Modern Algebra

A Constructive Introduction

Modern Algebra

A Constructive Introduction

Ian Connell
McGill University

North Holland
New York • Amsterdam • Oxford

Elsevier North Holland, Inc.
52 Vanderbilt Avenue, New York, New York 10017

Distributors outside the United States and Canada:

Edward Arnold (Publishers), Ltd.
41 Bedford Square, London, WC1B 3DQ

Library of Congress Cataloging in Publication Data

Connell, Ian.
Modern algebra: a constructive introduction.

Includes index.
1. Algebra, Abstract. I. Title.
QA162.C66 512 81-9804
ISBN 0-444-00609-5 AACR2

Manufactured in the United States of America

Contents

Preface

This is a textbook of algebra intended for students interested in pure mathematics. Starting from Peano's axioms it builds the basic objects of mathematics, as pictured in the following "tree":

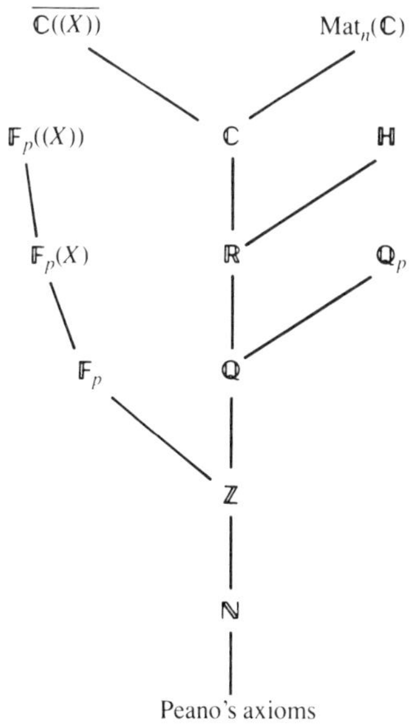

The treatment is self-contained and very thorough. As the text progresses up the branches of the tree it develops a good deal of important mathematics. The fundamental concepts of modern algebra (including rings, fields, groups, vector spaces, and homomorphisms) are introduced as they are needed and are thus seen "at work" in natural settings. This motivational approach gives a fine blend of modern and classical algebra that avoids the disjointed presentation (Chapter 0: Sets; Chapter 1: Groups; and so on) often seen in contemporary texts. And the student sees the whole story, instead of being fobbed off with such phrases as "we assume a knowledge of the real numbers" or "it can be shown that the field of complex numbers is algebraically closed." Of course, there are many topics not indicated explicitly in the tree; a more detailed idea of the contents can be gained by reading the introductory paragraphs at the beginning of each chapter.

The text can be used for a course of one, two, or three semesters, depending on the level of the students. For instance, a one-semester course would be suitable for the advanced undergraduate who has already been exposed to some modern algebra and linear algebra. For students of any level there should be plenty that is new and interesting.

We have grouped a selection of exercises into 12 assignments, which we hope the instructor will find useful. These problems (unlike the exercises at the end of sections and the supplementary exercises at the end of chapters) are treated as part of the main text and the results are occasionally used. (A3.5 refers to Assignment 3, problem 5.) The assignment questions contain important facts and ideas but are not intended to be difficult, and certainly not tricky. Hints are included when there is any danger of the student being unduly delayed.

From classroom experience we have anticipated a number of stumbling blocks and have taken pains to make the book at all times readable by the student. On a few occasions we refer to other texts, but only to mention that further development of certain ideas can be found there. This book is entirely self-contained.

List of Grammatical Abbreviations

$=$	is
$\in$	is in, is an element of, belongs to
$\notin$	is not in, is not a member of
$\forall$	for all, for every
$\exists$	there is, there are, there exist(s)
$\exists!$	there is precisely one, there exists uniquely
$\nexists$	there is no, there does not exist
$\ni$	such that
$\Rightarrow$	implies, only if, is sufficient that
$\Leftarrow$	is implied by, if, is necessary that
$\Leftrightarrow$, iff	if and only if, is equivalent to
/	over
I.H.	Inductive hypothesis (see Section 2 of Chapter 1)
$\hat{}$	the symbol under the "hat" is absent; for example, $x_1+\cdots+\hat{x}_i+\cdots+x_n$ means $x_1+\cdots+x_{i-1}+x_{i+1}+\cdots+x_n$
■	the end of a proof or discussion

A table of axiom schemes and a list of symbols appear as an appendix.

The Natural Numbers

1

In this first chapter we introduce by means of Peano's axioms the set $\mathbb{N}$ of natural numbers $1,2,3,\ldots$. We deduce the basic properties of addition, multiplication, and inequalities, the proofs providing good illustrations of the use of induction. We then go through the standard definitions from set theory: *map* (or *function*) and (more generally) *relation*, *domain*, *codomain*, *injective*, *surjective*, *bijective*, the various symbols $\subset$, $\cap$, $\setminus$ (complement), and so on. Next we define *finite* and *infinite* and indicate what is involved in proving that a nonempty set that is not finite must be infinite; this introduces the axiom of (disjoint) unions and the axiom of choice.

Many instructors will prefer to skip this chapter (and Assignment 1),[1] assuming that $\mathbb{N}=\{1,2,3,\ldots\}$ is already known; they will probably also prefer to postpone discussion of the axiom of choice. It is then a matter of ensuring that the students are familiar with induction (and complete induction) and with the standard terminology and symbolism of set theory.

The style of this chapter is not formal in the sense of mathematical logic; we do not describe what sequences of symbols are allowed as meaningful statements and what the rules of inference are. In fact, a strictly logical development from scratch would no doubt expand the chapter to several hundred pages. On the contrary, the style is that of ordinary mathematics, the kind that is normally accepted without comment except when we get close to the foundations: natural numbers and sets.

1. PEANO'S AXIOMS

Our knowledge of mathematics begins with the natural numbers $1,2,3,\ldots$. We use them for counting and we know how to add and multiply them. This familiarity, however, is not a solid enough foundation on which to build our

[1] The role of the assignments is discussed in the Preface.

subject. We wish to define the natural numbers in a precise way and not use any of their familiar properties until we have given a rigorous proof.

The definition we adopt consists of the following five statements, known as Peano's axioms:

(P1) There is a natural number 1.
(P2) To every natural number a there is associated a natural number $S(a)$, called the **successor** of a.
(P3) 1 is not the successor of any natural number.
(P4) If $S(a)=S(b)$, then $a=b$.
(P5) If a set of natural numbers contains 1 and the successor of every natural number of the set, then the set contains all the natural numbers.

These five statements form our starting point. In familiar terms, $S(1)=2$, $S(2)=3,\ldots,$ and $S(a)=a+1$, but again we stress that we must not rely on any previously acquired knowledge such as $a+1=1+a$. In fact, $S(a)=a+1$ will itself be part of the definition of addition.

2. ADDITION

If a and b are natural numbers, we define

$$a+1=S(a), \tag{1.1}$$

$$a+S(b)=S(a+b). \tag{1.2}$$

These equations are to be interpreted as follows. If the right side is a known natural number, then the left side is defined to be that natural number.

First we must check that these equations never lead to conflicting definitions. Equation (1.2) can never conflict with (1.1); that is, (1.2) cannot give a conflicting definition of $a+1$, since $S(b)$ is never 1 by (P3). Two of the equations (1.2), say, with left sides $a+S(b)$ and $a+S(c)$, cannot both purport to define the same sum $a+d$, since then $d=S(b)=S(c)$, which by (P4) implies that $b=c$.

Axiom (P5), known as the **principle of induction**, guarantees that $a+b$ is defined for all a and b for the following reason. Take any a, regard it for the moment as fixed, and consider the set B of natural numbers b for which $a+b$ is defined. Equation (1.1) says that 1 is in B (we write this in the abbreviated form $1\in B$), and (1.2) says that if a particular $b\in B$, then $S(b)\in B$. Thus by (P5), B consists of all the natural numbers; in other words, $a+b$ is defined for every b and, of course, for every a since there was no restriction on the a we began with.

We say that addition has been defined **inductively** or **by induction**. We also use induction in proofs, as we now see.

(1.3) PROPOSITION. *Addition is associative*:

$$(a+b)+c=a+(b+c)$$

for all natural numbers a, b, and c.

Proof. The proof will be by induction on c. First,

$$\begin{aligned}(a+b)+1 &= S(a+b) && \text{by (1.1)}\\ &= a+S(b) && \text{by (1.2)}\\ &= a+(b+1) && \text{by (1.1),}\end{aligned}$$

so the statement is true for $c=1$. Thinking of a and b as fixed, we have $1 \in C$, where C is the set of c for which the statement is true. If we now take any $c \in C$ and deduce that $S(c) \in C$, the proof will be complete.

Suppose, then, that $c \in C$; this is called the **inductive hypothesis**, which we abbreviate I.H. Then

$$\begin{aligned}(a+b)+S(c) &= S((a+b)+c) && \text{by (1.2)}\\ &= S(a+(b+c)) && \text{by I.H.}\\ &= a+S(b+c) && \text{by (1.2)}\\ &= a+(b+S(c)) && \text{by (1.2),}\end{aligned}$$

so $S(c) \in C$. ■

The convenient symbol ■ will mark the end of proofs. In the remainder of the text, the set underlying the induction (C here) is not usually named.

The standard symbols $2, 3, \ldots, 9$ are defined in succession by $2 = S(1), 3 = S(2), \ldots, 9 = S(8)$; we postpone discussion of the general decimal representation of natural numbers until Section 4 of Chapter 2. Tracing through the various definitions we can begin to build the addition table: $1+1=S(1)=2$, $1+2=1+S(1)=S(1+1)=S(2)=3$, and so on. We can now see examples of the associative law:

$$(2+2)+3=4+3=7,$$

$$2+(2+3)=2+5=7.$$

The agreement of the answers is too familiar to be amazing, but it is comforting to know that we have proved, on the basis of Peano's axioms, that it is true in *all* cases.

(1.4) PROPOSITION. *Addition is commutative*:

$$a+b=b+a$$

for all natural numbers a and b.

Proof. We first prove that $a+1=1+a$ by induction on a. This is obviously true when $a=1$, and, inductively,

$$\begin{aligned} S(a)+1 &= (a+1)+1 && \text{by (1.1)} \\ &= (1+a)+1 && \text{by I.H.} \\ &= 1+(a+1) && \text{by (1.3)} \\ &= 1+S(a) && \text{by (1.1),} \end{aligned}$$

so $a+1=1+a$ is true for all a.

We now prove $a+b=b+a$ by induction on b. We have just seen that it is true when $b=1$, and, inductively,

$$\begin{aligned} a+S(b) &= S(a+b) && \text{by (1.2)} \\ &= S(b+a) && \text{by I.H.} \\ &= (b+a)+1 && \text{by (1.1)} \\ &= b+(a+1) && \text{by (1.3)} \\ &= b+(1+a) && \text{since } a+1=1+a \\ &= (b+1)+a && \text{by (1.3)} \\ &= S(b)+a && \text{by (1.1).} \quad \blacksquare \end{aligned}$$

In the proofs that follow we state matters more economically, not giving the justification for each little step. Also, in the statements of the next few propositions we omit the obviously intended phrase "for all natural numbers $a, b, \ldots$."

(1.5) PROPOSITION. *Cancellation law for addition*:

$$a+b=a+c \quad \Rightarrow \quad b=c.$$

(The symbol $\Rightarrow$ means "implies.")

Proof by induction on a. $1+b=1+c \Rightarrow S(b)=S(c) \Rightarrow b=c$ by (P4). Inductively, $S(a)+b=S(a)+c \Rightarrow S(a+b)=S(a+c) \Rightarrow a+b=a+c \Rightarrow b=c$ by I.H. $\blacksquare$

3. MULTIPLICATION

We define the product of two natural numbers inductively:

(1.6) $$a1=a,$$

(1.7) $$aS(b)=ab+a.$$

In (1.7) the right side is the customary simplification of $(ab)+a$. It is understood that the multiplication is to be performed before the addition.

We leave it to the reader to verify that this defines the product of any two natural numbers unambiguously (compare the case of addition).

(1.8) PROPOSITION. *Left distributive law*:

$$a(b+c)=ab+ac.$$

Remark. As in (1.7), it is understood that on the right side of this equation the multiplications are performed before the addition.

Proof by induction on c. We have $a(b+1)=aS(b)=ab+a=ab+a1$, and, inductively,

$$\begin{aligned} a(b+S(c)) &= aS(b+c) \\ &= a(b+c)+a \\ &= ab+ac+a && \text{by I.H.} \\ &= ab+aS(c) && \text{by (1.7).} \end{aligned}$$ ■

(1.9) PROPOSITION. *Multiplication is associative*:

$$(ab)c=a(bc).$$

Proof. The result is true when $c=1$ by (1.6); inductively,

$$\begin{aligned} (ab)S(c) &= (ab)c+ab \\ &= a(bc)+ab && \text{by I.H.} \\ &= a(bc+b) && \text{by (1.8)} \\ &= a(bS(c)). \end{aligned}$$ ■

(1.10) LEMMA. $1a=a$ *and* $S(b)a=ba+a$.

Note. A **lemma** is an intermediate result, or "stepping stone," needed to prove an ostensibly more important or more general result. While we are on the subject, it has become fairly common practice in mathematics to reserve the title **theorem** for a difficult or "deep" result, relegating a result more easily obtained to the status of a **proposition**.

Proof. The first statement is true for $a=1$ by (1.6), and inductively $1S(a)=1a+1$, by (1.7), which in turn is equal to $a+1=S(a)$. The second statement of the lemma is clearly true when $a=1$; inductively,

$$\begin{aligned} S(b)S(a) &= S(b)a+S(b) && \text{by (1.7)} \\ &= (ba+a)+(b+1) && \text{by I.H.} \\ &= (ba+b)+(a+1) && \text{by (1.3), (1.4)} \\ &= bS(a)+S(a) && \text{by (1.7),} \end{aligned}$$

and this completes the proof. ■

(1.11) PROPOSITION. *Multiplication is commutative*:

$$ab = ba.$$

This follows from the lemma by an obvious induction that is left as an exercise.

In view of (1.8) an immediate consequence is

(1.12) COROLLARY. *Right distributive law*:

$$(a+b)c = ac + bc.$$

The remaining basic fact to be proved concerning multiplication is the cancellation law. It is convenient first to develop the notion of inequality.

EXERCISE[2]

Let $a \in \mathbb{N}$ be fixed and for any $x, y \in \mathbb{N}$ let $x\$y$ denote $x + y + axy$. Then \$ is associative: $(x\$y)\$z = x\$(y\$z)$, $\forall x, y, z$. Also, $x\$(y+z)$ and $(x\$y)+(x\$z)$ are never equal.

4. INEQUALITIES

We write $a < b$ and say a is less than b if there is a c such that $a + c = b$; if there is no such c we write $a \not< b$. In these statements of course c is understood to be a natural number: at present they are the only numbers within our purview. Later we shall construct negative numbers, fractional numbers, real numbers, and so on, using the natural numbers, but they are not yet at our disposal.

As usual, $a > b$ means $b < a$; $a \leqslant b$ means that either $a < b$ or $a = b$; $a \nleqslant b$ means that $a \leqslant b$ is not true (we shall see in a moment that this is exactly the same thing as $a > b$); similar remarks apply to $\geqslant$ and $\ngeqslant$. Comparisons between two natural numbers of the form $a \sharp b$, where $\sharp$ stands for one of $<, >, \leqslant, \geqslant$, are known as **inequalities**; if $\sharp$ is $<$ or $>$ one may speak of a **strict inequality**, when it is necessary to draw attention to this. One would hesitate to call $a \nleqslant b, a \ngeqslant b, a \neq b$ inequalities. (The last of these means that a and b are different natural numbers.)

(1.13) PROPOSITION. *The* **law of trichotomy**: *for each pair of natural numbers a, b exactly one of the following is true*:

$$a < b, \qquad a = b, \qquad a > b.$$

---

[2] In the exercises we often omit the phrase "prove that" when there can be no doubt what is expected. $\mathbb{N}$ denotes the set of all natural numbers.

Proof. First we prove that at most one of these relations is true for given a and b. Suppose we had $a<b$, say $a+c=b$, and also $a=b$. Then $b+c=b$, whence $b+c+1=b+1$, and by (1.5) $c+1=1$, which contradicts (P3). Similarly $a<b$ and $a>b$ are incompatible.

Conversely we must prove that at least one of the three relations is true, and this we do by induction on a. That is, if A is the set of a such that a is comparable to every b, we wish to show that A satisfies the requirements of (P5). The next lemma shows that $1 \in A$.

(1.14) LEMMA. $1 \leqslant a, \forall a$.

Note. The symbol $\forall$ is the initial letter of "All" inverted and stands for the phrase "for all" or "for every." Similarly it is standard to use $\exists$, the mirror image of the initial of "Exist," as short for "there is" or "there are."

Proof of the lemma. We prove that the set X consisting of those a for which the lemma is true satisfies (P5). First, $1 \in X$ by definition of $\leqslant$. Secondly, if $a \in X$ then $1<1+a=S(a)$ by definition of $<$. (In fact we did not need the assumption $a \in X$.) This implies the weaker statement $1 \leqslant S(a)$, and hence $S(a) \in X$, which completes the proof of the lemma by induction. ■

Returning to the proof of (1.13), suppose $a \in A$ and b is any natural number; we wish to compare $a+1$ with b. If $a>b$, say $a=b+c$, then $a+1=b+c+1$, hence $a+1>b$. If $a=b$, then $a+1>b$ by definition. Finally, if $a<b$, say $a+c=b$, we have, by the lemma, either $c=1$, and then $a+1=b$, or $c=1+d$ for some d, and in that case $a+1+d=b$, so $a+1<b$. ■

(1.15) PROPOSITION

$$a<b \quad \textit{and} \quad c \leqslant d \qquad \Rightarrow \qquad a+c<b+d \quad \textit{and} \quad ac<bd.$$

Proof. Let $b=a+e$, so $b+c=a+e+c$ and $bc=ac+ec$, which proves the results in the equality case $c=d$.

Now when $c<d$, applying the equality cases twice we obtain

$$\begin{array}{ccc} a+c<b+c & \text{and} & b+c<b+d, \\ ac<bc & \text{and} & bc<bd. \end{array}$$

The desired conclusions follow from the **transitive law** for inequalities

$$u<v \quad \text{and} \quad v<w \qquad \Rightarrow \qquad u<w, \tag{1.16}$$

whose simple proof we leave as an exercise. ■

(1.17) COROLLARY. *Cancellation law for multiplication*:

$$ab=ac \qquad \Rightarrow \qquad b=c.$$

If $b \neq c$ we have either $b<c$ or $b>c$, which leads to the contradictions $ab<ac$ or $ab>ac$, respectively.

5. WELL ORDERING

It is intuitively obvious that in any collection of natural numbers there is a smallest, provided of course the collection is not vacuous; we can actually prove this fact.

(1.18) PROPOSITION. *The* **well-ordering principle**: *Every nonempty set of natural numbers contains a smallest.*

Proof. Let C be a set with no smallest; we wish to prove that $C = \varnothing$, the **empty set**, i.e., the set with no members. Let A be the set of a with the property that for every $b \leqslant a$, $b \notin C$ (read "b is not in C"); in particular, if $a \in A$ then $a \notin C$. We proceed to prove that A satisfies (P5) and therefore contains all the natural numbers. $C = \varnothing$ then follows immediately.

First, $1 \in A$; otherwise $1 \in C$, but then 1 would be a smallest element in C since $1 \leqslant c$ for every natural number c, in particular those in C. Supposing $a \in A$ it remains to prove that $a+1 \in A$. If not, $b \in C$ for some $b \leqslant a+1$. Either $b = a+1$ or $b \leqslant a$ by A1.1.[3] Neither $b = a$ nor $b < a$ is possible since $a \in A$, so we are left with $b = a+1 \in C$. Now every $c \in C$ satisfies $c \geqslant a+1$ because $c < a+1$ leads to $c \leqslant a$, contradicting $a \in A$. Thus $a+1$ would be a smallest element in C, contrary to hypothesis. We must have $a+1 \in A$ after all, and this completes the proof. ■

By trichotomy, the smallest element in a nonempty set is unique: If a and b were both smallest, then $a \leqslant b$ and $b \leqslant a$, which imply $a = b$.

We now deduce a useful variant of the principle of induction.

(1.19) COROLLARY. *The principle of* **complete induction**: *Let A be a set of natural numbers such that $a \in A$ whenever all natural numbers less than a are in A. Then A contains all the natural numbers.*

Proof. Let B be the set of natural numbers not in A. If $B \neq \varnothing$, let b be the smallest element in B. By definition, if $a < b$, then $a \in A$. But then by the assumption on A, this implies that $b \in A$, a contradiction. Hence $B = \varnothing$. ■

Notice that it is not necessary to assume explicitly that $A \neq \varnothing$. This is a consequence of the assumption; indeed $1 \in A$ because A contains every b that satisfies $b < 1$—certainly, there are no such b!

We follow with an example of how complete induction can be used in a proof that would be awkward to recast in terms of ordinary induction.

First some terminology.

---

[3]At this point a start can be made on Assignment 1 (at the end of this chapter). A1.1 refers to Assignment 1, question 1.

(1.20) DEFINITION. The natural number p is **prime** if $p>1$ and

$$p=ab \quad \Rightarrow \quad a=1 \quad \text{or} \quad b=1;$$

the natural number c is **composite** if $c>1$ and is not prime.

The first few primes are 2,3,5,7, whereas $4=2\cdot 2$, $6=2\cdot 3$, $8=4\cdot 2=2\cdot 2\cdot 2$, $9=3\cdot 3$ are not prime; they are composite.

We say that a is a **factor** of c or a **divisor** of c or that a **divides** c when there exists a b such that $c=ab$; we then write $a|c$ and in the contrary case $a\nmid c$. Thus $1|c\ \forall c$ since $c=1c$; $2|4$ since $4=2\cdot 2$ but $2\nmid 3$ (cf. A1.1).

(1.21) PROPOSITION. *Every composite natural number can be written as a product of primes.*

Proof. Let A be the set of natural numbers consisting of 1, the primes, and those composite numbers that admit such a factorization, and let a be a natural number such that $b<a \Rightarrow b\in A$. We wish to deduce that $a\in A$. This is true if a is 1 or a prime (even without the I.H.), so we may assume that a is composite, say $a=bc$, where $b<a$, $c<a$ (cf. A1.1). By the I.H., both b and c are products of primes and therefore so is their product $bc=a$. ■

EXERCISES

1.
$$a|b \text{ and } a|S(b) \quad \Leftrightarrow \quad a=1;$$
$$(a+1)|(a^2+1) \quad \Leftrightarrow \quad a=1;$$
$$a|b \text{ and } S(a)|b \quad \Rightarrow \quad b\geqslant a^2+a.$$

2. For $m,n\in\mathbb{N}$ define $m\vee n$ (resp. $m\wedge n$) to be the larger (resp. smaller) of m and n. Thus $m\vee n=m\wedge n$ iff $m=n$. ("iff" and the symbol $\Leftrightarrow$ both mean if and only if.) Prove the associative and distributive laws,
$$(k\vee m)\vee n=k\vee(m\vee n),$$
$$k\vee(m\wedge n)=(k\vee m)\wedge(k\vee n),$$
and the two dual laws obtained by interchanging $\vee$ and $\wedge$.

6. SOME NOTATION FROM SET THEORY

The standard symbol for the set of all natural numbers is $\mathbb{N}$. A set is often described by displaying its members or elements, between braces { }; for example {5,4,7,8}. When it is not convenient or possible to list all the elements explicitly one can use the notation { : }, where to the left of the colon a typical element of the set is indicated; and to the right the requirements for that element to be a member of the set are listed. For example, $\{a\in\mathbb{N} : a\leqslant 9\}$ is another, perhaps more quickly comprehended, way of describing {1,2,3,4,5,6,7,8,9}. A more cogent example is $\{a\in$

$\mathbb{N}:2|a\}$, the set of **even** natural numbers, and again $\{a \in \mathbb{N}:2\nmid a\}$, the set of **odd** natural numbers.

If X and Y are sets, $X \subset Y$ means that every element of X is in Y: $a \in X \Rightarrow a \in Y$. We then say that X is **contained in** Y and that X is a **subset** of Y. Equivalently we write $Y \supset X$ and say that Y **contains** X. Since $\varnothing$ has no members, $\varnothing \subset Y$ for any Y, the condition for $\subset$ being vacuously fulfilled. At the other extreme, $Y \subset Y$ is always true; in particular, $\varnothing \subset \varnothing$. The equality $X = Y$ means that both $X \subset Y$ and $Y \subset X$. Notice that repetitions are disregarded; for example, the set of prime factors of $9 = 3 \cdot 3$ is $\{3,3\} = \{3\}$. (*Exercise*: No other prime divides 9.) Notice also that $\{3,2\} = \{2,3\}$. What this example really points out is that the apparent ordering of the elements, i.e., one is first and the other is second, is only an accidental feature of the particular way of describing the set: the set possesses no such ordering. Of course we might want to consider a set *together with* a particular ordering of its elements, for example, $\mathbb{N}$ with the usual $<$; however, this is a more elaborate structure than a simple bald set; it is an example of a relation, a notion that we are about to define.

First some simple, intuitive examples. Let a, b, c stand for the three students Alan, Betty, and Charles and let $X = \{a, b, c\}$. Suppose their ages are 18, 18, and 20, respectively. We can indicate these values by $f(a) = 18$, $f(b) = 18$, $f(c) = 20$. We say that f is a *function* or *map* from X to $\mathbb{N}$, the idea being that to each element x in X is associated a value $f(x)$ in $\mathbb{N}$. We indicate the direction of f by the notation $f\colon X \to \mathbb{N}$. Notice that if we go in the opposite direction, the two elements a and b are associated with 18, while no element is associated with 19, for instance; these associations do not give a map but only what is called a *relation*.

Here is another example of a relation. Suppose that from the set of available courses $Y = \{A, B, C, D\}$ Alan takes B, C, and D, Betty takes A and B, and Charles takes none. The relation between the students and courses can be specified by the set of pairs $\{(a, B), (a, C), (a, D), (b, A), (b, B)\}$, which is called the *graph* of the relation. Here are the general definitions.

If X and Y are sets, their **product** is the set $X \times Y$ of all pairs (x, y) where $x \in X$ and $y \in Y$. A **relation** between X and Y is a trio (X, Y, Z) where $Z \subset X \times Y$. The three sets X, Y, and Z are, respectively the **domain**, **codomain**, and **graph** of the relation. For example, if $X = Y = \mathbb{N}$, the relation less than has the graph $Z = \{(a, b) \in \mathbb{N} \times \mathbb{N} : a < b\}$. We then have $(2,3) \in Z$, but $(3,2) \notin Z$, $(3,3) \notin Z$.

If $\rho = (X, Y, Z)$ and $\sigma = (U, V, W)$ are relations, then $\rho = \sigma$ means, by definition, that $X = U$, $Y = V$, and $Z = W$. We shall not always be so precise in our notation: often it does not lead to ambiguity to blur the distinction between a relation and its graph, as in the phrase "consider a relation $\rho \subset X \times Y$." Similarly, $(x, y) \in \rho$ means that (x, y) is in the graph of ρ; this is also indicated by the notation $x \rho y$, as in the familiar relations $x<y$ and $x=y$.

To illustrate this and other definitions concerning the notion of relation, let $A=\{a,b,c\}$ be a set of three elements, $B=\{d,e\}$ a set of two, and C the subset $\{a,b\}$ of A. The relation $\rho=\{(a,e),(b,e)\} \subset A \times B$ between A and B is not equal to the relation $\sigma=\{(a,e),(b,e)\} \subset C \times B$ between C and B because their domains are not the same. This might seem to be pedantic, but we shall encounter situations where it is important to be clear about the meaning of equality of two relations.

Consider next the relation $f=\{(a,d),(b,d),(c,e)\} \subset A \times B$. It is sometimes helpful to visualize a relation as in Figure 1.1. This particular f is a map according to the next definition. A relation $f \subset X \times Y$ is a **function**, or **mapping**, or simply **map** from X to Y if $\forall x \in X$, the graph of f contains exactly one pair of the form (x, y) for some $y \in Y$.

In this case one usually writes $f(x)=y$ for $(x, y) \in f$. Also, $f\colon X \rightarrow Y$ is standard notation to indicate that f is a map from X to Y. The map f above is completely specified by the following data: its domain is A, its codomain is B, and $f(a)=d, f(b)=d, f(c)=e$. The relation $\gamma=\{(a,d),(b,d)\}$ is not a map from A to B because it is not everywhere defined on A: $\gamma(c)$ is not defined. $\{(a,d),(b,d),(c,d),(c,e)\}$ is not a map because it is not single valued: It is multiple valued at c, where it has the two values d and e.

If $\rho \subset X \times Y$ is a relation, the **inverse relation** $\rho^{-1} \subset Y \times X$ is defined by $y \rho^{-1} x \Leftrightarrow x \rho y$. If f is a map, f^{-1} is commonly called the **inverse map** (or **inverse function**) even when it is not in fact a map.

If $\alpha \subset X \times Y$ and $\beta \subset Y \times Z$ are relations we define their **product** (or **composition**) to be the relation $\beta\alpha \subset X \times Z$ determined by

$$x \beta\alpha z \quad \Leftrightarrow \quad \exists y \in Y \ni x \alpha y \quad \text{and} \quad y \beta z$$

(where $\ni$ stands for such that). In order that $\beta\alpha$ be defined it is necessary that the codomain of α be the domain of β. If α and β are maps, then

Figure 1.1

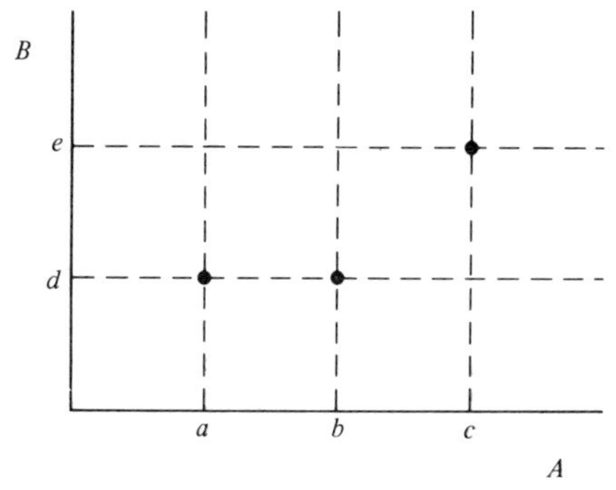

clearly $(\beta\alpha)(a)=\beta(\alpha(a))$. This is the reason for the right-to-left order of the factors. To borrow an example from analysis, sin log means the function whose values are given by $(\sin\log)(a)=\sin(\log(a))$.

For example, if $\alpha=\{(a,2),(a,3),(b,3)\}\subset A\times\mathbb{N}$ and $\beta=\{(1,d),(3,d),(3,e)\}\subset\mathbb{N}\times B$, then

$$\beta\alpha=\{(a,d),(a,e),(b,d),(b,e)\}.$$

The map $f\colon X\to Y$ is **injective** if $f(a)=f(b)\Rightarrow a=b$, and **surjective** (or **onto**) if

$$\forall y\in Y\,\exists x\in X\ni f(x)=y;$$

it is **bijective** if both injective and surjective. In other words, f is injective (resp. surjective, bijective) when for each $y\in Y$ there exists at most one (resp. at least one, precisely one) $x\ni f(x)=y$. One also says that f is an **injection** (resp. **surjection, bijection**). We avoid the expression "one to one," which has been used to mean both injective and bijective.

For example, the **identity map** $1_X\colon X\to X$ defined by $1_X(a)=a$, $\forall a\in X$ is a bijection. Notice that for any $\rho\subset X\times Y$, $\rho 1_X=1_Y\rho=\rho$. A bijection of a set with itself is also called a **permutation**; thus 1_X (also written simply as 1 when this is not likely to be misconstrued) is also called the **identity permutation** on X. The map $f\colon\mathbb{N}\to\{e,o\}$ defined by $f(a)=e$ if a is even and $f(a)=o$ if a is odd is surjective but not injective whereas the map $\{e,o\}\to\mathbb{N}$ given by $e\mapsto 4$ and $o\mapsto 4$ (we often indicate the effect of a map by the special arrow $\mapsto$, particularly when we do not wish to bother naming the map), is neither injective nor surjective. Axiom (P4) says that the successor function $S\colon\mathbb{N}\to\mathbb{N}$ is injective; (P3) guarantees that it is not surjective. While we are on the subject, (P1) amounts to the statement $\mathbb{N}\neq\varnothing$.

The **image** of $f\colon X\to Y$, abbreviated $\operatorname{Im}(f)$, is the subset $\{b\in Y : \exists a\in X\ni f(a)=b\}$ of Y; f is surjective iff $\operatorname{Im}(f)=Y$. If $U\subset X$ then, by definition, $f(U)$ denotes $\{f(a): a\in U\}$, the set of all elements of Y of the form $f(a)$ as a "runs through" U. Thus $f(X)$ is another way of writing $\operatorname{Im}(f)$.

Given any $f\colon X\to Y$, define $g\colon X\to\operatorname{Im}(f)$ by $g(a)=f(a)$ and $h\colon\operatorname{Im}(f)\to Y$ by $h(b)=b$. Then g is surjective, h is injective, and $f=hg$. Thus every map can be factored into a product of a surjection followed by an injection.

If $f\colon X\to Y$ and $U\subset X$, the **restriction** of f to U, denoted $f|U$, is the map $U\to Y$ given by $a\mapsto f(a)$, $\forall a\in U$. If f is injective, so is $f|U$ since $f|U(a)=f|U(b)\Rightarrow f(a)=f(b)\Rightarrow a=b$. Again, if $\operatorname{Im}(f)\subset V\subset Y$, then f defines a map, for which we have no special notation, $X\to V$ via $a\mapsto f(a)$. If f is injective, so is this map obtained by restricting the codomain.

(1.22) LEMMA. (i) *If $f\colon X\to Y$ is a bijection, so is f^{-1}, and $f^{-1}f=1_X$, $ff^{-1}=1_Y$.*

(ii) *If* $f\colon X \to Y$ *and* $g\colon Y \to Z$ *are both injective, or both surjective, or both bijective, then* gf *has the same property.*

We leave the proof as a simple exercise.

EXERCISES

1. Let $f\colon X \to Y$ and $g\colon Y \to Z$.
   - **(i)** gf injective $\Rightarrow f$ injective; gf surjective $\Rightarrow g$ surjective. Hence if $Z = X$ and $gf = 1$, then f is injective and g is surjective.
   - **(ii)** If f is surjective and g' is another map $Y \to Z \ni gf = g'f$, then $g = g'$. (It is common practice to use the sign $'$, called prime, to create new symbols. Thus g', read "g prime," is in effect a new letter of the alphabet, and the mathematical object it represents has no necessary connection with that represented by g. This process can be iterated: g'' is read "g double prime," g''' "g triple prime," and so on.)
   - **(iii)** Similarly, if g is injective, then $gf = gf' \Rightarrow f = f'$.
   - **(iv)** Suppose that $X \neq \varnothing$, $Z = Y$, and that f is right cancelable in the sense of (ii), i.e., suppose that for every pair of maps $g, g'\colon Y \to Y \ni gf = g'f$ we have $g = g'$. Then f is surjective.
   - **(v)** Formulate and prove an analogous converse to (iii).

2. An aviator (a) must transport a bird (b), a cat (c), and a dog (d) from airport A to airport B with the constraints that at most one animal can be ferried at a time and neither (b) and (c) nor (c) and (d) may be left alone together. The following flight plan is one solution, where the state of the system is indicated by the set at A:

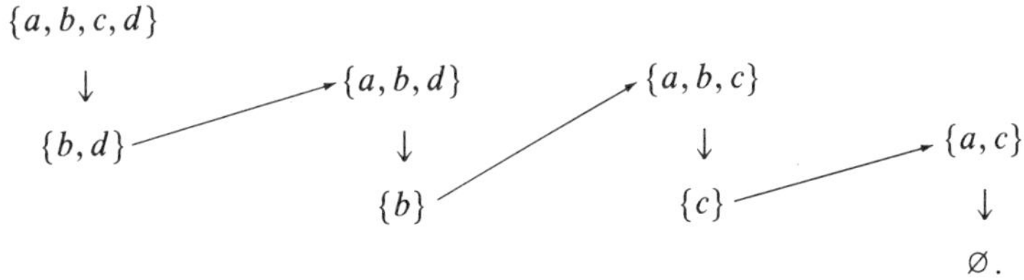

   Find the other solution.

7. COUNTING

When we say that $6 = 2\cdot 3$ has two prime factors we mean that the prime factors 2,3 can be paired up with the first two natural numbers, in other words, there is a bijection from $\{1,2\}$ to $\{2,3\}$. Similarly, we say that 5,4,8,7 comprise a set of four elements since there is a bijection (in fact, several bijections) from $\{1,2,3,4\}$ to $\{5,4,8,7\}$. Here are some general definitions.

As a temporary notation, let (n) denote $\{a \in \mathbb{N} : a \leqslant n\}$. The set X is **finite** if there exists a bijection $(n) \to X$; then n is called the **cardinality** of X, we write $|X|=n$, and we say that X contains n elements.[4] (We prove in the next proposition that this is well defined, i.e., we cannot also have a bijection $(m)\to X$ with $m\neq n$.) A set X is **infinite** if there exists an injection $\mathbb{N}\to X$. For example, $\mathbb{N}$ is infinite: any one of the injections $1_{\mathbb{N}}$, $S(a)=a+1$, $a\mapsto 3a+5$, $a\mapsto a^2$ (cf. A1.2),... shows this.

The basic fact concerning the counting of finite sets is given in the next lemma. One further bit of notation: $A\setminus B=\{a\in A: a\notin B\}$, the **complement** of B in A. This notation does not require $B\subset A$; for example, $\{1,2\}\setminus\{2,3\}=\{1\}$.

(1.23) LEMMA. *If there exists an injection* $(m)\to(n)$, *then* $m\leqslant n$.

Proof by induction on m. When $m=1$ the conclusion $1\leqslant n$ is true. (The hypothesis that there exists an injection $(1)\to(n)$ is also true $\forall n$ since we can take, for example, $1\mapsto 1$, but this is irrelevant.) Inductively we assume the result for m and deduce it for $m+1$. (The set underlying the induction is $\{m\in\mathbb{N}:$ for each $n\in\mathbb{N}$ either $m\leqslant n$ or there does not exist an injection $(m)\to(n)\}$.) Suppose we have an injection $f:(m+1)\to(n)$ for some n. Now $n>1$, for if $n=1$ we would have $f(1)=f(m+1)=1\Rightarrow$(since f is injective) $1=m+1$, a contradiction. This allows us to write $n=k+1$, say. If $n\notin\operatorname{Im}(f)$ then we can restrict the codomain to $(n)\setminus\{n\}=(k)$ to get an injection $(m+1)\to(k)$, and then restrict the domain to get an injection $(m)\to(k)$. By I.H., $m\leqslant k$, whence $m+1\leqslant k+1=n$, as required.

There remains the case $n\in\operatorname{Im}(f)$, say $f(a)=n$. Since f is injective, $f(b)\neq n$ for each $b\neq a$ in $(m+1)$. Define $g:(m)\to(m+1)$ by

$$g(b)=\begin{cases} b & \text{if } b<a\\ b+1 & \text{if } b\geqslant a.\end{cases}$$

g is injective and $n\notin\operatorname{Im}(fg)$. This yields an injection $(m)\to(k)$, and the argument is completed as before. ∎

(1.24) PROPOSITION. *A set is precisely one of the following: empty, finite, infinite. If finite, its cardinality is uniquely determined.*

Proof. We first verify that a set X cannot have more than one of the three attributes. If X is either finite or infinite there is a map $f: Y\to X$, where Y is some (n) or $\mathbb{N}$, so X contains $f(1)$ and therefore is not empty. Suppose we had both a bijection $f:(n)\to X$ and an injection $g:\mathbb{N}\to X$. Then we would have an injection $f^{-1}g:\mathbb{N}\to(n)$ that would restrict to an injection $(n+1)\to(n)$; but this is not possible by (1.23).

Next, the cardinality of a finite set X is well defined: suppose $f:(m)\to X$ and $g:(n)\to X$ are bijections. Then so are $g^{-1}f:(m)\to(n)$ and $f^{-1}g:(n)\to(m)$, hence $m\leqslant n$ and $n\leqslant m$ by (1.23), and therefore $m=n$.

---

[4]Alternative standard notation is card $X=n$.

Finally, we must prove that a nonempty set X is either finite or infinite. We define injective maps $(n) \to X$ inductively on n. First, when $n=1$ we choose any element $a \in X$ and define $(1) \to X$ by $1 \mapsto a$. If an injection $f:(n) \to X$ has been defined, there are two possibilities: the set $X \setminus \mathrm{Im}(f)$ is either empty or nonempty. In the former case f is surjective; hence X is finite, of cardinality n. In the latter case choose any $b \in X \setminus \mathrm{Im}(f)$ and define the injection $g:(n+1) \to X$ by $g(m)=f(m)$ for $m \leqslant n$ and $g(m+1) = b$.

Thus if X is not finite or empty, then given any n, no matter how large, we can construct an injection $f=(n) \to X$ by making n choices of elements from various nonempty sets of the form $X \setminus Y$. However, it is a nontrivial step to pass to an injection $\mathbb{N} \to X$ by making infinitely many choices simultaneously. (We can say infinitely many because there is one choice necessary for each $n \in \mathbb{N}$.) What we have proved by induction is that

$$\{n \in \mathbb{N} : \exists \text{ an injection } (n) \to X\} = \mathbb{N},$$

but this does not imply that there is an injection $\mathbb{N} \to X$. The completion of (this final part of) the proof depends on a new principle that we shall enunciate formally in (1.26).

Informally, this principle says that if we have a collection F of nonempty sets (we sometimes replace "set of sets" with "collection of sets" simply because it sounds less monotonous) then it is possible to choose one element from each member Z of F. In other words, there exists a **choice function** $h: F \to X$ such that $h(Z) \in Z \; \forall Z \in F$. To use this to complete the proof of (1.24) we take F to be the collection of all nonempty subsets of X. Then we can define an injection $f: \mathbb{N} \to X$ inductively by $f(n) = h(X \setminus \{f(m) : m < n\})$. All the necessary choices have been made beforehand by h.

However, to state this idea generally we have to specify the codomain of h as a set X in some sense containing all the given sets $Z \in F$. Such a universal set is provided by the following axiom of set theory. If F is a collection of subsets of a set X then the **union** of the collection is the set

$$\bigcup F = \{x \in X : x \in Z \text{ for some } Z \in F\}$$

and the **intersection** of the collection is the set

$$\bigcap F = \{x \in X : x \in Z \text{ for each } Z \in F\}.$$

One also denotes $\cup F$ by $\cup_{Z \in F} Z$ or more simply $\cup Z$ when that is not ambiguous. Moreover, if F is finite, for instance $\{A, B, C\}$, then $\cup F$ is also written $A \cup B \cup C$. Similarly one writes $\cap Z$, $A \cap B$, and so on. A and B are said to be **disjoint** if $A \cap B = \varnothing$.

As in the case of set notation, where we observed that for instance $\{3,2\} = \{2,3\}$, the notation here introduces a spurious suggestion of order. Yet $A \cup B = B \cup A$ does not call for a proof; it is a mere tautology.

$(A \cup B) \cup C = A \cup (B \cup C)$ is also true by definition, and similar remarks apply to $\cap$.

Notice that if $F = \varnothing$ then $\cup F = \varnothing$ and $\cap F = X$. The latter points out the incompleteness of the notation: the symbolism does not indicate that X is the universe. But this rarely causes problems in practice.

(1.25) AXIOM OF UNIONS. For each collection F of sets there exists a set $\amalg F$, called the **disjoint union** of F, and a collection of injections $\mu_Z: Z \to \amalg F$, one for each $Z \in F$, such that

(i) $\cup \mu_Z(Z) = \amalg F$ and

(ii) $Y, Z \in F,\ Y \neq Z \Rightarrow \mu_Y(Y) \cap \mu_Z(Z) = \varnothing$.

This axiom, which is an assumption we make about the sets we work with in mathematics, says that there always exists a set that contains as mutually disjoint subsets copies of given sets Z. As with $\cup$ and $\cap$ we also write $\amalg Z$, $A \amalg B$, and so on. If A, B are subsets of a set X such that $A \cap B = \varnothing$, and $C = A \cup B$, then we sometimes write $C = A \amalg B$ as a convenient way of making the two statements $C = A \cup B$ and $A \cap B = \varnothing$. For this purpose the notation $C = A \dot{\cup} B$ is also used (especially when we wish to emphasize that A and B are both subsets of a common set X). Thus $\dot{\cup}$, unlike $\cup$, is not an operation that can be performed between any two subsets of X.

(1.26) AXIOM OF CHOICE. If F is a collection of nonempty mutually disjoint subsets of a set X, then there exists a subset S of X such that

$$|S \cap Z| = 1, \qquad \forall Z \in F.$$

The unique element in $S \cap Z$ is the chosen element of Z.

To derive the informal version of the axiom of choice discussed above we apply (1.26) to the collection of subsets $\mu_Z(Z)$ of $\amalg Z$. Then we take $h(Z)$ to be the element of Z sent onto the chosen element of $\mu_Z(Z)$ by the injection μ_Z.

The axiom of choice is elementary if F is empty or finite (it can then be proved by induction), but not so in general. Certain other important principles that are logically equivalent to this axiom will be discussed in Chapter 4.

EXERCISES

1. Let X and Y be sets, let λ and μ be the canonical injections of X and Y into $X \amalg Y$, and let $x, x' \in X$ and $y, y' \in Y$. Then

$$\{\{\lambda(x)\}, \{\lambda(x), \mu(y)\}\} = \{\{\lambda(x')\}, \{\lambda(x'), \mu(y')\}\}$$

iff $x = x'$ and $y = y'$. (Thus we can define the **ordered pair** (x, y) set theoretically as $\{\{\lambda(x)\},\{\lambda(x),\mu(y)\}\}$ even when X and Y have elements in common, e.g., when $X = Y$.)

2. Explain why the sets $\{\varnothing\},\{\varnothing,\{\varnothing\}\},\{\varnothing,\{\varnothing\},\{\varnothing,\{\varnothing\}\}\}$ have cardinalities 1,2,3, respectively, and by induction extend the construction to all $n \in \mathbb{N}$.

3. Let $f: X \to Y$. Then

   Y finite and f injective $\Rightarrow X$ empty or finite;

   Y infinite and f surjective $\Rightarrow X$ infinite;

   X finite and f surjective $\Rightarrow Y$ finite;

   X infinite and f injective $\Rightarrow Y$ infinite.

4. For relations $\rho, \rho' \subset X \times Y$ and $\sigma \subset Y \times Z$ we have

$$(\sigma\rho)^{-1} = \rho^{-1}\sigma^{-1} \quad \text{and} \quad \sigma(\rho \cup \rho') = (\sigma\rho) \cup (\sigma\rho'),$$

   where $\rho \cup \rho'$ stands for the relation whose graph $|\rho \cup \rho'|$ is the union $|\rho| \cup |\rho'|$ of the graphs of ρ and ρ'; $\cap$ is used similarly. Give an example where $\sigma(\rho \cap \rho') \neq (\sigma\rho) \cap (\sigma\rho')$.

8. FINITE SUMS AND PRODUCTS

The statement "for every $n \in \mathbb{N}$ the sum of the elements of the set $\{n+1, 2n\}$ is at least 4" is not literally true. For when $n = 1$, $n + 1 = 2n$, and the set consists of, strictly speaking, the single element 2. The concept of a "set with repetitions" is often needed, for instance when listing the prime factors of 9. The standard notational device for this is an index set, as we now explain.

If $f: X \to Y$, we sometimes use a notation such as y_x for $f(x)$. For instance if $f:(n) \to Y$ we may denote $f(1), f(2), \ldots, f(n)$ by $y_1, y_2, \ldots, y_n$. We refer to the subscript x in the symbol y_x as an **index** and to X as an **index set**. Then in the graph $\{(x, y_x)\}$, $x \neq x' \Rightarrow (x, y_x) \neq (x', y_{x'})$ even when $y_x = y_{x'}$. However, this notation is cumbersome, and we usually revert to $\{y_x\}$, which we can refer to as a **list** rather than a set to emphasize that repetitions are to be preserved. Thus the sum of the elements in the list $\{y_1, y_2\}$, where $y_1 = n + 1$, $y_2 = 2n$, is $3n + 1$ even when $n = 1$.

Now let $a_1, a_2, \ldots, a_n$ be natural numbers. (The notation implicitly defines a map $(n) \to \mathbb{N}$ that can remain anonymous. As just explained, the a_i need not all be different.) We define their **sum**, denoted $\Sigma_{i=1}^n a_i$ or $a_1 + a_2 + \cdots + a_n$, to be $s(n)$, where, inductively, $s(1) = a_1$ and $s(i+1) = s(i) + a_{i+1}$. Of course if $n = 1$ or 2, $a_1 + a_2 + \cdots + a_n$ is to be understood as a_1 or $a_1 + a_2$. The i in $\Sigma_{i=1}^n a_i$ is a *dummy index*; it plays no part in the definition of the sum and can be replaced by any other symbol not currently assigned a meaning.

Similarly the **product** of the a_i, denoted $\Pi_{i=1}^n a_i$ or $a_1 a_2 \cdots a_n$, is $p(n)$, where $p(1) = a_1$ and $p(i+1) = p(i) a_{i+1}$.

The proof that the sum is well defined, i.e., depends only on the natural numbers $a_1, \ldots, a_n$ and not on the choice $f:(n) \to \mathbb{N}$ of indices, is a straightforward induction on n. If $n=1$, there is only one f and no problem. Inductively, suppose $n>1$ and that for each i with $1 \leqslant i \leqslant n$,

$$\sum_{\substack{j=1 \\ j \neq i}}^{n} a_j = s_i \qquad \text{(say)},$$

is well defined. s_i is sometimes written $a_1 + \cdots + \hat{a}_i + \cdots + a_n$, the hat labeling a term that is to be omitted. In terms of f, $a_j = f(j)$ and the sum is $a_1 + \cdots + a_n = s_n + a_n$. If g is another choice of indices and $g(n) = a_i$, the sum according to g is $s_i + a_i$, and we wish to prove this coincides with $s_n + a_n$; we can assume $i<n$. If $n=2$, then $s_2 = a_1$, $s_1 = a_2$ and the result is clear. If $n>2$, $\Sigma_{j \in (n) \setminus \{i,n\}} a_j = t$, say, is well defined by (complete) induction and $s_n = t + a_i$, $s_i = t + a_n$, so $s_n + a_n = t + a_i + a_n = s_i + a_i$.

Similarly it is a direct consequence of the associativity and commutativity of multiplication that $a_1 a_2 \cdots a_n$ is well defined and independent of the order of the factors.

We conclude this chapter with a famous result of Euclid.

(1.27) PROPOSITION. *The set of primes is infinite.*

Proof. Suppose the set P of primes were finite, say $P = \{p_1, \ldots, p_n\}$. If $q = p_1 \cdots p_n$ then, from the discussion above, we know that for each i, $q = q_i p_i$, where $q_i = p_1 \cdots \hat{p}_i \cdots p_n$.

Let $N = q+1$. Now $N > p_i \ \forall i$, i.e., N is greater than every prime, so by (1.21) N is a product of various p_i (possibly with repetitions). However, if $p_i | N$, say $N = p_i a$, then we must have $a > q_i$ since $a \leqslant q_i \Rightarrow p_i a \leqslant p_i q_i < N$. Then $N = p_i a \geqslant p_i(q_i + 1) = q + p_i > q + 1 = N$, the contradiction proving the result. ■

Assignment 1

A1.1. Give rigorous proofs of the following statements supposing that you have just completed the proof of the result indicated.

- **(i)** After (1.14), $a < b+1 \Rightarrow a \leqslant b$.
- **(ii)** After (1.16), $2 \nmid 3$.
- **(iii)** After (1.19), a is composite iff there exists a factorization $a = bc$ with $b<a$ and $c<a$.
- **(iv)** After (1.23), if there exists a surjection $(m) \to (n)$, then $m \geqslant n$.
- **(v)** After (1.24), if the set X is infinite and $x \in X$ then $x \setminus \{x\}$ is also infinite.

A1.2. For $a, b \in \mathbb{N}$, a^b is defined inductively by $a^1 = a$ and $a^{b+1} = a^b a$. In the expression a^b, b is called the **exponent**. Prove the following:

- **(i)** $a^b a^c = a^{b+c}$.

more instructive. We think of the *pair* of natural numbers (1,2) as representing a solution of $2+x=1$. What we have in mind is $(1,2)=1-2=-1$. We cannot say as much because minus is not yet defined, but there is no harm in letting our intuition guide us in arriving at useful definitions. From $(2,3)=2-3=-1$ we would like to regard (1,2) and (2,3) as representing the same thing; and in general we would like to identify, in some sense, the pairs (a,b) and (c,d) whenever $a+d=b+c$.

The idea we are approaching, pervasive in mathematics, has the following general definition.

An **equivalence relation** on the set A is a relation $\sim$ between A and itself that has the properties

(i) $\sim$ is **reflexive**: $a\sim a \ \forall a\in A$.
(ii) $\sim$ is **symmetric**: $a\sim b \Rightarrow b\sim a$.
(iii) $\sim$ is **transitive**: $a\sim b$ and $b\sim c\Rightarrow a\sim c$.

The equality relation $=$ is the smallest equivalence relation in the sense that its graph is contained in the graph of every equivalence relation; at the other extreme is the equivalence relation whose graph is $A\times A$.

Let us look at the example suggested by our discussion above. We define a relation $\sim$ on $\mathbb{N}\times\mathbb{N}$ (so the graph of $\sim$ consists of pairs of pairs) as follows: $(a,b)\sim(c,d)$ iff $a+d=b+c$. That $\sim$ is reflexive and symmetric follows from the commutativity of addition. Suppose now $(a,b)\sim(c,d)$ and $(c,d)\sim(e,f)$; that is, $a+d=b+c$ and $c+f=d+e$. Adding these equations we have $(a+d)+(c+f)=(b+c)+(d+e)$, and, by an obvious sequence of applications of the associative, commutative, and cancellation laws for addition, we obtain $a+f=b+e$, whence $(a,b)\sim(e,f)$. Thus $\sim$ is an equivalence relation.

Given an equivalence relation $\sim$ on a set A, for each $a\in A$ we define

$$[a]=\{b\in A: a\sim b\}.$$

This set is called the **equivalence class** determined by a; any member of this class, in particular a, is a **representative** of the class. (*Class* is the word traditionally used here, and in this context is synonymous with *set*.) Since $a\in[a]$ these equivalence classes cover A:

$$A=\bigcup_{a\in A}[a].$$

We shall see in a moment that two equivalence classes for a given equivalence relation $\sim$ either consist of exactly the same elements or else are disjoint. Symbolically,

$$[a]\neq[b] \quad\Rightarrow\quad [a]\cap[b]=\varnothing.$$

If R denotes a set of representatives, so that $|R\cap[a]|=1 \ \forall a$, these facts can be summarized by

$$A = \coprod_{a \in R} [a].$$

It is useful to picture a continent divided into nonoverlapping countries. In general, we call the splitting of a set A into nonoverlapping subsets a **partition** of A.

(2.1) PROPOSITION. *Let $\sim$ be an equivalence relation on the set A. Then the equivalence classes for $\sim$ constitute a partition of A. Conversely, given a partition of A, there is a uniquely determined equivalence relation whose equivalence classes form the partition.*

Proof. If $\sim$ is an equivalence relation, if $[a]$ and $[b]$ are $\sim$ equivalence classes, and $[a] \cap [b] \neq \varnothing$, say $c \in [a] \cap [b]$, we wish to prove that $[a] \subset [b]$; for then by the same argument $[b] \subset [a]$ and therefore $[a] = [b]$. Now if $d \in [a]$ then, by definition, $a \sim d$. We also have $a \sim c$, and hence $c \sim a$ and $b \sim c$. Applying transitivity to $b \sim c \sim a \sim d$, we obtain $b \sim d$, or $d \in [b]$, as required.

Conversely, given a partition $\{A_i : i \in I\}$ of A, so $A = \cup\{A_i : i \in I\}$ and $A_i \cap A_j = \varnothing$ if $i \neq j$, we define $a \sim b$ iff a and b are in the same A_i. Obviously $\sim$ is an equivalence relation, and the equivalence classes are precisely the A_i. ■

$A/\sim$ denotes the set of equivalence classes and is called the **quotient set** of A by $\sim$; thus $[a]$ is a *single element* of $A/\sim$.

EXERCISES

1. The relation $\rho \subset X \times X$ is an equivalence relation iff ρ is reflexive and $a \rho b$ and $b \rho c \Rightarrow c \rho a$.

2. Let ρ, σ be symmetric relations on the set X, i.e., $\rho^{-1} = \rho, \sigma^{-1} = \sigma$. Then ρ and σ commute ($\rho\sigma = \sigma\rho$) iff $\rho\sigma$ is symmetric.

3. Let $X_1, X_2, \ldots$ be a sequence of sets indexed by $\mathbb{N}$, $f_i : X_i \to X_{i+1}$ maps, one for each i, and let $\mu_i : X_i \to X = \coprod X_i$ be the canonical injections. Show that the relation $\sim$ defined on X in the following way is an equivalence relation: If $a \in X_i$ and $b \in X_j$, then $\mu_i(a) \sim \mu_j(b)$ if for all sufficiently large n, $f_n \cdots f_{i+1} f_i(a) = f_n \cdots f_{j+1} f_j(b)$. ($\sim$ identifies elements that are eventually sent onto the same image.)

2. DEFINITION OF $\mathbb{Z}$

We use the standard notation

$$\mathbb{Z} = \mathbb{N} \times \mathbb{N}/\sim,$$

where $\sim$ is the particular equivalence relation discussed in the last section, and call the elements of $\mathbb{Z}$ **integers**. We write $[a,b]$ instead of $[(a,b)]$ for the integer containing the pair (a,b). We define five operations on $\mathbb{Z}$ in the sense of the following terminology: A **binary operation** on the set X is a map $X \times X \to X$; for example, $(x,y) \mapsto x+y$ is a binary operation on $\mathbb{N}$. A **ternary operation** is a map $X \times X \times X \to X$, the domain consisting of all triplets (x,y,z) of elements from X. An ***n*-ary operation** is a map $X \times X \times \cdots \times X$ (n times) $\to X$. In the other direction, a **unary operation** on X is simply a map $X \to X$. Finally, **nullary operations** are simply elements of X, these being referred to also as **constants, special elements,** or **distinguished elements**.

First we define two constants: $[1,1]$, called **zero** and denoted 0; $[2,1]$, called **one** and denoted 1. Remember that 0 and 1 are single elements of $\mathbb{Z}$. Thus we use the symbol 1 to denote both a natural number and an integer (and on occasion also the identity permutation on a set), but this will not be a serious ambiguity.

Next we have the unary operation called **negative** or **minus**, denoted $-$: $\mathbb{Z} \to \mathbb{Z}$, which is given by $-[a,b]=[b,a]$.

Finally there are two binary operations called **addition** and **multiplication**:

$$[a,b]+[c,d]=[a+c,b+d],$$
$$[a,b][c,d]=[ac+bd,ad+bc].$$

Before we accept these definitions of $-$, $+$, and $\times$ (multiplication) as bona fide, we must verify that they are well defined, that is, the answers are not dependent on the choice of representatives. For example, $[1,2]=[3,4]$ and $[5,3]=[4,2]$. Now the product of these two classes is $[1,2][5,3]=[11,13]$ according to the first-named representatives (we explain decimal notation in Section 4) and $[3,4][4,2]=[20,22]$ according to the second representatives. If we did not have $[11,13]=[20,22]$, multiplication would not be a mapping from $\mathbb{Z}\times\mathbb{Z}$ to $\mathbb{Z}$ and the definition would have to be abandoned.

We now prove that such difficulties never arise.

(2.2) PROPOSITION. (i) *The operations* $-,+,\times$ *on* $\mathbb{Z}$ *are well defined.*

(ii) $+$ *and* $\times$ *are associative.*

(iii) $+$ *and* $\times$ *are commutative.*

(iv) $0+\alpha=\alpha$ *and* $-\alpha+\alpha=0$ $\forall\alpha\in\mathbb{Z}$.

(v) $1\alpha=\alpha$ $\forall\alpha\in\mathbb{Z}$.

(vi) *Multiplication is distributive over addition.*

Proof. (i) Suppose $[a,b]=[a',b']$ and $[c,d]=[c',d']$. We have $a+b'=b+a', c+d'=d+c'$. Thus $b'+a=a'+b$, i.e., $-[a',b']=-[a,b]$, so $-$ is well defined. Adding the two equations gives, after some rearrangement, $a+c+b'+d'=b+d+a'+c'$ i.e., $[a+c,b+d]=[a'+c',b'+d']$, that is, $[a,b]+[c,d]=[a',b']+[c',d']$, which proves that $+$ is well defined.

The case of $\times$ is a little tricky. We start by pulling out of the hat the equation

$$a(c'+d)+b(c+d')+c'(a'+b)+d'(a+b')=a(c+d')+b(c'+d)$$
$$+c'(a+b')+d'(a'+b),$$

which is true because $a'+b=a+b'$ and $c'+d=c+d'$. Expanding these terms and applying the cancellation law for $+$ in $\mathbb{N}$ yields

$$ad+bc+c'a'+d'b'=ac+bd+c'b'+d'a',$$

which proves

$$[a'c'+b'd', a'd'+b'c']=[ac+bd, ad+bc],$$

or

$$[a',b'][c',d']=[a,b][c,d].$$

(ii) The associative law for the addition of integers follows immediately from that for the natural numbers:

$$([a,b]+[c,d])+[e,f]=[(a+c)+e,(b+d)+f]$$
$$=[a,b]+([c,d]+[e,f]).$$

The remaining statements of the proposition are just as straightforward to prove and are left to the reader. ■

In the following corollary a, b, and c denote integers.

(2.3) COROLLARY.
(α) $a+b=a+c \Rightarrow b=c$.
(β) $0a=0$.
(γ) *$a+x=b$ has a unique solution x, namely $x=b-a$ (which means, as usual, $b+(-a)$).*
(δ) $(-a)b=a(-b)=-(ab)$.
(ε) $-(-a)=a$.

Proof. (α) $a+b=a+c \Rightarrow (-a+a)+b=(-a+a)+c$ by (ii), which in turn $\Rightarrow b=c$ by (iv).

(β) $0a=(0+0)a=0a+0a$ by (iv) and (vi), hence $0=0a$ by (α) in conjunction with (iii) and (iv).

(γ) Clearly $x=b-a$ is a solution and uniqueness follows by (α).

(δ) $0=0b=(-a+a)b=(-a)b+ab$, but also $-(ab)+ab=0$, so $(-a)b=-(ab)$ by (iii) and (α). Similarly, $0=a(-b+b)$ implies $a(-b)=-(ab)$.

(ε) We have both $a+(-a)=0$ and $-(-a)+(-a)=0$. ■

3. THE EMBEDDING $\mathbb{N} \to \mathbb{Z}$

We leave as an exercise the verification that inequalities on $\mathbb{Z}$ are well defined by declaring $[a,b]<[c,d]$ if $a+d<b+c$. Once this is done we see that the law of trichotomy still holds in $\mathbb{Z}$: Given two integers $[a,b]$ and $[c,d]$ exactly one of $<,=,>$ obtains between $a+d$ and $b+c$.

(2.4) PROPOSITION. *The mapping* $f\colon \mathbb{N} \to \mathbb{Z}$ *given by* $f(a)=[a+1,1]$ *is injective. Moreover, f preserves* 1, *sums, products, and inequalities*: $f(1)=1$, $f(a+b)=f(a)+f(b)$, $f(ab)=f(a)f(b)$, *and* $a<b \Rightarrow f(a)<f(b)$.

Proof. $f(a)=f(b) \Rightarrow [a+1,1]=[b+1,1] \Rightarrow a+2=b+2 \Rightarrow a=b$, so f is injective; $f(1)=[2,1]=1$; $f(a+b)=[a+b+1,1]=[a+b+2,2]$ $=[a+1,1]+[b+1,1]=f(a)+f(b)$; $f(ab)=[ab+1,1]=[ab+a+b+2,$ $a+b+2]=[a+1,1][b+1,1]=f(a)f(b)$; $a<b \Rightarrow a+2<b+2 \Rightarrow [a+$ $1,1]<[b+1,1]$, i.e., $f(a)<f(b)$. ■

Thus there is a bijective correspondence between integers of the form $[a+1,1]$ and natural numbers a. Since the integer 1 corresponds to the natural number 1 and $[a+1,1]+1$ corresponds to $a+1$, we see that this set of integers satisfies the Peano axioms, and, because all the properties of $\mathbb{N}$ were deduced from the axioms, is in fact a "copy" of $\mathbb{N}$ inside $\mathbb{Z}$ (cf. A2.1). There is no harm in making this bijection an identification:

$$a=[a+1,1].$$

We now have a tripartite division of $\mathbb{Z}$:

(2.5) PROPOSITION. $\mathbb{Z}$ *is partitioned into three classes*:

(α) 0;
(β) *the* **positive integers**, *or natural numbers* a, *where* $a \in \mathbb{N}$;
(γ) *the* **negative integers** $-a$, *where* $a \in \mathbb{N}$.

Proof. By trichotomy, $-a<0<a$ for $a \in \mathbb{N}$, which shows that the three sets are mutually disjoint, so it remains to check that every integer $[a,b]$ falls into one of the sets. If $a=b$, then $[a,b]=0$; if $a>b$, say $a=b+c$, where $c \in \mathbb{N}$, then $[a,b]=[c+1,1]=c$. Finally, if $a<b$, say $a+c=b$, where $c \in \mathbb{N}$, then $[a,b]=-[b,a]=-c$. ■

We can now discard the pair notation and write the elements of $\mathbb{Z}$ as usual:

$$\mathbb{Z}=\{\ldots,-3,-2,-1,0,1,2,3,\ldots\},$$

where $\cdots<-3<-2<-1<0<1<\cdots$.

(2.6) PROPOSITION. *Let a, b, c be integers.*

(i) $a < b$ *iff* $a + n = b$ *for some* $n \in \mathbb{N}$.
(ii) $a < b$ *and* $b < c \Rightarrow a < c$.
(iii) $a \leqslant b$ *and* $c < d \Rightarrow a + c < b + d$.
(iv) $a < b$ *and* $c > 0 \Rightarrow ac < bc$, *whereas* $a < b$ *and* $c < 0 \Rightarrow ac > bc$.
(v) $ab = ac$ *and* $a \neq 0 \Rightarrow b = c$.
(vi) $a \neq 0$ *and* $b \neq 0 \Rightarrow ab \neq 0$.

Proof. (i) Let $a = [r, s]$, $b = [u, v]$, where $r, s, u, v \in \mathbb{N}$. (This will almost certainly be our final recourse to the pair notation.) If $a < b$, then by definition $r + v < s + u$. We may therefore say $r + v + n = s + u$, where $n \in \mathbb{N}$. It follows that $a + n = b$. Conversely, let $a + n = b, n \in \mathbb{N}$. Then $r + n + 1 + v = s + 1 + u$, so $r + v < s + u$, whence $a < b$.

(ii) Let $a + m = b$, $b + n = c$, where $m, n \in \mathbb{N}$. Then $a + m + n = c$, hence $a < c$. A similar application of (i) proves (iii).

(iv) Let $a + n = b$, $n \in \mathbb{N}$, so $bc = ac + nc$. If $c > 0$, i.e., if $c \in \mathbb{N}$, then $nc \in \mathbb{N}$ and therefore $bc > ac$ by (i). On the other hand if $c < 0$, then $n(-c) \in \mathbb{N}$ and $bc < ac$ follows from $bc + n(-c) = ac$.

(v) By (iv), $b \neq c$ and $a \neq 0 \Rightarrow ab \neq ac$.

(vi) If $a \neq 0$ yet $ab = 0$ then (v) applied to $ab = a0$ gives $b = 0$. ■

EXERCISES

1. $1^2 - 2^2 + 3^2 - \cdots + (-1)^{n-1}n^2 = (-1)^{n-1}n(n+1)/2$.

2. For $a, b \in \mathbb{Z}$ and odd $m, n \in \mathbb{N}$, $a^m = b^m \Leftrightarrow a^n = b^n$.

3. Evaluate $1 - (2 - (3 - (4 - \cdots - (n))) \cdots)$.

4. THE ARCHIMEDEAN PRINCIPLE

A subset S of $\mathbb{Z}$ is **bounded below** if there exists an $a \in \mathbb{Z}$ such that $a \leqslant s$ $\forall s \in S$; such an a is called a **lower bound** for S. Notice that we do not require a to be in A. Thus $\varnothing$ is bounded below since every a is a lower bound. $\mathbb{N}$ is bounded below, any one of $1, 0, -1, -2, \ldots$ serving as a lower bound, but $\mathbb{Z}$ itself is not.

(2.7) PROPOSITION. (i) *The* **well-ordering principle** *for* $\mathbb{Z}$: *Let S be a nonempty subset of $\mathbb{Z}$ that is bounded below. Then S has a greatest lower bound, abbreviated g.l.b., and this g.l.b. is in S.*

(ii) *The* **Archimedean principle** *for* $\mathbb{Z}$: *Given integers a and b with $b > 0$, $\exists n \in \mathbb{N} \ni nb > a$.*

Proof. (i) Let a be a lower bound for S and consider the set $T = \{s + 1 - a : s \in S\}$ of natural numbers. By the well-ordering principle for $\mathbb{N}$, T

contains a smallest member, say s_0+1-a. Thus $s_0+1-a \leqslant s+1-a$, hence $s_0 \leqslant s$, $\forall s \in S$, which shows that s_0 is a lower bound for S. Since a is a lower bound for S and $s_0 \in S$, we have $s_0 \geqslant a$, proving that $s_0 = \text{g.l.b.}(S)$. Of course the g.l.b. is unique by trichotomy.

(ii) If $a \leqslant 0$, $n=1$ works; if $a>0$, $n=a$ works. ■

Since $a<b \Rightarrow -a>-b$, if S is a nonempty subset of $\mathbb{Z}$ bounded above, then $\{-s : s \in S\}$ is bounded below; and if c is the g.l.b. then clearly $-c$ is the least upper bound of S, abbreviated l.u.b. We have

(2.8) COROLLARY. *Every nonempty subset S of $\mathbb{Z}$ bounded above has a unique l.u.b., and this l.u.b. is in S.*

(2.9) PROPOSITION. *Given integers a and b with $b>0$, there exist unique integers q and r satisfying*

$$a=bq+r, \qquad 0 \leqslant r<b.$$

Proof. The set $S=\{c \in \mathbb{Z} : c=a-bd \text{ for some } d \in \mathbb{Z} \text{ and } c<b\}$ is bounded above by b and is nonempty by the Archimedean principle. If $r=\text{l.u.b.}(S)$, say $r=a-bq$, we wish to prove that $r \geqslant 0$. But if r were negative then $r<a-b(q-1)=r+b<b$, so $r+b$ would be an element of S greater than r, a contradiction.

It remains to prove uniqueness. Suppose that we also had $a=bq'+r'$, $0 \leqslant r'<b$; then $b(q'-q)=r-r'$. The inequalities satisfied by the rs imply $-b<r-r'<b$. Thus $q'>q$, which implies $b(q'-q) \geqslant b$, is not possible, nor is $q'<q$ for a similar reason. We must have $q'=q$, whence $0=r-r'$, and therefore also $r'=r$. ■

Some familiar terms: Given a and b, a process that determines q and r is called **division** of a by b; q is the **quotient** and r is the **remainder**.

We leave to the reader the simple proofs of the following supplementary remarks: (i) if $a \geqslant 0$ (in addition to $b>0$), then $q \geqslant 0$; (ii) if $b<0$, then $\exists! q, r \ni a=bq+r$ and $0 \leqslant r<-b$; (iii) we extend the definition of $b|a$ to all of $\mathbb{Z}$: this means $\exists c \in \mathbb{Z} \ni bc=a$. When $b \neq 0$, $b|a$ iff the remainder is 0 when we divide a by b. When applied to natural numbers $b|a$ retains its original meaning: necessarily $c \in \mathbb{N}$ also.

As an application of division we explain the **decimal notation** for integers; for the moment let us write $9+1=t$.

(2.10) PROPOSITION. *Each positive integer n is uniquely representable in the form*

$$n=d_0+d_1t+d_2t^2+\cdots+d_mt^m$$

for some $m \geqslant 0$ where $0 \leqslant d_i \leqslant 9$ for each i and $d_m>0$.

Remark. The d_i are called the **digits** of n; using the familiar positional notation for the digits, one writes the representation in the condensed form $n = d_m d_{m-1} \ldots d_0$. In particular, $t = 0 + 1 \cdot t = 10$.

Proof. Given n, we divide by t writing the result in the form

$$n = d_0 + tn_1, \qquad 0 \leqslant d_0 < t \quad (\text{i.e., } \ 0 \leqslant d_0 \leqslant 9).$$

If $n_1 = 0$, then $n = d_0$ is already a representation in the required form, so we can suppose that $n_1 > 0$ to complete the existence half of the proof. There are two ways of doing this. On the one hand we can argue by complete induction: since $n_1 < n$ we have such a representation for n_1, say $n_1 = e_0 + e_1 t + \cdots + e_r t^r$, and then $n = d_0 + e_0 t + \cdots + e_r t^{r+1}$ is of the required form. This existence proof is *nonconstructive* in that it does not give an explicit procedure for determining all the digits.

Of course, it is easily converted into a constructive proof. Instead of relying on induction, we deal with n_1 directly. Divide by t to get $n_1 = d_1 + tn_2$. Either $n_2 = 0$ and the procedure stops, or else we repeat the operation: $n_2 = d_2 + tn_3$. We continue until we arrive at some $n_i = 0$ (as we must: the set $\{n_j\}$ thus obtained is bounded below by 0, and if n_i is the g.l.b. then $n_i = 0$ because otherwise $n_{i+1} < n_i$).

The uniqueness part of the proof is an easy induction and is left to the reader. ■

A set of rules by which a result can be obtained mechanically, without ingenuity, is known as an **algorithm**. The procedure just discussed is an example, granted that one knows how to perform division.

EXERCISES

1. Devise an explicit algorithm to obtain the quotient and remainder in $a = bq + r$ given any integers a and $b \neq 0$.

2. Let q be a natural number > 1. Then q is prime iff $p \nmid q$ for every prime p satisfying $p^2 \leqslant q$. Thus 113 is prime since it is not divisible by 2, 3, 5, or 7.

3. A generalization of (2.10): Let $a_1, a_2, \ldots$ be integers, each $\geqslant 2$, and put $b_i = a_1 a_2 \cdots a_i$. Then each natural number n is a unique finite sum

   $$(*) \qquad n = d_0 + d_1 b_1 + d_2 b_2 + \cdots, \qquad 0 \leqslant d_i < a_{i+1}.$$

   (When each $a_i = a$ so that $b_i = a^i$, $(*)$ is called the ***a*-adic expansion** of n, or the representation of n in the **base** (or **scale** of) a. Two cases that are important in computer technology are the **binary** scale ($a = 2$) and the **hexadecimal** scale ($a = 16$). In the latter case it is customary to write A, B, C, D, E, F as digits for the numbers from 10 to 15. Thus in positional hexadecimal notation, $10B$ denotes $1 \cdot 16^2 + 0 \cdot 16 + 11 = 267$ in the usual base ten notation.) In any scale a, the number 10101 is composite.

Assignment 2

A2.1. Show that $\mathbb{N}$ is essentially unique: If $\mathbb{N}', S', 1'$ constitute another system satisfying Peano's axioms, in an obvious notation, prove that there is a bijection $f: \mathbb{N} \to \mathbb{N}'$ satisfying $f(1) = 1'$ and $fS = S'f$.

A2.2. Let n be a fixed integer. Show that the relation θ on $\mathbb{Z}$ defined by $a\theta b$ iff $n|(a-b)$ is an equivalence relation. Show that when $n = 0$, θ is the equality relation; that when $n > 0$ there are n equivalence classes, represented by the integers $0, 1, 2, \ldots, n-1$, and the representative of a is the remainder when a is divided by n.

A2.3. Let $\{A_i : i \in I\}$ be a collection of subsets of the set A.

(i) If B is another subset of A prove the distributive laws:

$$B \bigcap \left(\bigcup_{i \in I} A_i \right) = \bigcup_{i \in I} \left(B \bigcap A_i \right),$$

$$B \bigcup \left(\bigcap_{i \in I} A_i \right) = \bigcap_{i \in I} \left(B \bigcup A_i \right).$$

(I is not required to be finite.)

(ii) Prove **DeMorgan's laws**:

$$A \setminus \bigcup A_i = \bigcap (A \setminus A_i),$$

$$A \setminus \bigcap A_i = \bigcup (A \setminus A_i),$$

where $i \in I$ is understood.

Remark. In analyzing these and more complicated expressions involving $\cup$, $\cap$ and $\setminus$, it is often helpful to represent the sets by simple regions in the plane, thinking of the elements as points. Such pictographs, called **Venn diagrams** (see, e.g., Figure 2.1), are of course only aids and not substitutes for proofs.

A2.4. List the five equivalence relations on the set $A = \{1,2,3\}$ by specifying their graphs (without detailed explanation).

Figure 2.1 A Venn diagram.

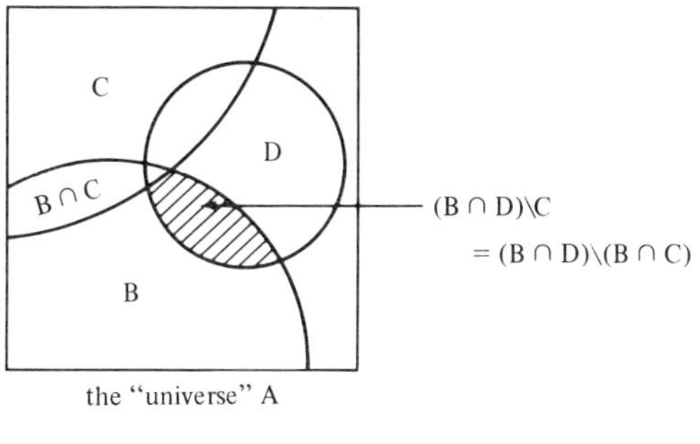

A2.5. If $\{\rho_i : i \in I\}$ is a collection of equivalence relations on A show that $\cap \rho_i$ is (the graph of) an equivalence relation. Hence deduce that if S is any subset of $A \times A$ there is a unique smallest equivalence relation containing S. If B is a subset of A, what is this equivalence relation when $S = B \times B$?

A2.6. (i) Let $a \in \mathbb{Z}$ and let S be a subset of $\mathbb{Z}$ satisfying

(α) $a \in S$,

(β) $s \in S \Rightarrow s+1 \in S$.

Prove that $S \supset \{b \in \mathbb{Z} : b \geqslant a\}$. (*Hint*: $\{n \in \mathbb{N} : n = s+1-a$ for some $s \in S\}$ satisfies (P5). This result is a generalization of (P5) known as **induction starting at *a*.**)

(ii) ***n* factorial**, denoted $n!$ (in some older books one finds $\underline{|n}$) is defined for nonnegative integers by induction starting at 0: $0! = 1$ and $(n+1)! = (n+1) \cdot n!$. Thus $1! = 1 \cdot 1 = 1, 2! = 2 \cdot 1 = 2, 3! = 3 \cdot 2 \cdot 1 = 6$, and so on. Second, the **binomial coefficients** for integers m, n satisfying $0 \leqslant m \leqslant n$, are defined by

$$\binom{n}{0} = \binom{n}{n} = 1$$

and

$$\binom{n+1}{m} = \binom{n}{m-1} + \binom{n}{m} \qquad \text{for } 1 \leqslant m \leqslant n.$$

A formula such as this, which defines a sequence of numbers in terms of previously calculated ones, is known as a **recurrence relation**. The results for successively higher values of n can be displayed in **Pascal's triangle**:

$$\begin{array}{ccccccccccc}
 & & & & & 1 & & & & & \\
 & & & & 1 & & 1 & & & & \\
 & & & 1 & & 2 & & 1 & & & \\
 & & 1 & & 3 & & 3 & & 1 & & \\
 & 1 & & 4 & & 6 & & 4 & & 1 & \\
1 & & 5 & & 10 & & 10 & & 5 & & 1 \\
 & & & & & \vdots & & & & &
\end{array}$$

The top number is $\binom{0}{0} = 1$; the second row consists of $\binom{1}{0} = 1$ and $\binom{1}{1} = 1; \ldots$; the sixth row of $\binom{5}{0} = 1$, $\binom{5}{1} = 5$, $\binom{5}{2} = 10, \ldots$. According to the recurrence relation each entry, apart from the 1s along the borders, is the sum of the two immediately overhead.

Prove that

$$m!(n-m)!\binom{n}{m} = n!.$$

Hence deduce that the product of any m consecutive integers is a multiple of $m!$ (i.e., of the form $m!x$ for some $x \in \mathbb{Z}$).

5. RINGS

A wide variety of mathematical systems share certain properties with $\mathbb{Z}$ and, in the spirit of modern algebra, we *abstract* these properties; that is, we separate them from the more special properties that are not of sufficiently general occurrence, in order to define a useful general or "abstract" algebraic notion.

(2.11) DEFINITION. A **ring** is a set R (say) with binary operations $+$ and $\times$, a unary operation $-$, and constants 0 and 1 satisfying the following axioms:

(R1) $+$ and $\times$ are associative;
(R2) $+$ is commutative;
(R3) $0+a=a$ and $-a+a=0\ \forall a\in R$;
(R4) $1a=a1=a\ \forall a\in R$;
(R5) $a(b+c)=ab+ac$ and $(a+b)c=ac+bc\ \forall a,b,c\in R$.
The ring R is **commutative** if it also satisfies the axiom
(R6) $\times$ is commutative.

$\mathbb{Z}$ certainly satisfies this definition and (R6) as well: $\mathbb{Z}$ is a commutative ring. We shall see examples of noncommutative rings in the next section. The phrase "R is a ring" does not exclude the possibility that R is commutative; thus it is quite correct to say "$\mathbb{Z}$ is a ring," just as "$0 \leqslant 1$" and "$1 \leqslant 1$" are true statements.

The most obvious advantage in making this definition is that all results deduced from the axioms are true for every ring and need not be reproved for each ring as it comes along. For example, if a,b,c are elements of a particular ring R and $a+b=a+c$, then we can conclude that $b=c$. The proof is identical to that used for $\mathbb{Z}$ in (2.3). We have $-a+(a+b)=-a+(a+c)$, whence $(-a+a)+b=(-a+a)+c$ using (R1); then $0+b=0+c$ by (R3), and therefore $b=c$ again by (R3). (*Exercise*: Verify that the proofs of the remaining statements in (2.3) depend only on the properties enunciated in the ring axioms, and that all the statements of (2.3) are therefore true for rings in general.) Our definition of ring and similar definitions of other algebraic structures have further advantages that will become clearer as these concepts are used.

As we shall see, it is not confusing to use the same symbols $+,\times,-,0,1$ for various rings. There are indeed many different rings, which puts the ring axioms in a different light from the Peano axioms, the latter being satisfied only by $\mathbb{N}$, as we saw in A2.1. In mathematical logic one would say that the ring axioms have different *models*, whereas the Peano axioms have only one model.

We now describe a construction that creates a new ring out of a given collection of rings. We begin with an example. We define ring operations on the set $R=\mathbb{Z}\times\mathbb{Z}$ of all pairs (a,b) of integers as follows:

$$
\begin{aligned}
(a,b)+(c,d)&=(a+c,b+d),\\
(a,b)(c,d)&=(ac,bd),\\
-(a,b)&=(-a,-b),\\
0&=(0,0),\\
1&=(1,1).
\end{aligned}
\tag{2.12}
$$

The new operations on R occurring on the left are defined in terms of the known operations on $\mathbb{Z}$ on the right. The ring axioms are very easy to check. For example, $(1,1)(a,b)=(1a,1b)=(a,b)$ shows that $1\alpha=\alpha\ \forall\alpha\in R$. This ring is indeed a new ring: It is not $\mathbb{Z}$ somehow in disguise because $x=(1,0)\neq 0$, $y=(0,1)\neq 0$, yet $xy=0$, a behavior unknown in $\mathbb{Z}$ (2.6 (vi)).

This construction extends to $R=R_1\times R_2\times\cdots\times R_n$, the set of all n-tuples $(a_1,\ldots,a_n)$, where a_i, called the **ith component**, is in the ith ring R_i and the operations are componentwise:

$$
\begin{aligned}
(a_1,\ldots,a_n)+(b_1,\ldots,b_n)&=(a_1+b_1,\ldots,a_n+b_n),\\
&\ \ \vdots\\
1&=(1,\ldots,1).
\end{aligned}
$$

We would like to generalize this to an arbitrary nonempty set of rings $\{R_i: i\in I\}$. Intuitively we picture the elements as having the form $(\ldots,a_i,\ldots)$, where $a_i\in R_i$, and the operations as performed componentwise: $(\ldots,a_i,\ldots)+(\ldots,b_i,\ldots)=(\ldots,a_i+b_i,\ldots)$. However, since I is allowed to be infinite a more careful definition is called for. The idea is to think of $(\ldots,a_i,\ldots)$ as a function with domain I whose value at i is a_i.

Recall that the disjoint union $\amalg R_i$ comes equipped with injections μ_i: $R_i\to\amalg R_i$. When it does not lead to ambiguity, we often identify R_i with $\mu_i(R_i)$ and then $R_i\subset\amalg R_i$. This notational simplification is used in the second part of the next definition.

(2.13) DEFINITION. (i) If X and I are sets, X^I denotes the set of all maps from I to X.

(ii) The **product** of the collection of sets $\{X_i: i\in I\}$ is the set

$$\prod_{i\in I}X_i=\left\{f\in\left(\amalg X_i\right)^I: f(i)\in X_i,\ \forall i\in I\right\}.$$

When I is finite, say $\{1,2,\ldots,n\}$, an alternative notation for the product, which we have already used, is $X_1\times\cdots\times X_n$.

EXERCISE

Show that the statement

$$I \neq \varnothing \quad \text{and} \quad X_i \neq \varnothing \quad \forall i \in I \qquad \Rightarrow \qquad \prod X_i \neq \varnothing$$

(in words, the product of a nonempty collection of nonempty sets is nonempty) is equivalent to the axiom of choice. That is, derive each statement from the other.

(2.14) PROPOSITION. *Let $\{R_i : i \in I\}$ be a collection of rings and $R = \prod R_i$. Then R is a ring if we define the ring operations componentwise: If $f, g \in R$, then*

$$(f+g)(i) = f(i) + g(i),$$
$$(fg)(i) = f(i)g(i),$$
$$(-f)(i) = -(f(i)),$$
$$1(i) = 1,$$
$$0(i) = 0,$$

where the operations on the right of these equations are the given operations on R_i.

Remarks. R is called the **product** or **direct product** of the rings R_i. Only on rare occasions will it be necessary to write $f \times g$ or $f \cdot g$ for fg to avoid confusion with the composition of maps.

Proof. Let $*$ stand for either $+$ or $\times$. Then $((f*g)*h)(i) = (f*g)(i)*h(i) = (f(i)*g(i))*h(i) = f(i)*(g(i)*h(i))$, since $*$ is associative in R_i, and by definition this is $(f*(g*h))(i)$. This being true $\forall i$, we can conclude that $(f*g)*h = f*(g*h)$, which proves both cases of (R1) for R. The proofs of the other ring axioms are equally straightforward and are left to the reader. ■

Notice that $\prod R_i$ is commutative iff each R_i is. (The existence of even a single pair a, b such that $ab \neq ba$ makes the ring noncommutative.)

We conclude this section with two more examples of rings. First an "extreme" example, the **one-element ring**, which we shall denote $\not{1}$. (This notation is *not* standard in the mathematical literature.) The single element serves as both 0 and 1; in $\not{1}$, $0 = 1$. (The axioms do not preclude this.) For the other operations we have no choice: $0 + 0 = 0$, $0 \times 0 = 0$, $-0 = 0$. The ring axioms are satisfied and $\not{1}$ is a ring, albeit a not very interesting one. (It would, however, be awkward in certain discussions to disallow $\not{1}$, as do some authors, by making $1 \neq 0$ an additional ring axiom. Incidentally, in certain specialized applications there is a need for the concept of "ring not necessarily with 1," whose definition is obtained from that of ring by removing the requirement that there exist a constant 1 and (R4). Their theory is more complicated and less extensive than that of rings and is best developed in the context where it is needed. In this book ring always means "ring with 1.")

If R is a ring in which $1=0$, then R is (a copy of) $\not{1}$ because $a=1a=0a=0$, $\forall a \in R$.

Thus if R contains exactly two elements these elements must be 0 and 1, with $0 \neq 1$. (R3), (R4), and (2.3)(β) immediately determine all sums and products except $1+1$. We could not have $1+1=1$, because then (2.3)(α) $\Rightarrow 1=0$, so $1+1=0$ and the addition and multiplication tables are as below; the third figure indicates the arrangement of the tables:

+	0	1
0	0	1
1	1	0

×	0	1
0	0	0
1	0	1

*	y
x	$x*y$

A table of negatives would be redundant since $-a$ is the unique solution of $x+a=0$, and this can be read from the addition table. One always has $-0=0$, and in this example $-1=1$. The ring axioms can be verified by checking all cases. In Section 4 of Chapter 3 we shall introduce concepts that permit us to tell "at a glance" that the axioms are satisfied.

This ring is denoted either GF(2) or $\mathbb{F}_2$ or $\mathbb{Z}/2\mathbb{Z}$ (cf. Section 5 of Chapter 3); all are standard. Some writers use $\mathbb{Z}_2$ for this ring, but this should be avoided because $\mathbb{Z}_2$ is standard notation for another ring (introduced in Chapter 5).

If R is a finite ring, or indeed any finite set equipped with a set of operations subject to a set of axioms, one refers to $|R|$ as the **order** of R. The discussion above shows that there is, up to copies, only one ring of order 2.

EXERCISES

1. Assuming the fact that there is a ring of order 3, say $R=\{0,1,r\}$, show that the + and × tables must be

+	0	1	r
0	0	1	r
1	1	r	0
r	r	0	1

×	0	1	r
0	0	0	0
1	0	1	r
r	0	r	1

(The unique ring of order 3 is denoted either GF(3) or $\mathbb{F}_3$ or $\mathbb{Z}/3\mathbb{Z}$.)

2. In the definition of ring, (R2) is redundant: it is a consequence of the other axioms.

3. For elements a, b, c in a commutative ring,

$$a^3+b^3+c^3=0 \Rightarrow \left((a^3-c^3)b\right)^3+\left((b^3-a^3)c\right)^3+\left((c^3-b^3)a\right)^3=0.$$

6. POLYNOMIALS

The operations $+$ and $\times$ in a ring have common features that can be profitably abstracted:

(2.15) DEFINITION. A **semigroup** is a set equipped with an associative binary operation. With the operation denoted $(a,b)\mapsto a*b$, the semigroup is **commutative** if $a*b=b*a$, $\forall a,b$.

For example $\mathbb{N}$ with $+$ is a commutative semigroup; $\mathbb{N}$ is a different commutative semigroup with respect to multiplication. If A is a set then the set A^A of all maps from A to itself with composition of maps as the operation is a semigroup (cf. A1.4), which is in general noncommutative.

For instance, if $A=\{1,2\}$, then A^A consists of four elements, say $1, r, s, t$, whose values are given in the accompanying table:

x	$x(1)$	$x(2)$
1	1	2
r	1	1
s	2	2
t	2	1

To determine a product, say rs, we work out its values: $(rs)(1)=r(s(1))=r(2)=1, (rs)(2)=r(s(2))=r(2)=1$; and inspection of the table shows that these values correspond to those of r, so $rs=r$. Similarly, we find $sr=s$; hence $rs\neq sr$ and this semigroup is noncommutative. The complete multiplication table for this semigroup is as follows; the entry in the table is xy as in the tables for $\mathbb{Z}/2\mathbb{Z}$ given earlier.

$x \backslash y$	1	r	s	t
1	1	r	s	t
r	r	r	r	r
s	s	s	s	s
t	t	s	r	1

In a general discussion about semigroups we usually write the operation as multiplication; when such a discussion is specialized, say to the additive semigroup of a ring, naturally we choose to switch to additive notation. Of course, there is only one concept of semigroup: A phrase such as "additive semigroup" is merely a convenient way of saying "semigroup whose operation is written $+$."

A **subsemigroup** of a semigroup B is a subset $C\subset B$ that is closed under (or with respect to) the oper-tion. That is,

$$x, y\in C \quad\Rightarrow\quad xy\in C.$$

With the operation restricted to $C \times C \to C$, C is itself a semigroup. In the example $B = A^A$, the following subsets are subsemigroups: $\varnothing$, $\{1\}$, $\{r\}$, $\{s\}$, $\{1,t\}$, $\{r,s\}$, $\{1,r,s\}$, and B itself. $\{t\}$ is not a subsemigroup because $t \times t = 1 \notin \{t\}$.

If A is a semigroup and a_i denote elements of A, the associative law says that $a_1a_2a_3$ is unambiguous: the two possible interpretations $(a_1a_2)a_3$ and $a_1(a_2a_3)$ give the same element of A. There are five meaningful ways of bracketing four factors:

$$(a_1a_2)(a_3a_4), \qquad ((a_1a_2)a_3)a_4,$$
$$(a_1(a_2a_3))a_4, \qquad a_1(a_2(a_3a_4)), \qquad a_1((a_2a_3)a_4).$$

The next result says that these all agree, so we may write the product unambiguously as $a_1a_2a_3a_4$.

(2.16) PROPOSITION. *The general associative law: Let A be a semigroup written multiplicatively and $a_1, \ldots, a_n \in A$. Then the product $a_1a_2 \cdots a_n$ is unambiguous.*

Proof by complete induction on n. We can suppose that $n > 3$. By I.H., $a_1 \cdots a_{n-1} = b$ is uniquely defined. Now consider any particular, meaningful bracketing of $a_1a_2 \cdots a_n$. The fact that the bracketing is meaningful implies that the product is separated into two factors: $(a_1 \cdots a_m)(a_{m+1} \cdots a_n)$, where $1 \leqslant m < n$, and there are in general further parentheses that have not been indicated. We would like to say that this equals $(a_1 \cdots a_{n-1})a_n$, where $a_1 \cdots a_{n-1}$ is bracketed in any meaningful way, since this has the unambiguous value ba_n, which would complete the proof. This is true if $m = n-1$, so we can suppose $m < n-1$.

By I.H. the term $a_{m+1} \cdots a_n$ calculated according to the given bracketing is equal to ca_n, where $c = a_{m+1} \cdots a_{n-1}$ is unambiguous. Again by I.H., $d = a_1 \cdots a_m$ is unambiguous and the given product is $d(ca_n) = (dc)a_n$ by the key case of three factors. ■

The order of the factors $a_1, a_2, \ldots$ in $a_1a_2 \cdots a_n$ is significant unless the semigroup is commutative, in which case the order of the factors does not matter; this was proved together with the general associative law for additive ℕ in Section 8 of Chapter 1. Clearly what we proved there can be restated as a result about commutative semigroups.

A **monoid** is a semigroup A with a constant denoted e (or sometimes simply 1), called the **neutral element**, satisfying the axiom

$$ea = a = ae, \quad \forall a \in A.$$

Notice that there can be only one such e: If f is an element of A such that also $fa = a = af\ \forall a \in A$, then $e = ef = f$. This remark applied to the additive monoid of a ring R gives the fact that 0 (the e of this monoid) is the only element of R with the property $0 + a = a\ \forall a \in R$; applied to the multiplicative monoid of R it shows that 1 is the only element satisfying $1a=a=a1$ $\forall a\in R$.

Another example of a monoid is the semigroup A^A mentioned earlier; in this case 1_A serves as e. (*Mental exercise*: If $\{X_i : i\in I\}$ is a set of semigroups (resp. monoids), then ΠX_i with componentwise operation(s) is a semigroup (resp. monoid). It is called the **product** or **direct product** of the X_i.)

A particular monoid we shall use presently is

$$\mathbb{M}=\{0\}\cup\mathbb{N}=\{0,1,2,3,\ldots\},$$

where the operation is addition of integers. $\mathbb{M}$ will keep this meaning throughout. Unlike $\mathbb{N}$ and $\mathbb{Z}$, the symbol is not standard in the literature.

A *polynomial* over a ring R is an expression like

$$a_0+a_1X+\ +a_2X^2+\cdots+a_nX^n,$$

where the coefficients $a_0, a_1,\ldots$ are elements of R. Addition is performed by adding coefficients of like powers of X; e.g.,

$$(2-3X+5X^3)+(-2+2X+X^2)=-X+X^2+5X^3$$

(which is $0+(-1)X+1X^2+5X^3$ with obvious notational abbreviations), and in general,

$$\sum a_iX^i+\sum b_iX^i=\sum(a_i+b_i)X^i.$$

An example of multiplication is

$$\begin{aligned}(2-3X&+5X^3)(-2+2X+X^2)\\ &=2(-2)+(2\cdot 2+(-3)(-2))X+(2\cdot 1+(-3)2)X^2\\ &\quad+((-3)1+0\cdot 2+5(-2))X^3+(5\cdot 2)X^4+(5\cdot 1)X^5\\ &=-4+10X-4X^2-13X^3+10X^4+5X^5.\end{aligned}$$

The general rule is

$$\begin{aligned}(a_0+a_1X+\cdots+a_mX^m)&(b_0+b_1X+\cdots+b_nX^n)\\ &=c_0+\cdots+c_{m+n}X^{m+n},\end{aligned}$$

where $c_i=a_0b_i+a_1b_{i-1}+a_2b_{i-2}+\cdots+a_ib_0$. The remaining ring operations are defined by

$$-(a_0+a_1X+\cdots)=(-a_0)+(-a_1)X+\cdots,$$

which we write simply as $-a_0-a_1X-\cdots$, and

$$0=0+0X+0X^2+\cdots,$$

$$1=1+0X+0X^2+\cdots.$$

One may ask, what is X? Where does it come from? A good way to answer this is to regard the polynomial $f=a_0+\cdots+a_nX^n$ as a function

f: $\mathbb{M} \to R$ whose values are $f(0)=a_0$, $f(1)=a_1,\ldots, f(n)=a_n$, and $f(i)=0$ for $i>n$. Then $X=0+1X+0X^2+\cdots$ stands for the function $\mathbb{M} \to R$ whose values are 0 everywhere except for the value 1 at 1. Notice that by replacing elements m, n of $\mathbb{M}$ by X^m, X^n (with $X^0=1$ and $X^1=X$) we convert the addition $m+n$ into the multiplication $X^m X^n = X^{m+n}$.

It will be useful to us later (and really not much more work) to generalize these ideas by replacing $\mathbb{M}$ by an arbitrary monoid M. Here are the formal definitions. Recall that R^M denotes the ring of all functions $M \to R$ with componentwise operations (cf. 2.13 and A3.2ii).

Given a ring R and a monoid M, the **monoid ring** denoted $R[M]$ is the set of all functions a: $M \to R$ that have only finitely many nonzero values (with ring operations to be defined presently). If $m_1,\ldots, m_n$ are the $m \in M$ for which $a(m) \neq 0$, we use the following convenient notation:

$$a = a(m_1)m_1 + \cdots + a(m_n)m_n = \sum a(m)m.$$

The neutral element of M is normally written as 1, and the term $a(1)1$ is simplified to $a(1)$ (and of course can be omitted if $a(1)=0$). $1m$ is simplified to m, and $(-1)m$ to $-m$. One refers to R as the **ground ring** of $R[M]$.

In $\Sigma\, a(m)m$, $a(m)$ are called the **coefficients** of a. Thus two elements a, b of the monoid ring are equal iff they have the same coefficients: $a(m)=b(m)$ $\forall m$.

The operations $0, -, +$ are defined componentwise: 0 is the map $M \to R$ with the value 0 $\forall m$,

$$-(a(m_1)m_1 + a(m_2)m_2 + \cdots) = -a(m_1)m_1 - a(m_2)m_2 - \cdots,$$

and the sum of two elements a, b is

$$a + b = \sum a(m)n + \sum b(m)m = \sum (a(m)+b(m))m.$$

Notice that the $+$s in $a(m_1)m_1 + a(m_2)m_2 + \cdots$ really do denote addition and are not merely serving as separators or commas. In this notation the single term $a(m_i)m_i$ denotes the function $M \to R$ whose value is $a(m_i)$ at m_i and 0 elsewhere, and when we add these according to the above definition we obtain the function $a(m_1)m_1 + a(m_2)m_2 + \cdots$ whose value at m_i is $a(m_i)$ $\forall i$.

We now have an additive submonoid of the ring R^M. We next define 1 and multiplication in $R[M]$. It is *not* componentwise and $R[M]$ is not a subring of R^M. (As in the special case of polynomials, 1 is not $1+1X+1X^2+\cdots$ and the product of $a_0+a_1X+\cdots$ and $b_0+b_1X+\cdots$ is not $a_0b_0+a_1b_1X+a_2b_2X^2+\cdots$.) We define the 1 of $R[M]$ to be the function $M \to R$ whose value is 1 at the neutral element of M and 0 elsewhere. The product of two elements, say $ab = c = \Sigma\, c(m)m$, is given by

$$c(m) = \sum_{\substack{s,t \\ st=m}} a(s)b(t).$$

The sum is taken over all pairs s and t such that $st = m$. For general M there may be infinitely many such pairs, but only finitely many figure into the sum, namely those with both $a(s) \neq 0$ and $b(t) \neq 0$. With these definitions $R[M]$ is a ring; see (2.17).

In the polynomial case we change the notation slightly because $\mathbb{M}$ is written additively:

$$\sum a(s)X^s \sum b(t)X^t = \sum_{\substack{s,t \\ s+t=m}} a(s)b(t)X^m.$$

For instance, $X^2 = XX$ is the function

$$X^2(m) = \sum X(s)X(t)$$
$$= \begin{cases} X(1)X(1) = 1 & \text{if} \quad m = 2, \\ 0 & \text{if} \quad m \neq 2, \end{cases}$$

and in general for $k \in \mathbb{M}$,

$$X^k(m) = \delta_{km}.$$

Here we are using the **Kronecker δ-function**, defined (over any domain and appropriate codomain) by $\delta_{km} = 1$ or 0 according to whether $k = m$ or $k \neq m$. The Kronecker δ is also written $\delta_k(m)$. The polynomial ring $R[\mathbb{M}]$ is more commonly denoted $R[X]$ to display the symbol chosen for the special function δ_{1m}. The elements of $R[X]$ are referred to as polynomials in the **variable** or **indeterminate** X. Later we shall consider polynomials in more than one variable. For example, an element of $\mathbb{Z}[X][Y]$ is a polynomial in the variable Y whose coefficients are polynomials in the variable X over $\mathbb{Z}$.

Let us now consider an explicit nonpolynomial example: $\mathbb{Z}[M]$, where $M = \{1, r, s, t\}$ is the monoid A^A for $A = \{1,2\}$ that was discussed earlier in this section. The element $a = 2 - 3s + t$ stands for the function $a\colon M \to \mathbb{Z}$ with values $a(1) = 2$, $a(r) = 0$, $a(s) = -3$, and $a(t) = 1$. Since $(-a)(1) = -(a(1)) = -2$, and so on, we have $-a = -2 + 3s - t$. If $b = r - t$, then $a + b = (2+0) + (0+1)r + (-3+0)s + (1-1)t = 2 + r - 3s$ because $(a+b)(r) = a(r) + b(r) = 0 + 1 = 1$, and so on. For ab we have

$$(ab)(1) = \sum_{x,y \ni xy=1} a(x)b(y) = a(1)b(1) + a(t)b(t)$$
$$= 2\cdot 0 + 1\cdot(-1) = -1,$$

and similarly we can calculate $(ab)(r)$, etc. However, it is easier to calculate ab by simply applying the distributive laws and collecting like terms:

$$ab = (2 - 3s + t)(r - t) = 2r - 2t - 3sr + 3st + tr - t^2$$
$$= 2r - 2t - 3s + 3s + s - 1 = -1 + 2r + s - 2t.$$

The general case is

$$\left(\sum_x a(x)x\right)\left(\sum_y b(y)y\right) = \sum_{x,y} a(x)b(y)xy$$

(where the sum is over all pairs x, y). When we collect like terms this becomes

$$\sum_m \Bigg(\sum_{\substack{x,y \ni \\ xy=m}} a(x)b(y) \Bigg) m,$$

which is correct according to the original definition of the product.

(2.17) PROPOSITION. *The monoid ring $R[M]$, in particular, the polynomial ring $R[X]$, satisfies the ring axioms.*

Sketch of proof. First one easily checks that the operations are closed on $R[M]$: If an operation produced an $a \in R^M$ with infinitely many $a(m) \neq 0$ we would not have a ring. Next we observe that the axioms involving only $+$, $-$, and 0 are true for all elements in $R[M]$ since they are true in fact for all elements in R^M.

We conclude by indicating the proof of the associative law for multiplication, the proofs of the remaining axioms being rather easier. (To the reader unaccustomed to juggling multiple sums, some examples are offered in A3.6.)

$$\begin{aligned}((fg)h)(m) &= \sum_{st=m} (fg)(s)h(t) \\ &= \sum_{st=m} \Bigg(\sum_{uv=s} f(u)g(v) \Bigg) h(t) \\ &= \sum_{uvt=m} f(u)g(v)h(t)\end{aligned}$$

(the sum over all triples u, v, t, with $uvt = m$)

$$\begin{aligned} &= \sum_{uw=m} f(u) \Bigg(\sum_{vt=w} g(v)h(t) \Bigg) \\ &= (f(gh))(m). \quad \blacksquare \end{aligned}$$

$R[M]$ is commutative iff both R and M are. Noncommutative monoids are easily come by, e.g., A^A with $|A| > 1$, so we have the promised examples of noncommutative rings.

As in the case of subsemigroup, we define a **subring** of the ring U as a subset V that is closed with respect to all the operations, that is,

$$a \text{ and b} \in V \quad \Rightarrow \quad a+b \text{ and } ab \in V;$$

$$a \in V \quad \Rightarrow \quad -a \in V, \quad 0,1 \in V.$$

R may be regarded as a subring of $R[M]$ by means of the identification $a = ae$. An element $a = a + 0 \cdot X + 0 \cdot X^2 + \cdots$ of R regarded as an element of $R[X]$ is called a **constant polynomial**. (*Exercise*: If A and B are rings, explain why $\{(a,0\} : a \in A\}$ is *not* a subring of $A \times B$ unless $B = \not{1}$.)

Assignment 3

A3.1. When $f: X \to Y$ and $Z \subset Y$ we use the notation

$$f^{-1}(Z) = \{x \in X: f(x) \in Z\}.$$

When $Z = \{y\}$ consists of a single element we write simply $f^{-1}(y)$. Show that the inverse map preserves $\cup$s and $\cap$s: If $\{Z_i : i \in I\}$ is a collection of subsets of Y, then

$$f^{-1}\left(\bigcup Z_i\right) = \bigcup f^{-1}(Z_i),$$
$$f^{-1}\left(\bigcap Z_i\right) = \bigcap f^{-1}(Z_i).$$

Show that maps similarly preserve unions; give an example to show that in general maps do not preserve intersections.

A3.2. (i) Let Y be a set containing a copy of each of the sets X_i, $i \in I$, that is to say, there are injections $\nu_i: X_i \to Y$. (The $\nu_i(X_i)$ are not assumed to be mutually disjoint.) Establish a bijection between $\prod X_i$ and $\{g \in Y^I : g(i) \in \nu_i(X_i), \forall i \in I\}$. (Thus in practice $\amalg X_i$ can be replaced by any such Y in the definition of $\prod X_i$.) Hence explain how X^I is a product of copies of X. (Thus by (2.14), if R is a ring and I any set, then R^I is a ring, called the **ring of R-valued functions on I**.)

(ii) Let X, Y, Z be sets (empty, finite, or infinite). Show that there is a bijection $(X^Y)^Z \to X^{Y \times Z}$.

A3.3. We define the cardinality $|\varnothing| = 0$.

(i) Show that for finite or empty sets X, Y

$$|X \amalg Y| = |X| + |Y|,$$
$$|X \times Y| = |X| \cdot |Y|,$$
$$|X^Y| = |X|^{|Y|},$$

where in the last case 0^0 is to be interpreted as 1. (To elaborate on this last point, for an element a of any multiplicatively (resp. additively) written monoid and a nonnegative integer n we define a^n (resp. na) by $a^0 = e$ and $a^{n+1} = a^n a$ (resp. $0a = e$ and $(n+1)a = na + a$). Thus in $\mathbb{M}$, $0 \cdot 0 = 0$; in the monoid $\{0, 1, 2, \ldots\}$ with multiplication of integers as the binary operation, $0^0 = 1$. Notice that A1.2 (i and ii), with the notation appropriately modified for the additive case, are still true in this generality and that (iii) is true whenever $ac = ca$ (or $a + c = c + a$), in particular when the monoid is commutative. In the case of a ring there are two monoid structures and both types of notation, na and a^n.) In particular,

in every ring $\quad 0^0 = 1$.

(ii) If $X_1, \ldots, X_n$ are finite subsets of a set show that $X_1 \cup \cdots \cup X_n$ is finite and

$$|X_1 \cup \cdots \cup X_n| \leqslant |X_1| + \cdots + |X_n|.$$

A3.4. (i) Let S be a set. Show that $a \mapsto \{s \in S : a(s) = 1\}$ sets up a bijection between $(\mathbb{Z}/2\mathbb{Z})^S$, which is a ring by A3.2, and the set of all subsets of S. (This explains the standard notation 2^S for the latter set. By "transport of structure," 2^S becomes a ring and as such is called the **Boolean ring**, or **Boolean algebra** of subsets of S. The general definition of the term algebra will be given later.)

(ii) Write the ring operations $+$ and $\times$ of 2^S in terms of the set theoretic operations $\cup$, $\cap$ and $\backslash$. (*Hint*: We give the answer for the more difficult one. $a + b = (a \backslash b) \cup (b \backslash a)$ or, what is the same thing, $(a \cup b) \backslash (a \cap b) =$ the set of elements in a or in b but not in both. In some contexts this $+$ is referred to as "exclusive or," as opposed to the "inclusive or" of $\cup$. The latter, which can be rendered as "a or b or both," is what is always intended in mathematical English by the unqualified word "or." $a + b$ is also called the **symmetric difference** of the sets a and b.) Also interpret 0, 1, and $-a$ in terms of subsets; conversely, write $\cup$, $\cap$, and $\backslash$ in terms of $+$ and $\times$.

(iii) Let $S = \{1,2,3\}$. With the notation $R = 2^S = \{\varnothing, a = \{1\}, b = \{2\}, c = \{3\}, d = \{1,2\}, e = \{1,3\}, f = \{2,3\}, S\}$, write out the addition and multiplication tables of R.

A3.5. The **Binomial Theorem**: Let x, y be elements of a commutative ring and n a nonnegative integer. Prove that

$$(x+y)^n = x^n + \binom{n}{1}x^{n-1}y + \binom{n}{2}x^{n-2}y^2 + \cdots$$
$$+ \binom{n}{n-2}x^2y^{n-2} + \binom{n}{n-1}xy^{n-1} + y^n.$$

Deduce that for $n \geqslant 0$

$$\sum_{m=0}^{n} \binom{n}{m} = 2^n, \qquad \sum_{m=0}^{n} (-1)^m \binom{n}{m} = \delta_{0n} \quad \text{(Kronecker } \delta\text{)}.$$

Next, if $a, n \in \mathbb{N}$, show that $(1+a)^n \geqslant 1 + na$. Then deduce the following multiplicative version of the archimedean principle: if $b, c \in \mathbb{Z}$ with $c > 1$, then $\exists n \in \mathbb{N} \ni c^n > b$.

A3.6. All index sets in this exercise are finite. If the index set I of the sum $S = \Sigma_{i \in I} a_i$ is a subset of $J \times K$, shown in Figure 2.2 as a set of points

Figure 2.2

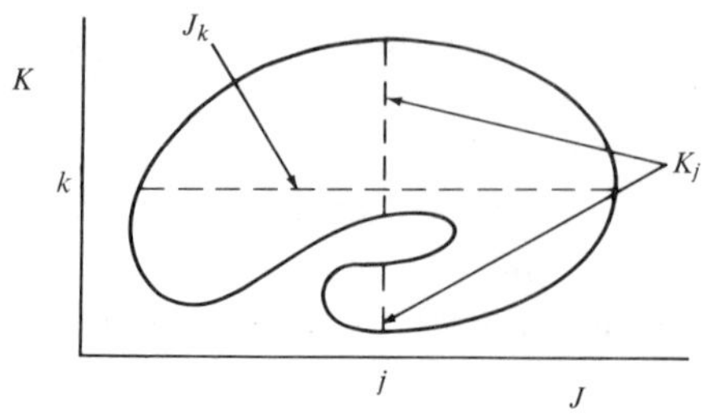

enclosed by the curve, then there are two natural ways of breaking S up into "subsums."

$$S=\sum_{j\in J}\sum_{k\in K_j}a_{jk}=\sum_{k\in K}\sum_{j\in J_k}a_{jk}.$$

We have used the standard notational simplification a_{jk} for $a_{(j,k)}$. The meaning of these **iterated sums** will become plain with an example. Suppose $I=\{(1,2),(1,3),(2,1),(4,1),(4,3)\}\subset\{1,2,3,4\}\times\{1,2,3\}$. Then

$$K_1=\{2,3\},\qquad K_2=\{1\},\qquad K_3=\varnothing,\qquad K_4=\{1,3\},$$

$$J_1=\{2,4\},\qquad J_2=\{1\},\qquad J_3=\{1,4\},$$

so $\sum_{k\in K_1}a_{1k}=a_{12}+a_{13}$, etc., and

$$S=\sum_{j\in J}\sum_{k\in K_j}a_{jk}=(a_{12}+a_{13})+(a_{21})+(0)+(a_{41}+a_{43}).$$

With the order of summation inverted, i.e., using the second iterated sum we have

$$S=\sum_{k\in K}\sum_{j\in J_k}a_{jk}=(a_{21}+a_{41})+(a_{12})+(a_{13}+a_{43}).$$

(i) For N a nonnegative integer show that

$$\sum_{m=0}^{N}(-1)^m\sum_{n=m}^{N}\binom{n}{m}=1.$$

(*Hint*: Invert the order of summation.)

(ii) Let $m,n,N\in\mathbb{M}$ with $m\leqslant N$ and $n\leqslant N$. By comparing coefficients of $X^{m+n(N+1)}$ in

$$(1+X)^N(1+X^{N+1})^N=(1+X+X^{N+1}+X^{N+2})^N$$

in $\mathbb{Z}[X]$, prove that

$$\binom{N}{m}\binom{N}{n}=\sum_{s=0}^{m}\binom{N}{s+n}\binom{s+n}{m}\binom{m}{s}.$$

(iii) Let f: $\mathbb{N}\to\mathbb{N}$ be nondecreasing ($m<n\Rightarrow f(m)\leqslant f(n)$) and "eventually increasing" so that a map f^*: $\mathbb{N}\to\mathbb{M}$ is defined by

$$f^*(n)=\text{number of } m\ni f(m)<n.$$

For example, if $f(n)=p_n$, the nth prime, then $f^*(n)$ is the number of primes $<n$, or $\pi(n-1)$ in the standard notation. Show that

$$\sum_{k=1}^{n}\sum_{j=1}^{f(k)}a_{jk}=\sum_{j=1}^{f(n)}\sum_{k=f^*(j)+1}^{n}a_{jk}.$$

A3.7. Let $a,m,n\in\mathbb{N}$, $a>1$. Prove that

$$(a^m-1)|(a^n-1)\qquad\text{iff}\qquad m|n.$$

(*Hint*: $a^{n-m}-1=a^n-1-a^{n-m}(a^m-1)$.)

SUPPLEMENTARY EXERCISES

1. [Section 4] Let $a, b, m, n \in \mathbb{N}$.

(i) If $m|n$, then $(a^m - b^m)|(a^n - b^n)$.

(ii) If $a^n - 1$ is prime, then $a = 2$ and n is prime. (A prime of the form $2^n - 1$ is called a **Mersenne prime**. The first few are $2^2 - 1 = 3$, $2^3 - 1 = 7$, $2^5 - 1 = 31$, $2^7 - 1 = 127$; but $23|2^{11} - 1$.)

(iii) If $2^n + 1$ is prime, then n is a power of 2, say $n = 2^m$. (Such primes $F_m = 2^{2^m} + 1$ are called **Fermat primes**. The first few are $F_0 = 3$, $F_1 = 5$, $F_2 = 17$, $F_3 = 257$, $F_4 = 65{,}537$. The next few F_m are composite $(641|F_5)$ and, as far as I know, no further Fermat primes have been found.)

2. [A2.3] Let A, B be subsets of a set C and let $\bar{A}$ denote the complement $C \backslash A$. Then

$$(A \cap \bar{B}) \cup (\bar{A} \cap B) = (A \cup B) \cap \overline{(A \cap B)},$$

hence, by De Morgan's laws, the dual statement

$$(A \cup \bar{B}) \cap (\bar{A} \cup B) = (A \cap B) \cup \overline{(A \cup B)}.$$

Also

$$A = (A \cap \bar{B}) \cup (\bar{A} \cap B) \Rightarrow B = \varnothing.$$

3. [Section 5] A ring R is **regular** if $\forall x \in R$, $\exists y \in R \ni xyx = x$. Secondly, R is **strongly regular** if $\forall x$, $\exists y \ni x^2y = x$. Next, an element $x \in R$ is **nilpotent** (resp. **idempotent**) if $x^n = 0$ for some $n \geqslant 1$ (resp. $x^2 = x$). R is **reduced** if 0 is the only nilpotent element.

(i) If R is strongly regular, then R is reduced. ($\mathbb{Z}$ is reduced but not (strongly) regular.)

(ii) If R is reduced and $x^2y = x$, then $xy = yx$. (*Hint*: Show in succession $(xyx - x)^2 = 0$ and hence $xyx = x$; similarly $yx^2 = x$; $xy^2x = xy$ (by calculating xy^2x^2y in two ways); hence $(xy - yx)^2 = 0$.) Therefore strongly regular $\Rightarrow$ regular.

(iii) If the rings R_i are reduced (resp. regular, strongly regular), then $\prod R_i$ has the same property.

(iv) In any ring, if $xyx = x$, then xy and yx are idempotents; if j is idempotent, so is $1 - j$.

(v) If every element of R is idempotent, then $2x = 0$ $\forall x \in R$, R is commutative and R is strongly regular. (*Hint*: $(1 + 1)^2 = 1 + 1$.)

(vi) If R is regular and $x \in R$, then $\exists z \ni xzx = x$ and $zxz = z$. When R is strongly regular z is uniquely determined by x.

4. [Section 6] For any set S, the definition $xy = x$ makes S into a semigroup. It is a monoid iff $|S| = 1$.

5. [Section 6] By induction, the number of maps $f: \{1, 2, \ldots, m\} \to \mathbb{N}$ satisfying $\Sigma f(i) \leqslant n$ is $\binom{m+n}{m}$.

6. [Section 6] Let a, b be elements of a commutative ring. Factorize $X^4 - 2(a^2 + b^2)X^2 + (a^2 - b^2)^2$ into polynomials of the form $X + c$.

7. [A3.5] By comparing coefficients in $(1+X)^n(1+X)^n=(1+X)^{2n}$, show that

$$\binom{n}{0}^2+\binom{n}{1}^2+\cdots+\binom{n}{n}^2=\binom{2n}{n}.$$

8. [A3.5] Find the coefficients of the polynomial $(1-X)\prod_{i=1}^{n}(1+X^{2^i})$.

9. [Section 6] For $f\in\mathbb{Z}[X]$ and $a,b\in\mathbb{Z}$, $(a-b)|(f(a)-f(b))$.

10. [Section 6] If $u_n=\sum_{m=0}^{n}\binom{n+m}{n-m}X^m$, then $u_{n+1}u_{n-1}-u_n^{\,2}=X$.

11. [A3.3] For finite subsets X,Y of a set, show that

$$|X\cup Y|=|X|+|Y|-|X\cap Y|.$$

Give a formula for three finite subsets.

12. [A3.5] Let a,b be elements of a ring and define inductively $c_0=a, c_{n+1}=c_nb-bc_n$. Then for $n\geqslant 0$,

$$\sum_{m=0}^{n} b^m a b^{n-m}=\sum_{m=0}^{n}\binom{n+1}{m+1}b^{n-m}c_m.$$

13. [A3.6] Prove the general distributive law for ring elements:

$$\left(\sum_{i=1}^{m}a_i\right)\left(\sum_{j=1}^{n}b_j\right)=\sum_{i=1}^{m}\sum_{j=1}^{n}a_ib_j.$$

14. [A3.4] Let S be a collection of subsets of an n element set such that any two members of S have nonempty $\cap$. Then $|S|\leqslant 2^{n-1}$. (*Hint*: If $X_1, X_2,\ldots$ are the members of S, consider their complements $X_1', X_2',\ldots$.)

Rational Numbers and Rational Functions

3

In this chapter we construct rational numbers (fractions like $\frac{3}{2}$ or $-\frac{5}{9}$) from integers, and rational functions (fractions like $(2-X)/(X+5X^3)$) from polynomials. The general procedure, known as localization, is described in Section 1. Then we introduce the concepts of integral domain, field, in particular the field $\mathbb{Q}$ of rational numbers, and homomorphisms (more generally, homomorphic relations; in particular, congruence relations). This is followed by Assignment 4, which includes our first example of a universal property.

We then explain the quotient R/θ of a ring R by a congruence relation, along with the equivalent, more convenient, notion R/I of dividing a ring by an ideal. These ideas are illustrated by the immediately accessible example $\mathbb{Z}/n\mathbb{Z}$, where, for instance, when $n=3$, we write $8\equiv 2 \bmod 3$, which means simply that the difference $8-2=2\cdot 3$ is a multiple of the *modulus*, 3.

Next we define groups, prove a few simple properties, and discuss the example R^* of the group of units of a ring. In particular we define Euler's function $\varphi(n)=|(\mathbb{Z}/n\mathbb{Z})^*|$. Then we define prime ideals (a natural generalization of prime numbers) and their connection with localization. That requires Zorn's lemma, which we introduce in the simple form for chains of subsets of a set. Assignment 5 is designed to help the student gain confidence in using the foregoing concepts.

The next major topic is the unique factorization of integers into primes and the analog for polynomials over a field k. In the spirit of modern algebra, we find a common generalization of $\mathbb{Z}$ and $k[X]$ to avoid going through essentially the same proofs twice, namely principal ideal domains (P.I.D.s). We then prove uniqueness of factorization for elements of a P.I.D., where the noetherian (ascending chain) condition on ideals plays an important role. The next two sections deal with consequences of unique factorization, and with the euclidean algorithm used to calculate greatest common divisors (g.c.d.s) in $\mathbb{Z}$ and $k[X]$.

Assignment 6 contains further examples concerning factorization as well as Lagrange's theorem on finite groups. The chapter closes with a section that provides some finer tools for tackling factorization problems, including Eisenstein's criterion and reduction mod p.

1. LOCALIZATION

We construct fractions such as $\frac{3}{2}$ by a process similar to the one that gave us the integers. On the set $X = \mathbb{Z} \times (\mathbb{Z} \setminus \{0\})$ of pairs of integers (a, b) in which the second component is nonzero, we define the relation $(a,b) \sim (c,d)$ to mean $ad = bc$; for example, $(3,2) \sim (-6,-4)$, which is, of course, a preliminary version of the familiar $3/2 = -6/-4$. This relation is an equivalence relation and it is clear how we should proceed: define ring operations on the quotient set $X/\sim$, check that they are well defined, verify the ring axioms, make an identification $a = a/1$, and finally check that the ring operations match up as in (2.4).

However, before we carry out this program we wish to generalize it in two directions. First, it is not only integers that we need as denominators. For example, in the case of polynomials, from $(1 + X + X^2 + \cdots + X^n)(1 - X) = 1 - X^{n+1}$ we should like to conclude that

$$1 + X + \cdots + X^n = \frac{1 - X^{n+1}}{1 - X}.$$

Second, it is a technical advantage to be able to introduce a restricted class of denominators. A significant example occurs in (3.25). As a simple example, in the case of $\mathbb{Z}$ we may wish to introduce all fractions of the form a/b with b odd. It is a familiar fact that these fractions form a ring because when we add or multiply fractions the denominators are multiplied and the product of odd integers is odd.

These considerations lead to the following. Let A be a commutative ring and S a multiplicatively closed subset containing 1; i.e.,

$$(3.1) \qquad 1 \in S \quad \text{and} \quad s, s' \in S \;\Rightarrow\; ss' \in S.$$

In more ponderous terms, S is a **submonoid** of the multiplicative monoid of A. Indeed (3.1) are the defining properties that a subset of a monoid be a submonoid. ($\mathbb{Z}$ has quite an extensive menagerie of multiplicative submonoids, as evidenced by the examples

$$\{1,2,4,\ldots,2^n,\ldots\},\ \{1,-1,4,-4,\ldots,\pm 4^n,\ldots\},$$

$$\{1,2,3,4,6,\ldots,2^m3^n,\ldots\}, \{1,10,11,12,\ldots\},$$

$\{0,1\}$, $\{1,-1\}$, and $\mathbb{Z}$ itself.)

On the set $X = A \times S$ we define the relation $\sim$ by $(a,s) \sim (a',s') \Leftrightarrow \exists t \in S \ni as't = a'st$. The reason for the factor t is the possibility of S containing **zero divisors**, that is, elements s for which $\exists y \neq 0 \ni sy = 0$. (The relation $\approx$ defined by $(r,s) \approx (r',s') \Leftrightarrow rs' = r's$ is not transitive in general; e.g., when $A = S = \mathbb{Z}$.) When S contains no zero divisors $(as' - a's)t = 0,\ t \in S \Rightarrow as' - a's = 0$, i.e., $as' = a's$, so we can take $t = 1$ or, in effect, disregard t.

$\sim$ is reflexive: Take $t = 1$ so $as = as \Rightarrow (a,s) \sim (a,s)$.

$\sim$ is obviously symmetric.

$\sim$ is transitive: If $(a_1,s_1) \sim (a_2,s_2)$ and $(a_2,s_2) \sim (a_3,s_3)$ say $a_1s_2s_4 = a_2s_1s_4$ and $a_2s_3s_5 = a_3s_2s_5$, then the former multiplied by s_3s_5 and the latter by s_1s_4 give

$$a_1s_2s_4s_3s_5 = a_2s_1s_4s_3s_5 = a_3s_2s_5s_1s_4,$$

whence $a_1s_3s = a_3s_1s$, where $s = s_2s_4s_5 \in S$, and therefore $(a_1,s_1) \sim (a_3,s_3)$.

We denote

$$a/s \quad \text{or} \quad \frac{a}{s}$$

the equivalence class containing (a,s). Thus $a/s = a'/s'$ iff $\exists t \in S \ni as't = a'st$. The word **fraction** is used loosely to mean either the class a/s or a particular representative of it. Taken in the second sense we define a to be the **numerator** and s the **denominator** of the fraction a/s.

(3.2) DEFINITION. The **localization of A with respect to S**, denoted $S^{-1}A$, is the quotient set $A \times S/\sim$, with ring operations defined as follows:

$$\frac{a}{b} + \frac{c}{d} = \frac{ad+bc}{bd},$$

$$\frac{a}{b} \cdot \frac{c}{d} = \frac{ac}{bd},$$

$$-\frac{a}{b} = \frac{-a}{b},$$

$$1 = \frac{1}{1}, \qquad 0 = \frac{0}{1}.$$

(3.3) PROPOSITION. *$S^{-1}A$ is a commutative ring.*

Proof. Suppose $a/b = a'/b'$, say $ab'e = a'be$, $e \in S$.

$+$ is well defined: We have $(ad+bc)b'de = (a'd+b'c)bde$, so

$$\frac{a}{b} + \frac{c}{d} = \frac{ad+bc}{bd} = \frac{a'd+b'c}{b'd} = \frac{a'}{b'} + \frac{c}{d}.$$

Now $+$ is obviously commutative, so by interchanging the two terms this calculation shows that c/d also can be replaced by an equal fraction c'/d'.

$\times$ is well defined: $\times$ is clearly commutative and, as in the case of $+$, it is sufficient to observe that since $ab'cde = a'bcde$ we have

$$\frac{a}{b} \cdot \frac{c}{d} = \frac{a'}{b'} \cdot \frac{c}{d}.$$

$-$ is well defined: $ab'e = a'be \Rightarrow -ab'e = -a'be \Rightarrow -a/b = -a'/b'$.

All the ring axioms are easy to check by direct calculations, of which one example will suffice: Noting the rule $xy/xz = y/z$,

$$\frac{a}{b}\left(\frac{c}{d} + \frac{e}{f}\right) = \frac{a}{b} \cdot \frac{cf + de}{df} = \frac{a(cf+de)}{b(df)} = \frac{acf + ade}{bdf}$$

$$= \frac{acf}{bdf} + \frac{ade}{bdf} = \frac{ac}{bd} + \frac{ae}{bf} = \frac{a}{b} \cdot \frac{c}{d} + \frac{a}{b} \cdot \frac{e}{f}. \quad \blacksquare$$

EXERCISES

1. In a ring R the set $S = \{s \in R : sx = 0 \Rightarrow x = 0\}$ of nonzero divisors is a multiplicative submonoid.

2. If S_i are submonoids of the monoid M then so is $\cap S_i$.

3. $S^{-1}A = \not{1}$ iff $0 \in S$.

4. Complete the details of the proof of (3.3).

2. HOMOMORPHISMS

Now that we have constructed the ring $S^{-1}A$ we want to consider the natural map $A \to S^{-1}A$ given by $a \mapsto a/1$. Because of certain special properties this map is called a ring homomorphism, as we now explain. We begin with a general definition in the simpler case of semigroups.

A relation ρ between semigroups A and B is said to be **homomorphic** if it preserves the algebraic structure,

$$a\rho b \quad \text{and} \quad a'\rho b' \qquad \Rightarrow \qquad (aa')\rho(bb'),$$

where we assume that both semigroups are written multiplicatively. Using ρ also to denote the graph of the relation, as in Chapter 1, this condition can be rewritten

$$(a,b) \in \rho \quad \text{and} \quad (a',b') \in \rho \qquad \Rightarrow \qquad (aa',bb') \in \rho$$

and this shows that a relation is homomorphic iff its graph is a subsemigroup of $A \times B$. In the context of monoids, in order to qualify as homomorphic ρ has to satisfy also $(e_A, e_B) \in \rho$, where we have distinguished the es by subscripts.

Similarly, a homomorphic relation ρ between rings A and B is a relation that preserves all the operations, equivalently, one whose graph is a subring of $A \times B$:

$$(a,b) \text{ and } (a',b') \quad \text{in } \rho \quad \Rightarrow \quad (a+a', b+b') \text{ and } (aa', bb') \quad \text{in } \rho,$$
$$(a,b) \in \rho \quad \Rightarrow \quad (-a,-b) \in \rho,$$
$$(0,0) \in \rho, \quad \text{and} \quad (1,1) \in \rho.$$

Two particular types of ρ are especially important:

(i) a homomorphic map $\rho: A \to B$ is called a **homomorphism.**
(ii) (When $A = B$) a homomorphic equivalence relation is a **congruence relation.**

Congruence relations are discussed in Section 4. Translating i) in the case of rings, a map $f: A \to B$ is a homomorphism when

$$f(a+a') = f(a) + f(a'), \qquad f(aa') = f(a)f(a'), \qquad f(1) = 1.$$

We do not need to include $f(-a) = -f(a)$ and $f(0) = 0$ because these are consequences of the conditions listed: $f(0) = f(0+0) = f(0) + f(0)$, so $f(0) = 0$; further, $0 = f(0) = f(-a+a) = f(-a) + f(a)$, so $f(-a) = -f(a)$. *Caution*: the same omissions cannot be made in the definition of subring; for example, the subset $\{0,1,2,\ldots\}$ of $\mathbb{Z}$ is closed with respect to $+$, $\times$, 0 and 1 but not with respect to $-$ and therefore is not a subring.
The following result is immediate from the definitions.

(3.4) PROPOSITION. *With the notation of* (3.3), $a \mapsto a/1$ *defines a ring homomorphism* $A \to S^{-1}A$.

The analogs of the remaining statements of (2.4) are not correct here. For one thing, inequalities are not involved; only very special rings admit a relation $<$ that behaves at all sensibly with respect to $+$ and $\times$. For example, in $\mathbb{F}_2$, the equation $1+1=0$ indicates that neither definition $1>0$ or $1<0$ would be of much use.

Of more interest is the possibility that the homomorphism $a \mapsto a/1$ may not be injective. Analyzing this will lead us to important new ideas in the next few sections.

If R is any ring the one and only map $R \to \not{1}$ is a ring homomorphism, obviously. In the other direction we have the

(3.5) PROPOSITION. *Let R be any ring. There is one and only one ring homomorphism* $\mathbb{Z} \to R$.

Proof. We define $f: \mathbb{Z} \to R$ inductively by $f(0) = 0$, and if $f(m)$ is defined for some $m \geqslant 0$, then $f(-m) = -f(m)$ and $f(m+1) = f(m) + 1$. Thus $f(1) = 1$,

$f(-1)=-1, f(2)=1+1$, and so on. Since any homomorphism satisfies this definition, if there is a homomorphism at all it must be f.

To complete the proof we must show that f preserves sums and products. We first prove that $f(m+n)=f(m)+f(n)$ for m and n both nonnegative by induction on n. Since $f(0)=0$ it is true when $n=0$. Assuming it true for n we have

$$\begin{aligned} f(m+n+1) &= f(m+n)+1 && \text{by the definition of } f, \\ &= f(m)+f(n)+1 && \text{by I.H.,} \\ &= f(m)+f(n+1) && \text{by the definition of } f. \end{aligned}$$

Next we observe that $f(-x)=-f(x)\ \forall x\in\mathbb{Z}$ by the definition of f; therefore if m and n are both negative, then, using the result just proved, $f(m+n)=-f(-m-n)=-(f(-m)+f(-n))=f(m)+f(n)$. Suppose just one of m, n is negative, say m. Then if $m+n\geqslant 0$, $f(n)=f(-m+(m+n))=f(-m)+f(m+n)$, which gives the result. Otherwise $m+n<0$, and then $-f(m)=f(-m)=f(n-(m+n))=f(n)-f(m+n)$, and again the result follows.

The case of multiplication is less troublesome and is left to the reader. ■

EXERCISES

1. If $f: A\to B$ is a homomorphism of rings (resp. semigroups, monoids) then $\operatorname{Im}(f)$ is a subring (resp. subsemigroup, submonoid) of B.

2. There are precisely two ring homomorphisms $\mathbb{Z}\times\mathbb{Z}\to\mathbb{Z}$.

3. If $\rho\subset A\times B$ is a homomorphic relation between the rings A and B, and A' and B' are subrings of A and B respectively, then

$$\{a\in A: a\rho b \text{ for some } b\in B'\}, \qquad \{b\in B: a\rho b \text{ for some } a\in A'\}$$

are subrings. State and prove similar results for semigroups and monoids.

3. INTEGRAL DOMAINS AND FIELDS

(3.6) PROPOSITION. *The canonical homomorphism $A\to S^{-1}A$ is injective iff S contains no zero divisors.*

Remark. The word "canonical" is used in mathematics to mean natural, standard, or obvious. There may be other homomorphisms $A\to S^{-1}A$, but $a\mapsto a/1$ recommends itself as being the most natural and therefore qualifies as "canonical."

Proof. Suppose $a\neq b$ yet $a/1=b/1$. Then $\exists t\in S\ni at=bt$, so $t(a-b)=0$ and t is a zero divisor. Conversely, if $tc=0$, then $c/1=0/1$. ■

When S satisfies the condition of the proposition we can make the identification $a = a/1$ and regard A as a subring of $S^{-1}A$.

(3.7) DEFINITION. An **integral domain** is a commutative ring with $1 \neq 0$ that satisifies

$$xy = 0 \quad \Rightarrow \quad x = 0 \quad \text{or} \quad y = 0.$$

Other ways of putting this condition are to state that there are no nonzero zero divisors or that $S = A \setminus \{0\}$ is multiplicatively closed. In this case we use the special notation $Q(A)$ for $S^{-1}A$ and call this ring the **field of quotients** of the integral domain A. Thus $Q(A)$ is obtained by introducing all nonzero denominators.

$\mathbb{Z}$ is an integral domain (2.6(vi)) and for its field of quotients there is a standard symbol $\mathbb{Q}$. The elements of $\mathbb{Q}$ are called **rational numbers** and $\mathbb{Q}$ is called the **rational field** or the **field of rationals**. Under the identification $a = a/1$, integers are a special type of rational number and they comprise a subring of $\mathbb{Q}$. We can now write the result of A2.6(ii)

$$\binom{n}{m} = \frac{n!}{m!(n-m)!}. \tag{3.8}$$

We know that the binomial coefficients are integers, in other words, we know the denominator on the right divides the numerator (in $\mathbb{Z}$), but it is obviously a convenience to be able to express this result in the larger ring $\mathbb{Q}$. Similarly, the fractions in A1.3 can now be properly interpreted.

To construct $\mathbb{Q} = S^{-1}\mathbb{Z}$ we can take S to be the set of all nonzero integers or the set of positive integers. (A negative sign in the denominator can always be transferred to the numerator.) There are a variety of further possibilities for S; this phenomenon will be analyzed in (3.24).

$\mathbb{Q}$ is an integral domain: If

$$\frac{a}{b} \cdot \frac{c}{d} = 0, \qquad \frac{a}{b} \neq 0,$$

then $a \neq 0$, and multiplying the first equation by b/a gives

$$\frac{b}{a}\frac{a}{b}\frac{c}{d} = 0; \qquad \text{hence} \quad \frac{c}{d} = 0.$$

In fact the same argument shows that $Q(A)$ is an integral domain for every integral domain A. The essential property is that $x(a/b) = 1$ has a solution, provided $a \neq 0$, namely $x = b/a$. Thus, according to (3.9), the fields of quotients are actually fields.

(3.9) DEFINITION. A **field** is a commutative ring k with $1 \neq 0$ such that for every nonzero element $a \in k$, $ax = 1$ has a solution $x \in k$.

Remarks

1. When $a \neq 0$ the solution x of $ax = 1$ is unique, for suppose also that $ay = 1$. Then, since the ring is commutative, $x = x1 = x(ay) = (ax)y = 1y =$

y. The unique solution is denoted a^{-1} and is called the **inverse** of a. Thus in the case of $Q(A)$, $(a/b)^{-1} = b/a$, provided of course $a \neq 0$. See Section 6 for a general discussion of invertible elements.

2. The argument used above (of the form $uv = 0 \Rightarrow u^{-1}uv = 0 \Rightarrow v = 0$) shows that *every field is an integral domain*. $\mathbb{Z}$ is an example of an integral domain that is not a field.

3. The ring $A = \mathbb{Z} \times \mathbb{Z}$ is not an integral domain (therefore certainly not a field) since if we take $x = (1,0)$, so $x^2 = x$, and $y = 1 - x = (0,1)$, then neither x nor y is 0 yet $xy = 0$. When $S = \{1, x\}$ we know by (3.6) that $A \to S^{-1}A$ is not injective; in fact, both $0 \mapsto 0/1 = 0$ and $y \mapsto y/1 = 0$.

To have at hand further examples of integral domains we observe

(3.10) PROPOSITION. $R[X]$ *is an integral domain iff* R *is an integral domain.*

Proof. Clearly every subring of an integral domain is an integral domain and, since R can be regarded as a subring of $R[X]$, one half of the proof is clear.

Conversely suppose R is an integral domain. Then $R[X]$ is certainly a commutative ring with $1 \neq 0$, and it remains to show that the product of two nonzero polynomials $a = a_0 + a_1X + \cdots + a_mX^m$ and $b = b_0 + \cdots + b_nX^n$ is nonzero. We can assume that $a_m \neq 0$; then a_m is called the **leading coefficient** of a (as opposed to the **constant coefficient** a_0, which may be 0) and the **degree** of a is defined by $\deg(a) = m$. (Of course these terms are used for polynomials over any ground ring.) In other words, $\deg(a)$ is the highest exponent of X occurring with nonzero coefficient. $\deg(0)$ is not defined. Similarly we can suppose that $b_n \neq 0$ and $\deg(b) = n$.

Now in the product

$$ab = a_0b_0 + (a_1b_0 + a_0b_1)X + \cdots + a_mb_nX^{m+n},$$

the leading coefficient is $a_mb_n \neq 0$. It follows that $ab \neq 0$. ■

The last point in the proof is worth restating: *For nonzero polynomials over an integral domain* we have the formula

$$\deg(ab) = \deg(a) + \deg(b). \tag{3.11}$$

It is also clear that if a, b, and $a + b$ are all nonzero,

$$\deg(a+b) \leqslant \max\{\deg(a), \deg(b)\}, \tag{3.12}$$

where max means simply "the larger of." Because of cancellation there may be strict inequality; for example, if $a = 1 + X$, $b = -X$, then $\deg(a) = \deg(b) = 1$ but $\deg(a+b) = \deg(1) = 0$.

$R[X]$ is never a field because X for instance has no inverse in $R[X]$. If k is a field then $Q(k[X])$ is denoted $k(X)$ and is called the **field of rational functions** (in the **variable** or **indeterminate** X over the **ground field** k). Here are some elements of $\mathbb{Q}(X)$: $1, 0, -2, 3/4, X^{-1} = 1/X$, $(\frac{5}{3} + 8X^3 - \frac{1}{2}X^4)/(\frac{1}{5}X^2 + X^3)$.

EXERCISES

1. For $m, n, t \in \mathbb{N}$,

$$\binom{n+t}{m}\binom{m}{t} = \binom{n+t}{n}\binom{n}{m-t}.$$

2.

$$\sum_{i=0}^{n} \binom{m-1+i}{i} = \binom{m+n}{m}.$$

3. If a, b, c, d are elements of an integral domain $A \ni a/b = c/d$ (in $Q(A)$), then $\forall x, y, u, v \ni au + bv \neq 0$,

$$\frac{ax+by}{au+bv} = \frac{cx+dy}{cu+dv}.$$

4. Since $\Sigma_{i=1}^{n}(a_i - a_{i-1}) = a_n - a_0$, therefore

$$n^2 = \sum_{i=1}^{n}\left(i^2 - (i-1)^2\right) = \sum_{i=1}^{n}(-1+2i) = -n + 2\sum_{i=1}^{n} i.$$

This gives the formula $\Sigma_{i=1}^{n} i = (n^2+n)/2$. Use this technique to find in succession the next few $I_k = \Sigma_{i=1}^{n} i^k$. Deduce $I_3 | 3I_5$.

5. Two identities in $\mathbb{Q}$: If n is even, then

$$1 - \frac{1}{2} + \frac{1}{3} - \cdots - \frac{1}{n} = 2\left(\frac{1}{n+2} + \frac{1}{n+4} + \cdots + \frac{1}{2n}\right),$$

while if n is odd,

$$1 - \frac{1}{2} + \frac{1}{3} - \cdots + \frac{1}{n} = 2\left(\frac{1}{n+1} + \frac{1}{n+3} + \cdots + \frac{1}{2n}\right).$$

6. In a field if $x^2 + y^2 + z^2 = -1$ and $y^2 + z^2 \neq 0$, then

$$\left(\frac{xy+z}{y^2+z^2}\right)^2 + \left(\frac{xz-y}{y^2+z^2}\right)^2 = -1.$$

7. Let $a, b, c, d \in \mathbb{N}$ satisfy $ad - bc = 1$. Then no cancellation is possible in the fraction $(a+b)/(c+d)$.

Assignment 4

A4.1. Show that in $\mathbb{Q}$

$$\sum_{i=1}^{n} \frac{1}{i(i+1)} = \frac{n}{n+1}.$$

A4.2. If σ and τ are homomorphic relations, then so are $\sigma\tau$, when defined, and σ^{-1}. Prove this in the ring case.

A4.3. If $f\colon A \to B$ is a map of sets, let $\sim$ denote the equivalence relation defined by $a \sim a' \Leftrightarrow f(a) = f(a')$. The quotient set $A/\sim$ is called the **coimage** of f.

(i) Show that $f^{-1}(f(a)) \mapsto f(a)$ defines a bijection between the coimage and the image of f.

(ii) If f is a homomorphism, then $\sim$ is a congruence relation. Verify this in the case of rings.

Remark. If $\sim$ is an equivalence relation on the set A, the surjection $f\colon A \to A/\sim$ given by a $\mapsto$ the equivalence class containing a is called the **canonical projection**. Notice that the equivalence relation associated to f as in (i) is the $\sim$ we started with.

A4.4. Let S be a multiplicative submonoid of the commutative ring A and let $\gamma_S\colon A \to S^{-1}A$ denote the canonical homomorphism. If $f\colon A \to B$ is a homomorphism of rings such that $f(s)$ is a unit in B $\forall s \in S$, prove there is a unique ring homomorphism $g\colon S^{-1}A \to B \ni g\gamma_S = f$. (This is the **universal property of localization.**) Hence explain the following cases:

(i) If $S \subset S_1$, where S_1 is also a multiplicative submonoid of A, then there is a unique homomorphism $g\colon S^{-1}A \to S_1^{-1}A \ni g\gamma_S = \gamma_{S_1}$. (This generalizes (3.4), which is the case $S = \{1\}$.)

(ii) If $f\colon A \to B$ is a homomorphism of commutative rings then $f(S)$ is a multiplicative submonoid of B and $\exists!$ homomorphism, $S^{-1}A \to f(S)^{-1}B$, denoted $S^{-1}f$, satisfying $S^{-1}f \cdot \gamma_S = \gamma_{f(S)} \cdot f$.

The reader may find the following diagrams helpful:

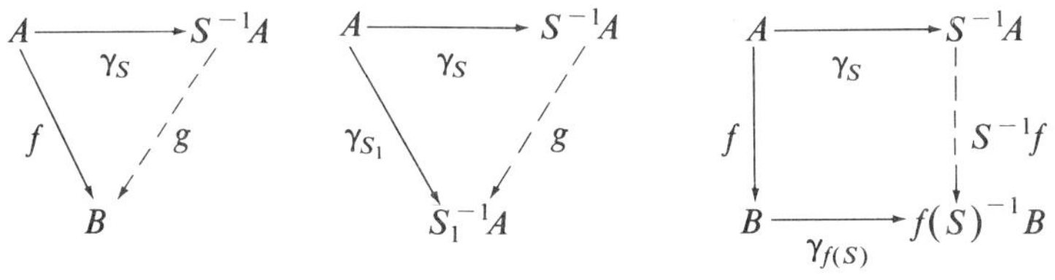

A4.5. **(i)** Let $a = q/r$ and $b = s/t$ be rational numbers where the integers r and t are positive, as we can assume without loss of generality. Show that $<$ is well defined on $\mathbb{Q}$ by $a < b \Leftrightarrow qt < rs$, that this restricts to the usual $<$ on $\mathbb{Z}$, that statements (ii)–(iv) of (2.6) are valid for $a, b, c, d \in \mathbb{Q}$, and that the archimedean principle is valid: if $a, b \in \mathbb{Q}$ and $b > 0$, then $\exists n \in \mathbb{N} \ni nb > a$.

(ii) Prove by induction that

$$1 + \frac{1}{2} + \frac{1}{3} + \cdots + \frac{1}{2^n} > \frac{n+1}{2}.$$

(iii) Show that if $a \in \mathbb{Q}$, then $\{n \in \mathbb{Z} : n \leqslant a\}$ is nonempty and bounded above in $\mathbb{Z}$. The l.u.b. (in $\mathbb{Z}$) is denoted $\lfloor a \rfloor$ and called the **integral part** of a. (For example, $\lfloor 0 \rfloor = \lfloor \frac{1}{2} \rfloor = 0$, $\lfloor -1 \rfloor = \lfloor -\frac{1}{2} \rfloor = -1$.) Finally, show that if $m \in \mathbb{Z}$ then $\lfloor a + m \rfloor = \lfloor a \rfloor + m$.

4. QUOTIENT RINGS

The main point about congruence relations, which were defined in Section 2 as homomorphic equivalence relations, is that the quotient set inherits all the operations of the original set in a natural way. We explain this for rings in the next proposition, but the reader should satisfy himself that similar statements are true for semigroups and monoids.

First a simple example to fix our ideas. The equivalence relation θ of A2.2 is actually a congruence relation for the ring structure on $\mathbb{Z}$ because if $a\theta a'$, say $a = a' + nx$, and $b\theta b'$, say $b = b' + ny$, then $a + b = a' + b' + n(x + y)$, $ab = a'b' + n(a'y + b'x + nxy)$, and $-a = -a' + n(-x)$, that is, $(a+b)\theta(a' + b')$, $(ab)\theta(a'b')$, $(-a)\theta(-a')$, and, of course $0\theta 0$ and $1\theta 1$. For ease of reference later in this section we denote this θ by $\tilde{n}$. Since $\widetilde{-n} = \tilde{n}$, we can assume $n \geqslant 0$.

(3.13) PROPOSITION. *Let R be a ring, let θ be a congruence relation on R, and let $[a]$ denote the θ-equivalence class of an element $a \in R$. Then R/θ becomes a ring if we define*

$$[a] + [b] = [a + b], \qquad [a][b] = [ab],$$

$$-[a] = [-a], \qquad 0 = [0], \quad 1 = [1].$$

If R is commutative, so is R/θ.

Remarks. This way of forming a new ring does not encompass the construction $S^{-1}A = A \times S/\sim$ since $A \times S$ is not a ring.

It is worth recalling the metaphor that R/θ is a continent whose members are the countries $[a]$. It is true that each country is composed of citizens, with a and b of the same citizenship iff $a\theta b$, but as far as R/θ is concerned, $[a]$ is a single entity.

Proof. Let $[a] = [a']$ and $[b] = [b']$; i.e., $a\theta a'$ and $b\theta b'$. The fact that θ is a congruence relation implies that $(a + b)\theta(a' + b')$, $(ab)\theta(a'b')$, and $(-a)\theta(-a')$. Hence $[a + b] = [a' + b']$, $[ab] = [a'b']$, and $[-a] = [-a']$. In other words, the operations are well defined.

The truth of the ring axioms for R/θ is visibly a consequence of their truth for R:

$$([a][b])[c] = [ab][c] = [(ab)c] = [a(bc)] = [a]([b][c]),$$

$$0 + [a] = [0] + [a] = [0 + a] = [a],$$

and so on. Similarly the commutativity axiom (R6) for R/θ follows from that for R: $[a][b] = [ab] = [ba] = [b][a]$. ■

The ring axioms are all of the form "$f(x, y, \ldots) = g(x, y, \ldots)\ \forall x, y, \ldots,$" where f and g stand for operations, or compositions of operations, possibly involving constants: The ring axioms are *of equational type*. Some axioms not of equational type are "$1 \neq 0$" and "$xy = 0 \Rightarrow x = 0$ or $y = 0$." The axioms for commutative rings, for semigroups, and for monoids are of equational type; but not all the axioms, as we have stated them, for integral domains or for fields. It is possible to state and prove (3.13) in the general context of a set with a set of operations subject to a set of axioms of equational type, but we shall not take the trouble to do this. It is possible similarly to generalize (2.14). Because $\mathbb{Z} \times \mathbb{Z}$, for instance, is not an integral domain ($(1,0)(0,1) = 0$), this points to the *impossibility* of finding axioms of equational type for the concept of integral domain. For the same reason fields are not equationally defined.

This point of view is further reinforced by the observation that in (3.13) we can always take θ to be the "blanket" relation with graph $R \times R$ (obviously a congruence relation); then $R/\theta = \not{1}$, which is not an integral domain, a fortiori not a field, regardless of the nature of the original ring R. In the case of $\mathbb{Z}$ this θ is $\tilde{1}$.

As a less trivial example, the commutative ring $\mathbb{Z}/\tilde{n}$ is not an integral domain if n is a composite natural number, say $n = ab$, where $1 < a < n$ and $1 < b < n$. For then $[a] \neq 0$, $[b] \neq 0$, but $[a][b] = [n] = 0$. For instance, $[2] \neq 0$ in $\mathbb{Z}/\tilde{4}$ yet $[2]^2 = 0$. Since $\tilde{0}$ is the equality relation, $\mathbb{Z}/\tilde{0} = \mathbb{Z}$.

Now for any $n > 0$, each $[a] \in \mathbb{Z}/\tilde{n}$ has a canonical (here meaning standard) representative, namely the remainder r in $a = nq + r$, $0 \leqslant r < n$. Indeed, $[a] = [r]$ and the canonical character is a consequence of the uniqueness of the remainder: If $[a] = [r']$, say $a = nq' + r'$, and $0 \leqslant r' < n$, then $r' = r$. Thus the elements of $\mathbb{Z}/\tilde{n}$ are $[0] = 0$, $[1] = 1$, $[2], \ldots, [n-1]$ and $|\mathbb{Z}/\tilde{n}| = n$. In particular, $\mathbb{Z}/\tilde{2}$ must be *the* two-element ring. Although the notation $\mathbb{Z}/2\mathbb{Z}$ for this ring still awaits explanation, the previous proposition does provide a verification of the ring axioms without a case-by-case examination. This ring is in fact a field and is usually called the **two-element field.**

Replacing a by $r = a - nq$ can be a help in calculations. For example, if $n = 7$ then $[1000] = [6]$, $[-5] = [2]$, so

$$[1000] + [-5] = [6] + [2] = [8] = [1],$$

and

$$[1000][-5] = [6][2] = [12] = [5].$$

Sometimes it is convenient to use representatives in the range from $-n$ to 0. For example, if $n = 17$ and we wish to calculate $[15^{50}]$ expeditiously, we notice that

$$[15^{50}] = [15]^{50} = [-2]^{50} = [-1]^{50}[2]^{50} = [2]^{50},$$

and since $[2]^4 = [-1]$, this is

$$[2]^{50} = [2]^{4 \cdot 12 + 2} = [-1]^{12}[2]^2 = [4].$$

This allows us to predict confidently that when 15^{50} is divided by 17 the remainder will be 4.

A set of integers representing the n elements of $\mathbb{Z}/\tilde{n}$ is known as a **complete residue system**. We have already mentioned the canonical system $\{0,1,\ldots,n-1\}$. Another useful set is $\{a\in\mathbb{Z}: -n<2a\leqslant n\}$; for example, when $n=5$ this is $\{-2,-1,0,1,2\}$ and when $n=6$ it is $\{-2,-1,0,1,2,3\}$. When we choose such a system, let us say $\{0,1,\ldots,n-1\}$, we have defined an injection $\mathbb{Z}/\tilde{n}\to\mathbb{Z}$, but it must not be supposed that this is a ring homomorphism. For example, when $n=10$, sums and products are preserved for the smaller integers. $[2]+[3]=[5]$ corresponds to $2+3=5$ and $[2][3]=[6]$ to $2\cdot 3=6$, but this soon breaks down: $[5]+[7]=[2]$, $[2][5]=0$. There is in fact *no* homomorphism $\mathbb{Z}/\tilde{n}\to\mathbb{Z}$ when $n>0$ because such a homomorphism would necessarily map $1=[1]\mapsto 1$ and hence $[2]=[1]+[1]\mapsto 1+1=2$ and so on up to $[n]=[n-1]+[1]\mapsto n-1+1=n$. However, $[n]=0\mapsto 0\neq n$, a contradiction.

The quotient set R/θ with this ring structure is called the **quotient ring** of R by θ. This is rather similar to the term ring of quotients sometimes used for the quite dissimilar object $S^{-1}A$ and for this reason some authors prefer **factor ring** for R/θ. The equivalence classes $[a]$ are also called **residue classes**. (*Exercise*: In the ring $\mathbb{Z}/\widetilde{11}$, show by calculation that $[a]^{11}=[a]$ for all $a\in\mathbb{Z}$. This is an example of Fermat's "little theorem" (3.53).)

5. IDEALS AND CONGRUENCES

(3.14) DEFINITION. An **ideal** of the ring R is a subset I satisfying

(I1) $0\in I$;
(I2) $a,b\in I\Rightarrow a+b\in I$; and
(I3) $a\in I$ and $r\in R\Rightarrow ar\in I$ and $ra\in I$ (hence $-a=(-1)a\in I$).

Thus $\{0\}$ and R itself are ideals. $\{0\}$ is customarily denoted simply 0. The ideal I is **proper** if $I\neq R$. Notice that I is proper iff $1\notin I$, for if $I=R$ certainly $1\in I$, and conversely if $1\in I$ then $r=r\cdot 1\in I$ $\forall r\in R$.

We shall find the following notation convenient. If a is an element and X a subset of the ring R, then $a+X$ denotes the set $\{a+b: b\in X\}$ and aX denotes $\{ab: b\in X\}$.

If A is a commutative ring and $a\in A$, then aA is an ideal, as the following calculations show: $0=a0\in aA$, $ab+ac=a(b+c)\in aA$, and $ab\cdot c=c\cdot ab=a(bc)\in aA$. Thus the set $2\mathbb{Z}$ of even integers is an ideal of $\mathbb{Z}$. Such an ideal is called principal. In other words, an ideal I of a commutative ring A is **principal** if $\exists a\in A\ni I=aA$. For example, $0=0A$ and $A=1A$ are always principal.

(3.15) PROPOSITION. *Let R be a ring, θ a congruence relation on R, and let $[a]$ denote the θ-equivalence class containing the element a of R. Then*

(i) $[0]$ *is an ideal of* R;
(ii) $\theta \mapsto [0]$ *gives a bijection between the set of congruence relations on R and the set of ideals of R*;
(iii) $[a] = a + [0]$.

Proof. (i) Let us write I for $[0] = \{a \in R : a\theta 0\}$. Then $0 \in I$; if a and $b \in I$ then $(a+b)\theta(0+0)$, whence $a+b \in I$; and if $r \in R$ then $(ar)\theta(0r)$ and $(ra)\theta(r0)$, whence $ar \in I$ and $ra \in I$.

(ii) One way to show a map of sets $\alpha: X \to Y$ is bijective is to show that $\exists$ a map $\beta: Y \to X \ni \alpha\beta = 1_Y$ (which tells us that α is surjective) and $\beta\alpha = 1_X$ (which tells us that α is injective). Then of course $\beta = \alpha^{-1}$.

In the present situation, X is the set of all congruence relations on R, Y is the set of ideals in R, and $\alpha: X \to Y$ is defined by $\alpha(\theta) = [0]_\theta$, where we have attached a subscript as a reminder that $[0]_\theta$ depends on θ. Given $I \in Y$, $\beta(I) \in X$ is defined by $a\beta(I)b \Leftrightarrow a - b \in I$. This relation is reflexive since $0 \in I$, symmetric since $a - b \in I \Rightarrow (-1)(a-b) = b - a \in I$, transitive since $a-b$ and $b - c \in I \Rightarrow (a-b)+(b-c) = a - c \in I$, and homomorphic since $a - b \in I$ and $c - d \in I \Rightarrow (a-b)+(c-d) = (a+c) - (b+d) \in I$, $(a-b)c + b(c-d) = ac - bd \in I$, and $(-1)(a-b) = (-a) - (-b) \in I$.

Now $a \in \alpha(\beta(I)) \Leftrightarrow a\beta(I)0 \Leftrightarrow a - 0 \in I$. Thus $\alpha\beta(I) = I$, so $\alpha\beta = 1_Y$ in the explanatory notation above. Further, $\beta\alpha = 1_X$ because $a\beta(\alpha(\theta))b \Leftrightarrow a - b \in \alpha(\theta) \Leftrightarrow (a-b)\theta 0 \Leftrightarrow ((a-b)+b)\theta(0+b) \Leftrightarrow a\theta b$, so $\beta(\alpha(\theta)) = \theta$.

(iii) $b \in [a]$ iff $b\theta a$ and, as we just saw, this is equivalent to $(b-a)\theta 0$; i.e., $b - a = i$ (say) $\in [0]$. In other words, $b = a + i \in a + [0]$. ■

In view of (ii) we can express ourselves in terms of the ideal $I = [0]$ rather than the congruence relation θ. We write R/I for R/θ, e.g., $\mathbb{Z}/2\mathbb{Z}$, and for $a\theta b$ the customary notation is

$$a \equiv b \mod I.$$

This statement is called a **congruence** and is read "a is congruent to b modulo I." I is the **modulus** of the congruence. When $I = cA$ is principal, and the context makes clear the identity of A, one can write simply mod c. For instance, since $5 - (-4) \in 3\mathbb{Z}$,

$$5 \equiv -4 \mod 3 \qquad (\text{with } A = \mathbb{Z} \text{ understood});$$

$$X^2 + X + 1 \equiv 1 - X \mod X + 2$$

(with some $A = B[X]$ determined by the context).

The characteristic properties of the congruence relation θ are expressed as the following congruences, where for brevity we have omitted mod I:

$$a \equiv a \quad \forall a \in R,$$
$$a \equiv b \quad \Rightarrow \quad b \equiv a,$$
$$a \equiv b \text{ and } b \equiv c \quad \Rightarrow \quad a \equiv c,$$
$$a \equiv b \quad \Rightarrow \quad -a \equiv -b,$$
$$a \equiv b \text{ and } c \equiv d \quad \Rightarrow \quad a+c \equiv b+d \text{ and } ac \equiv bd.$$

Since $10 \equiv 1 \bmod 9$, we have $10^m \equiv 1^m \equiv 1 \bmod 9$ for $m \geqslant 0$; therefore, if the integer n has the decimal representation $n = d_m \ldots d_0 = d_m 10^m + \cdots + d_0$, then

$$n \equiv d_m + \cdots + d_0 \mod 9.$$

For example, $3017 \equiv 3+0+1+7 \equiv 11 \equiv 2 \bmod 9$ and $7756 \equiv 7+7+5+6 \equiv 25 \equiv 2+5 \equiv 7 \equiv -2 \bmod 9$. Had we erroneously calculated the product $3017 \cdot 7756$ as $23{,}398{,}852 \equiv 4$, we could detect the error by noticing that $2 \cdot -2 \not\equiv 4 \bmod 9$. This method, known as **casting out nines**, can similarly be used to check sums and more complicated calculations. We are simply using the fact that the equality of two expressions involving the ring operations and elements of a ring R must survive as an equality in any quotient ring R/I. For instance, if $ab + c = d^2$ in $\mathbb{Z}$, then $ab + c \equiv d^2 \bmod n$, $\forall n$. A comprehensive way of stating this occurs in A5.1(β).

One can also cast out elevens: $10 \equiv -1 \bmod 11$, so if $n = d_m \ldots d_0 = d_0 + d_1 10 + \cdots$ then $n \equiv d_0 - d_1 + d_2 - \cdots + (-1)^m d_m \bmod 11$. The incorrect value 23,398,952 for $3017 \cdot 7756$ would slip through the mod 9 test but would be caught by casting out elevens, as the reader can verify.

An element of R/I can be written $a + I$, as we just saw in (3.15)(iii), and $a + I = b + I$ is another way of saying $a \equiv b \bmod I$. At first the notation may seem dangerous: $0 + I = I$ is the 0 of the ring R/I but of course I need not be the 0 ideal. However, this causes no problem in practice. Notice that the equivalence classes $a + I$ partition the ring into subsets that appear to be "congruent" in the sense that $a + i \mapsto b + i$ defines a bijection $a + I \to b + I$ between any two of them and in a quite natural way that only depends on the choice of a and b. For example, the two elements of the ring $\mathbb{Z}/2\mathbb{Z}$, regarded as subsets of $\mathbb{Z}$, are the set $2\mathbb{Z}$ of even integers and the set $1 + 2\mathbb{Z}$ of odd integers; $x \mapsto 1 + x$ is a bijection between the two. Similarly mod 3, $\mathbb{Z}$ is split into three sets: $3\mathbb{Z}$, $1 + 3\mathbb{Z}$, and $2 + 3\mathbb{Z}$. It is sometimes helpful to have in mind a picture (Figure 3.1).

The set $2\mathbb{Z} \cup 3\mathbb{Z}$ contains 2 and 3 but not $2 + 3$. Thus the union of a collection $\{I_t : t \in T\}$ of ideals need not be an ideal. To obtain an ideal containing all the I_t we need only put in all sums that obviously must be there, as we now explain. First let us take the case of two ideals I and J. The set of all sums $i + j$ where $i \in I$ and $j \in J$, which we naturally denote $I + J$,

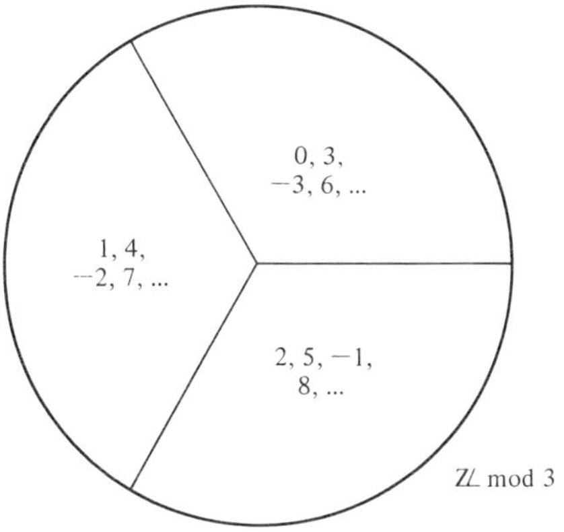

Figure 3.1

is an ideal:

$$\begin{aligned} 0 &= 0+0 \in I+J; \\ (i+j)+(i'+j') &= (i+i')+(j+j') \in I+J; \\ (i+j)r &= ir+jr \in I+J; \\ r(i+j) &= ri+rj \in I+J. \end{aligned}$$

Since $i+0 \in I+J$, $I \subset I+J$ and, similarly, $J \subset I+J$. Hence $I \cup J \subset I+J$, and $I+J$ is the smallest ideal containing I and J. This is because if K is any ideal containing I and J and $i \in I, j \in J$, then from $i \in K, j \in K$, and the (I2) property we have $i+j \in K$; hence $I+J \subset K$. ($I+J=\langle I \cup J \rangle$ in the sense of A5.3.) Notice that if $I \subset J$ then $I+J=J$.

Here is a numerical example:

$$8\mathbb{Z} + 12\mathbb{Z} = 4\mathbb{Z}.$$

For $8\mathbb{Z} \subset 4\mathbb{Z}$ (every multiple of 8 is a multiple of 4), and similarly $12\mathbb{Z} \subset 4\mathbb{Z}$. It follows that $8\mathbb{Z} + 12\mathbb{Z} \subset 4\mathbb{Z}$. Conversely, since $4n = -8n + 12n \in 8\mathbb{Z} + 12\mathbb{Z}$ $\forall n$, $4\mathbb{Z} \subset 8\mathbb{Z} + 12\mathbb{Z}$.

We treat the general case the same way. If $\{I_t : t \in T\}$ is a collection of ideals, we define ΣI_t to be the set of all finite sums $r_1 + \cdots + r_n$, where the rs are allowed to be elements from any of the I_t. To make this logically correct, in the case $T=\varnothing$, we must allow $n=0$. This obliges us to make the formal definition, long overdue, that in a monoid an empty sum (or product, depending on how the operation is written) is e, the special element of the monoid. In particular for elements r_α in a ring we have $\Sigma_{\alpha \in \varnothing} r_\alpha = 0$ and $\Pi_{\alpha \in \varnothing} r_\alpha = 1$.

With this clarification we certainly have $0 \in \Sigma I_t$. If i and j are two elements of ΣI_t, we can choose the notation so that $i = r_1 + \cdots + r_m$, $j = r_{m+1} + \cdots + r_n$, where each r_α is in some I_t, say $r_\alpha \in I_{t_\alpha}$. Then $i+j=$

$r_1 + \cdots + r_n \in \Sigma I_t$. If r is any element of the ring, $rr_\alpha \in I_{t_\alpha}$ and $ri = rr_1 + \cdots + rr_n \in \Sigma I_t$. Similarly, $ir \in \Sigma I_t$, and therefore ΣI_t is an ideal, again plainly the smallest ideal containing all the original ideals.

(3.16) DEFINITION. The collection $\{I_t : t \in T\}$ of subsets of the set R is a **chain** if $\forall s, t \in T$ either $I_s \subset I_t$ or $I_t \subset I_s$, that is, any two members of the collection are comparable.

Since $2\mathbb{Z} \not\subset 3\mathbb{Z}$ ($\not\subset$ means that $\subset$ is not true) and $3\mathbb{Z} \not\subset 2\mathbb{Z}$, $\{2\mathbb{Z}, 3\mathbb{Z}\}$ is not a chain. (*Exercise*: The following collections of ideals in $\mathbb{Z}$ are chains: $\{2^n\mathbb{Z} : n = 0, 1, 2, \ldots\}$, and $\{n!\mathbb{Z} : n = 1, 2, 3, \ldots\}$.)

Now let $\{I_t : t \in T\}$ be a nonempty chain of ideals and $i = r_1 + \cdots + r_n \in \Sigma I_t$, with $n > 0$, say $r_\alpha \in I_{t_\alpha}$. By $n-1$ pairwise comparisons we find that one of the I_{t_α} contains all the others; in detail, either $I_{t_1} \supset I_{t_2}$ or $I_{t_1} \subset I_{t_2}$, say the former. Next we have either $I_{t_1} \supset I_{t_3}$ or $I_{t_1} \subset I_{t_3}$, and so on. If, say, I_{t_1} contains I_{t_α} for $\alpha = 2, \ldots, n$, then each $r_\alpha \in I_{t_1}$ and therefore $i \in I_{t_1} \subset \cup I_t$. Also, $0 \in \cup I_t$ since the chain contains at least one I_t, T being assumed nonempty, and $0 \in I_t$. For future reference we state our results as

(3.17) PROPOSITION. *If $\{I_t : t \in T\}$ is a collection of ideals in the ring R, ΣI_t is an ideal and is the smallest ideal containing all the I_t. If the collection is a nonempty chain, this ideal coincides with $\cup I_t$.*

EXERCISES

1. Verify that the following sets are ideals in the indicated rings:

(i) $\{-4n : n \in \mathbb{Z}\}$ in $\mathbb{Z}$,

(ii) $\{0, 2\}$ in $\mathbb{Z}/4\mathbb{Z}$,

(iii) $\{0, 2, 4\}$ and $\{0, 3\}$ in $\mathbb{Z}/6\mathbb{Z}$,

(iv) all polynomials $a_0 + a_1X + \cdots$ with a_0 even in $\mathbb{Z}[X]$.

2. For every $n \in \mathbb{N}$ and $x, y, z \in \mathbb{Z}$,

$x^3 \equiv x \bmod 6$;

$x^2 + y^2 \equiv 0 \bmod 3 \Leftrightarrow x^2 + y^2 \equiv 0 \bmod 9$;

the sum of the cubes of three consecutive integers is congruent to 0 mod 9;

$2 \cdot 3^n - (-3)^n \equiv 1 \bmod 8$;

$(3^{2n} + 1)/2$ and $(3^{2n+1} + 1)/4$ are odd integers;

to the modulus 17, $2x + 3y \equiv 0 \Leftrightarrow 9x + 5y \equiv 0$;

$n^2 + 4$ is not a perfect square (i.e., of the form x^2);

$1 + 2^{2^n} + 2^{2^{n+1}} \equiv 0 \mod 21$;

$x^2 - 2y^2 + 8z = 3$ has no solution.

3. For $n\in\mathbb{N}$,

$$\left\lfloor\frac{n}{3}\right\rfloor+\left\lfloor\frac{n+2}{6}\right\rfloor+\left\lfloor\frac{n+4}{6}\right\rfloor=\left\lfloor\frac{n}{2}\right\rfloor+\left\lfloor\frac{n+3}{6}\right\rfloor,$$

$$\left\lfloor\frac{n+1}{2}\right\rfloor+\left\lfloor\frac{n+2}{4}\right\rfloor+\cdots+\left\lfloor\frac{n+2^n}{2^{n+1}}\right\rfloor+\cdots=n,$$

$$1+\frac{1}{2}+\cdots+\frac{1}{n}\in\mathbb{N}\quad\Leftrightarrow\quad n=1.$$

4. Let $x_1,\ldots,x_n\in\mathbb{Z}$, $n\geqslant 1$.
 (i) For some nonempty $I\subset\{1,\ldots,n\}$, $\Sigma_{i\in I}x_i\equiv 0 \bmod n$.
 (ii) If $x=\Pi(x_i-x_j)$ is the product over all pairs i,j with $i\neq j$, then $x\equiv 0 \bmod m^{n-m}\ \forall m\leqslant n$.

5. $S=\{a\in\mathbb{Z}:a\equiv 1 \bmod 4\}$ is a nonsaturated multiplicative set, and $\mathbb{N}\setminus S$ contains infinitely many primes. (*Hint*: If $p_1=2, p_2=3, p_3=7,\ldots,p_n$ were the complete list, consider $N=2^2 3\ldots p_n-1$ as in the proof of (1.27).) Similarly there are infinitely many primes congruent to 5 mod 6.

6. GROUPS AND UNITS

Let M be a monoid written multiplicatively with neutral element 1. An element $a\in M$ is called a **unit** or **invertible element** if there exists an element $x\in M\ni$

$$ax=xa=1.$$

When such an x exists it is unique. For if we also had $ay=ya=1$, then $x=x1=x(ay)=(xa)y=1y=y$. This unique x is written a^{-1} and is called the **inverse** of a. (For general noncommutative M we must require a^{-1} to "work on both sides." Later we shall see an example of elements a, x in a monoid where $ax=1$ but $xa\neq 1$.)

For example, when $M=E^E$ is the monoid of all maps from the set $E=\{1,2,3\}$ to itself, then $a\in M$ defined by $a(1)=2$, $a(2)=3$, $a(3)=1$ is a unit since the inverse map, whose values are $a^{-1}(1)=3$, $a^{-1}(2)=1$, $a^{-1}(3)=2$, satisfies $aa^{-1}=a^{-1}a=1_E=1$. In fact, for any set E, an element a of E^E is a unit iff it is a bijection. For if a is a bijection then $aa^{-1}=a^{-1}a=1$, and conversely the existence of an $x\ni ax=1$ implies that a is surjective, while $xa=1$ implies that a is injective.

The set of all units in a monoid M is denoted M^*. When we speak of units in a ring R we are referring to the multiplicative monoid of R:

$$R^*=\{r\in R:\exists x\in R,\ rx=xr=1\}.$$

For instance, $\mathbb{Z}^*=\{1,-1\}$ and $\mathbb{Q}^*=\mathbb{Q}\setminus\{0\}$. In fact, for any field k, $k^*=k\setminus\{0\}$. In words, a field can be defined as an integral domain in which every nonzero element is a unit. (This has an unfortunate popular extrapolation. For example, in the *Petit Larousse, dictionnaire encyclopédique* one finds, in effect, $N = \{0,1,2,\ldots\}$ and $N^* = N \setminus \{0\}$.)

Here are some further remarks to clarify the notion of unit:

1. In the monoid $\mathbb{Z}^{\mathbb{Z}}$, let a denote the surjective map $n \mapsto \lfloor n/2 \rfloor$ (the integral part of $n/2$, cf. A4.5), and b the injective map $n \mapsto 2n$. Then $ab = 1$ but $ba \neq 1$.

2. However, when an element a has both a left inverse and a right inverse, say $xa = ay = 1$, then necessarily $x = y$ by the calculation used earlier: $x = x1 = x(ay) = (xa)y = 1y = y$. Then a is a unit with $a^{-1} = x = y$. This proves that the a in (1) has no left inverse in $\mathbb{Z}^{\mathbb{Z}}$; the only candidate b does not work. Similarly, b has no right inverse. Even if we embed $\mathbb{Z}^{\mathbb{Z}}$ in a larger monoid the same reasoning shows that a can never acquire a left inverse. Thus in the ring $\mathbb{Z}[M]$, where $M = \mathbb{Z}^{\mathbb{Z}}$, a has a right inverse but is not a unit.

3. If $f\colon M \to N$ is a homomorphism of monoids or rings and $xy = 1$ in M, then $f(x)f(y) = f(1) = 1$ in N. This proves that $f(M^*) \subset N^*$, and if $x \in M^*$, then $f(x)^{-1} = f(x^{-1})$.

4. M^* is a submonoid of M since

(i) $1 \cdot 1 = 1$, hence $1 \in M^*$ with $1^{-1} = 1$;

(ii) if $a, b \in M^*$, then $(ab)(b^{-1}a^{-1}) = a1a^{-1} = 1$ and $(b^{-1}a^{-1})(ab) = 1$; hence $ab \in M^*$ with $(ab)^{-1} = b^{-1}a^{-1}$. More generally, if $a_1, \ldots, a_n \in M^*$, then $a_1 \cdots a_n \in M^*$ with inverse

$$(a_1 a_2 \cdots a_n)^{-1} = a_n^{-1} a_{n-1}^{-1} \cdots a_1^{-1}. \tag{3.18}$$

The submonoid M^* has the following additional property:

(iii) If $a \in M^*$ then $a^{-1} \in M^*$ with inverse $a^{-1-1} = a$.

This means that M^* is a group:

(3.19) DEFINITION. A **group** is a monoid G (say) with an additional operation $^{-1}\colon G \to G$ and the additional axiom (here written multiplicatively)

$$aa^{-1} = 1 = a^{-1}a \qquad \forall a \in G.$$

The two main cases that will concern us are

(i) the **group of units** R^* of the ring R, and

(ii) the **symmetric group** $\mathrm{Sym}(E) = (E^E)^*$ of bijections $E \to E$. In this context these bijections are usually called **permutations** of E. When E is the finite set $\{1,2,\ldots,n\}$ this group is also denoted $\mathrm{Sym}(n)$. A detailed discussion of permutations including the cyclic notation for the elements of $\mathrm{Sym}(n)$ is given in Section 19 of Chapter 4.

Actually the axioms entailed in (3.19) are redundant and can be pared down to the following, which is potentially useful since less checking is then involved in verifying that a given G is a group: G is a set with the three operations $\cdot$, $^{-1}$, and 1 such that

(G1) $(ab)c=a(bc)$ (hence (2.16));
(G2) $1a=a$;
(G3) $a^{-1}a=1$.

To prove that such a G is a group we must show that $a1=a$ and $aa^{-1}=1$. We do this by an artfully chosen sequence of applications of the three axioms (Gi):

$$a=1a=(a^{-1-1}a^{-1})a=a^{-1-1}(a^{-1}a)=a^{-1-1}1.$$

Multiplying this on the right by a^{-1} gives

$$aa^{-1}=(a^{-1-1}1)a^{-1}=a^{-1-1}(1a^{-1})=a^{-1-1}a^{-1}=1.$$

Hence $a1=a(a^{-1}a)=(aa^{-1})a=1a=a$.

Caution. Despite (G3), one still needs both $ax=1$ and $xa=1$ in the definition of a unit $a\in M^*$ for the following reason. If $a\in M^*$, then (G3) requires $xa=1$ to have a solution *in* M^*, so that (G3) again requires $yx=1$ to have a solution $y\in M^*$. But then a simple argument we have already seen implies that $y=a$, and this fact may as well be incorporated into the definition of unit.

A group G is **commutative** or **abelian** if $ab=ba\ \forall a,b\in G$. Additive notation, that is, $a+b,-a,0$, is almost exclusively reserved for abelian groups, as for the additive group of a ring (which we have been calling the additive monoid).

Let G be a group, $a\in G$ and $n\in\mathbb{Z}$. We extend the notation a^n (or na in additive notation) to negative n by defining, for $m\in\mathbb{N}$, $a^{-m}=(a^{-1})^m$ (or $(-m)a=-(ma)$).

(3.20) PROPOSITION. *Let a,b be elements of the multiplicatively written group G.*

(i) *$ax=b$ has a unique solution $x\in G$, namely $x=a^{-1}b$; $ax=az\Rightarrow x=z$;*
(ii) *similarly $ya=b$ has the unique solution $y=ba^{-1}$; $ya=za\Rightarrow y=z$;*
(iii) *for $m,n\in\mathbb{Z}$, $a^ma^n=a^{m+n}$, in particular $a^na^{-n}=1$, $(a^m)^n=a^{mn}$, in particular $(a^{-1})^n=a^{-n}$, and if $ab=ba$ (in particular, if G is abelian), then $(ab)^n=a^nb^n$.*

We leave the proof to the reader; the proof of (iii) is rather tedious because of the different cases one has to deal with as in the proof of (3.5).

The additive group of the ring $\mathbb{Z}/n\mathbb{Z}$ is called the **cyclic group** of order n and is denoted $C(n)$. Thus $C(3)$ consists of three elements [0], [1], [2] in the notation of Section 5, with addition mod 3: $[1]+[2]=[0]$, $[2]+[2]=[1]$, and so on. Often we convert to multiplicative notation such as $C(3)=$

$\{1, a, a^2\}$ where the exponents are calculated mod 3, so $a^3 = 1$, $a^2a^2 = a^4 = a$, and so on. In general, $C(n) = \{1, a, a^2, \ldots, a^{n-1} : a^n = 1\}$. Of course other letters can be used, e.g., $C(n) = \{1, t, \ldots, t^{n-1} : t^n = 1\}$. The groups $\mathbb{Z}^* = \{1, -1\}$ and $C(2) = \{1, a\}$ can be identified as abstract groups since they both contain one element $\neq 1$, and its square is 1.

In this notation $C(0)$ denotes the additive group of $\mathbb{Z}$, called the **infinite cyclic group**. It is also commonly denoted $C(\infty)$ and in multiplicative notation appears as $\{1, a, a^{-1}, a^2, a^{-2}, a^3, \ldots\}$. A detailed discussion of cyclic groups is given in Section 21 of Chapter 5 in connection with roots of unity.

If G_i, $i \in I$, is a collection of groups, then the **direct product**, or simply **product**, is $G = \Pi G_i$ with componentwise operations:

$$1 = (\ldots, 1, \ldots),$$
$$(\ldots, g_i, \ldots)^{-1} = (\ldots, g_i^{-1}, \ldots),$$
$$(\ldots, g_i, \ldots)(\ldots, h_i, \ldots) = (\ldots, g_i h_i, \ldots).$$

In the case of finitely many factors one can also write $G_1 \times \cdots \times G_n$. The example $C(2) \times C(2) = \{1 = (1,1), (a,1), (1,a), (a,a)\}$ is known as the **Klein 4-group**. As for the product of semigroups and monoids, we leave the verification of the group axioms of the product as a very easy exercise.

A relation ρ between groups G and H is **homomorphic** if, as usual, all operations are preserved: $1\rho 1$; $a\rho b \Rightarrow a^{-1}\rho b^{-1}$; $a\rho b$ and $c\rho d \Rightarrow ac\rho bd$. The conditions that a map be a **homomorphism** can be reduced to the single requirement

$$f(ab) = f(a)f(b)$$

because then $f(1)f(1) = f(1\cdot 1) = f(1)$, hence $f(1) = 1$ by (3.20), and consequently $1 = f(1) = f(a^{-1}a) = f(a^{-1})f(a) \Rightarrow f(a^{-1}) = f(a)^{-1}$.

Here are some explicit examples of group homomorphisms $f\colon G \to H$. We leave it to the reader to check the homomorphic property of f in each case.

(i) $G = C(2) = \{1, a\}$, $H = C(4) = \{1, b, b^2, b^3\}$, $f(a) = b^2$ (and of course $f(1) = 1$).

(ii) $G = C(4) = \{1, a, a^2, a^3\}$, $H = C(6) = \{1, b, \ldots, b^5\}$ and $f(a) = b^3$, hence $f(a^2) = (b^3)^2 = 1$ and $f(a^3) = b^3$.

(iii) $B = C(0) = \{a^n : n \in \mathbb{Z}\}$, $H = \text{Sym}(3)$, and $f(a) = b$, where b denotes the permutation $b(1) = 2$, $b(2) = 3$, $b(3) = 1$. Thus $f(a^2) = b^2 = b^{-1}$, $f(a^3) = b^3 = 1$, $f(a^{-1}) = b^{-1}$, and so on.

A homomorphism $G \to G$ is called an **endomorphism** of G. (This term is also used for other algebraic objects, such as rings, and semigroups.) For example $a \mapsto a^2$ defines an endomorphism of every abelian group since $(ab)^2 = a^2b^2$; but it is not an endomorphism of nonabelian groups. When the group is written additively this becomes $a \mapsto 2a$. Anticipating definition (3.22), an **automorphism** is a bijective endomorphism. For example, $a \mapsto 2a$ is an automorphism of the additive of group $\mathbb{Q}$ (but of course this is not a ring automorphism since it does not preserve 1 and products).

A **subgroup** of the group G is a subset X that is closed with respect to the three group operations: $1 \in X$, $a, b \in X \Rightarrow ab \in X$, and $a^{-1} \in X$. Thus $\{1\}$, which is usually denoted simply 1, and G itself are subgroups. It is not hard to verify that the following is a complete list of the subgroups of $C(6) = \{1, a, \ldots, a^5\}$: $1, \{1, a^3\}, \{1, a^2, a^4\}, C(6)$. The list for the Klein 4-group G is $1, \{1, (a, 1)\}, \{1, (1, a)\}, \{1, (a, a)\}, G$.

(3.21) PROPOSITION. *Let f: $G \to H$ be a homomorphism of groups. Then* $\operatorname{Ker}(f) = \{g \in G : f(g) = 1\}$ *is a subgroup of G (called the* **kernel** *of f). f is injective iff* $\operatorname{Ker}(f) = 1$.

Remark. The subgroups K of a group G that occur as kernels are of a special type called **normal subgroups**. They are characterized by the property that, $\forall g \in G$, $gK = Kg$, where $gK = \{gk : k \in K\}$ and $Kg = \{kg : k \in K\}$. We shall discuss this more fully in Chapter 5; see (5.324). The ring analog occurs in A5.1.

Proof. We abbreviate $\operatorname{Ker}(f)$ as K. Since $f(1) = 1$, $1 \in K$. If $g \in K$, then $f(g^{-1}) = f(g)^{-1} = 1^{-1} = 1$, and hence $g^{-1} \in K$. Third, if $g, k \in K$, then $f(gk) = f(g)f(k) = 1 \cdot 1 = 1$, so $gk \in K$. This completes the verification that K is a subgroup.

If f is injective and $g \in K$ then from $f(g) = f(1) = 1$ we have $g = 1$. Hence $K = 1$. Conversely, suppose $K = 1$ and $f(g_1) = f(g_2)$. Then $f(g_1 g_2^{-1}) = f(g_1) f(g_2)^{-1} = 1$, and hence $g_1 g_2^{-1} \in K$, so $g_1 g_2^{-1} = 1$, or $g_1 = g_2$. In other words, f is injective. ■

In the examples of homomorphisms given above, $\operatorname{Ker}(f)$ has the following values:

(i) 1,
(ii) $\{1, a^2\}$,
(iii) $\{a^n : n \equiv 0 \bmod 3\}$.

Let us look at some examples of R^* where $R = \mathbb{Z}/n\mathbb{Z}$. The order $|R^*|$ of the finite group $(\mathbb{Z}/n\mathbb{Z})^*$ is denoted $\varphi(n)$; φ is called **Euler's function**. When $n = 0$, $R = \mathbb{Z}$ and $R^* = \{1, -1\}$. When $n = 1$, $R = \not{1}$, $R^* = \{0\}$ (a "pathological" example), and $\varphi(1) = 1$. When $n = 2$, $R = \{0, 1 : 1 + 1 = 0, \text{etc.}\}$, $R^* = \{1\}$, and $\varphi(2) = 1$. When $n = 3$, $R = \{0, 1, [2]\}$, where $1 + [2] = 0$ (i.e., $1 + 2 \equiv 0 \bmod 3$), $[2][2] \equiv 1$ (i.e., $2 \cdot 2 \equiv 1 \bmod 3$), and so on. In this case $R^* = \{1, [2]\}$, where $[2]^{-1} = [2]$, and $\varphi(3) = 2$. Next when $n = 4$, $R^* = \{1, [3]\}$, where $[3]^{-1} = [3]$ and $\varphi(4) = 2$. In this ring $[2]^2 = 0$ and obviously a zero divisor is never a unit. Incidentally, an element r of a ring is **nilpotent** if $r^n = 0$ for some n. The smallest possible exponent n is the **index** of nilpotency. Thus in the ring $\mathbb{Z}/4\mathbb{Z}$ the element [2] is nilpotent with index 2. In any ring, 0 is nilpotent with index 1 (except in $\not{1}$ when the index is 0).

We list the next few cases in the accompanying table. Under $(\mathbb{Z}/n\mathbb{Z})^*$ we list the canonical representatives of the residue classes in R^*.

n	$(\mathbb{Z}/n\mathbb{Z})^*$	$\varphi(n)$
5	1,2,3,4	4
6	1,5	2
7	1,2,3,4,5,6	6
8	1,3,5,7	4
9	1,2,4,5,7,8	6
10	1,3,7,9	4
11	1,...,10	10
12	1,5,7,11	4
13	1,...,12	12

Notice that $\mathbb{Z}/n\mathbb{Z}$ is a field when $n=2,3,5,7,11,13$ and is not a field for any other n in the range $0 \leqslant n \leqslant 13$.

In the case of $k[X]$, k a field, $ab=1 \Rightarrow \deg(a)+\deg(b)=0$, whence $\deg(a)=\deg(b)=0$, which immediately leads to

$$(k[X])^* = k^*;$$

i.e., only the nonzero constant polynomials have inverses. Of course a nonconstant polynomial, e.g., $1+X$, has an inverse $1/(1+X)$ in the larger ring $k(X)$, but the notation R^* requires the inverse to be in R.

The elements a, b of the commutative ring A are said to be **associates** if $\exists u \in A^* \ni a = bu$. It is a simple matter to check that being associates is an equivalence relation. In the case $A = \mathbb{Z}$, since $\mathbb{Z}^* = \{1, -1\}$, the equivalence classes are $\{0\}, \{1,-1\}, \{2,-2\}, \ldots$. If $a = bu$, then the equations $ac = b(uc)$ and $bc = a(u^{-1}c)$ show that $aA = bA$. The converse that $aA = bA$ implies that a and b are associates is true when A is an integral domain, as the reader will easily verify, but is not true for commutative rings in general.

A polynomial with 1 as its leading coefficient is called **monic**. From the example $\frac{3}{2}(\frac{2}{3}X+\frac{1}{2}) = X + \frac{3}{4} \in \mathbb{Q}[X]$ it is clear that every nonzero polynomial over a field has a unique monic associate.

EXERCISES

1. The four elements of the group $(\mathbb{Z}/8\mathbb{Z})^*$ satisfy $x^2 = 1$.

2. **(i)** Make a table of integer representatives of the elements of $(\mathbb{Z}/n\mathbb{Z})^*$ along with their inverses for $10 \leqslant n \leqslant 20$.

(ii) A ring homomorphism $f: R \to S$ restricts to a group homomorphism $f^*: R^* \to S^*$.

(iii) For rings R_i, $(\prod R_i)^* = \prod R_i^*$ (the latter being regarded as a subset of $\prod R_i$ as usual).

(iv) The group $C(5) = \{1, g, g^2, g^3, g^4 : g^5 = 1\}$ ($\approx$ additive group of $\mathbb{Z}/5\mathbb{Z}$) is not the group of units of any ring. (*Hint*: Such an R^* would contain -1 and $1+g^2+g^3$.)

3. In a group G,

$x^2=1\ \forall x \Rightarrow G$ is abelian;

more generally, $(xy)^2=x^2y^2\ \forall x,y \Rightarrow G$ is abelian;

$(xy)^n=x^ny^n$ for three consecutive integers $n \Rightarrow xy=yx$;

given $g \in G$, $x^2gx=g^{-1}$ has a solution $x \in G$ iff g is a cube.

The last two are a little harder.

4. List the five subgroups of $(\mathbb{Z}/8\mathbb{Z})^*$.

5. The definition of a subgroup X can be compressed to $1 \in X$ and $a,b \in X \Rightarrow ab^{-1} \in X$ but cannot be compressed to $1 \in X$ and $a,b \in X \Rightarrow ab \in X$.

6. If G is a group and $g \in G$, then $\sigma_g(x)=gx$ defines a permutation $G \to G$; i.e., $\sigma_g \in \mathrm{Sym}(G)$. Similarly $x \mapsto xg$ and $x \mapsto x^{-1}$ define element τ_g and θ of $\mathrm{Sym}(G)$, and $\tau_g\theta\sigma_g=\theta$.

7. Let $G=\{g_1,\ldots,g_n\}$ be a finite group.

(i) If $s=g_1+\cdots+g_n \in R[G]$ (R any ring), then $s^2=ns$. Hence when $n \in R^*$ the element $t=s/n$ is idempotent.

(ii) When G is abelian $g_1{}^2g_2{}^2\cdots g_n{}^2=1$.

8. Let A be an integral domain and let $A[X,X^{-1}]$ denote $S^{-1}A[X]$ where $S=\{1,X,X^2,\ldots\}$. Then $A[X,X^{-1}]^*=\{uX^n : u \in A^*, n \in \mathbb{Z}\}$.

9. Let p be a prime and a an integer satisfying $0<a<p$. Verify the algorithm of Figure 3.2 to calculate the inverse of a mod p. The value of a is changed during the calculation, its final value being 1, and the required inverse is the final value of b; $f(x)=x-p\lfloor x/p\rfloor$ denotes the least positive residue of x mod p. Use this to calculate 23^{-1} and 24^{-1} mod 67.

Figure 3.2 Algorithm for a^{-1} mod p.

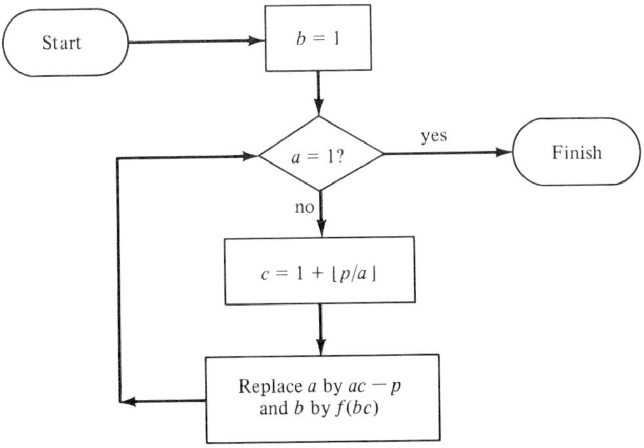

7. RATIONAL ARITHMETIC

Mod 11 we have $2^{-1}\equiv 6$, $3^{-1}\equiv 4$, $6^{-1}\equiv 2$, and $5\cdot 6^{-1}\equiv 5\cdot 2\equiv 10\equiv 2^{-1}+3^{-1}$, in perfect analogy with the equation $\frac{5}{6}=\frac{1}{2}+\frac{1}{3}$ in $\mathbb{Q}$. Of course this coincidence is no accident; the explanation follows in (3.25).

(3.22) DEFINITION. A bijective homomorphism $f: A\to B$ is an **isomorphism**; an isomorphism $f: A\to A$ is an **automorphism**.

For example, if A is a commutative ring and $S=\{1\}$, then in $S^{-1}A$, $a/1=b/1 \Leftrightarrow a=b$, so the canonical homomorphism $A\to S^{-1}A$ is bijective and is therefore an isomorphism.

If $f: A\to B$ is an isomorphism, then so is the inverse map $f^{-1}: B\to A$. (*Exercise*: prove this in the case of rings; cf. A4.2. Also show that if $g: B\to C$ is another ring isomorphism then $gf: A\to C$ is again an isomorphism.) One then says that A and B are **isomorphic**, which is sometimes indicated $A\approx B$. Then A and B are "abstractly the same" or "copies of one another" insofar as all the structure that is incorporated into the sense of "homomorphism" is concerned. To elucidate the last phrase, the map $a\mapsto 2a$ is an automorphism of $\mathbb{Q}$ *qua* additive group: it is an abelian group automorphism. However, it is not a ring automorphism since 1 and products are not preserved.

(3.23) LEMMA. *Let A be a commutative ring and S a multiplicative submonoid. Then $\bar{S}=\{a\in A: ab\in S$ for some $b\in A\}$ is a multiplicative submonoid containing S and $\bar{\bar{S}}=\bar{S}$.*

Remarks. In the definition of $\bar{S}$ such an element b will of course also be in $\bar{S}$. $\bar{S}$ is the **saturation** of S and the last statement can be phrased "the saturation is saturated." Notice the particular case $\overline{\{1\}}=A^*$.

Proof. $s\cdot 1\in S$ $\forall s\in S$ so $\bar{S}\supset S$ and in particular $1\in\bar{S}$. If $a,c\in\bar{S}$, say $ab, cd\in S$, then $ab\cdot cd=ac\cdot bd\in S$ so $ac\in\bar{S}$. We already know that $\bar{S}\subset\bar{\bar{S}}$. If $a\in\bar{\bar{S}}$, say $ab\in\bar{S}$, then $\exists c\ni abc\in S$. Hence $a\in\bar{S}$. ■

(3.24) PROPOSITION. *Let A be a commutative ring, S and S_1 multiplicative submonoids with $S\subset S_1$, and $f: S^{-1}A\to S_1{}^{-1}A$ the canonical homomorphism (cf. A4.4). Then f is an isomorphism iff $S_1\subset\bar{S}$.*

Proof. First suppose that $S_1\subset\bar{S}$. Let us use the notation a/s for elements in $S^{-1}A$ and $a/s)_1$ for elements in $S_1{}^{-1}A$. Thus $f(a/s)=a/s)_1$. Now if $s,s'\in S$ and $a/s)_1=a'/s')_1$, then $\exists t\in S_1\ni as't=a'st$. However, then $\exists b\in A\ni tb\in S$, and since $as'tb=a'stb$ we have $a/s=a'/s'$. This proves that f is injective. It is surjective because if we take any $a/s)_1\in S_1{}^{-1}A$ where $s\in S_1$, then, since $s\in\bar{S}$, $\exists b\ni sb\in S$. Hence $(ab)/(sb)\in S^{-1}A$ and $f((ab)/(sb))=a/s)_1$.

Conversely, suppose f is bijective. Given $s \in S_1$ we wish to show that $\exists b \ni sb \in S$. Since f is surjective $\exists s' \in S$ and $a \in A \ni f(a/s') = 1/s$; i.e., $\exists t \in S_1 \ni ast = s't$. However, then $(as)/1)_1 = s'/1)_1$ and, since f is injective, $(as)/1 = s'/1$, i.e., $\exists t' \in S \ni ast = s't'$. Since $s't' \in S$ we can take $b = at$. ∎

Taking $S = \{1\}$ and $s_1 = \bar{S} = A^*$ and composing the isomorphism $A \to S^{-1}A$ with the isomorphism of the proposition we obtain

(3.25) COROLLARY. *If* $S = A^*$, *the canonical map* $A \to S^{-1}A$ *is a ring isomorphism.*

In particular, we can identify a with $a/1$ and hence also a^{-1} with $1/a$ when $a \in A^*$. We then have, for example, for $a, b \in A^*$

$$a^{-1} + b^{-1} = 1/a + 1/b = (b+a)/ab = (a+b)a^{-1}b^{-1}.$$

This corollary provides the full justification for rational arithmetic, that is, ring operations with fractions in $A^{*-1}A$. The corollary also shows that if A is an integral domain then iterating the field of quotients construction gives nothing new: we have $Q(A) \xrightarrow{\sim} Q(Q(A))$. The $\sim$ above $\to$ indicates that the map is an isomorphism. (*Exercise*: Making this isomorphism an identification, show that $(a/b)/(c/d) = (ad)/(bc)$.)

The proposition shows that in the construction of the rings $S^{-1}A$ we can restrict our attention to saturated S, because $S^{-1}A$ and $\bar{S}^{-1}A$ are effectively the same. (*Exercise*: Prove that in this ring a fraction is a unit iff its numerator is in $\bar{S}$.)

In the next section we explain the connection between saturated S and a certain type of ideal.

EXERCISES

1. For $m, n \in \mathbb{Z}$, there exists a ring homomorphism $\mathbb{Z}/n\mathbb{Z} \to \mathbb{Z}/m\mathbb{Z}$ iff $m \mid n$.

2. If I, J are ideals in the ring R and $I \subset J$, exhibit a ring homomorphism $R/I \to R/J$.

3. If $R = \mathbb{Z}^{\mathbb{N}}$ (direct product of copies of the ring $\mathbb{Z}$), find a nonzero element $a \in R$ such that the rings R and R/aR are isomorphic.

8. PRIME IDEALS AND ZORN'S LEMMA

(3.26) DEFINITION. The ideal P of the commutative ring A is **prime** if $A \setminus P$ is a submonoid of A, that is, $1 \notin P$ and $a \notin P$, $b \notin P \Rightarrow ab \notin P$. Equivalently, P is proper and

(3.27) $\qquad ab \in P \quad \Rightarrow \quad a \in P \quad \text{or} \quad b \in P.$

For example $4\mathbb{Z}$ is not prime since $2\cdot 2 \in 4\mathbb{Z}$ but $2 \notin 4\mathbb{Z}$. Similarly, $6\mathbb{Z}$ is not prime since it contains $2\cdot 3$ but neither 2 nor 3. However, $2\mathbb{Z}$ is prime since

$$a, b \notin 2\mathbb{Z} \quad \Rightarrow \quad a \equiv b \equiv 1 \mod 2 \quad \Rightarrow \quad ab \equiv 1 \mod 2$$
$$\Rightarrow \quad ab \notin 2\mathbb{Z}.$$

The ideal 0 is also prime in $\mathbb{Z}$. In fact,

(3.28) PROPOSITION. *The ideal I in the commutative ring A is prime iff A/I is an integral domain. In particular, 0 is a prime ideal in A iff A is an integral domain.*

Proof. The element $a+I$ of A/I is the 0-element of this ring iff $a \in I$. Thus

$$(a+I)(b+I) = ab + I = 0 \quad \Leftrightarrow \quad ab \in I.$$

Suppose first that I is prime. Then $1 \notin I$; hence $1 + I \neq I$ and $1 \neq 0$ in A/I. If $a+I, b+I$ are nonzero elements of A/I, then their product is also nonzero in A/I since $ab \notin I$. In other words, A/I is an integral domain.

Conversely, let A/I be an integral domain. Then $1 \neq 0$ in A/I i.e., $1 + I \neq I$, so $1 \notin I$ and I is a proper ideal. If $ab \in I$ then $(a+I)(b+I) = 0$ in A/I, hence either $a+I$ or $b+I$ is I, that is, a or b is in I, and therefore I is prime. As to the final statement, recall that the ideal 0 corresponds to the congruence relation $=$ and $A/0 = A$. ∎

As a temporary abbreviation, let "monoid" stand for "multiplicative submonoid of A."

(3.29) PROPOSITION. *Let A be a commutative ring and $\{P_i : i \in I\}$ a collection of prime ideals. Then $A \setminus \cup P_i$ is a saturated monoid. Conversely, every saturated monoid is of this form.*

Proof. An element a of A is in $S = A \setminus \cup P_i$ iff $a \notin P_i \ \forall i$. Since the latter is true of $a = 1$, we have $1 \in S$. Now

$$a, b \in S \quad \Rightarrow \quad a, b \notin P_i \quad \forall i \quad \Rightarrow \quad ab \notin P_i \quad \forall i \quad \Rightarrow \quad ab \in S,$$

so S is multiplicatively closed. It is saturated because

$$a \notin S \quad \Rightarrow \quad a \in \text{some } P_i \quad \Rightarrow \quad ab \in P_i \quad \Rightarrow \quad ab \notin S \quad \forall b \in A.$$

Conversely if S is a saturated monoid we shall show that $S = A \setminus \cup P_i$, where the union is over all prime ideals P_i that do not meet S, i.e., for which $P_i \cap S = \varnothing$. Certainly no other Ps could be allowed and obviously $S \subset A \setminus \cup P_i$. It remains to prove that given $a \in A \setminus S$ then $\exists P_i$ containing a (cf. Figure 3.3). In a nutshell, the construction of P_i is as follows. Let C be the collection of all ideals (prime or not) that contain a and do not meet S. Then we can take P_i to be any maximal member in C. (By **maximal** in C we mean that if $J \in C$ then $P_i \subset J \Rightarrow P_i = J$. This does not imply that P_i contains every member of C, nor that P_i is a maximal ideal in the sense of

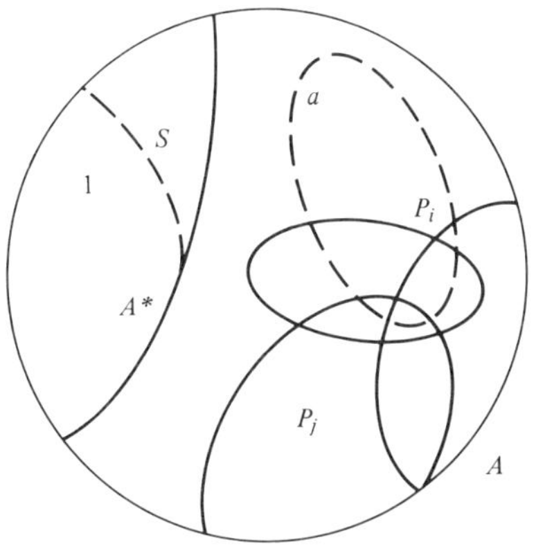

Figure 3.3

A5.6. For instance, in the collection $\{3\mathbb{Z}, 4\mathbb{Z}\}$ both members are maximal.) The proof splits up into three statements:

(α) $C \neq \varnothing$.
(β) Every maximal member of C is a prime ideal.
(γ) C has a maximal member.

To prove (α), aA is an ideal containing a and it does not meet S because $a \notin S$ and S is saturated.

For (β) let M be a maximal member of C and b, c two elements of $A \ni bc \in M$. We wish to prove that either b or c is in M. If $b \notin M$, then by (3.17) $M + bA$ is an ideal and $M \subsetneq M + bA$. ($\subsetneq$ denotes **proper containment** and means that both $\subset$ and $\neq$ are true.) Since M is maximal in C it must be that $M + bA \notin C$, hence $M + bA$ meets S, say $m + bx = s \in S$. Similarly, if we also had $c \notin M$, then we would have an equation $m' + cy = s' \in S$. Now the element

$$ss' = (m + bx)(m' + cy) = mm' + mcy + bxm' + bcxy$$

is in both S and M because $ss' \in S$ and all the terms on the right are in M, the last term because $bc \in M$ by assumption. Yet $M \in C$ so $M \cap S = \varnothing$, a contradiction that proves the result.

It remains to prove (γ). Intuitively we start with any member of C, say aA. Either that member is already maximal and we are finished or it is contained in a larger member, to which we transfer our attention. If that member is maximal we are done; otherwise we consider a yet larger member, "and so on." The problem is that ordinary induction is not a powerful enough tool. It produces a sequence $J_1 \subset J_2 \subset \cdots$ of members of C. It is easy to see that $J = \cup J_i$ is again a member of C, but J may still not be maximal. What we need to consider are *chains* in C (cf. 3.16). So let $\{J_i : i \in I\}$ be a nonempty chain of ideals in C. By (3.17), $J = \cup J_i$ is an ideal,

$a \in J$ since $a \in$ each J_i, and $J \cap S = \varnothing$ since $J_i \cap S = \varnothing$ $\forall i$. Hence $J \in C$ and J serves as an upper bound for the chain in the sense of the following result, which completes the proof of (γ) and of the proposition.

(3.30) ZORN'S LEMMA (subset version). *Let C be a collection of subsets of a set for which*

(i) *$C \neq \varnothing$, and*
(ii) *every nonempty chain $\{X_i : i \in I\} \subset C$ has an upper bound $X \in C$, that is, $X_i \subset X$ $\forall i \in I$.*

Then C has a maximal member.

The maximal member need not be unique, indeed there may be infinitely many of them. For example, if C consists of all proper subsets of $\mathbb{N}$, i.e., $C = 2^{\mathbb{N}} \setminus \{\mathbb{N}\}$, then the maximal members are the subsets $\mathbb{N} \setminus \{n\}$ which are missing a single number.

Since $\varnothing$ is a chain we could amalgamate (i) and (ii) into the single requirement that every chain have an upper bound in C. However, the way we have stated it is clearer and safer in the sense that it is less liable to be misapplied in a complicated situation.

This version of Zorn's lemma is a consequence of the axiom of choice (1.25). We do not give the proof here because a more abstract formulation of the lemma will be needed in Chapter 4. (It will amount simply to replacing C and $\subset$ by a set equipped with a relation $\leqslant$ subject to suitable axioms.)

Assignment 5

A5.1. (α) If $f: R \to S$ is a homomorphism of rings the **kernel** of f is

$$\operatorname{Ker}(f) = \{r \in R : f(r) = 0\}.$$

Show that $\operatorname{Ker}(f)$ is an ideal and that f is injective iff $\operatorname{Ker}(f) = 0$.

(β) If I is an ideal in the ring R and $f: R \to R/I$ is the canonical projection (cf. A4.3), show that f is a homomorphism with kernel I. (Hence every ideal occurs as a kernel.)

(γ) If $f: R \to S$ is a ring homomorphism with kernel I, show that the "induced" map $g: R/I \to S$ given by $r + I \mapsto f(r)$ is well defined and an injective ring homomorphism. (Hence every ring homomorphism f factors into a surjective ring homomorphism $R \to R/I$ followed by an injective ring homomorphism $R/I \to S$.)

(δ) A ring R is **simple** if $1 \neq 0$ in R and the only ideals in R are 0 and R. Show that the commutative simple rings are precisely the fields and deduce that a homomorphism of a field to any ring other than $\not{1}$ is necessarily injective.

A5.2. (α) Find x^{-1} mod 25 for $x=1,2,3,4$ and then show that $1+1/2+1/3+1/4\equiv 0$ mod 25.

(β) Solve the following congruences (that is, for a congruence mod n, find which values $x=0,1,\ldots,n-1$ satisfy the congruence):

i. $6x\equiv 15$ mod 9,
ii. $6x+4\equiv 0$ mod 9,
iii. $x^2\equiv 0$ mod 8,
iv. $x^2\equiv 1$ mod 8,
v. $x^2\equiv 2$ mod 8,
vi. $x^2\equiv 2$ mod 7,
vii. $x^2\equiv 3$ mod 7,
viii. $x^5\equiv x$ mod 5.

A5.3. (α) If $\{I_j : j\in J\}$ is a collection of ideals in a ring R show that $\cap I_j$ is an ideal. (Hence there is a unique smallest ideal containing a given subset S of R, namely the intersection of all ideals containing S. The ideal is denoted $\langle S\rangle$, which is simplified to $\langle r_1,\ldots,r_n\rangle$ in the case $S=\{r_1,\ldots,r_n\}$. For example, $\langle\varnothing\rangle=0$ and $\langle u\rangle=R$ if $u\in R^*$.)

(β) Show that $\langle S\rangle$ consists of all sums of the form $\Sigma x_\alpha s_\alpha y_\alpha$, where x_α, y_α can be any elements of R, the s_α any elements of S, and where α runs over any finite or empty index set.
(*Hint*: Break the proof up into two parts: (i) the set of all such sums is an ideal containing S, and (ii) any ideal containing S must contain all these sums. Note that in (α), $\langle S\rangle$ is approached from above, so to speak, and here it is built up from below. $\langle S\rangle$ is the ideal **generated** by the set S. Of course different sets can generate the same ideal.)

(γ) Deduce that if $\{I_t : t\in T\}$ is a collection of ideals, $\langle\cup I_t\rangle=\Sigma I_t$, and that if R is commutative,

$$\langle r_1,\ldots,r_n\rangle = r_1R+\cdots+r_nR.$$

A5.4. Let $\{R_i : i\in I\}$ be a collection of rings, R their product and $\pi_i: R\to R_i$ the map, called the ***i*th projection**, given by $r\mapsto r(i)=$ the ith component of r.

(α) Show that π_i is a ring homomorphism.

(β) If, for each i, J_i is an ideal of R_i show that ΠJ_i, identified as a subset of ΠR_i in the obvious way, is an ideal of R, and express Ker(π_i) in this form. Prove that if I is finite then conversely every ideal of R has this form. (*Hint*: If J is an ideal of R and $x\in J$ then $w_ix\in J$, where w_i is the element of R whose ith component is 1 and all other components are 0.)

(γ) If S is another ring and we have ring homomorphisms $\sigma_i: S\to R_i$, one for each i, show that there is a unique ring homomorphism $\sigma: S\to R\ni \pi_i\sigma=\sigma_i\ \forall i$. (This result is referred to as the **universal property** of the product of rings. The phrase "factors through the product" is a convenient aid to remember the direction of σ.)

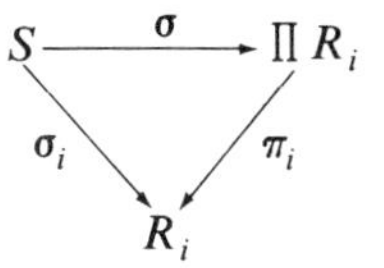

A5.5. Let $\alpha: M \to R$ be an element of the monoid ring $R[M]$.

(α) Lef $f: R \to S$ be a ring homomorphism and let $f\alpha$ denote the usual composition of maps: for $m \in M$, $(f\alpha)(m) = f(\alpha(m))$. Show that $\alpha \mapsto f\alpha$ defines a ring homomorphism $R[M] \to S[M]$ and the kernel consists of those α with $\alpha(m) \in \operatorname{Ker}(f)$ $\forall m$. (Note the particular case $R[X] \to S[X]$, where $S = R/I$, arising from the canonical surjection $R \to S$.)

(β) If $g: M \to N$ is a monoid homomorphism show that a ring homomorphism $R[M] \to R[N]$ is defined by $\alpha \mapsto \beta$, where

$$\beta(n) = \sum_{m \in g^{-1}(n)} \alpha(m).$$

A5.6. An ideal M of the ring R is **maximal** if it is proper and if it is not properly contained in any other proper ideal. That is, $1 \notin M$, and if I is an ideal such that $M \subset I \subset R$, then either $I = M$ or $I = R$.

(α) Let J be any proper ideal in R. Show that J is contained in a maximal ideal. (*Hint*: Apply Zorn's lemma to the collection of proper ideals containing J, noting that an element of the collection that is Zorn maximal is actually maximal in the sense just defined.)

(β) Let A be a commutative ring and J a proper ideal in A. Show that J is maximal iff

$$J + aA = A \quad \forall a \in A \setminus J.$$

(γ) Let J be an ideal in the commutative ring A. Show that J is maximal iff A/J is a field. (Hence by (3.28) every maximal ideal is prime.)

A ring is **local** if it has precisely one maximal ideal. (For example, a simple ring is local; its maximal ideal is 0.)

(δ) Let A be a commutative local ring with maximal ideal M. Show that $A^* = A \setminus M$.

(ε) Let P be a prime ideal in the commutative ring A and $S = A \setminus P$. Show that $S^{-1}A$ is local. (This ring is called the **local ring at P** and is customarily denoted A_P.)

A5.7. Let G be a group and for each $x \in G$ define $\sigma_x(y) = xy$.

(i) σ_x is a bijection. Hence $\sigma_x \in \operatorname{Sym}(G)$.

(ii) $x \mapsto \sigma_x$ is an injective group homomorphism $G \to \operatorname{Sym}(G)$. (This homomorphism is called the **left regular representation** of G.) Thus every finite group of order n is isomorphic to a subgroup of $\operatorname{Sym}(n)$—**Cayley's theorem**.

(iii) Similarly, $\tau_x(y) = yx^{-1}$ defines an element $\tau_x \in \operatorname{Sym}(G)$ and $x \mapsto \tau_x$ defines an injective homomorphism $G \to \operatorname{Sym}(G)$ (called the *right* regular representation).

9. PRINCIPAL IDEAL DOMAINS

A **principal ideal domain**, abbreviated P.I.D., is an integral domain in which every ideal is principal.

(3.31) PROPOSITION. *$\mathbb{Z}$ and $k[X]$, where k is a field, are P.I.D.s.*

Proof. Let I be any ideal in $\mathbb{Z}$. Since $0=0\mathbb{Z}$ is principal we can assume that $I\neq 0$, in other words, that I contains some $a\neq 0$. Then I also contains $(-1)a=-a$, so I contains a positive integer. By the well-ordering principle I contains a smallest positive integer b, say. Then I contains all elements of the form bx so $I\supset b\mathbb{Z}$. If c is any element in I let $c=bq+r$, where $0\leqslant r<b$. Then $r=c-bq\in I$ and the minimality of b forces $r=0$ hence $c=bq\in b\mathbb{Z}$. Thus $I=b\mathbb{Z}$.

We prove the result for $k[X]$ in an entirely similar manner with "smallest positive integer" replaced by "any nonzero polynomial in the ideal of least degree." We first prove an analog of (2.9).

(3.32) LEMMA. *Let A be a commutative ring and let a and b be polynomials over A where the leading coefficient of b is in A^*. Then $\exists! q,r\in A[X]\ni$*

$$a=bq+r \quad \text{with} \quad r=0 \quad or \quad \deg(r)<\deg(b).$$

Proof. Let $a=a_mX^m+\cdots+a_0, b=b_nX^n+\cdots+b_0, b_n\in A^*$. First we prove the existence of q and r by describing the **division algorithm** for polynomials. This algorithm, which is the familiar process of long division, produces a sequence of pairs $(q_1,r_1),\ldots,(q_t,r_t)$ where $\deg(r_1)>\deg(r_2)>\cdots>\deg(r_{t-1})$ and either $r_t=0$ or $\deg(r_{t-1})>\deg(r_t)$. The pairs (q_i,r_i) for $i=1,2,\ldots$ can be thought of as successively closer approximations to the final pair $(q_t,r_t)=(q,r)$, which is the required answer. The details are as follows.

We begin with $q_1=0$, $r_1=a$. Inductively, having defined (q_i,r_i), if $r_i=0$ or $\deg(r_i)<n$ then the algorithm is terminated with $t=i$. Otherwise we set $q_{i+1}=q_i+cb_n^{-1}X^{d-n}$, where c is the leading coefficient of r_i and $d=\deg(r_i)$, and we put $r_{i+1}=a-q_{i+1}b=a-(q_i+cb_n^{-1}X^{d-n})b=r_i-cb_n^{-1}X^{d-n}b$. In the last expression the terms of degree d cancel out so that either $r_{i+1}=0$ or $\deg(r_{i+1})<\deg(r_i)$. Since these degrees cannot decrease indefinitely, the algorithm must eventually terminate, say with (q_t,r_t). This can only happen if $r_t=0$ or $\deg(r_t)<n$ and therefore $(q,r)=(q_t,r_t)$ satisfies the requirements of the lemma.

As to the uniqueness, suppose we also had $a=bQ+R$, where $R=0$ or $\deg(R)<n$, so $b(Q-q)=r-R$. Then, since the leading coefficient of b is a unit hence not a zero divisor, $Q\neq q\Rightarrow \deg(b(Q-q))=\deg(b)+\deg(Q-q)\geqslant\deg(b)$, whereas $r-R$ is either 0 or of degree $<n$ by (3.12), a contradiction that shows that we must have $Q=q$ and therefore also $R=r$.

Returning to the proof (3.31), if $I\neq 0$ let b be any nonzero member of I of least degree and let a be any member of I. Since k is a field, the leading coefficient of b is a unit and we can apply the lemma: $r=a-bq\in I\Rightarrow r=0$. Thus we have $I=bk[X]$ as in the case of $\mathbb{Z}$. ■

The division algorithm for polynomials is summarized in the flowchart of Figure 3.4. The subscript i has been suppressed and the final value of a is r.

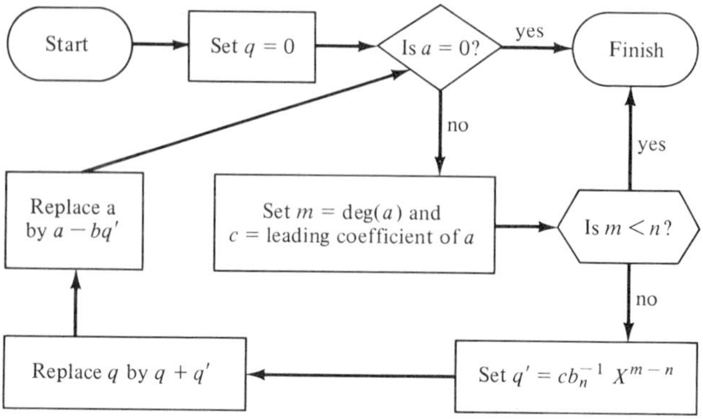

Figure 3.4 Division algorithm for polynomials.

EXERCISES

1. In $(\mathbb{Z}/8\mathbb{Z})[X]$, divide $6X^3$ by $5X^2+4X+2$.

2. In $A[X]$ where $A=\mathbb{Z}[Y]$, divide X^4 by $X-Y$.

In the case of $\mathbb{Z}$ each ideal I has a canonical generator (see A5.3 for the definition of *generate*), namely 0 or the least positive member of I. It follows that the ideals of $\mathbb{Z}$ are precisely $0, \mathbb{Z}, 2\mathbb{Z}, 3\mathbb{Z}, \ldots$. This basic fact is used in

(3.33) DEFINITION. Let R be a ring and let the kernel of the unique ring homomorphism $\mathbb{Z} \to R$ be $n\mathbb{Z}$, where $n \geqslant 0$ (cf. (3.5) and A5.1). Then n is the **characteristic** of R, denoted char(R).

If one forms the successive sums $1, 1+1, 1+1+1, \ldots$ in R, one of two things happens: Either these sums are all nonzero, which means that char$(R)=0$, or there is a smallest positive n for which the n-fold sum $\Sigma_{i=1}^{n} 1 = 0$, and this means char$(R)=n$. Then $\forall r \in R$, $nr = (1+\cdots+1)r = r+\cdots+r = 0$. For example, if $n \geqslant 0$ then char$(\mathbb{Z}/n\mathbb{Z}) = n$. One often uses the symbol 2 for the element $1+1$ of R. Thus $2=0$ in $\mathbb{Z}/2\mathbb{Z}$. Similarly, 3 stands for $1+1+1$, -2 stands for $-(1+1)$, and so on. Notice that the characteristic of an integral domain, in particular that of a field, is 0 or a prime; for if char$(R)=n=ab$, where a and b are integers strictly between 1 and n then, in R, $a \neq 0, b \neq 0$ but $ab=0$. Of course the converse is not true; e.g., $(\mathbb{Z}/2\mathbb{Z}) \times (\mathbb{Z}/2\mathbb{Z})$ has characteristic 2 but is not an integral domain.

Applying the remark at the end of A5.1 for any ring R of characteristic $n \geqslant 0$, we have an injective ring homomorphism $\mathbb{Z}/n\mathbb{Z} \to R$. The usual argument that $1 \mapsto 1$, hence $1+1 \mapsto 1+1$, and so on shows that this homomorphism is unique. Thus

(3.34) COROLLARY of (3.5). *Let R be a ring of characteristic $n \geqslant 0$. Then there exists a unique injective ring homomorphism $\mathbb{Z}/n\mathbb{Z} \to R$.*

The ideals of $k[X]$ also have canonical generators. For the ideal $0 = 0k[X]$ there is no choice: 0 is the canonical generator. If I is a nonzero ideal and $I = ak[X] = bk[X]$ then, since $k[X]$ is an integral domain, a and b are associates. Thus $a = bc$, where $c \in k^*$ (since $k[X]^* = k^*$). Among the associates of a we can choose the unique monic one as the canonical generator of I.

EXERCISES

1. Let A be a commutative ring, $u \in A^*$, and I an ideal in A. Then the set $\{ux : x \in I\}$, which is denoted uI, coincides with I. In particular, for any $a \in A$, a and ua generate the same principal ideal: $aA = uaA$.

2. The characteristic of a simple ring is 0 or a prime.

3. In a field of characteristic $\neq 3$,
$$a^3 + b^3 + c^3 = (a+b+c)^3 \quad \Rightarrow \quad (a+b)(b+c)(c+a) = 0.$$

10. THE SUBSTITUTION HOMOMORPHISM AND THE MINIMUM POLYNOMIAL

Given a ring A and an element $a \in A$, consider the map $A[X] \to A$ that sends a polynomial f to the "value" obtained by substituting a for X. For instance when $a = -2$, $f = X^3 - 3X + 5$ is mapped to $(-2)^3 - 3(-2) + 5 = 3$. This is customarily indicated by $f(-2) = 3$. Similarly, $f(0) = 5$, and so on. We sometimes write $f(X)$ to denote the original polynomial.

In some circumstances we can substitute elements not in A, for example, when $f = X^2 + 1 \in \mathbb{Z}[X]$:
$$f(1/2) = 5/4 \in \mathbb{Q},$$
$$f(Y + 1/Y) = Y^2 + 3 + 1/Y^2 \in \mathbb{Q}(Y),$$
$$f(1) = 0 \in \mathbb{Z}/2\mathbb{Z}.$$
However, the polynomial $g = X^2 + \frac{1}{2} \in \mathbb{Q}[X]$, for instance, cannot be evaluated at any $a \in \mathbb{Z}/2\mathbb{Z}$ since $\frac{1}{2}$ has no meaning in $\mathbb{Z}/2\mathbb{Z}$. The problem is that there is no ring homomorphism $\mathbb{Q} \to \mathbb{Z}/2\mathbb{Z}$. The following **universal property of polynomial rings** clarifies the general case. In order to avoid complications that need not concern us here, it is stated only for commutative rings.

(3.35) PROPOSITION. *Let $\rho: A \to B$ be a homomorphism of commutative rings and let $b \in B$. Then ρ has a unique extension to a ring homomorphism*

$s_b\colon A[X]\to B$ satisfying $s_b(X)=b$. This homomorphism is given by substitution of b for X:

$$s_b(a_0+a_1X+\cdots)=\rho(a_0)+\rho(a_1)b+\cdots.$$

Proof. This is the only possible s_b since it extends ρ (and hence $s_b(a_i)=\rho(a_i)$), preserves products (and hence $s_b(a_iX^i)=s_b(a_i)s_b(X)^i=\rho(a_i)b^i$), and preserves sums. It remains to check that s_b defined this way is a ring homomorphism. This is done by direct calculation using the fact that ρ is a ring homomorphism. If $f=\Sigma a_iX^i$ and $g=\Sigma a_i'X^i$, then

$$\begin{aligned} s_b(f+g)&=s_b\left(\sum(a_i+a_i')X^i\right)=\sum\rho(a_i+a_i')b^i\\ &=\sum\rho(a_i)b^i+\sum\rho(a_i')b^i\\ &=s_b(f)+s_b(g);\\ s_b(fg)&=s_b\sum a_i''X^i \qquad \left(\text{where } a_i''=\sum_j a_ja_{i-j}'\right)\\ &=\sum\rho(a_i'')b^i=\sum_i\sum_j\rho(a_j)\rho(a_{i-j}')b^i\\ &=\left(\sum\rho(a_m)b^m\right)\left(\sum\rho(a_n')b^n\right)=s_b(f)s_b(g); \end{aligned}$$

and $s_b(0)=0$, $s_b(1)=1$. ■

Let us apply this to the special case $B=A$ (and $\rho=1$). Now $X-b\in A[X]$, and for any $f\in A[X]$ we have by division

$$f=(X-b)q+r, \qquad r\in A.$$

Applying the homomorphism s_b gives $f(b)=0q(b)+r=r$. For example, $f=X^{18}+X+1$ divided by $X+1$ leaves remainder $f(-1)=1$. Thus $s_b(f)=f(b)=r$; hence $f\in \operatorname{Ker}(s_b)\Leftrightarrow r=0\Leftrightarrow (X-b)\mid f$. Writing a for b, we have

(3.36) COROLLARY. *Let A be a commutative ring, $a\in A$, and $f\in A[X]$.*

(i) $\operatorname{Ker} s_a$ *is the principal ideal* $(X-a)A[X]$.
(ii) *The* **remainder theorem**: *the remainder of division of f by $X-a$ is $f(a)$.*
(iii) *The* **factor theorem**: $(X-a)\mid f$ iff *a is a* **root** *of f, that is, $f(a)=0$.*

Examples. 1. $\frac{2}{3}$ is a root of $f=3X^3+X^2+X-2$, so the factor theorem guarantees that $X-\frac{2}{3}$ is a factor of f in $\mathbb{Q}[X]$. Indeed

$$f=(3X-2)(X^2+X+1).$$

2. If $f=3X^3+2X+4\in(\mathbb{Z}/9\mathbb{Z})[X]$, then $f(1)=0$ (in $\mathbb{Z}/9\mathbb{Z}$). Hence $(X-1)\mid f$, and in fact,

$$f=(X-1)(3X^2+3X+5) \qquad \text{in } (\mathbb{Z}/9\mathbb{Z})[X].$$

3. An element e of a ring is **idempotent**, or is an idempotent if $e^2 = e$. Unlike the case of nilpotent, the exponent here must be 2; there is no special name for elements that only satisfy $e^n = e$ for some $n > 2$. A ring always has the *trivial* idempotents 0 and 1 and since $e(1-e) = 0$, these are the only idempotents in an integral domain. (*Exercise*: If e is idempotent, so is $1-e$ and $e = e^2 = e^3 = \cdots$.) Thus an idempotent e is a root of the polynomial $X^2 - X$, and therefore $X - e \mid X^2 - X$. In fact,

$$X^2 - X = (X-e)(X-(1-e)).$$

As we saw in A3.4, every element e in the boolean ring $A = 2^S$ is idempotent and, taking S infinite, this shows that a polynomial can have infinitely many roots. However,

(3.37) PROPOSITION. *Let f be a nonzero polynomial of degree n over the integral domain A. Then f has at most n roots in A.*

Proof. Let $c, c', \ldots$ be distinct elements of A such that $f(c) = f(c') = \cdots = 0$. Now $f = (X-c)g$ for some $g \in A[X]$ of degree $n-1$. Applying $s_{c'}$ we have $0 = (c'-c)g(c')$, and since A is an integral domain we must have $g(c') = 0$. Hence $g = (X-c')h$ for some h of degree $n-2$, and $f = (X-c)(X-c')h$. Inductively, the general situation is

$$f = (X-c)(X-c')\cdots(X-c^{(i)})t,$$

where $\deg(t) = n - i$, which forces i to satisfy $i \leqslant n$. ■

As a matter of terminology, polynomials of degrees $0, 1, 2, \ldots$ are called, respectively, **constant**, **linear**, **quadratic**, **cubic**, **quartic**, **quintic**, and **sextic** (one should draw the line at **septic**). The **discriminant** of the quadratic $aX^2 + bX + c$ is the constant $b^2 - 4ac$.

Example. If $c \in \mathbb{Q}$ and $c \geqslant 0$, then $c^2 \geqslant 0$, whereas if $c < 0$, then $c^2 = (-c)(-c) > 0$. Thus in any case squares are positive, and more generally, $c^{2n} = (c^n)^2 \geqslant 0$ $\forall c \in \mathbb{Q}$. Thus $f = 3X^8 + X^6 + \frac{1}{2}$ has no root in $\mathbb{Q}$ since $f(c) \geqslant \frac{1}{2}$ $\forall c \in \mathbb{Q}$. In the same vein, the quadratic $f = aX^2 + bX + c \in \mathbb{Q}[X]$ has no root in $\mathbb{Q}$ if its discriminant is negative, as we can see by the old trick of **completing the square**,

$$4af = (2aX + b)^2 - (b^2 - 4ac).$$

For example, $f = -X^2 + X - 1$ has discriminant -3, $-4f = (2X-1)^2 + 3$, and f has no root in $\mathbb{Q}$ since this shows that $f(c) \leqslant -\frac{3}{4}$ $\forall c \in \mathbb{Q}$.

There is one more deduction we wish to make from (3.35). We can reverse the roles of f and a and consider the **polynomial function** $f\colon A \to A$ whose value at a is $f(a)$. We must, however, be careful with the notation, at least for certain "small" A. For instance when $A = \mathbb{Z}/2\mathbb{Z}$, we have $a = a^2 = a^3 = \cdots$ for all $a \in A = \{0, 1\}$, and therefore the functions associated with the polynomials $X, X^2, X^3, \ldots$ all coincide. For the purpose of the next proposition let us write $\bar{f}$ for the polynomial function. Thus $f \in A[X]$ while $\bar{f} \in A^A$.

(3.38) PROPOSITION. *Let A be a commutative ring. The map $f \mapsto \bar{f}$ is a ring homomorphism s: $A[X] \to A^A$.*

Proof. We apply the universal property of products (A5.4(γ)) to the family of homomorphisms s_a: $A[X] \to A$, where a runs over the elements of A. This gives a homomorphism s: $A[X] \to \prod_{a \in A} A = A^A$ such that $\pi_a s = s_a$ $\forall a \in A$, where π_a is the ath projection. Hence

$$s(f) = (\ldots, s_a(f), \ldots) = (\ldots, f(a), \ldots) = \bar{f}. \quad \blacksquare$$

As noted above, in the case $A = \mathbb{Z}/2\mathbb{Z}$, Ker($s$) contains $X^2 - X$, $X^3 - X, \ldots$. For more on this see (3.54)(ii).

Returning to the general case ρ: $A \to B$, there is one more idea associated with the substitution homomorphism s_b that we wish to introduce. Ker(s_b) is not always a principal ideal but there are important cases when it is, for example, when A is a field, by (3.31). If Ker(s_b) is a principal ideal, say $mA[X]$, then m is called the **minimum polynomial** of b over A. (This leaves m ambiguous to the extent of a unit factor u, since for any unit u, $umA[X] = mA[X]$. When A is a field we can divide by the leading coefficient, and in this case m is always understood to be chosen monic.) Thus when m exists, that is, when Ker(s_b) is principal, for $f \in A[X]$ we have

$$f(b) = 0 \quad (\text{in } B) \qquad \Leftrightarrow \qquad m \mid f \quad (\text{in } A[X]).$$

Only multiples of m have b as a root.

Examples. 1. A clear example can be given if we anticipate from Chapter 5 the construction of the real field $\mathbb{R}$. This field contains $\mathbb{Q}$ as a subfield and an element denoted $\sqrt{2}$ with the property that $(\sqrt{2})^2 = 2$. The homomorphism $\mathbb{Q}[X] \to \mathbb{R}$ determined by $X \mapsto \sqrt{2}$ has kernel $(X^2 - 2)\mathbb{Q}[X]$, so $m = X^2 - 2$ is the minimum polynomial of $\sqrt{2}$ over $\mathbb{Q}$. In $\mathbb{R}[X]$, m has the factorization $(X - \sqrt{2})(X + \sqrt{2})$, hence the two roots $\pm\sqrt{2}$, and m is also the minimum polynomial of $-\sqrt{2}$. In other words, $m\mathbb{Q}[X]$ is also the kernel of the substitution $X \mapsto -\sqrt{2}$.

2. An example similar to that in (1) can be constructed from materials already at hand. Let $G = \{1, g, g^2, \ldots, g^{n-1} : g^n = 1\}$ be the cyclic group of order n and let $A[G]$ denote, as usual, the monoid ring—now called the **group ring**. Substituting g for X gives a homomorphism $A[X] \to A[G]$ with kernel $(X^n - 1)A[X]$.

3. From (3.36) we see that the minimum polynomial of an element a of A is simply $X - a$.

4. Our definition allows $m = 0$, and then the element is said to be **transcendental** over A. For instance, X in $A[X]$ is transcendental over A since the substitution homomorphism determined by $X \mapsto X$ is just $1_{A[X]}$ and the kernel is 0. An element α with $m \neq 0$ is said to be **algebraic** over A, and deg m is called the **degree** of α.

5. Given any $m \in A[X]$ we can construct a ring B with an element b whose minimum polynomial/A is m, as follows. Let I denote the ideal $mA[X]$ and take B

to be the factor ring $A[X]/I$ and b the element $X+I$ of B. (b is the equivalence class containing X when $A[X]$ is partitioned according to congruence mod I.) The canonical projection $\pi: A[X] \to B$ has kernel I (by A5.1) and restricts to a homomorphism that we denote $\rho: A \to B$. Now

$$\pi(a_0 + a_1 X + \cdots) = (a_0 + a_1 X + \cdots) + I$$
$$= (a_0 + I) + (a_1 + I)(X + I) + \cdots$$

(by definition of the ring operations in B)

$$= \rho(a_0) + \rho(a_1) b + \cdots = s_b(a_0 + a_1 X + \cdots).$$

Thus $s_b = \pi$ has kernel $I = mA[X]$, and therefore by definition b has minimum polynomial m. When m is monic of positive degree n, the nonzero polynomials in $I = mA[X]$ are all of degree $\geqslant n$, and hence $A \cap I = \operatorname{Ker}(\rho) = 0$. Thus $\rho: A \to B$ is injective, and in this case A can be regarded as a subring of B. Moreover, the division algorithm is applicable, so for any $f \in A[X]$ we can write $f = mq + r$; hence $f \equiv r \bmod I$. In other words, every element $f + I$ in the factor ring is represented by an element of the form

$$r = a_0 + a_1 X + \cdots + a_{n-1} X^{n-1},$$

where n is the degree of m and $a_i \in A$. If we write b for $X + I$, then, as in the calculation above,

$$r + I = a_0 + a_1 b + \cdots + a_{n-1} b^{n-1}.$$

The uniqueness of the remainder in division immediately implies the following (we use the more distinctive symbol θ instead of b):

(3.39) PROPOSITION. *Let A be a commutative ring and m a monic polynomial of positive degree n. Let I denote the ideal $mA[X]$, B the ring $A[X]/I$, and θ the element $X + I$ of B. Then the elements of B are uniquely representable in the form*

$$a_0 + a_1 \theta + \cdots + a_{n-1} \theta^{n-1}, \qquad a_i \in A.$$

For example, the element $\theta = X + I$ of the ring $B = \mathbb{Q}[X]/(X^2 - 2)\mathbb{Q}[X]$ satisfies $\theta^2 = 2$ (θ is a root of its minimum polynomial $m = X^2 - 2$) and the elements of B are uniquely of the form $a + b\theta$, where $a, b \in \mathbb{Q}$. (We shall see in Section 13 of Chapter 5 that B is a field containing $\mathbb{Q}$ as a subfield.) Addition is performed by adding corresponding coefficients,

$$(2 + \theta) + (-2 + \tfrac{1}{3}\theta) = \tfrac{4}{3}\theta,$$

multiplication by applying the relation $\theta^2 = 2$,

$$(2 + \theta)(-2 + \tfrac{1}{3}\theta) = -4 + (\tfrac{2}{3} - 2)\theta + \tfrac{1}{3}\theta^2$$
$$= -4 - \tfrac{4}{3}\theta + \tfrac{2}{3} = -\tfrac{10}{3} - \tfrac{4}{3}\theta.$$

The general rule is

$$(a_0 + a_1\theta + \cdots)(b_0 + b_1\theta + \cdots) = c_0 + c_1\theta + \cdots$$

where

$$(a_1+a_1X+\cdots)(b_0+b_1X+\cdots)=mq+r$$

and $r=c_0+c_1X+\cdots$ is obtained by the division algorithm.

One final example: $A=\mathbb{F}_2, m=X^2+X+1$. The elements of B are uniquely of the form $a+b\theta$, where $a,b\in\mathbb{F}_2$ (so $-1=1$) and $\theta^2=-1-\theta=1+\theta$. Thus B consists of the four elements $0,1,\theta,1+\theta$. Since $\theta(1+\theta)=\theta+\theta^2=2\theta+1=1$, we have $\theta^{-1}=1+\theta$ and $(1+\theta)^{-1}=\theta$. Hence every nonzero element of B is invertible: B is a **four-element field** (and because a field certainly not the four-element ring $\mathbb{Z}/4\mathbb{Z}$ in which $2\neq 0$, $2^2=0$). This field is denoted GF(4) or $\mathbb{F}_4$.

EXERCISES

1. Use the factor theorem to determine for which a, X^2+aX+1 has $\frac{1}{2}$ as a root.

2. By (3.37), for distinct a,b,c in a field
$$\frac{(X-b)(X-c)}{(a-b)(a-c)}+\frac{(X-c)(X-a)}{(b-c)(b-a)}+\frac{(X-a)(X-b)}{(c-a)(c-b)}=1.$$

3. Every nonconstant polynomial in $A[X]$ is transcendental over A iff A is an integral domain.

4. With $A=\mathbb{Z}/3\mathbb{Z}$ and $m=X^2-2$, show that $A/mA=\{a+b\theta: a,b\in A$ and $\theta^2=2\}$ is a field of nine elements (denoted $\mathbb{F}_9$). Show that this field is not isomorphic to the ring $\mathbb{Z}/9\mathbb{Z}$.

5. Let k be a field, $a_1,\ldots,a_n$ distinct elements of k, and $b_1,\ldots,b_n$ any elements of k. Prove $\exists! f\in k[X]\ni \deg(f)<n$ and $f(a_i)=b_i$ for $i=1,\ldots,n$, namely
$$f(X)=\frac{(X-a_2)(X-a_3)\cdots(X-a_n)}{(a_1-a_2)(a_1-a_3)\cdots(a_1-a_n)}b_1 + \frac{(X-a_1)(X-a_3)\cdots(X-a_n)}{(a_2-a_1)(a_2-a_3)\cdots(a_2-a_n)}b_2+\cdots.$$
f is called the **Lagrange interpolation polynomial** for the data (a_i,b_i).

11. UNIQUE FACTORIZATION

We know from Chapter 1 that every composite natural number is a product of primes. It follows that every nonzero integer a can be expressed in the form

(3.40) $$a=up_1^{e_1}\cdots p_n^{e_n},$$

where $u\in\mathbb{Z}^*$, the p_i are primes, no two the same, the e_i are positive integers, and $n\geqslant 0$. (When $n=0$, $a=u$.) It is almost a truism that this factorization is unique: We can vary the factorization of $1001 = 7 \cdot 11 \cdot 13$ in trivial ways such as $1001 = 11 \cdot 7 \cdot 13 = (-13) \cdot (-7) \cdot 11$ and so on, but we shall never find a really different factorization into primes such as $19 \cdot 59$. Or will we?—perhaps some large integer has distinct factorizations? Here is a cautionary example.

In the multiplicative monoid $M = \{1,4,7,10,\dots\}$ of all positive integers $\equiv 1 \bmod 3$, one can define "prime" and "composite" in the obvious way. Thus 4 is a "prime" since it has no nontrivial factorization in M and similarly 10 and 25 are "primes." The argument used in (1.21) obviously can be adapted to prove that every "composite" member of M is a product of "primes," but the example

$$100 = 10 \cdot 10 = 4 \cdot 25$$

shows that this factorization is not always unique. (For an example of an integral domain exhibiting nonunique factorization see A6.4.) However we shall prove that in a P.I.D., in particular in $\mathbb{Z}$ and $k[X]$, no such aberrant behavior occurs.

To frame our statements properly we need some new terms. If A is any commutative ring we partition its elements into four classes:

(i) the 0-divisors;
(ii) the units A^*;
(iii) the **irreducible elements**, i.e., elements p that are neither 0-divisors nor units and that have the property

$$p = ab \quad \Rightarrow \quad a \text{ or } b \text{ is a unit;}$$

(iv) the **composite elements**—whatever elements are left over from the first three classes.

Examples. 1. If A is a field then classes (iii) and (iv) are empty.

2. If $A = \mathbb{Z}$ then (iii) consists of the primes together with their negatives and (iv) is $\{\pm 4, \pm 6, \pm 8, \pm 9, \dots\}$.

3. If $A = \mathbb{Q}[X]$ then a small sampling of (iii) is X, $-\frac{2}{7}X + 1$, $X^3 + X + 1$, and $5x^2 - 10$ (remember that $5 \in \mathbb{Q}^*$). The verification of the last two examples must await the development of certain tools helpful in deciding when a polynomial is irreducible.

4. If A is a finite commutative ring, e.g., $\mathbb{Z}/n\mathbb{Z}$, then (iii) and (iv) are empty: Every nonzero divisor is a unit. Since it involves only a little extra work, we prove this for all (not necessarily commutative) finite rings.

(3.41) PROPOSITION. *Let R be a finite ring and r an element of R with the property $rx = 0 \Rightarrow x = 0$. Then $r \in R^*$ and therefore also $yr = 0 \Rightarrow y = 0$. Similarly if r has the property $yr = 0 \Rightarrow y = 0$ then $r \in R^*$.*

Proof. Let $|R| = n$, say $R = \{r_1, \dots, r_n\}$. Of course $0, 1$, and r are somewhere in this list. Now $rr_i = rr_j \Rightarrow r(r_i - r_j) = 0 \Rightarrow r_i - r_j = 0 \Rightarrow r_i = r_j$. Hence the n elements $rr_1, \dots, rr_n$ are distinct and must therefore be $r_1, \dots, r_n$ in some order. In particular 1 occurs so we have $rr_i = 1$ for some i. Now $r(1 - r_i r) = r - rr_i r = r - 1r = 0$. Hence $1 - r_i r = 0$; i.e., $r_i r = 1$. Thus $r \in R^*$ with $r^{-1} = r_i$. Finally, $yr = 0 \Rightarrow yrr^{-1} = 0 \Rightarrow y = 0$. ■

(3.42) COROLLARY. *Every finite integral domain is a field.*

Returning to the general discussion, notice that if p is irreducible then so is any associate pu of p. In $\mathbb{Z}$, among the associates $\{p, -p\}$ of a given p we can choose the positive one; in the case of $k[X]$ we can choose the monic one. Although in general there need not be a canonical representative, in order to discuss factorizations of the form (3.40) it is convenient to make some choice. In this generality we must invoke the axiom of choice (1.26) to obtain a set P of irreducible elements such that (i) no two elements of P are associates and (ii) every irreducible element of A is an associate of some element of P.

If $a = uq_1^{e_1}\ldots$ is a factorization of type (3.40), then we have $q_i = p_i u_i$ with $p_i \in P$, $u_i \in A^*$. Hence the factorization can be converted into one involving only the chosen representatives, namely $a = u' p_1^{e_1}\ldots$ where $u' = uu_1^{e_1}\ldots \in A^*$ and with no change in the exponents e_i. With this observation in mind, we make the

(3.43) DEFINITION. The integral domain A is a **unique factorization domain**, abbreviated U.F.D., if

(U1) every nonzero $a \in A$ has a factorization

$$a = u \prod p^{e_p},$$

where $u \in A^*$ and only finitely many (or no) $e_p > 0$, and

(U2) this factorization is unique: a uniquely determines e_p for each $p \in P$.

A field is a U.F.D. in a trivial way: Each nonzero $a = u$, $P = \varnothing$, and (U2) is vacuously fulfilled.

As a general observation, if p is not a zero divisor in the commutative ring A,

$$(3.44) \qquad pA \text{ prime} \quad \Rightarrow \quad p \text{ irreducible.}$$

To see this suppose pA is prime. Then $pA \neq A$, so $p \notin A^*$. If $p = ab$, then $ab \in pA$, so $a(\text{say}) \in pA$, whence $a = pc$ for some c. Then $p = pbc$ or $p(1 - bc) = 0$ and since p is not a zero divisor $1 - bc = 0$, or $bc = 1$ and hence $b \in A^*$. This proves that p is irreducible. (*Exercise*: In $A = \mathbb{Z}/4\mathbb{Z}$ find a zero divisor $a \ni aA$ is prime.)

The converse of (3.44) is not invariably true and is the key property that guarantees uniqueness of factorizations:

(3.45) LEMMA. *In the definition of U.F.D., (U2) can be replaced by*

$$(U2') \qquad p \text{ irreducible} \quad \Rightarrow \quad pA \text{ prime}.$$

Proof. We first assume (U1) and (U2) and prove (U2′). Let p be irreducible and $ab \in pA$, say $ab = pc$. When we factorize a, b, and c according to (U1), substitute in the equation $ab = pc$, and compare exponents according to (U2), we see that p, or at any rate an associate of p, must occur in the factorization of either a or b. Hence $a \in pA$ or $b \in pA$.

Conversely, assume (U1) and (U2′) and suppose that the element a has two factorizations, say, $a = u\prod p^{e_p} = u'\prod p^{f_p}$ where $e_q \neq f_q$ and q denotes a particular p. If, say, $e_q < f_q$ then by canceling a factor q^{e_q} we can suppose that $e_q = 0 < f_q$. Since $f_q > 0$, $a \in qA$, so $u\prod p^{e_p} \in qA$. By (U2′), qA is a prime ideal and, by an obvious induction, (3.27) implies that one of the factors of $u\prod p^{e_p}$ is in qA, i.e., qA contains either u or one of the ps other than q (since $e_q = 0$). However, $u \notin qA$ because qA is proper. Moreover, if $p \neq q$ were in qA, say $p = qb$, then since p is irreducible $b \in A^*$. This implies that p and q are associates, which is not possible since they are distinct members of P. This contradiction proves that we could not have had the two factorizations of a. ∎

We are now ready to address the principal result of this section. Since the total effort to obtain this result is fairly substantial, we call it a theorem. The particular corollary of this theorem that $\mathbb{Z}$ is a U.F.D. is known as the **fundamental theorem of arithmetic**.

(3.46) THEOREM. *Every P.I.D. is a U.F.D.*

Proof. Let A be a P.I.D. We first prove that it satisfies (U2′). Suppose $ab \in pA$, say, $ab = pc$. The ideal $aA + pA$ is principal, say dA, which amounts to equations

$$d = ae + pf, \qquad a = dg, \quad p = dh$$

for certain $e, f, g, h \in A$. Since p is irreducible either d or h is a unit. If d is a unit then multiplying the first equation by bd^{-1} we get $b = abd^{-1}e + pfbd^{-1} = p(cd^{-1}e + fbd^{-1})$, so $b \in pA$. If h is a unit, then $d = ph^{-1}$, $a = ph^{-1}g$ and hence $a \in pA$.

It remains to prove (U1). We lead up to this proof, which really begins with (3.47), to motivate the introduction of a new idea. Let a denote the element for which we wish to prove (U1). If a is a unit or is irreducible there is nothing more to prove. Otherwise $a = a_1 b_1$, where neither a_1 nor b_1 is a unit. Let us call such a factorization **proper**. We repeat the procedure on a_1 (and b_1): Either a_1 is irreducible or can be replaced by a proper factorization and the procedure repeated on each of the factors. We simply wish to prove that this process cannot continue indefinitely, that eventually all the factors are irreducible. In the case of $\mathbb{Z}$ this is because the process involves a decreasing sequence of natural numbers (to paraphrase the proof of (1.21)). For example, $48=6\cdot 8$, $6=2\cdot 3$ and $8=2\cdot 4$, and finally $4=2\cdot 2$ so $48=2\cdot 3\cdot 2\cdot 2\cdot 2=2^4\cdot 3$. There is a similar reason in the case $k[X]$; this time the reins are decreasing sequences of degrees. However the reason in general is slightly subtle because a P.I.D. need not possess a "division algorithm."

The clue is to look at a proper factorization $a=a_1b_1$ from the point of view of ideals. We have $a\in a_1A$, so that $aA\subset a_1A$, and moreover this containment is proper, i.e., $aA\neq a_1A$. For if we had equality, then $a_1\in aA$, say $a_1=ax$, and then $a=axb_1\Rightarrow 1=xb_1\Rightarrow b_1$ is a unit, contrary to assumption. Thus a sequence of proper factorizations $a=a_1b_1, a_1=a_2b_2, a_2=a_3b_3\cdots$ gives rise to $aA\subsetneq a_1A\subsetneq a_2A\subsetneq\cdots$.

(3.47) DEFINITION. A commutative ring B is **noetherian** if every ascending chain of ideals

$$I_1\subsetneq I_2\subsetneq I_3\subsetneq\cdots$$

is finite.

Put another way, if we have ideals $I_1\subset I_2\subset\cdots$ then $\exists n\ni I_n=I_{n+1}=I_{n+2}=\cdots$. We also say that a noetherian B satisfies the **ascending chain condition** on ideals.

The proof of the theorem will be complete when we have proved the following two statements:

(α) Every P.I.D. is noetherian.
(β) Every noetherian domain (as we call a noetherian integral domain) satisfies (U1).

Proofs. (α) Consider any ascending chain of ideals $I_1\subset I_2\subset\cdots$ in the P.I.D. A. By (3.17), $I=\cup I_i$ is an ideal, say $I=cA$. Now c must be in some I_i, say $c\in I_n$. However, then I is forced to coincide with I_n, which in turn obliges $I_n=I_{n+1}=\cdots$.

(β) Let b be a composite element of the noetherian domain B. We first prove that b is divisible by some irreducible element p. Since b is composite there is a proper factorization $b=b_1c_1$. If b_1 is irreducible we can take $p=b_1$; otherwise we have a proper factorization $b_1=b_2c_2$, so $b=b_2c_1c_2$. Either b_2 is irreducible and we can take $p=b_2$, or we iterate the procedure. We thus obtain $bB\subsetneq b_1B\subsetneq b_2B\subsetneq\cdots$, and the ascending chain condition implies that this process stops, say at b_n. This means that b_n is irreducible and we can take $p=b_n$.

Thus $b=pd_1$, say. Either d_1 is a unit or, by the result just proved, $d_1=p_1d_2$, where p_1 is irreducible. Repeated application of this gives $bB\subsetneq d_1B\subsetneq d_2B\subsetneq\cdots$, which must come to an end, say at d_mB, and this means that d_m is a unit. We have $b = d_m p p_1 \cdots p_{m-1}$, which completes the proof. ■

EXERCISES

1. Let a, b, c, d, m be integers (more generally elements of a U.F.D.) $\ni ab \equiv ad - bc \equiv cd \equiv 0 \bmod m$. Then $ad \equiv bc \equiv 0 \bmod m$.

2. Let A be a commutative ring and $S \subset A$ multiplicatively closed, not containing 0. If A is a P.I.D. or is noetherian, $S^{-1}A$ has the same property.

3. Let $n \in \mathbb{N}$ and define $f(X) = X + a_1 X + \cdots + a_{n-1} X^{n-1} + X^n$ by

$$a_k = \begin{cases} 1 & \text{if } k \mid n, \\ 0 & \text{if } k \nmid n. \end{cases}$$

For example when $n = 6$, $f(X) = X + X^2 + X^3 + X^6$. Then

$$f(-1) \begin{cases} < 0 & \text{if } 2 \nmid n, \\ = 0 & \text{if } 2 \mid n \text{ but } 4 \nmid n, \\ > 0 & \text{if } 4 \mid n. \end{cases}$$

12. CONSEQUENCES OF UNIQUE FACTORIZATION

The situation thus far can be indicated schematically as in Figure 3.5. These are all strict inclusions. For example, $\mathbb{Z}[X]$ is a U.F.D. but not a P.I.D. and $\mathbb{Z}[X]/(X^2 + 5)\mathbb{Z}[X]$ is an integral domain that is not a U.F.D. (Compare Section 14 and A6.4.)

From (3.28), (3.44), and (U2′) we have immediately

Figure 3.5 Hierarchy of types of rings.

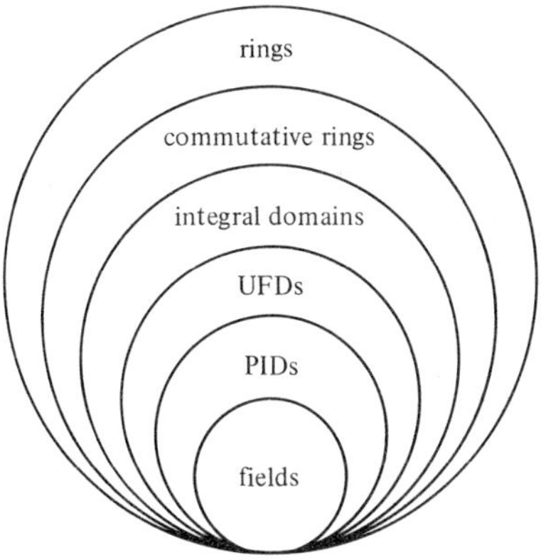

(3.48) COROLLARY. *Let a be a nonzero element in the U.F.D. A. Then A/aA is an integral domain iff a is irreducible.*

In conjunction with (3.42) this gives

(3.49) COROLLARY. *If $n \geqslant 0$, $\mathbb{Z}/n\mathbb{Z}$ is a field iff n is prime.*

Thus when $n=p$ is prime the Euler function has the value

$$\varphi(p)=p-1. \tag{3.50}$$

In (3.62) we shall see that more generally A/aA is a field when A is a P.I.D. and a is an irreducible element.

It turns out that there is, up to isomorphism, precisely one finite field of order q for each prime power q. That is, there is one field of each of the orders $q=2,3,4=2^2,5,7,8=2^3,9=3^2,11,13,16,17,\ldots$, but no field of any of the orders $6,10,12,14,15,\ldots$. This field is denoted $\mathrm{GF}(q)$ or $\mathbb{F}_q$. In particular $\mathrm{GF}(p)=\mathbb{F}_p=\mathbb{Z}/p\mathbb{Z}$ for each prime p. The example $\mathbb{F}_4$ was introduced in Section 10 and, to repeat a reminder given then when $q=p^e$ with $e>1$, $\mathbb{F}_q$ is *not* $\mathbb{Z}/q\mathbb{Z}$ since the latter ring is not a field. We return to these matters later.

If k is a field of characteristic $p>0$, then by (3.34) we can regard $\mathbb{F}_p$ as a subring of k or, to use an obvious term, $\mathbb{F}_p$ is a subfield of k. On the other hand, if k is a field of characteristic 0, then k contains $\mathbb{Q}$ as a subfield. Put simply, k contains $\mathbb{Z}$ since $\mathrm{char}(k)=0$, and since k is a field every nonzero integer b has an inverse. Hence k contains every rational fraction $a/b=ab^{-1}$. Put more carefully, the reasoning goes as follows.

By (3.34) the canonical homomorphism $f\colon \mathbb{Z}\to k$ is injective and, since k is a field, $f(b)$ has an inverse $\forall b(\neq 0)\in\mathbb{Z}$. The universal property of the localization $\mathbb{Z}\to\mathbb{Q}$ (cf. A4.4) extends f to a homomorphism $\mathbb{Q}\to k$, given by $a/b\mapsto f(a)f(b)^{-1}$, and this homomorphism is obviously injective (cf. A5.1(δ)). Thus we can identify $\mathbb{Q}$ with a subfield of k.

From this discussion it is clear that every field k contains a unique smallest subfield, which is one of $\mathbb{Q}$, $\mathbb{F}_2,\mathbb{F}_3,\mathbb{F}_5,\ldots$. This subfield is called the **prime subfield** of k. Another approach is to observe that if $\{F_i\colon i\in I\}$ is any collection of subfields of the field k then $\cap\, F_i$ is again a subfield. Thus the prime subfield is the $\cap$ of all subfields of k.

In terms of the notation $a|b$, which stands for $b\in aA$, the property (U2′) is

$$p \text{ irreducible and } p|ab \quad\Rightarrow\quad p|a \text{ or } p|b,$$

which extends immediately to $p|a_1\cdots a_n \Leftrightarrow p|a_i$ for some i.

(3.51) LEMMA. *If p is prime and the integer m satisfies $0<m<p$, then $p|\binom{p}{m}$.*

Proof. The prime p divides the product $p! = \binom{p}{m} m!(p-m)!$ and therefore divides one of $\binom{p}{m}$, $m!$, $(p-m)!$. But p does not divide $m! = m(m-1)\cdots 2\cdot 1$ since it divides none of $m, m-1, \ldots, 1$ and for a similar reason does not divide $(p-m)!$. ■

An inspection of Pascal's triangle shows that it is necessary to assume in the lemma that p is prime.

(3.52) PROPOSITION. *If p is a prime and A is a commutative ring of characteristic p then $a \mapsto a^p$ defines a ring homomorphism $F: A \to A$. If A is a field, F is injective, and if A is a finite field, then it is an automorphism.*

Proof. $1^p = 1$ and $(ab)^p = a^p b^p$ so the main thrust of the proof is that F preserves sums:

$$(a+b)^p = a^p + \binom{p}{1} a^{p-1}b + \binom{p}{2} a^{p-2}b^2 + \cdots + \binom{p}{p-1} ab^{p-1} + b^p$$

$$= a^p + b^p$$

since each of the intervening binomial coefficients is 0 in A.

If A is a field then by A5.1, $\operatorname{Ker}(F) = 0$ and F is injective. If A is finite, then any injective map from A to itself is necessarily also surjective, as follows from Section 6 of Chapter 1. ■

The map F is called the **Frobenius endomorphism**. In view of (3.34), F must be the identity automorphism 1 when $A = \mathbb{F}_p$. In other words,

(3.53) COROLLARY. *If p is a prime and a is any integer then*

$$a^p \equiv a \mod p.$$

This result, known as **Fermat's little theorem**, is easy to prove directly. It is true when $a \equiv 0$. When $a \not\equiv 0$ then a represents a unit. Hence, as in the proof of (3.41), $a, 2a, \ldots, (p-1)a$ must be congruent to $1, 2, \ldots, p-1$ in some order, so $a \cdot 2a \cdots (p-1)a \equiv 1 \cdot 2 \cdots (p-1)$, whence $a^{p-1} \equiv 1$ and $a^p \equiv a$.

Consider the Frobenius endomorphism F on the infinite field $\mathbb{F}_p(X)$:

$$F\left(\frac{a_0 + a_1 X + \cdots}{b_0 + b_1 X + \cdots}\right) = \frac{a_0^p + a_1^p X^p + \cdots}{b_0^p + b_1^p X^p + \cdots}.$$

Since $X \notin \operatorname{Im}(F)$, F is not surjective. We have $F(1+X) = (1+X)^p = 1 + X^p$ and therefore, by induction,

$$F^e(1+X) = (1+X)^{p^e} = (1 + X^{p^{e-1}})^p = 1 + X^{p^e}.$$

Comparing coefficients in

$$(1+X)^{np^e} = (1 + X^{p^e})^n,$$

we have the first part of the following corollary, generalizing (3.51):

(3.54) COROLLARY. (i) *If* p *is a prime and* $e, m, n \in \mathbb{N}$, *then*

$$\binom{np^e}{m} \equiv 0 \mod p$$

unless $p^e | m$, *say* $m = lp^e$, *and then*

$$\binom{np^e}{lp^e} \equiv \binom{n}{l} \mod p.$$

(ii) *If* $A = \mathbb{F}_p$ *and* $s\colon A[X] \to A^A$ *is the homomorphism of* (3.38) *then* $Ker(s)$ *is the principal ideal* $(X^p - X)A[X]$.

Proof of (ii). By the previous corollary, the function associated to the polynomial $X^p - X$ is the 0-function and so Ker(s) contains at least this principle ideal. Conversely, if $f \in$ Ker(s) and we write $f = (X^p - X)q + r$, where $r = 0$ or deg$(r) < p$, then $r \in$ Ker(s); i.e., r vanishes at all elements of A: $r(0) = r(1) = \cdots = r(p-1) = 0$. By (3.37) we must have $r = 0$. ■

Let a be a nonzero element of the U.F.D. A and let its factorization be $a = u\Pi\, p^{v_p(a)}$. By definition of U.F.D., the integer $v_p(a)$ is uniquely determined by a and, as observed in the last section, it does not depend on the choice of representative for the irreducible element: If p is replaced by an associate $p' = up$, then $v_{p'}(a) = v_p(a)$. The integer $v_p(a)$ is called the **p-adic value** of a. If $b = u_1 \Pi\, p^{v_p(b)}$ is another nonzero element of A, $ab = uu_1 \Pi\, p^{v_p(a) + v_p(b)}$ must be the unique factorization of ab, and we have

(3.55) $$v_p(ab) = v_p(a) + v_p(b).$$

Also, if $a + b \neq 0$, we have

(3.56) $$v_p(a+b) \geqslant \min\{v_p(a), v_p(b)\}.$$

(min means "the smaller of.") If the smaller is $v_p(a)$, say, and for convenience we write v for v_p and $a = p^{v(a)}a'$, $b = p^{v(b)}b'$, then $a + b = p^{v(a)}(a' + p^{v(b)-v(a)}b')$. Thus p occurs in $a + b$ with exponent at least $v(a)$. For instance, in $\mathbb{Z}$, $v_2(4) = 2$, $v_2(6) = 1$, $v_2(4 \cdot 6) = v_2(24) = 2 + 1 = 3$, $v_2(4+6) = v_2(10) = 1$, which coincides with $\min\{v_2(4), v_2(6)\}$. An example of inequality in (3.56) is $v_5(-2) = v_5(27) = 0$, $v_5(-2+27) = 2$.

Here is an example in the U.F.D. $\mathbb{Q}[X]$. To find the $(X-2)$-adic value of $f = \frac{1}{2}X^6 - \frac{1}{2}X^5 - 3X^4 + 2X^3 + 4X^2$ we first observe that $f = \frac{1}{2}X^2 g$ where $g = X^4 - X^3 - 6X^2 + 4X + 8$. Now, the monic irreducible polynomial $X - 2$ occurs to exponent 0 in the factorization of $\frac{1}{2}X^2$, so $v_{X-2}(\frac{1}{2}X^2) = 0$ and $v_{X-2}(f) = v_{X-2}(\frac{1}{2}X^2) + v_{X-2}(g) = v_{X-2}(g)$. We keep dividing by $X - 2$ until we get a nonzero remainder. Since $g(2) = 0$ we divide, getting $g = (X-2)h$, where $h = X^3 + X^2 - 4X - 4$. Since $h(2) = 0$ we divide again: $h = (X-2)q$, where $q = X^2 + 3X + 2$; since $q(2) \neq 0$ we have $v_{X-2}(f) = 2$.

Returning to the general situation and writing v for v_p, it is convenient to introduce the symbol ∞, called **infinity**, and make the definitions $v(0)=\infty$, $n+\infty=\infty+n=\infty+\infty=\infty$, and $\infty>n$, $\forall n\in\mathbb{Z}$. Notice that (3.55) and (3.56) remain valid for this extended v.

Next we extend the definition of v to the field of quotients $Q(A)=K$, say, in the obvious way: If $a\in K$, say $a=r/s$, where $r,s\in A$, we put $v_p(a)=v(a)=v(r)-v(s)$.

(3.57) PROPOSITION. $v\colon K\to\mathbb{Z}\amalg\{\infty\}$ *is well defined and* (3.55) *and* (3.56) *are true* $\forall a,b\in K$.

Proof. If $a=r/s=q/t$, then $rt=qs$, and since (3.55) is valid at least for elements of A, $v(r)+v(t)=v(q)+v(s)$. Hence $v(r)-v(s)=v(q)-v(t)$ and therefore $v(a)$ is well defined (even when $a=0$).

Now let $a=r/s$, $b=q/t$ be any two fractions in K. Clearly (3.55) is true. To prove (3.56) we suppose, as we can, that $v(a)\leqslant v(b)$, i.e., $v(rt)\leqslant v(qs)$. Using (3.56) for elements of A, we have

$$\begin{aligned} v(a+b)&=v(rt+qs)-v(st)\\ &\geqslant\min\{v(rt),v(qs)\}-v(st)\\ &=v(rt)-v(st)=v(a). \quad\blacksquare \end{aligned}$$

The map $v=v_p$ is called the ***p*-adic valuation** on K. (*Exercise*: Show that there is equality in (3.56) if $v(a)\neq v(b)$, and that more generally

$$v(a_1+\cdots+a_n)\geqslant\min\{v(a_1),\ldots,v(a_n)\}, \tag{3.58}$$

with equality if just one of the $v(a_i)$ has the minimum value.)

It follows from this proposition that every $a\in K^*$ is uniquely representable in the form

$$a=u\prod p^{v_p(a)},$$

where $v_p(a)\in\mathbb{Z}$ and $u\in A^*$. (This is not to be confused with the trivial statement that the field K is a U.F.D. because in the latter context there are no primes and a is a unit. In any case the exponents in (U1) are required to be nonnegative.)

For instance, in $\mathbb{Q}$ $-\frac{18}{32}=-2^{-4}\cdot 3^2$ and in $k[X]$, k any field, $X+2+1/X=(X+1)^2X^{-1}$.

Notice that if $a\in K$ then $a\in A$ iff $v_p(a)\geqslant 0$ $\forall p$, and $a\in A^*$ iff $v_p(a)=0$ $\forall p$. Thus if $r,s\in A$, then $r\mid s$ (i.e., $rt=s$ for some $t\in A$) iff $v_p(r)\leqslant v_p(s)$ $\forall p$. Hence r and s are associates iff $v_p(r)=v_p(s)$ $\forall p$.

For example, $-15\mid 300$ in $\mathbb{Z}$ because $v_2(-15)=0<2=v_2(300)$; $v_3(-15)=1=v_3(300)$; $v_5(-15)=1<2=v_5(300)$; and for $p\geqslant 7$, $v_p(-15)=0=v_p(300)$.

We say that $a\in K^*$ is a **square** or has a **square root** in K if $\exists b\in K\ni a=b^2$. When this is so we have $v_p(a)=2v_p(b)$ so a necessary condition is that

$v_p(a)$ be even $\forall p$. Thus there is no rational number $b \ni b^2 = 2$ since $v_2(2)$ is odd. Similarly, in order that $a \in K^*$ be a **cube** or have a **cube root** in K it is necessary that $3 | v_p(a)$ $\forall p$, and in general, for any positive integer m, in order that a be an ***m*th power** or that a have an ***m*th root** in K it is necessary that $v_p(a)$ be a multiple of m, $\forall p$.

In the case $K = \mathbb{Q}$, since the structure of $\mathbb{Z}^*$ is uncomplicated, we can complete the description.

(3.59) COROLLARY. *Let $a \in Q^*$ and let m be a positive integer. In order that a have an mth root in $\mathbb{Q}$ it is necessary and sufficient that $m | v_p(a)$ for all primes p and when m is even that $a > 0$.*

Proof. When $a = b^m$ and m is even, as observed earlier, $b^m > 0$, so the conditions are necessary. Conversely, if $v_p(a) = me_p$, say, and we take $b = u \Pi p^{e_p}$, where $u = 1$ or -1 according to whether a is positive or negative, then since $(-1)^m = -1$ when m is odd we see that $a = b^m$ under the conditions stated. ■

In a notation to be explained fully in Chapter 5, we write $\sqrt[m]{a} \in K$ (or $\notin K$) as an abbreviation for the statement that a has an mth root in K (or has not). When $m = 2$ it is omitted from the symbol. Thus $\sqrt{1} \in \mathbb{Q}$, $\sqrt{-1} \notin \mathbb{Q}$, $\sqrt[3]{8/9} \notin \mathbb{Q}$; and for any field k, $\sqrt{X} \notin k(X)$, $\sqrt[4]{(1+X)^3/X^4} \notin k(X)$. In the case of $\sqrt[m]{a} \notin \mathbb{Q}$ we also use the more colorful language "$\sqrt[m]{a}$ is irrational." Thus $\sqrt{p}$ is irrational $\forall p$ prime.

As a general observation, if f is a nonconstant polynomial over a field k of degree $\leqslant 3$ and with no root in k, then f is irreducible, for in a proper factorization $f = gh$ we have $\deg(f) = \deg(g) + \deg(h) \leqslant 3$. Either $\deg(g)$ or $\deg(h)$ is therefore 1; say, $g = aX + b$. However, $-b/a$ is then a root of f. Thus we can conclude that the following polynomials are irreducible over $\mathbb{Q}$: $X^2 + 1$, $X^3 - 2$, and $5X^2 - 10$ because $\sqrt{-1}$, $\sqrt[3]{2}$, and $\sqrt{10/5}$ (i.e., $\sqrt{2}$) are irrational. However, the situation is not as simple for higher degrees. For example, $\sqrt[4]{4}$ is irrational but $X^4 - 4 = (X^2 - 2)(X^2 + 2)$ is reducible.

EXERCISES

1. List all nonzero $v_p(a)$ for $a = 47/45$ and all nonzero $v_p(b)$ for $b = -1/63$. Verify (3.55) and (3.56) for these a, b and $p = 2,3,5$.

2. By pairing x with x^{-1}, in every finite field $\mathbb{F}_q$, $\Pi\{x : x \in \mathbb{F}_q^*\} = -1$. (The case $(p-1)! \equiv -1 \bmod p$ for every prime p is known as **Wilson's theorem.**) Conversely, if n is an integer $> 1 \ni (n-1)! \equiv -1 \bmod n$, then n is prime.

3. The automorphism group of $\mathbb{F}_4$ is the cyclic group of order 2, consisting of the Frobenius automorphism F and $F^2 = 1$.

4. Let k be a field of characteristic $p>0$, $a\in k$, and suppose $f=X^p-X+a$ has a root $r\in k$. Then $r+1, r+2,\ldots,r+p-1$ are also roots. *Harder*: f is either irreducible or factors into p distinct linear factors in $k[X]$.

5. Let the map $v\colon \mathbb{Q}^*\to\mathbb{Z}$ satisfy (3.55) and (3.56). Then v is either trivial or one of the p-adic valuation maps.

13. THE EUCLIDEAN ALGORITHM

(3.60) DEFINITION. If a, b are elements of the U.F.D. A, their **greatest common divisor** is the element

$$\text{g.c.d.}(a,b)=\prod p^{\min\{v_p(a),\,v_p(b)\}},$$

with the convention that g.c.d.$(0,0)=0$. Their **least common multiple** is the element

$$\text{l.c.m.}(a,b)=\prod p^{\max\{v_p(a),\,v_p(b)\}},$$

with the convention that l.c.m.$(a,b)=0$ if $ab=0$.

Notice that g.c.d.$(a,0)=$ g.c.d.$(0,a)=au$ for a unit u because of the conventions concerning ∞.

These definitions depend on the choice of representatives for the irreducible elements so in that sense the g.c.d. and l.c.m. are ambiguous to the extent of a unit factor. In the case of $\mathbb{Z}$ (resp. $k[X]$) when we speak of *the* g.c.d. and *the* l.c.m. of course we mean the one that is positive (resp. monic) or zero.

For example in $\mathbb{Z}$, g.c.d.$(-84,198)$ can be obtained by comparing the factorizations $-84=(-1)2^2\cdot 3\cdot 7$, $198=2\cdot 3^2\cdot 11$ and taking the smaller exponent for each prime. Thus g.c.d.$(-84,198)=2\cdot 3=6$. Taking the larger exponent in each case we get l.c.m.$(-84,198)=2^2\cdot 3^2\cdot 7\cdot 11=2772$.

If $c=$ g.c.d.(a,b), then by definition

(i) $c\mid a$ and $c\mid b$, i.e., c is a common divisor of a and b; and
(ii) c is "greatest" or "universal" with respect to property (i), that is, if d is any other common divisor of a and b then $d\mid c$.

(Of course in general there is no notion of $<$ on A; we carry over the word "greatest" from the familiar case of $\mathbb{N}$ where $d\mid c\Rightarrow d\leqslant c$.)

(*Exercise*: Show that conversely if c has properties (i) and (ii), then $c=u\cdot$g.c.d.(a,b), where $u\in A^*$.)

The explanation of the term "least" in l.c.m. is similar.

The following equations illustrate the next proposition (using the numerical example above and $(-84)\mathbb{Z}=84\mathbb{Z}$):

$$84\mathbb{Z}+198\mathbb{Z}=6\mathbb{Z},$$

$$84\mathbb{Z}\cap 198\mathbb{Z}=2772\mathbb{Z}.$$

(3.61) PROPOSITION. *If a, b are elements of the P.I.D. A then*

$$\text{g.c.d.}(a,b)A = aA + bA,$$
$$\text{l.c.m.}(a,b)A = aA \cap bA.$$

Remark. Since A is an integral domain, $cA = dA$ iff c and d are associates. So the formulas here are consistent with the unit factor ambiguity of the g.c.d. and l.c.m.

Proof. The ideal $aA + bA$ is principal, say $aA + bA = cA$. This equality between ideals amounts to three equations as follows. For some $x, y, s, t \in A$ we have

$$a = cx \qquad (\text{i.e., } aA \subset cA),$$

$$b = cy \qquad (\text{i.e., } bA \subset cA),$$

$$c = as + bt \qquad (\text{i.e., } cA \subset aA + bA).$$

The first two say that c is a common divisor of a and b, i.e., $v_p(c) \leqslant \min\{v_p(a), v_p(b)\}$, $\forall p$. Now, $v_p(as) = v_p(a) + v_p(s) \geqslant v_p(a)$ and similarly $v_p(bt) \geqslant v_p(b)$, so (3.56) applied to the third equation implies that $v_p(c) \geqslant \min\{v_p(a), v_p(b)\}$. Hence $v_p(c) = \min\{v_p(a), v_p(b)\}$, $\forall p$, and consequently $c = \text{g.c.d.}(a, b)$.

The statement concerning the l.c.m. is clear from the general fact that for $a, d \in A$, $a | d \Leftrightarrow aA \supset dA$. ■

This proposition implies that g.c.d.$(-84, 198) = 6$, for instance, can be written in the form $-84s + 198t$ for some $s, t \in \mathbb{Z}$; in fact we can take $s = 7$, $t = 3$. In the P.I.D. $\mathbb{Q}[X]$, g.c.d.$(X + 1, X^4 + 2X^2 + 3) = 1$ because $a = X + 1$ is irreducible and does not divide $b = X^4 + 2X^2 + 3$. We have $1 = as + bt$, where $s = (X^3 - X^2 + 3X - 3)/6$ and $t = \frac{1}{6}$.

(3.62) COROLLARY. *If a, b are elements of the P.I.D. A then $a + bA \in (A/bA)^*$ iff* g.c.d.$(a, b) = 1$. *Hence if b is irreducible then A/bA is a field.*

Remark. When g.c.d.$(a, b) = 1$, a and b are said to be **relatively prime** or **coprime**.

Proof. First suppose that $a + bA$ is a unit in the quotient ring A/bA. Then $\exists c \in A \ni ac \equiv 1 \bmod b$, i.e., $ac = 1 + bd$ for some $d \in A$. Then $1 = ac - bd \in aA + bA$, and hence $aA + bA = A = 1A$ and g.c.d.$(a, b) = 1$.

Conversely let $aA + bA = A$, say $ax + by = 1$, where $x, y \in A$. Then $ax \equiv 1 \bmod b$, so a represents a unit in A/bA. ■

Caution. This result is not true for U.F.D.s in general. For instance, it will be seen in the next section that $A = \mathbb{Z}[X]$ is a U.F.D. and that 2 is an irreducible element. As explained in A5.5, $A/2A \approx GF(2)[X]$. (Passing from A to $A/2A$ amounts to interpreting the coefficients of a polynomial mod 2.) Now g.c.d.$(2, X) = 1$, yet X is not a unit in $A/2A$.

The particular case of $\mathbb{Z}$ is worth restating.

(3.63) COROLLARY. *Let a, n be integers. Then a represents a unit in $\mathbb{Z}/n\mathbb{Z}$ iff* g.c.d.$(a, b) = 1$. *Thus if $n > 0$, $\varphi(n)$ is the number of integers a with $1 \leqslant a \leqslant n$ that are relatively prime to n.*

We draw from this in turn the Corollary (3.64). The notation

$$\sum_{d|n}, \quad \prod_{d|n}$$

is usually used only when n is a positive integer and means that the sum or product is extended over all positive integer divisors of n. Thus

$$\sum_{d|6} \varphi(d) = \varphi(1) + \varphi(2) + \varphi(3) + \varphi(6) = 1 + 1 + 2 + 2 = 6.$$

(3.64) COROLLARY. $\forall n \in \mathbb{N}$, $\Sigma_{d|n} \varphi(d) = n$.

Proof. As a general definition, when A is a U.F.D. a fraction $a/b \in Q(a)$ is in **reduced form** or in **lowest terms** if g.c.d.$(a, b) = 1$. Any fraction a/b can be put in reduced from by canceling $g =$ g.c.d.(a, b) from both the numerator and denominator since if $a = gc$ and $b = gd$ then $a/b = c/d$ and (3.60) implies that g.c.d.$(c, d) = 1$.

Now there are n rational fractions a/n with $1 \leqslant a \leqslant n$ and each has a unique reduced form c/d with $d > 0$. Conversely, given a fraction c/d with $1 \leqslant c \leqslant d$ and $d | n$, say $n = gd$, we have $c/d = a/n$, where $a = gc$ satisfies $1 \leqslant a \leqslant n$. Thus the set of n fractions of the form a/n is partitioned into the subsets $X_d = \{c/d : 1 \leqslant c \leqslant d,\ \text{g.c.d.}(c, d) = 1\}$, one for each divisor d of n. By the previous corollary, $|X_d| = \varphi(d)$, which gives the result. ■

(3.65) LEMMA. *If a, b, and m are elements of the U.F.D. A and $a \equiv b$* mod *m, then*

$$\text{g.c.d.}(a, m) = \text{g.c.d.}(b, m).$$

Proof. The following simple remark will be useful here and elsewhere. If d divides each of $c_1, c_2, \ldots, c_n$, then d divides every **linear combination** of the c_i, that is, every element $c_1 x_1 + \cdots + c_n x_n$ $(x_i \in A)$ in the ideal generated by the c_i, because if $dd_i = c_i$, then $d(d_1 x_1 + \cdots) = c_1 x_1 + \cdots$.

Now we have $a = mq + b$ for some $q \in A$ and since g.c.d.(a, m) divides both a and m it divides the linear combination $a - mq = b$. It follows that g.c.d.$(a, m)|$g.c.d.(b, m); then by symmetry (i.e., interchanging the roles of a and b), g.c.d$(b, m)|$g.c.d.(a, m). Thus the two g.c.d.s are associates and are therefore equal because they are both of the form prescribed in (3.60). ■

We now describe a remarkable algorithm, applicable to elements a, b of either $\mathbb{Z}$ or $k[X]$, where k is any field, that produces g.c.d.(a, b) without using the (U1) factorizations of a and b, and that also shows how to write the g.c.d. as a linear combination of the two elements. We shall write r_0 and r_1 for a and b in order to make the notation uniform.

(3.66) DEFINITION of the **Euclidean algorithm**. Given nonzero elements r_0, r_1 of $\mathbb{Z}$ or of $k[X]$, we define elements $r_2, \ldots$ inductively as follows. If $r_n \neq 0$, then r_{n+1} is the remainder, subject to the usual constraints, in

$$r_{n-1} = r_n q_n + r_{n+1}.$$

If $r_n = 0$, the algorithm is finished.

Let us follow this prescription in $\mathbb{Z}$ in the case $r_0 = -84$, $r_1 = 198$:

$$-84 = 198(-1) + 114.$$

Since $r_2 = 114 \neq 0$ we can divide by r_2 (and we keep dividing until we get a zero remainder):

$$198 = 114 \cdot 1 + 84$$

$$114 = 84 \cdot 1 + 30$$

$$84 = 30 \cdot 2 + 24$$

$$30 = 24 \cdot 1 + 6$$

$$24 = 6 \cdot 4.$$

(*Exercise*: Explain why the algorithm always terminates after finitely many steps in both cases $\mathbb{Z}$ and $k[X]$.)

(3.67) PROPOSITION. *If the Euclidean algorithm for $\mathbb{Z}$ or $k[X]$ starting with r_0, r_1 continues to $r_n \neq 0$, $r_{n+1} = 0$, then $r_n =$ g.c.d.(r_0, r_1) (within a unit factor).*

Proof. Applying lemma (3.65) to each equation in the algorithm

$$\begin{aligned} r_0 &= r_1 q_1 + r_2, \\ r_1 &= r_2 q_2 + r_3, \\ &\vdots \\ r_{n-2} &= r_{n-1} q_{n-1} + r_n, \\ r_{n-1} &= r_n q_n, \end{aligned}$$

we have $\text{g.c.d.}(r_0, r_1) = \text{g.c.d.}(r_1, r_2) = \cdots = \text{g.c.d.}(r_{n-1}, r_n) = \text{g.c.d.}(r_n, 0) = r_n$ within a unit factor. ■

It is easiest to explain by example how we express the g.c.d as a linear combination of the starting data. From

$$\begin{aligned} 27263 &= 8494 \cdot 3 + 1781, \\ 8494 &= 1781 \cdot 4 + 1370, \\ 1781 &= 1370 \cdot 1 + 411, \\ 1370 &= 411 \cdot 3 + 137, \\ 411 &= 137 \cdot 3, \end{aligned}$$

we obtain by working backward, starting with the second to last equation,

$$\begin{aligned} \text{g.c.d.}(27263, 8494) = 137 &= 1370 - 411 \cdot 3 \\ &= 1370 - (1781 - 1370 \cdot 1) \cdot 3 = 1370 \cdot 4 - 1781 \cdot 3 \\ &= (8494 - 1781 \cdot 4) \cdot 4 - 1781 \cdot 3 = 8494 \cdot 4 - 1781 \cdot 19 \\ &= 8494 \cdot 4 - (27263 - 8494 \cdot 3) \cdot 19 \\ &= 8494 \cdot 61 - 27263 \cdot 19, \end{aligned}$$

a linear combination as required. The g.c.d was determined in ignorance of the factorizations into primes $27263 = 137 \cdot 199, 8494 = 2 \cdot 31 \cdot 137$.

(3.68) LEMMA. *If a, b, c are elements of the U.F.D. A, a and b are relatively prime and $a \mid bc$ then $a \mid c$.*

Proof. If p is any irreducible element for which $v_p(a) > 0$, then $v_p(b) = 0$ since $\text{g.c.d.}(a, b) = 1$. However, since $a \mid bc$ we have $v_p(a) \leqslant v_p(bc)$, so that $v_p(a) \leqslant v_p(c)$. ■

The following result is known as the **rational roots test**.

(3.69) PROPOSITION. *Let A be a U.F.D., $f = a_n X^n + \cdots + a_1 X + a_0 \in A[X]$ with $a_n \neq 0$ and let r/s be a fraction in $Q(A)$ in reduced form (i.e., $\text{g.c.d.}(r, s) = 1$) which is a root of f. Then $r \mid a_0$ and $s \mid a_n$.*

Proof. Multiplying the equation $f(r/s) = 0$ by s^{n-1} and transposing terms to the right side of the equation, we obtain

$$a_n r^n / s = -a_{n-1} r^{n-1} - a_{n-2} r^{n-2} s - \cdots - a_0 s^{n-1} \in A,$$

whence $s \mid a_n r^n$. However, $\text{g.c.d.}(s, r) = 1$; therefore $\text{g.c.d.}(s, r^n) = 1$ and the lemma implies that $s \mid a_n$. If $r = 0$, then $f(0) = a_0 = 0$, so the statement $r \mid a_0$ is true in this case. If $r \neq 0$, then s/r is a root of the so-called **reciprocal polynomial** $a_0 X^n + a_1 X^{n-1} + \cdots + a_n$ and $r \mid a_0$ follows from the result already proved. ■

It is instructive to follow the proof through in a particular case. (Of course the proof must remain valid when particular values are given to r, s, and the a_i.) For example, when $A=\mathbb{Z}$ and $f=3X^3-X^2+X+2$, the rational number $4=\frac{4}{1}$ cannot be a root since $4\nmid 2$. For assuming it were, to follow the above proof, $\frac{1}{4}$ would be a root of $2X^3+X^2-X+3$, i.e., $2(\frac{1}{4})^3+(\frac{1}{4})^2-(\frac{1}{4})+3=0$ and multiplying this by 4^2 leads to $2(\frac{1}{4})=-1+4-3\cdot 4^2\in\mathbb{Z}$, whence the contradiction $4|2$.

Indeed the only rational numbers that can possibly be roots of f are $\{r/s : r|2 \text{ and } s|3\}=\{\pm 1, \pm 2, \pm(1/3), \pm(2/3)\}$. At this point we can simply test these possibilities. A priori it could be that none is a root, but we find in fact that $f(-2/3)=0$. By the factor theorem we know that $(X+2/3)|f$, and indeed $f=(3X+2)(X^2-X+1)$. Now X^2-X+1 is irreducible since its discriminant is negative; alternatively, neither of the possibilities ± 1 allowed by the rational roots test is in fact a root. Thus

$$f=3(X+\tfrac{2}{3})(X^2-X+1)$$

is the unique factorization of f in $\mathbb{Q}[X]$.

As another example, $f=6X^3+X+1\in\mathbb{Q}[X]$ is irreducible since none of $-1, -\frac{1}{2}, -\frac{1}{3}, -\frac{1}{6}$ is a root. (We can dismiss the positive ones since $a>0\Rightarrow f(a)>0$.) Similarly, $g=6X^4+X+1$ has no rational root, but at this point we cannot assert that g is irreducible. In the next section we shall describe a technique for showing that g is not a product of two quadratics.

Since $f=6X^3+X+1$ is irreducible in $\mathbb{Q}[X]$, $I=f\mathbb{Q}[X]$ is a maximal ideal and $k=\mathbb{Q}[X]/I$ is a field (by (3.62) and A5.6). As explained in Section 10, if we write β for $X+I$, the elements of k are uniquely represented in the form $a+b\beta+c\beta^2$, where $a,b,c\in\mathbb{Q}$. Euclid's algorithm can be used to calculate inverses in k. For example, for $(1-2\beta^2)^{-1}$ the algorithm gives

$$1=(1-2X^2)s+ft,$$

where $s=(8-3X+12X^2)/7$. Therefore

$$1\equiv(1-2X^2)s \mod f,$$

and

$$(1-2\beta^2)^{-1}=(8-3\beta+12\beta^2)/7.$$

However, other methods may be more efficient in certain circumstances. For example, if $\gamma^2=c$, then

$$\frac{1}{a+b\gamma}=\frac{1}{a+b\gamma}\frac{a-b\gamma}{a-b\gamma}=\frac{a}{a^2-b^2c}-\frac{b}{a^2-b^2c}\gamma.$$

This procedure is called **rationalizing the denominator**.

EXERCISES

1. If a and b are relatively prime natural numbers and $ab=c^3$ for some $c\in\mathbb{N}$, then $\exists d,e\in\mathbb{N}\ni a=d^3$ and $b=e^3$.

2. For $n\in\mathbb{Z}$, g.c.d.$(2n-1, 9n+4)=1$ or 17.

3. For elements a,b of a U.F.D., g.c.d.$(a,b)=1 \Rightarrow$ g.c.d.$(a+b,a-b)|2$ and g.c.d.$(a+b,a^2-ab+b^2)|3$.

4. **(i)** Prove the **Chinese Remainder Theorem** for $\mathbb{Z}$: For $m_i \in \mathbb{N}$ and $a_i \in \mathbb{Z}$, the system of simultaneous congruences $x \equiv a_i \bmod m_i$, $1 \leqslant i \leqslant k$, has a solution iff g.c.d.$(m_i,m_j)|(a_i-a_j)$, $\forall i,j$. The solution is then unique mod l.c.m.$\{m_i\}$.

(ii) Use this to find the eight solutions of $x^2 \equiv 1 \bmod 1001 = 7 \cdot 11 \cdot 13$, and to prove that $x^3 \equiv x \bmod 24$ $\forall$odd x.

(iii) Solve the system

$$\begin{aligned} 2x &\equiv 5 \mod 15, \\ 4x &\equiv 13 \mod 21, \\ 6x &\equiv -5 \mod 35. \end{aligned}$$

5. If m and n are unequal positive integers, then

$$\text{g.c.d.}(2^{2^m}+1, 2^{2^n}+1) = 1.$$

6. Let a and b be elements of the P.I.D. A and let B be another P.I.D. containing A as a subring. If $Aa+Ab=Ac$, $c \in A$, then $Ba+Bb=Bc$. (Hence g.c.d.s do not change in going from A to B, apart from the ambiguity due to unit factors. Notice the case $k[X] \subset K[X]$ of **base field extension** for polynomials.)

7. Let $R=\mathbb{Z}/n\mathbb{Z}$. For which n are $f=X^3+2X^2+3X+4$ and $g=X^2+5X+6$ relatively prime in $R[X]$?

8. Let F be a field and $k=F(T)$. By the rational roots test, $\forall m \in \mathbb{N}$, X^3+TX+T^m is irreducible.

Assignment 6

A6.1. **(i)** If S is a subset of the group G, let $\langle S \rangle$ denote the subgroup generated by the S, that is, the intersection of all subgroups $\supset S$. For $a \in G$ show that $\langle a \rangle = \{1, a, a^{-1}, a^2, a^{-2}, \ldots\}$ and that if $a^n=1$ for some $n \in \mathbb{N}$ then $\langle a \rangle = \{1, a, \ldots, a^{n-1}\}$. (In the latter case the smallest such $n \in \mathbb{N}$ is called the **order** of a; it is in fact the order $|\langle a \rangle|$ of the subgroup generated by a. If $a^n \neq 1$ $\forall n \in \mathbb{N}$, one says that a has **infinite order**.)

(ii) Let H be a subgroup of G. Define the relation $\sim$ on G by $a \sim b$ iff $\exists h \in H \ni a=hb$. Show that $\sim$ is an equivalence relation and that the equivalence class containing a is $\{ha : h \in H\}$. (This set is denoted Ha and is called a **right coset** of H. **Left cosets** $aH=\{ah : h \in H\}$ arise in an analogous way.)

(iii) Show that a bijection between the set of right cosets and the set of left cosets of H in G is given by $Ha \mapsto a^{-1}H$.

(iv) For $a,b \in G$ prove that $ha \mapsto hb$ defines a bijection $Ha \to Hb$.

(v) Now suppose G is finite and let $(G:H)$ denote the number of distinct right cosets of H in G; this number is called the **index** of H in G. (For example, $(G:1)=|G|$.) From (ii) and (iv) deduce **Lagrange's theorem**: $|G|=(G:H)|H|$, hence $|H| \mid |G|$.

(vi) Deduce from (i) and (v) that if $|G| = n$ then $a^n = 1\ \forall a \in G$, so if R is a finite ring and $n = |R^*|$, then $r^n = 1\ \forall r \in R^*$. In particular, if $m \in \mathbb{N}$, $a \in \mathbb{Z}$, and g.c.d.$(a, m) = 1$, then by (3.63) (cf. also (3.50) and (3.53))

$$a^{\varphi(m)} \equiv 1 \mod m. \tag{3.70}$$

A6.2. (i) Write g.c.d.(a, b) as a linear combination of a and b in the following cases.

(α) $a = 73543, b = 52447$ in $\mathbb{Z}$;

(β) $a = X^4 + X^3 + X^2 + X$, $b = -X^4 - X^3 + 9X^2 + 9X$ in $\mathbb{Q}[X]$; and

(γ) a and b as in (β) regarded as elements in $\mathbb{F}_5[X]$.

(ii) Let $a, b \in \mathbb{N}$ and put $d =$ g.c.d.(a, b). Show that $ax \equiv ay \mod b \Leftrightarrow x \equiv y \mod (b/d)$. Hence prove that $ax \equiv c \mod b$ has a solution x iff $d|c$ and that there are then d solutions: If $x \equiv e$ is any one, the others are $e + b/d, e + 2b/d, \ldots, e + (d-1)b/d$. (Note that Euclid's algorithm gives an effective means of finding such an e: If $d = as + bt$, then one can take $e = sc/d$. This is an expeditious way of finding, for instance, that $21^{-1} \equiv 30 \mod 37$. See also Exercise 9 after Section 6.)

A6.3. Prove that in $A = \mathbb{Z}[X]$ the ideal $2A + XA$ is not principal and is maximal. Also show that the ideals $2A$ and XA are prime but not maximal.

A6.4. Let the symbol $\sqrt{-5}$ denote the element $X + I$ of $A = \mathbb{Z}[X]/I$ where $I = (X^2 + 5)\mathbb{Z}[X]$. As explained in Section 10, the elements of A are uniquely of the form $a + b\sqrt{-5}$, where $a, b \in \mathbb{Z}$. Prove by direct calculation that the map $N\colon A \to \mathbb{Z}$ defined by $N(a + b\sqrt{-5}) = (a + b\sqrt{-5})(a - b\sqrt{-5}) = a^2 + 5b^2$ is a multiplicative monoid homomorphism and deduce that

(i) A is an integral domain,

(ii) $A^* = \{\pm 1\}$, and

(iii) $6 = 2 \cdot 3 = (1 + \sqrt{-5})(1 - \sqrt{-5})$ are essentially different factorizations into irreducible elements and consequently A is not a U.F.D.

A6.5. Factorize completely the polynomials

(i) $2X^5 + 4X^4 - X^3 - 2X^2 + 5X + 4$ in $\mathbb{Q}[X]$ and

(ii) $X^3Y + X^2 + XY^2 + Y$ in $k[X]$, where k is the field $\mathbb{F}_2(Y)$ of rational functions in one variable over the prime field $\mathbb{F}_2$.

A6.6. Let A be a U.F.D., I a set of representatives of the irreducible elements, and S a multiplicative submonoid of A not containing 0.

(i) Show that $S^{-1}A$ is a U.F.D. (*Hint*: By (3.24) we can assume that S is saturated, and then a set of representatives of the irreducible elements of $S^{-1}A$ is $I \setminus S$.)

(ii) Consider the particular case A_P, the local ring at $P = pA$, where $p \in I$. (That is, $S = A \setminus P$, cf. A5.6(ε). P is a prime ideal by (3.48).) Show that $A_P = \{a \in Q(A) : v_p(a) \geqslant 0\}$, that this U.F.D. has (up to associates) the single irreducible element p, and that the nonzero ideals are $p^nA_P = \{a \in Q(A) : v_p(a) \geqslant n\}$ for $n = 0, 1, 2\ldots$. (*Hint*: If J is a nonzero ideal, consider an element in J of smallest p-adic value. This local ring is also called the **p-adic valuation ring** and will be studied further in Chapter 5.)

A6.7. Let R be a ring and let M be a multiplicatively written copy of the additive monoid $\mathbb{Q}^{\geqslant}=\{a\in\mathbb{Q}: a\geqslant 0\}$, say $M=\{X^a: a\in Q, a\geqslant 0\}$, where $X^aX^b=X^{a+b}$. (We made a similar change to multiplicative notation for $\mathbb{M}$ in Section 6 of Chapter 2. Notice that this use of exponents is consistent with $X^0=1$, $X^1=X$, $X^{n+1}=X^nX$.)

(i) Show that $R[M]$ is an integral domain iff R is an integral domain, but $R[M]$ is never a U.F.D. because (U1) fails.

(ii) Exhibit an ideal of $R[M]$ that is not finitely generated (i.e., that cannot be written, in the notation of A5.3, in the form $\langle x_1,\ldots,x_n\rangle$ for finitely many $x_i\in R[M]$. (However, it should be mentioned that the existence of a nonfinitely generated ideal does not in itself preclude an integral domain from being a U.F.D.)

14. POLYNOMIALS OVER U.F.D.s

Let A be a U.F.D., P a set of representatives of the irreducible elements of A, and $k=Q(A)$. For $f=a_nX^n+\cdots+a_0\in k[X]$ (with $a_n\neq 0$) define the **content** of f to be

$$(3.70)\quad c(f)=\prod_{p\in P}p^{e_p},\qquad\text{where}\quad e_p=\min\{v_p(a_n),\ldots,v_p(a_0)\}.$$

Then $f=c(f)f_1$, where $f_1\in A[X]$ and $c(f_1)=1$. Let

$$Q=\left\{c(f)^{-1}f: f\in k[X]\text{ and } f\text{ is monic, irreducible, of positive degree}\right\}.$$

(3.71) THEOREM. *$A[X]$ is a U.F.D. and $P\cup Q$ is a set of representatives of the irreducible elements.*

(3.72) LEMMA. *Let f, g be nonzero elements of $A[X]$. Then*

$$c(fg)=c(f)c(g).$$

Proof. Since $f\in A[X]$, $c(f)$ is simply the g.c.d of the coefficients a_i of f and similarly $c(g)$ is the g.c.d. of the coefficients b_j of g. Thus $c(f)c(g)$ divides each of the coefficients Σa_ib_j of fg and we can write $c(fg)=c(f)c(g)d$ for some $d\in A$. We wish to show that $d=1$.

If not, let $p\in P$ be a factor of d, let π: $A[X]\to\bar{A}[X]$ be the canonical ring homomorphism where $\bar{A}=A/pA$ (cf. A5.5) and write $f=c(f)f_1$, $g=c(g)g_1$, $fg=c(fg)h$, so that $f_1g_1=dh$. Then $\pi(f_1)\pi(g_1)=0$, which is a contradiction since $\pi(f_1)\neq 0$ (because $c(f_1)=1$), $\pi(g_1)\neq 0$, and $\bar{A}[X]$ is an integral domain. ■

Proof of the theorem. Let $f, g\in A[X]$. If $p\in P$ and $p=fg$, then $\deg(f)=\deg(g)=0$, so $f, g\in A$; hence f, say, is in $A^*=A[X]^*$. Thus the elements of P remain irreducible.

Now suppose $q \in Q$ and $q = fg$. Then $c(fg) = c(q) = 1$. Hence $c(f) = c(g) = 1$. Since q is irreducible in $k[X]$ therefore f, say, is in k^*. It follows that $f \in A^*$.

Thus the elements of $P \cup Q$ are irreducible and no two are associates in $A[X]$ since $A[X]^* = A^*$. Moreover, every nonzero element $f \in A[X]$ regarded as an element of $k[X]$ admits a factorization

$$f = a \prod_{q \in Q} q^{v_q(f)}, \qquad a \in k^*,$$

and since $c(q) = 1$ $\forall q$, $c(f) = c(a) = au^{-1}$ for some $u \in A^*$, so that $a \in A$. Thus

$$f = u \prod_{p \in P} p^{v_p(a)} \prod_{q \in Q} q^{v_q(f)}$$

and it remains to prove (U2).

If also

$$f = w \prod_{p \in P} p^{e_p} \prod_{q \in Q} q^{e_q}, \qquad w \in A^*,$$

then from (U2) for $k[X]$ we obtain $v_q(f) = e_q$, hence

$$u \prod p^{v_p(a)} = w \prod p^{e_p}.$$

Then from (U2) for A we obtain $v_p(a) = e_p$ and $u = w$. ∎

Thus $\mathbb{Z}[X[$ is a U.F.D. The elements 2 and $2X+1$ are irreducible but $4X+2 = 2(2X+1)$ is composite. Of course, in $\mathbb{Q}[X]$, $4X+2$ is irreducible since now $2 \in Q[X]^*$.

This theorem can be reapplied: The polynomial ring in two variables $\mathbb{Z}[X][Y]$ is a U.F.D. Similarly the ring of polynomials in three variables $k[X][Y][Z]$ over the field k is a U.F.D. Before proceeding to the next corollary, let us take a moment to discuss polynomial rings in several variables.

An element of $\mathbb{Z}[X][Y]$ is a polynomial $a_0 + a_1 Y + \cdots$ in the variable Y with coefficients $a_j = a_{0j} + a_{1j} X + \cdots$ in the ring $\mathbb{Z}[X]$. This can be written $\Sigma a_{ij} X^i Y^j$, and the symmetry between X and Y makes it clear that the rings $\mathbb{Z}[X][Y]$ and $\mathbb{Z}[Y][X]$ can be identified. This ring of polynomials in two variables is usually written $\mathbb{Z}[X, Y]$. Starting with any ground ring R, one can define inductively $R[X_1, \ldots, X_n] = R[X_1, \ldots, X_{n-1}][X_n]$. Alternatively, $R[X_1, \ldots, X_n]$ can be constructed at once as the monoid ring $R[M]$, where M is the direct product $\mathbb{M} \times \cdots \times \mathbb{M}$ of n copies of $\mathbb{M}$. As in the one-variable case discussed in Section 6 of Chapter 2, the additive notation $(m_1, \ldots, m_n) \in M$ is converted to the multiplicative notation $X_1^{m_1} X_2^{m_2} \cdots X_n^{m_n}$. It is a straightforward exercise to set up an isomorphism between the inductively defined $R[X_1, \ldots, X_n]$ and $R[M]$.

(3.73) COROLLARY. *If f is a polynomial of positive degree in $A[X]$ and $f=g_1g_2$, where $g_i \in k[X]$, then $\exists c \in k^* \ni c^{-1}g_1$ and cg_2 are in $A[x]$. In other words, if f factors in $k[X]$, it factors (with factors of the same degree) in $A[X]$. Moreover, when f is monic the factors in $A[X]$ can also be taken as monic; in particular, if $r \in k$ is a root of a monic $f \in A[X]$, then $r \in A$.*

Proof. Write $c(g_i)=b_i/c_i$, where $b_i, c_i \in A$ and g.c.d.$(b_i, c_i)=1$. Since $c(f)=c(g_1)c(g_2)=(b_1b_2)/(c_1c_2) \in A$, it follows that b_2/c_1 and b_1/c_2 are in A. Thus $c=c_2/c_1$ does what is required. If f is monic and $f=g_1g_2$, where $g_i \in A[X]$ and the leading coefficient of g_i is a_i, then $1=a_1a_2$ and hence $a_i \in A^*$ and $f=h_1h_2$, where $h_i=a_i^{-1}g_i$ is monic. ■

We now combine this corollary with the homomorphism $\pi: A[X] \to \bar{A}[X]$, where $\bar{A}=A/pA$ (cf. A5.5), to obtain a powerful technique for proving the irreducibility of $f \in k[X]$, or suggesting the form of possible factors.

We can assume $c(f)=1$, so $f \in A[X]$. If $f=g_1g_2$, we can assume that $g_i \in A[X]$ and then $\pi(f)=\pi(g_1)\pi(g_2)$. Thus if $\pi(f)$ is irreducible over A/pA for some p not dividing the leading coefficient of f, then we can conclude that f is irreducible in $k[X]$.

For instance, there remained at the end of the last section the possibility that $f=6X^4+X+1$ is a product of two quadratics in $\mathbb{Q}[X]$. By (3.73) the possible factorizations of f can be reduced to the following two types, where $a,\ldots,d \in \mathbb{Z}$:

$$f=(X^2+aX+b)(6X^2+cX+d),$$
$$f=(2X^2+aX+b)(3X^2+cX+d).$$

When we read these equations mod 2 (i.e., when we apply $\pi: \mathbb{Z}[X] \to \mathbb{F}_2[X]$) we see that neither is possible since $\deg(\pi(f))=\deg(X+1)=1$ while the right-hand sides have degrees $\geqslant 2$. Hence f is irreducible in $\mathbb{Q}[X]$.

Consider the example $f=X^4-5X^3+X+8 \in \mathbb{Z}[X]$. This is reducible mod 2, so we take it mod 3. None of $0, 1, -1$ is a root mod 3 and (3.73) enables us to conclude that f has no root in $\mathbb{Q}$. (This method can be quicker than the rational roots test.) There remains the possible factorization

(3.74) $\quad f=(X^2+aX+b)(X^2+cX+d), \qquad$ with $\; a,\ldots,d \in \mathbb{Z}$,

which we can take mod various p. (For a particular p there are only finitely many possibilities and usually shortcuts can be found. A factorization mod p imposes congruence conditions on the coefficients of any possible factorization in $\mathbb{Z}[X]$.) We find

$$f \equiv (X^2+1)(X^2+X-1) \mod 3,$$

which is compatible with (3.74), and we try another modulus, say $p=2$:

$$f \equiv X(X^3+X^2+1) \mod 2,$$

where X^3+X^2+1 is irreducible mod 2. This shows that (3.74) is not possible and f is irreducible in $\mathbb{Q}[X]$.

(3.75) EISENSTEIN'S IRREDUCIBILITY CRITERION. *Let A be a U.F.D., p an irreducible element of A with associated valuation map v, and let*

$$f=a_nX^n+a_{n-1}X^{n-1}+\cdots+a_0\in A[X],$$

where

$$v(a_0)=1, \qquad v(a_i)>0, \quad \text{for } 1\leqslant i\leqslant n-1, \qquad v(a_n)=0,$$

i.e., $p|a_i$, $\forall i<n$, $p^2\nmid a_0$, and $p\nmid a_n$. Then f is irreducible in the U.F.D. $A[X]$ (hence also in the U.F.D. $Q(A)[X]$ by (3.73)).

Proof. Suppose the contrary: By (3.73), $f=gh$, where $g=b_mX^m+\cdots+b_0$, $h=c_{n-m}X^{n-m}+\cdots+c_0\in A[X]$, with $0<m<n$, and $v(b_m)=v(c_{n-m})=0$. Now $v(a_0)=1=v(b_0c_0)\Rightarrow$ one of $v(b_0)$, $v(c_0)$, say $v(b_0)$, is 1. Hence $v(c_0)=0$. Define $r\leqslant m$ by $v(b_i)>0$ for $0\leqslant i<r$ and $v(b_r)=0$. The coefficient of X^r in $f=gh$ is

$$a_r=b_rc_0+b_{r-1}c_1+\cdots.$$

Now, $v(b_rc_0)=0$ while p divides each of the remaining terms $b_{r-1}c_1,\ldots$ on the right. This gives the required contradiction $v(a_r)=0$. ■

Examples. 1. $X^n-2\in\mathbb{Z}[X]$. For each $n\in\mathbb{N}$ this is irreducible (in $\mathbb{Z}[X]$ or, by (3.73), in $\mathbb{Q}[X]$) by Eisenstein's criterion with $p=2$. This is a good deal stronger than (3.59) or (3.69), which merely say that X^n-2 has no linear factor (when $n>1$). Similarly $X^n+18X-15$ is irreducible in $\mathbb{Q}[X]$ by the criterion with $p=3$. Thus there are irreducible polynomials of every degree over $\mathbb{Q}$.

2. Similarly there are irreducible polynomials of every degree over $k=Q(A)$, where A is any U.F.D. with at least one irreducible element p (to exclude the trivial case $k=A$). For instance, if A is the polynomial ring $F[T]$, where F is a field and T an indeterminate, so that $k=F(T)$, then X^n-T is an irreducible element of $k[X]$, $\forall n\in\mathbb{N}$.

3. If F is a field of characteristic $\neq 3$ then $f=X^3+Y^3+1$ is an irreducible element of the U.F.D. $F[X][Y]$. For we can apply the criterion with $A=F[X]$, $p=X+1$, thinking of $f=Y^3+a$ as a polynomial in the variable Y, where $a=X^3+1=(X+1)(X^2-X+1)=pg$, say. Since $g(-1)=3\neq 0$ in F, $p^2\nmid a$. By (3.73), f is also irreducible in $F(X)[Y]$ and, by symmetry, in $F(Y)[X]$. (In characteristic 3, $X^3+Y^3+1=(X+Y+1)^3$ by (3.52).)

4. $f=\frac{3}{2}X^4-10X+\frac{3}{7}$ is irreducible in $\mathbb{Q}[X]$ since

$$\tfrac{2}{3}f=X^4-\tfrac{20}{3}X+\tfrac{2}{7}$$

is irreducible by Eisenstein's criterion with $p=2$ and $A=S^{-1}\mathbb{Z}$ for appropriate S; such A are U.F.D.s by A6.6. For instance, we can take $S=\{21^n: n=0,1,\ldots\}$, $S=\{3^m7^n: m,n=0,1,\ldots\}$ (these give the same A), or in fact any S whose saturation contains 3 and 7 but not 2, so that 2 is still an irreducible element in A. The maximal such S is $\mathbb{Z}\backslash 2\mathbb{Z}$ and then $S^{-1}\mathbb{Z}$ is the 2-adic valuation ring $\{r\in\mathbb{Q}: v_2(r)\geqslant 0\}$ in $\mathbb{Q}$, as explained in A6.6.

EXERCISES

1. Of the 27 polynomials $X^3+a_2X^2+a_1X+a_0\in\mathbb{Q}[X]$, where $a_i\in\{0,\pm 1\}$, determine the 12 that are irreducible.

2. The following polynomials are irreducible over $\mathbb{Q}$: X^4+1, X^6+X^3+1, $X^4+2pX+p^2$ for any prime p.

3. If k is a field of characteristic $\neq 2$, X^2+Y^2-1 is irreducible in $k[X,Y]$.

4. If F is a field, T^2+XT+Y is irreducible in $F[X,Y,T]$

5. If F is a field of characteristic 0 and $n\in\mathbb{N}$, $X^n+Y^n+Z^n$ is irreducible in $F[X,Y,Z]$.

6. For p an odd prime, $(X+Y+Z)^p-(X^p+Y^p+Z^p)=p(X+Y)(Y+Z)(Z+X)f_p$ for some $f_p\in\mathbb{Z}[X,Y,Z]$; and $f_3=1$.

7. A generalization of Eisenstein's criterion: With the notation of (3.75), if $v(a_0)=1$ and, for some $k\leqslant n, v(a_i)>0$ for $0\leqslant i<k, v(a_n)=v(a_k)=0$, then f has an irreducible factor of degree $\geqslant k$.

8. Generalize the universal property of polynomial rings to several variables: A homomorphism ρ: $A\to B$ of commutative rings has a unique extension to $s_{(b_1,\ldots,b_n)}$: $A[X_1,\ldots,X_n]\to B$ in which $X_i\mapsto b_i$, where $b_1,\ldots,b_n$ are given elements of B. (The image of $f=f(X_1,\ldots,X_n)$ under $s_{(b_1,\ldots,b_n)}$ is denoted $f(b_1,\ldots,b_n)$.)

SUPPLEMENTARY EXERCISES

1. [Section 3] A sequence $a_1,a_2,\ldots$ of elements of a commutative ring is in **arithmetic progression** if $a_{i+1}-a_i$ have the same value $\forall i$. If all the a_i are units, then the sequence is in **geometric** (resp. **harmonic**) **progression** if a_{i+1}/a_i (resp. $1/a_{i+1}-1/a_i$) have the same value $\forall i$. Find the eighth term of the sequence in arithmetic (resp. geometric, harmonic) progression in $\mathbb{Q}$ whose fifth term is 1 and whose tenth term is 32. Second, find $f,g\in\mathbb{Z}[X]$ with $f\neq X$ such that X^2+X, f^2+f, g^2+g are in arithmetic progression.

2. [A4.5] For $a_1,\ldots,a_n$, $b_1,\ldots,b_n\in\mathbb{Q}$ with the b_i positive,

$$\min\left\{\frac{a_1}{b_1},\ldots,\frac{a_n}{b_n}\right\}\leqslant\frac{a_1+a_2+\cdots+a_n}{b_1+b_2+\cdots+b_n}\leqslant\max\left\{\frac{a_1}{b_1},\ldots,\frac{a_n}{b_n}\right\}.$$

(The middle quantity is called the **mediant** of the fractions a_i/b_i.) Usually the a_i and b_i are integers, but this is not necessary.)

3. [A4.5] $a/b+b/c+c/d+d/a=1$ has no solution in positive rationals but has infinitely many solutions when negative rationals are allowed.

4. [A4.5] Every arithmetic progression of increasing positive integers contains an integer whose decimal expansion begins with any given sequence of digits $d_0d_1\ldots d_n$ $(d_0\neq 0)$.

5. [A4.5] For $\alpha\in\mathbb{Q}$ let $\lceil\alpha\rceil=-\lfloor-\alpha\rfloor$ denote the least integer $\geqslant\alpha$. Starting with $0<\alpha_1<1$, for $n=1,2,\ldots$ define

$$a_n=\lceil 1/\alpha_n\rceil,\qquad \alpha_{n+1}=\alpha_n-1/a_n.$$

Show that $a_1<a_2<\cdots$ and that the algorithm always terminates, giving

$$\alpha_1=\frac{1}{a_1}+\cdots+\frac{1}{a_n}.$$

Describe a similar algorithm using $\lfloor\,\rfloor$ in place of $\lceil\,\rceil$, which leads to a representation $\alpha_1=1/b_1-1/b_2+\cdots+(-1)^{n-1}/b_n$.

6. [A4.5] If $a_1,\ldots,a_n$ are distinct natural numbers then

$$\sum_{i=1}^{n}\frac{1}{i}\leqslant\sum_{i=1}^{n}\frac{a_i}{i^2}.$$

7. [A4.5] For $\alpha,\beta,\gamma,\delta\in\mathbb{Q}$ and $(\alpha X+\beta Y)(\gamma X+\delta Y)=aX^2+bXY+cY^2$,

$$\max(a,b,c)\geqslant\tfrac{4}{9}(\alpha+\beta)(\gamma+\delta).$$

8. [Section 5] Let R satisfy all the rings axioms with the possible exception of (R4).

(i) On $R'=\mathbb{Z}\times R$ define

$$(a,x)+(b,y)=(a+b,x+y),$$
$$(a,x)(b,y)=(ab,ay+bx+xy).$$

Then R' is a ring with $1=(1,0)$ containing R as an ideal when we identify $(0,x)$ with $x\in R$.

(ii) On the set R'' of all maps $f\colon R\to R$ satisfying $f(x+y)=f(x)+f(y)$ and $f(xy)=f(x)y$ (sic), define

$$(f+g)(x)=f(x)+g(x),$$
$$(fg)(x)=f(g(x)).$$

Then R'' is a ring with $1=1_R$ and $h\colon R\to R''$, where $h(x)(y)=xy$ preserves sums and products.

(This gives two ways of supplying a missing 1. When R already has a 1, method (i) will not take cognizance of this and will produce a new 1; $(0,1)=(0,1)^2$ is an idempotent and R' is the direct product of the two rings R and $\mathbb{Z}$. Method (ii) does not have that shortcoming, but Ker(f) can be nonzero.)

9. [Section 6] If R is a "set with structure," for instance, a field, a group, or the like, if X is a set, and if $f\colon R\to X$ is a bijection, then f **transports the structure**

of R to X in an obvious sense. For example, if $+: R \times R \to R$ is a binary operation on R, then the corresponding operation on X, which we can denote $\oplus$, is given by $x \oplus y = f(f^{-1}(x) + f^{-1}(y))$. By taking R to be the ring $\mathbb{Z}$, X the set $\mathbb{Z}$, and appropriate f, show that the following define ring structures on X:

$$x \oplus y = x + y - 1, \qquad x \odot y = xy - x - y + 2;$$

$$x \oplus y = x + y - 1, \qquad x \odot y = x + y - xy.$$

What are the ring 0 and 1 in these cases?

10. [Section 6] Let G be a group, K and L subgroups, and $KL = \{xy : x \in K, y \in L\}$.

(i) $|KL| = |K||L|/|K \cap L|$ (e.g., in a group of order 20, two subgroups of order 5 must have nontrivial $\cap$ and hence coincide).

(ii) $K \cup L$ is a subgroup $\Leftrightarrow$ $K \subset L$ or $L \subset K$; the example $G = (\mathbb{Z}/8\mathbb{Z})^*$ shows that this does not extend to three subgroups.

(iii) If A is any subset of G, $B = G \setminus A$, and $\sigma \in \mathrm{Sym}(G)$ then

$$A\sigma(B) = B\sigma(A)$$

(e.g., we always have $AB = BA$ and $AB^{-1} = BA^{-1}$).

11. [Section 6] If G is a semigroup, $S = 2^G$ is a semigroup if we define, for $A, B \in S$, $AB = \{ab: a \in A, b \in B\}$. S is a monoid if G is a monoid but not a group when G is a group.

12. [Section 6] Let M be a *cancellative* commutative monoid $(xy = xz \Rightarrow y = z)$. Apply $\mathbb{Z}[M] \to S^{-1}\mathbb{Z}[M]$, where $S = M$, to embed M in a group. What group does the construction give in the case $M = \mathbb{N}$?

13. [Section 6] Let X be a ring and $X^{\mathbb{Q}}$ the ring of functions $f: \mathbb{Q} \to X$ with componentwise operations $((f+g)(a) = f(a) + g(a)$, and so on). f is **periodic** if $\exists p \neq 0 \ni$

$$(*) \qquad f(a+p) = f(a) \quad \forall a \in \mathbb{Q}.$$

(i) The set of such p, for a particular f, is an additive subgroup of $\mathbb{Q}$.

(ii) The periodic f comprise a subring R (say) of $X^{\mathbb{Q}}$.

(iii) For each $p > 0$, the set R_p of f satisfying $(*)$ is a subring of R.

(iv) $f \in R \setminus \cap_{p>0} R_p$ iff there is a smallest positive p for which $(*)$ is valid. (This p is called the **period** of f.)

14. [Section 6] If an element r of a ring has a unique right inverse then it is a unit. In fact, if $rx = 1$ and $xr \neq 1$, then r has infinitely many right inverses.

15. [Section 7] Let A be a ring, B a subgroup of A^*, $a \in A$, and $b \in B$.

(i) Let $\sigma_{a,b}: A \to A$ denote the map $x \mapsto a + bx$. Then $\sigma_{a,b}^{-1}$ and $\sigma_{a,b}\sigma_{c,d}$ are again of the form $\sigma_{e,f}$ and these maps form a group G (a subgroup of $\mathrm{Sym}(A)$).

(ii) $X \mapsto a + bX$ extends to a ring automorphism $\sigma'_{a,b}$ of $A[X]$ and these σ' comprise a group G'; G' is the group of *all* ring automorphisms of $A[X]$

leaving the elements of A fixed when A is an integral domain and $B=A^*$.

(iii) The groups G and G' are isomorphic (and, when $B=A^*$, either is called the **1-dimensional affine group**). Write out the multiplication table in the case $A=\mathbb{Z}/4\mathbb{Z}$, $B=\{\pm 1\}$. (This group is known as the **dihedral group** of order 8 and will occur in other contexts.)

16. [Section 7] Let A be a commutative ring. Then the set of nonzero divisors $S_1=\{s\in A: sa=0\Rightarrow a=0\}$ is a saturated multiplicative monoid. ((3.6) says that $A\to S^{-1}A$ is injective iff $S\subset S_1$.) If σ is a ring automorphism of A, then $\sigma(S_1)=S_1$ and a ring automorphism of $S_1{}^{-1}A$ is well defined by $\sigma(a/b)=\sigma(a)/\sigma(b)$.

17. [Section 8] The **Frattini subgroup** Φ of a group G is the $\cap$ of all maximal proper subgroups of G. (When G is infinite it can happen that there are no such subgroups and then $\Phi=G$.) Then, by Zorn's lemma, Φ consists of those elements that can be deleted from any set of generators:

$$x\in\Phi \quad\Leftrightarrow\quad (\langle S\cup\{x\}\rangle=G \;\Rightarrow\; \langle S\rangle=G).$$

18. [A5.1] Let K be an ideal in the ring R and π: $R\to R/K$ the canonical surjection.

(i) If J is an ideal in R/K, $\pi^{-1}(J)$ is an ideal in R containing K, and if J is maximal, so is $\pi^{-1}(J)$.

(ii) $J\mapsto\pi^{-1}(J)$ sets up a bijection between the ideals of R/K and the ideals of R that contain K.

(iii) If $\{J_i\}$ is a nonempty collection of ideals in R/K, then $f^{-1}\Sigma J_i=\Sigma f^{-1}J_i$.

19. [A5.6]

(i) Let f: $A\to B$ be a homomorphism of commutative rings and P a prime ideal in B. Then $f^{-1}(P)$ is a prime ideal in A. Give an example where M is maximal and $f^{-1}(M)$ is not.

(ii) Let S be a multiplicative submonoid of the commutative ring A not containing 0 and P a prime ideal of A not meeting S. Then the subset $\{p/s: p\in P\}$ of $S^{-1}A$, denoted $S^{-1}P$, is a prime ideal of $S^{-1}A$. Moreover, $P\mapsto S^{-1}P$ gives a bijection between the set of prime ideals of A not meeting S and the set of all prime ideals of $S^{-1}A$.

20. [Section 10] Let k be a field of characteristic $\neq 2$. There are exactly three pairs $(x,y)\in k\times k$ satisfying

$$x^2-3xy+2y^2+x-y=0,$$
$$x^2-2xy+y^2-5x+7y=0.$$

21. [Section 11] Find all nilpotent elements and all idempotent elements in the rings $\mathbb{Z}/n\mathbb{Z}$ (any $n\in\mathbb{N}$) and $\mathbb{Q}[X]/(X^2(X^2+1))\mathbb{Q}[X]$.

22. [Section 12] Find all solutions $(x,y)\in\mathbb{Q}^2$ of $x(x+1)=4y(y+1)$ in terms of a rational parameter. (That is, find rational functions $f,g\in\mathbb{Q}(X)$ such that the set of solutions is given by $x=f(\lambda)$, $y=g(\lambda)$, where the parameter λ runs through all rational numbers for which $f(\lambda)$ and $g(\lambda)$ are defined.)

23. [Section 12] The only integer solutions of $3^m-2^n=1$ are $3-2=1$ and $9-8=1$.

24. [Section 12] If $a,b,\dots,n$ are distinct natural numbers and none is divisible by any prime >3 then $1/a+1/b+\cdots+1/n<3$.

25. [Section 13] For $m,n\in\mathbb{N}$, g.c.d.$(m,((m+1)^n-1)/m)=$ g.c.d.(m,n).

26. [Section 13] Let a,b,m,n be positive integers with g.c.d.$(a,b)=1$ and $a>b$. Then g.c.d.$(a^m-b^m,a^n-b^n)=a^d-b^d$, where $d=$ g.c.d.(m,n).

27. [Section 13] Let a,b be relatively prime positive integers. Show that the integer n is of the form $n=ax+by$ for some $x,y\in\mathbb{M}$ iff $ab-a-b-n$ is not of this form. (Since negative integers are not of this form, it follows that every $n>ab-a-b$ is of this form—and of the n satisfying $0\leqslant n\leqslant ab-a-b$, exactly half are of this form.) Deduce that a nonzero (additive) submonoid M of $\mathbb{M}$ eventually consists of the multiplies of some $d\in\mathbb{N}$:

$$M=\{md\colon m\in\mathbb{M}\}\setminus X,\qquad \text{where}\quad X \text{ is finite or empty.}$$

28. [Section 13] For $m,n\in\mathbb{N}$ let $m\vee n$ denote l.c.m.(m,n) and $m\wedge n$ g.c.d.(m,n). Then $\vee$ and $\wedge$ satisfy the associative and distributive laws as in Exercise 2 of Section 1.5 and

$$(ab)\wedge(cd)=(a\wedge c)(b\wedge d)\left(\frac{a}{a\wedge c}\wedge\frac{d}{b\wedge d}\right)\left(\frac{c}{a\wedge c}\wedge\frac{b}{b\wedge d}\right).$$

29. [Section 13] The complete solution in integers of $x^2+y^2=z^2$ is given by

$$x,y=(\text{in either order})\ (m^2-n^2)t,\quad 2mnt,\qquad z=(m^2+n^2)t,$$

where $m,n,t\in\mathbb{Z}$. (*Hints*: (i) A common factor t can be divided out, so we can assume g.c.d.$(x,y,z)=1$. (ii) x,y cannot both be odd. Say x is even. (iii) $x^2=(z-y)(z+y)$, where g.c.d.$(z-y,z+y)=2$.)

30. [Section 13] $x+x^2=y+y^2+y^3$ has no integer solutions. (*Hint*: Write $y=ab$ and $x-y=ac$, where g.c.d.$(b,c)=1$.)

31. [Section 13] For which $n\in\mathbb{N}$ does $X^n+(2+X)^n+(2-X)^n$ have a rational root?

32. [Section 13] Find monic irreducible polynomials in $\mathbb{Z}/p\mathbb{Z}[X]$ of degrees 2, 3, and 4 in each of the cases $p=2$, 3, and 5.

33. [Section 13] If a,b are elements of an integral domain and m,n are relatively prime natural numbers such that $a^m=b^m$ and $a^n=b^n$, then $a=b$.

34. [Section 13] For $n \in \mathbb{N}$ let $S_n = \{1, n, n^2, n^3, \ldots\}$. Then $S_m^{-1}\mathbb{Z} = S_n^{-1}\mathbb{Z}$ (as subrings of $\mathbb{Q}$) iff m and n have the same prime divisors.

35. [A6.1] If G is an abelian group and $n \in \mathbb{Z}$, then $g \mapsto g^n$ is a group endomorphism. If G is finite of order N, it is an automorphism iff g.c.d.$(n, N) = 1$.

36. [A6.1] For elements a, b of a group, ab and ba have the same order (possibly infinite).

37. [A6.1] Let G be a group and let L denote the set of all left cosets of all subgroups of G together with the subset $\varnothing$. Similarly, let R denote the set of all right cosets and $\varnothing$. Then $L = R$ and $X_i \in L \Rightarrow \cap X_i \in L$.

38. [A6.6] If A is a commutative ring the intersection of all prime ideals in A is called the **prime radical** of A and is denoted rad(A). The $\cap$ of all maximal ideals of A is called the **Jacobson radical**, or simply the radical, and is denoted Rad(A).

(i) rad$(A) \subset$ Rad(A).

(ii) rad(A) consists of all nilpotent elements of A. (*Hint*: If a is not nilpotent apply (3.29) to the saturation of $\{1, a, a^2, \ldots\}$.)

(iii) rad$(A/\text{rad}(A)) = 0$.

(iv) By A5.6(β), Rad$(A) = \{a \in A : 1 - ab \in A^*, \forall b \in A\}$.

(v) If A is the local ring $\mathbb{Z}_{p\mathbb{Z}}$ (cf. A6.6), rad$(A) = 0$ and Rad$(A) = pA$.

(vi) If $A = \mathbb{Z}/\mathbb{Z}n$, then rad$(A) =$ Rad$(A) = Am$, where $m = 0$ if $n = 0$ and $m = p_1 p_2 \cdots$ if $n = p_1^{e_1} p_2^{e_2} \cdots > 1$.

(vii) $(A[X])^* = \{a_0 + \cdots + a_n X^n : a_0 \in A^* \text{ and } \forall i > 0,\ a_i \in \text{rad}(A)\}$.

(viii) In a P.I.D. A, every nonzero prime ideal P is maximal and there are infinitely many P iff Rad$(A) = 0$.

39. [Section 14] Let $R = \mathbb{Q}[X, Y]/I$.

(i) When $I = \langle X^2 + 1, Y^2 + Y + 1 \rangle$, R is a field; equivalently I is a maximal ideal.

(ii) When $I = \langle X^2 + 1, Y^2 + 2Y + 2 \rangle$, R is not an integral domain, i.e., I is not a prime ideal.

40. [Section 14] Find a quadratic factor in $\mathbb{Z}[X]$ of $X^{13} + X + 90$.

41. [A6.1] (Another application of Lagrange's theorem) If $a, n \in \mathbb{N}$, then $n \mid \varphi(a^n - 1)$.

42. [Section 14] Let K be a field, F a subfield, $R = F[X_1, \ldots, X_n]$, and $(b_1, \ldots, b_n) \in K^n$. Then, using the notation of Exercise 8 after Section 14, $\{f \in R : f(b_1, \ldots, b_n) = 0\}$ is a prime ideal in R.

43. [Section 14] Devise a practical algorithm to factor (in a finite number of steps) any given $f(X) \in \mathbb{Q}[X]$ based on the following:

(i) Removing the content, we can assume $f \in \mathbb{Z}[X]$ and $c(f) = 1$.

(ii) For $g \in \mathbb{Z}[X]$, $g(X) \mid f(X) \Leftrightarrow g(n) \mid f(n)\ \forall n \in \mathbb{Z}$.

(iii) Use the Lagrange interpolation formula.

4

Vector Spaces

This chapter is a self-contained introduction to the basic concepts of linear algebra that will be used in Chapter 5: vector space, subspace, linear dependence, basis, dimension, linear transformation (or vector space homomorphism), rank and nullity, matrix notation, determinant. Also discussed are permutations, algebras, and the resultant of two polynomials. The student familiar with these notions can proceed to Chapter 5, referring back to results quoted in this chapter as necessary.

We also include for the interested reader the following additional topics: infinite dimension (the partial fraction basis of $k(X)$ over k giving an important concrete example), certain facts about infinite sets such as the Schroeder–Bernstein theorem and $\text{card}(X \times X) = \text{card } X$ (all with proofs instead of the customary "it is shown in books on set theory..."), partially ordered sets and Zorn's lemma, and, in an appendix to the chapter, a proof of the equivalence of Zorn's lemma and the axiom of choice.

The chapter begins gently with a look at systems of linear equations.

1. SYSTEMS OF LINEAR EQUATIONS

Consider the set of all solutions $(x, y) \in \mathbb{Q} \times \mathbb{Q}$ of the set of equations

$$(4.1) \qquad x + 2y = 3, \qquad 4x + 5y = 6.$$

A solution is understood to satisfy both equations simultaneously. Thus $x + 2y = 3$ *and* $4x + 5y = 6$. These equations imply that

$$-4(x+2y) + (4x+5y) = (-4)3 + 6, \qquad \text{or}$$

$$-3y = -6, \qquad \text{or}$$

$$y = 2,$$

and from the first equations $x + 2y = 3$ we conclude that $x = -1$. Thus if

(x, y) is a solution, it must be $(-1,2)$, and conversely this is indeed a solution of (4.1): The system of linear equations (4.1) has the unique solution $(-1,2)$. The word "linear" refers to the fact that there are no quadratic or more complicated terms in the "unknowns" x, y.

Ordinarily we would compress the above calculations thus: Subtracting 4 times the first equation of (4.1) from the second we obtain $-3y=-6$; hence $y=2$, and therefore $x=-1$.

As we learned to do in school, we can plot the points (x, y) that satisfy each of the equations individually as lines in the plane of all points in $\mathbb{Q} \times \mathbb{Q}$ (Figure 4.1). The unique point common to both lines is the unique solution with coordinates (i.e., values) $x=-1$, $y=2$.

Of course such figures must not be used in any essential way in proofs, that is, in a way that cannot obviously be backed up with a rigorous algebraic proof. However, geometrical figures, in general, any pictographs or diagrams, whether drawn mentally or physically, can be among our most powerful allies in discovering proofs and new ideas.

As a simple example, we expect that two parallel lines should correspond to a system with no solution. Here is such a case.

$$2x-4y=6, \qquad -3x+6y=2. \tag{4.2}$$

If we add $\frac{3}{2}$ times the first equation to the second we obtain the statement $0=11$, which is false in $\mathbb{Q}$. This implies that no $(x, y) \in \mathbb{Q} \times \mathbb{Q}$ satisfies both equations simultaneously: The system is **inconsistent**. A system is said to be **consistent** if it has at least one solution.

If we modify this example so that the parallel lines become coincident, say to

$$2x-4y=6, \qquad -3x+6y=-9, \tag{4.3}$$

then we have a system with infinitely many solutions. The second equation is $-\frac{3}{2}$ times the first, so any (x, y) satisfying the first also satisfies the second. System (4.3) is therefore equivalent to the "system" of one equation

$$2x-4y=6$$

Figure 4.1

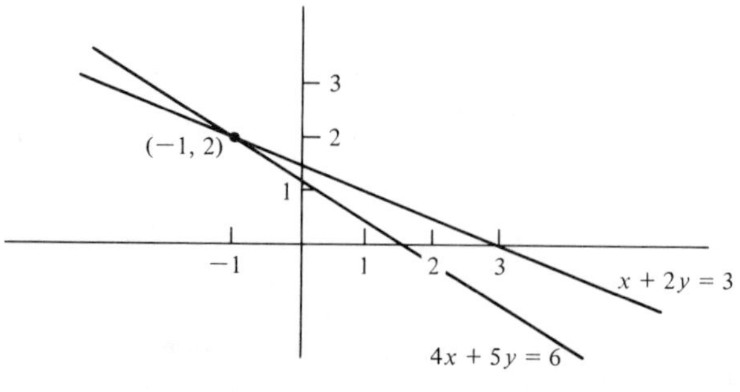

in the sense that the two systems have precisely the same solutions. These solutions are conveniently described as follows:

$$x = 3 + 2y, \qquad y \text{ arbitrary.}$$

That is, we can choose any value for y, then take $x = 3 + 2y$, and we have a solution. Conversely, every solution is obtained in this way. A "variable," y in this case, that can be assigned any value is called an **independent variable** or **parameter**; the remaining variables, in this case just x, are called **dependent variables.** Of course we could have chosen the alternative description

$$y = -\tfrac{3}{2} + \tfrac{1}{2}x.$$

and now x is a parameter. Thus the designations of parameter and dependent variable reflect the description of the solutions rather than an intrinsic property of the variables.

Sometimes it is convenient to use other parameters to describe the solutions. For instance, the general solution, let us say in rational numbers, of the single linear equation

$$a_1x_1 + a_2x_2 + a_3x_3 + b = 0,$$

where a_1, a_2, a_3 are distinct nonzero rational numbers, can be expressed in the form

$$(*) \qquad x_i = (s + t/a_i)(a_{i+1} - a_{i+2}) - b/3a_i,$$

where the subscripts are taken mod 3 (a_4 means a_1, and so on) and where s and t are parameters. We leave it as an exercise to verify that the x_i given by $(*)$ for $(s, t) \in \mathbb{Q}^2$ compose precisely the set of solutions.

Let us now solve (4.2) interpreted as a system defined over $\mathbb{F}_p$ for various primes p. First let $p = 2$. Then the equations reduce to $0 = 0$ and $x = 0$. Thus the set of solutions is given by

$$x = 0, \qquad y \text{ arbitrary} \quad (\text{i.e., } y = 0 \text{ or } 1).$$

Here y is a parameter and x is a dependent variable (which happens to be unaffected by the value chosen for the parameter). In this example x cannot be taken as a parameter.

Next, if $p > 2$, then $\frac{3}{2}$ is a well-defined element of $\mathbb{F}_p$ and we can proceed as we did in the case of $\mathbb{Q}$, obtaining $0 = 11$. Hence the system is inconsistent for $p > 2$, $p \neq 11$. Finally, over $\mathbb{F}_{11}$ the second equation of (4.2) is 4 times the first and the solutions are

$$x = 2y + 3, \qquad y \text{ arbitrary.}$$

The general system of linear equations, say m equations in n unknowns, can be written

$$(4.4)\qquad \begin{aligned} a_{11}x_1+a_{12}x_2+\cdots+a_{1n}x_n&=b_1,\\ a_{21}x_1+a_{22}x_2+\cdots+a_{2n}x_n&=b_2,\\ &\vdots\\ a_{m1}x_1+a_{m2}x_2+\cdots+a_{mn}x_n&=b_m. \end{aligned}$$

We allow any of the possibilities $m<n$, $m=n$, $m>n$. The coefficients a_{ij} have double subscripts as explained in A3.6. The a_{ij} and the b_i are elements of a field k and we seek information about solutions $(x_1,\ldots,x_n)\in k^n$. The study of such systems of linear equations is the starting point of the subject of linear algebra.

Of course, one could allow k to be a more general type of ring, but then the theory becomes much more complicated, if not intractable. The theory is most extensively developed when k is a field; indeed, the subject title "linear algebra" normally carries with it the understanding that the "ground ring" k is a field; we shall assume this until Section 20.

It is traditional in the subject of linear algebra to call the elements of k **scalars** and the elements $\mathbf{x}=(x_1,\ldots,x_n)$ of k^n **vectors**. We use the symbol 0 for the scalar zero and $\mathbf{0}$ for the vector $(0,\ldots,0)$.

The system (4.4) is **homogeneous** if $b_1=b_2=\cdots=b_m=0$. Notice that a homogeneous system is consistent since the $\mathbf{0}$ vector represents a solution. For any system (4.4), the **associated homogeneous system** is

$$(4.5)\qquad \begin{aligned} a_{11}y_1+\cdots+a_{1n}y_n&=0,\\ &\vdots\\ a_{m1}y_1+\cdots+a_{mn}y_n&=0, \end{aligned}$$

where we have taken the precaution of using ys for the unknowns so that they can be distinguished from the unknowns of (4.4).

(4.6) PROPOSITION. *Let H denote the set of all solutions of the homogeneous system* (4.5). *Then H is an additive subgroup of k^n. If the inhomogeneous system* (4.4) *is consistent, say, $\mathbf{x}=(x_1,\ldots,x_n)$ is a solution, then the set of all solutions of* (4.4) *is the coset*

$$\mathbf{x}+H=\{\mathbf{x}+\mathbf{y}:\mathbf{y}\in H\}.$$

Proof. Let $\mathbf{y}\in H$. Since

$$\begin{aligned} a_{i1}(x_1+y_1)+\cdots+a_{in}(x_n+y_n)&=(a_{i1}x_1+\cdots+a_{in}x_n)\\ &\quad+(a_{i1}y_1+\cdots+a_{in}y_n)\\ &=b_i+0=b_i \end{aligned}$$

for $i=1,\dots,m$, $\mathbf{x}+\mathbf{y}$ is a solution of (4.4). Applied to the case where all the $b_i=0$, this shows that H is additively closed. Plainly $\mathbf{0}\in H$ and $-\mathbf{y}=(-y_1,\dots)\in H$, and therefore H is an additive group.

If $(z_1,\dots,z_n)$ is a solution of (4.4), define $\mathbf{y}=\mathbf{z}-\mathbf{x}=(z_1-x_1,\dots)$ so that

$$\begin{aligned} a_{i1}y_1+\cdots+a_{in}y_n &= a_{i1}(z_1-x_1)+\cdots \\ &= (a_{i1}z_1+\cdots+a_{in}z_n)-(a_{i1}x_1+\cdots+a_{in}x_n) \\ &= b_i-b_i=0. \end{aligned}$$

Thus $\mathbf{y}$ is a solution of (4.5) and $\mathbf{z}=\mathbf{x}+\mathbf{y}$. ∎

This result can be summed up thus:

> The general solution = a particular solution,
> + the general homogeneous solution.

Thus the discussion of (4.4) breaks up into the following two parts:

(i) Find convenient criteria to decide when (4.4) is consistent; and
(ii) describe the solutions of (4.5).

These two matters are dealt within the following sections.

When dealing with a system (4.4) one often has to perform a series of manipulations such as adding twice the first equation to the second and so forth, and it is obviously unnecessary to repeat the xs in each equation. It is sufficient to write the coefficients in a rectangular array or **matrix** (we shall write the plural **matrices**). For instance, the system

$$\begin{aligned} x+2y-3z&=4, \\ -2x+\qquad 5z&=-6 \end{aligned}$$

can be written as the matrix

$$\begin{pmatrix} 1 & 2 & -3 & 4 \\ -2 & 0 & 5 & -6 \end{pmatrix}.$$

The system obtained by adding twice the first equation to the second is represented by

$$\begin{pmatrix} 1 & 2 & -3 & 4 \\ 0 & 4 & -1 & 2 \end{pmatrix}.$$

For the description of the general system (4.4) it is convenient to define two matrices:

$$(4.7)\qquad \begin{pmatrix} a_{11} & a_{12} & \cdots & a_{1n} \\ a_{21} & a_{22} & \cdots & a_{2n} \\ \vdots & \vdots & & \vdots \\ a_{m1} & a_{m2} & \cdots & a_{mn} \end{pmatrix}, \qquad \begin{pmatrix} a_{11} & a_{12} & \cdots & a_{1n} & b_1 \\ a_{21} & a_{22} & \cdots & a_{2n} & b_2 \\ \vdots & \vdots & & \vdots & \vdots \\ a_{m1} & a_{m2} & \cdots & a_{mn} & b_m \end{pmatrix}.$$

The first, with m rows and n columns, is the **coefficient matrix** of the system (4.4). The second, with m rows and $n+1$ columns, is known as the **augmented matrix** of the system.

However, we turn now to more theoretical matters and return to what might be called the practical aspects of linear algebra (manipulating matrices and in particular solving systems of equations) only in Section 13.

EXERCISES

1. For any field of scalars, the system $ax+by=e$, $cx+dy=f$ has a unique solution iff $ad-bc\neq 0$. (Prove by direct calculation.)

2. By considering $(X-r)(X^2+sX+t)$ describe parametrically all X^3+aX^2+bX+c that have r as a root.

2. VECTOR SPACES

The additive group H of solutions of the homogeneous system (4.5) contains certain products as we now explain. (H is not a subring of k^n in general since usually it does not contain $(1,\dots,1)$ and there is no reason for it to be multiplicatively closed.)

The **diagonal map**

$$\Delta : k \to k^n$$

given by $a \mapsto (a,a,\dots,a)$ is obviously an injective ring homomorphism. Making the identifications $a=(a,\dots,a)$, if $\mathbf{x}=(x_1,\dots,x_n)$, then $a\mathbf{x}=(ax_1,\dots,ax_n)$ and if $\mathbf{x}\in H$ it is clear that $a\mathbf{x}\in H$. The following equations for $a,b\in k$ and $\mathbf{x},\mathbf{y}\in H$ result from the ring axioms for k^n:

(V1) $a(\mathbf{x}+\mathbf{y})=a\mathbf{x}+a\mathbf{y}$;
(V2) $(a+b)\mathbf{x}=a\mathbf{x}+b\mathbf{x}$;
(V3) $a(b\mathbf{x})=(ab)\mathbf{x}$;
(V4) $1\mathbf{x}=\mathbf{x}$.

Thus H is a vector space according to the following abstract definition.

(4.8) DEFINITION. A **vector space** (over the field k) is an abelian group V, written additively say, together with a map $k\times V\to V$ called **scalar multiplication** satisfying (V1) to (V4) for all a,b in k and $\mathbf{x},\mathbf{y}$ in V.

From (V2) we deduce that $0\mathbf{x}=(0+0)\mathbf{x}=0\mathbf{x}+0\mathbf{x}$ and so $0\mathbf{x}=\mathbf{0}$, since V is a group. Similarly from (V1) we obtain $a\mathbf{0}=\mathbf{0}$. Thus $\mathbf{0}=0\mathbf{x}=(a-a)\mathbf{x}=a\mathbf{x}+(-a)\mathbf{x}$ and $\mathbf{0}=a\mathbf{0}=a(\mathbf{x}-\mathbf{x})=a\mathbf{x}+a(-\mathbf{x})$; hence

$$(-a)\mathbf{x}=-(a\mathbf{x})=a(-\mathbf{x}),$$

again using the group properties of V. In particular, if n is a positive integer regarded as an element of k via the canonical map $\mathbb{Z} \to k$, we have $(-n)\mathbf{x} = -(n\mathbf{x})$; from (V2) and (V4) we have $1\mathbf{x} = \mathbf{x}$ and $(1+n)\mathbf{x} = \mathbf{x} + n\mathbf{x}$. Thus the notation is consistent with that introduced in (3.20).

If k is a subring of a ring R, then R has the structure of a vector space over k if we take as scalar multiplication the restriction of the ring multiplication map $R \times R \to R$ to $k \times R \to R$, i.e., if we "forget" part of the multiplication table. This generalizes the case k^n above. We do not need to assume that multiplication is commutative: we may have $ar \neq ra$ for some $a \in k$, $r \in R$ (but of course $ab = ba\ \forall a, b \in k$).

In particular, every field can be regarded as a vector space over its prime subfield (cf. Section 12 of Chapter 3).

Another example that comes to mind is the polynomial ring $k[X]$. In this context every vector (i.e., polynomial) $a_0 + a_1X + \cdots$ is a sum of scalar multiples a_iX^i of the special vectors X^i.

Here is an example of a vector space from a different source in which the abelian group is written multiplicatively and which we would hesitate to write additively.

First let us rewrite the vector space axioms (V1)–(V4) in multiplicative notation. It is now more natural to write the scalars as exponents. Thus $a\mathbf{x}$ becomes $\mathbf{x}^a$ and the axioms are

(V1) $(\mathbf{x}\mathbf{y})^a = \mathbf{x}^a\mathbf{y}^a$,
(V2) $\mathbf{x}^{a+b} = \mathbf{x}^a\mathbf{x}^b$,
(V3) $(\mathbf{x}^b)^a = \mathbf{x}^{ba}$,
(V4) $\mathbf{x}^1 = \mathbf{x}$.

Now let A be any commutative ring and let $V = \{\mathbf{x} \in A : \mathbf{x}^2 = 1\}$. Clearly V is a subgroup of A^* and therefore V has the structure of an abelian group, written multiplicatively. With $k = \mathbb{F}_2$, we define scalar multiplication, or scalar exponentiation as it might reasonably be called, in the only possible way:

$$\mathbf{x}^0 = \mathbf{1}, \qquad \mathbf{x}^1 = \mathbf{x}.$$

It is now easy to check that V is a vector space$/\mathbb{F}_2$. (A solidus $/$ is often used as shorthand for "over" when it cannot be misconstrued as denoting a quotient structure.)

It is only for special examples that we use this multiplicative notation and we now return to additive notation and general ground field k.

(4.9) DEFINITION. A subset W of the vector space V is a **(vector) subspace** if

(VS1) $\mathbf{0} \in W$;
(VS2) $\mathbf{x}, \mathbf{y} \in W \Rightarrow \mathbf{x} + \mathbf{y} \in W$;
(VS3) $\mathbf{x} \in W, a \in k \Rightarrow a\mathbf{x} \in W$.

Taking $a=-1$ in (VS3) we see that $\mathbf{x}\in W \Rightarrow -\mathbf{x}\in W$, and this in conjunction with (VS1) and (VS2) shows that W is a subgroup of V. In view of (VS3), this shows that W itself is a vector space.

The set consisting solely of the $\mathbf{0}$-vector of V is a subspace and is denoted simply 0. At the other extreme, V is itself a subspace. Here are some subspaces of $\mathbb{Q}[X]$, regarded as a vector space/$\mathbb{Q}$:

all polynomials of degree $\leqslant 10$ (including the 0 polynomial);

$Q[X^2]$, i.e., all polynomials of the form $a_0+a_2X^2+a_4X^4+\cdots$;

more generally, all polynomials involving exponents from a specified subset of $\mathbb{N}$;

all polynomials (including 0) having 5 as a root;

all polynomials having 5 as a root and X^2+2 as a factor;

the intersection of any of the above.

The definition of subspace is reminiscent of that of ideal and in fact a number of results we have seen for ideals also hold for subspaces. For example, if $\{W_i : i\in I\}$ is a collection of subspaces of the vector space V, then $\cap W_i$ is again a subspace. Thus if S is a subset of V there is a unique smallest subspace containing S, namely the intersection of all subspaces containing S. We denote this subspace by $\langle S\rangle$ and call it the subspace **generated** or **spanned** by S. We also say that S is a **spanning set** for this subspace. The proofs of these statements are easy and can be copied from those of A5.3(α).

As in A5.3(β) we can describe $\langle S\rangle$ by an explicit construction: $\langle S\rangle$ coincides with the set T of all linear combinations of elements of S, that is, all finite or empty sums of the form $\Sigma a_\alpha \mathbf{s}_\alpha$, where $a_\alpha\in k$ and $\mathbf{s}_\alpha\in S$. For since $S\subset\langle S\rangle$, the axioms (VSx) imply that $T\subset\langle S\rangle$. Conversely, T contains each element $\mathbf{s}=1\cdot\mathbf{s}$ of S so it remains to check that T is a subspace. Now $\mathbf{0}$ (the empty sum) is in T; the sum of two such sums is again a sum of the same type, so T is additively closed; finally

$$a\Sigma a_\alpha\mathbf{s}_\alpha=\Sigma a(a_\alpha\mathbf{s}_\alpha)=\Sigma(aa_\alpha)\mathbf{s}_\alpha\in T$$

using (V1), appropriately extended, and (V3).

In particular, if $\{W_i : i\in I\}$ is a collection of subspaces then we write ΣW_i for $\langle\cup W_i\rangle$ and, just as in the case of ideals, ΣW_i consists of $\mathbf{0}$ and all finite sums of the form $\Sigma\mathbf{x}_j$ where each $\mathbf{x}_j$ comes from some W_i.

It is very helpful to visualize these concepts as in the following intuitive geometrical picture in $\mathbb{Q}^3$. First let us classify the subspaces W of $\mathbb{Q}^3$. If $W\neq 0$ it contains some vector $\mathbf{w}\neq\mathbf{0}$. Then W must contain the **line through 0 and w**, which is, by definition, $\langle\mathbf{w}\rangle=\{a\mathbf{w} : a\in\mathbb{Q}\}$. If W contains a vector $\mathbf{u}\notin\langle\mathbf{w}\rangle$ then W must contain the **plane** $\langle\mathbf{w},\mathbf{u}\rangle=\{a\mathbf{w}+b\mathbf{u} : a,b\in\mathbb{Q}\}$ through the three points $\mathbf{0},\mathbf{w},\mathbf{u}$. Finally, if W is still larger than this plane then, as will appear from the theory in Section 6, W must coincide with the whole space $\mathbb{Q}^3$.

The intersection of two different planes through $\mathbf{0}$ is a line through $\mathbf{0}$. This illustrates the fact that the intersection of subspaces is a subspace. If we intersect with a third plane we obtain either the line, if the plane happens to contain that line, or the 0-subspace.

As will be explained later (in (4.87)), a plane through $\mathbf{0}$ in $\mathbb{Q}^3$ consists of all points (x, y, z) satisfying a single linear equation of the form $ax+by+cz=0$, where a, b, c are not all 0. (The points satisfying $ax+by+cz=d$, where $d \neq 0$ comprise the points of a plane that has been "translated away from $\mathbf{0}$.")

Thus the solutions of a homogeneous system of m equations in three unknowns are the points in the intersection of m planes through $\mathbf{0}$. If that intersection is 0 the system has the unique solution $\mathbf{0}$; if it is a line the system has a one-parameter family of solutions; if it is a plane, in which case the m planes must all be the same, the solution involves two parameters.

The geometrical interpretation of Proposition (4.6), again let us say in $\mathbb{Q}^3$, is as follows. Suppose the point $\mathbf{P}$ with coordinates x_1, x_2, x_3 is a solution of the inhomogeneous system and $\mathbf{Q}=(y_1, y_2, y_3)$ is a typical member of the set H of solutions of the associated homogeneous system. Then the set of solutions $\mathbf{P}+\mathbf{Q}=(x_1+y_1, \ldots)$ of the inhomogeneous system comprise what is, by definition, the parallel translation of H from $\mathbf{0}$ to $\mathbf{P}$ and, depending on the nature of H, is what is called a plane through $\mathbf{P}$, a line through $\mathbf{P}$, or simply the point $\mathbf{P}$.

EXERCISES

1. Verify the examples of subspaces of $\mathbb{Q}[X]$ given just after (4.9).

2. If a is a scalar and $\mathbf{v}$ is a vector, then $a\mathbf{v}=\mathbf{0} \Leftrightarrow a=0$ or $\mathbf{v}=\mathbf{0}$.

3. Let k be a field. Which of the following subsets of $k[X]$ are subspaces?

$$\{f: f(1)=0\}, \qquad \{f: f(0)=1\}, \qquad \{f: f(0)=f(1)=0\},$$

$$\{f: 2f(0)=f(1)\}, \qquad \{f: f=0 \text{ or } \deg(f)<3\},$$

$$\left\{f: f \text{ has the form } a_0+a_1X+a_2X^4+\cdots+a_nX^{n^2}\right\},$$

$$\{f: f=0 \text{ or } \deg(f) \text{ is even}\}, \qquad \{f: f(X)=f(1-X)\}.$$

4. Let V be a vector space, W, W' subspaces, and for $\mathbf{v} \in V$ let $\mathbf{v}+W$ denote the coset $\{\mathbf{v}+\mathbf{w}: \mathbf{w} \in W\}$ as usual. Then

$$\mathbf{v}+W \subset \mathbf{v}'+W' \quad \Leftrightarrow \quad W \subset W' \text{ and } \mathbf{v}-\mathbf{v}' \in W'.$$

3. LINEAR DEPENDENCE

(4.10) DEFINITION. A subset S of a vector space is **linearly dependent** if there exist $r > 0$ distinct elements $\mathbf{v}_1, \ldots, \mathbf{v}_r$ of S and scalars $a_1, \ldots, a_r$ not all zero such that

$$a_1\mathbf{v}_1 + \cdots + a_r\mathbf{v}_r = 0. \tag{4.11}$$

For example, the subset $S = \{(1,2,3),(4,5,6),(7,8,9)\}$ of $\mathbb{Q}^3$ is linearly dependent because

$$(1,2,3) - 2(4,5,6) + (7,8,9) = 0. \tag{4.12}$$

Geometrically this means that any one of the three points is in the plane determined by $\mathbf{0}$ and the other two points; for instance, $(1,2,3) \in \langle (4,5,6),(7,8,9) \rangle$. In general if $a_i \neq 0$ in (4.11), then, using a caret $\hat{}$ as in Chapter 1 to indicate a term omitted,

$$\mathbf{v}_i = \frac{-a_1}{a_i}\mathbf{v}_1 - \cdots \in \langle \mathbf{v}_1, \ldots, \hat{\mathbf{v}}_i, \ldots, \mathbf{v}_r \rangle;$$

hence $\mathbf{v}_i \in \langle S \setminus \{\mathbf{v}_i\} \rangle$.

Any subset containing $\mathbf{0}$ is linearly dependent because $a_1\mathbf{v}_1 = \mathbf{0}$ when $a_1 = 1$, $\mathbf{v}_1 = 0$ and this satisfies (4.11) with $r = 1$.

If the set S is linearly dependent by virtue of the relation (4.11) and $S \subset T$, then (4.11) shows that T, too, is linearly dependent. For instance, (4.12) shows that $T = \{(1,2,3),(4,5,6),(7,8,9),(-7,8,9)\}$ is linearly dependent. However, the subset $I = \{(1,2,3),(4,5,6),(-7,8,9)\}$ is **linearly independent**, i.e., is not linearly dependent. To prove this we must show that the only linear combination of the elements of I that is $\mathbf{0}$ is the *trivial* linear combination, that is, the one in which all the coefficients are 0:

$$x(1,2,3) + y(4,5,6) + z(-7,8,9) = \mathbf{0} \quad \Rightarrow \quad x = y = z = 0. \tag{4.13}$$

The left side of (4.13) is the vector $(x + 4y - 7z, 2x + 5y + 8z, 3x + 6y + 9z)$ and the statement that this is $\mathbf{0}$ amounts to the statement that x, y, z comprise a solution of the homogeneous system

$$\begin{aligned} x + 4y - 7z &= 0, \\ 2x + 5y + 8z &= 0, \\ 3x + 6y + 9z &= 0. \end{aligned} \tag{4.14}$$

Thus we wish to show that (4.14) has only the trivial solution.

It is convenient to have a shorthand notation to describe the three types of transformations we apply to systems of equations:

$E_{ij}(c)$ means add c times the ith equation to the jth, where $i \neq j$;

$E_i(c)$ for $c \neq 0$ means multiply the ith equation by c; and

E_{ij} means interchange the ith and jth equations, where of course $i \neq j$.

We refer to these various Es as **elementary operations**. The third type E_{ij} will play a more significant role later (in Section 14) when the Es are interpreted in another context.

Applying $E_{12}(-2)$, then $E_{13}(-3)$, and then $E_{23}(-2)$ to (4.14) we obtain

$$\begin{aligned} x+4y-7z&=0,\\ -3y+22z&=0,\\ -14z&=0. \end{aligned} \tag{4.15}$$

Every solution of (4.14) satisfies (4.15), and conversely, since we can transform (4.15) back to (4.14) by the sequence $E_{23}(2)$, $E_{13}(3)$, $E_{12}(2)$. Reading this system from the bottom up gives in succession $z=0$, $y=0$, $x=0$ and this proves that I is linearly independent.

Notice that the order of application of the Es usually matters. In the above example the rearranged sequence $E_{23}(-2)$, $E_{12}(-2)$, $E_{13}(-3)$ does not produce the desired effect.

To rephrase the definition then, the set I is linearly independent if, for every r, for distinct elements $\mathbf{v}_1,\ldots,\mathbf{v}_r$ of I and scalars $a_1,\ldots,a_r$ we have

$$a_1\mathbf{v}_1+\cdots+a_r\mathbf{v}_r=\mathbf{0} \quad \Rightarrow \quad \text{every} \quad a_i=0. \tag{4.16}$$

Thus $\varnothing$ is linearly independent since the only linear combination of elements of $\varnothing$ is the empty one (whose sum is $\mathbf{0}$ and the implication $\Sigma a_i\mathbf{v}_i=\mathbf{0}\Rightarrow a_i=0\ \forall i$ is true by default).

The set $I=\{1, X, X^2, X^3,\ldots\}$ of monomials in the polynomial ring $k[X]$ regarded as a vector space over k is linearly independent since $a_0+a_1X+\cdots+a_nX^n=0$ means precisely that $a_0=\cdots=a_n=0$. The set I also spans the vector space $k[X]$.

Occasionally the notion of linear dependence is used in a mildly ambiguous way as in the following problem: Find the set of $t\in\mathbf{Q}$ such that $X=\{(1,2+t),(t,3)\}$ is linearly dependent/$\mathbf{Q}$. Calculation shows that X is linearly dependent when $t=-3$, collapses to a one-element set when $t=1$, and is linearly independent for all other values of t. As an answer to the problem, $\{-3,1\}$ is surely preferable to $\{-3\}$, but for this to be strictly correct we must regard X as a *list* rather than a set, as explained in the final section of Chapter 1. In minor matters of this nature, however, it is usual to leave the interpretation to the common sense of the reader.

EXERCISES

1. Which of the following sets are linearly independent?

$$\{(1,1,-1),(1,-1,1),(-1,1,1)\} \qquad \text{in } \mathbf{Q}^3,$$

$$\{(1,2,3),(3,-2,1),(-3,4,1)\} \qquad \text{in } \mathbf{Q}^3,$$

$$\{X+X^3+X^4, X^2+X^3, X+X^2+X^4, X+X^2\} \qquad \text{in } \mathbf{Q}[X].$$

2. The set of vectors I is linearly independent iff $\forall \mathbf{v} \in I$ we have $\mathbf{v} \notin \langle I \backslash \{\mathbf{v}\} \rangle$.

3. The singleton $I = \{\mathbf{v}\}$ is linearly independent iff $\mathbf{v} \neq 0$.

4. The subset M of the monoid ring $k[M]$ is linearly independent and also spans $k[M]$ as a vector space$/k$.

5. Let X be a linearly independent set of vectors and Y, Z subsets of X satisfying $Y \cap Z = \varnothing$. Then $\langle Y \rangle \cap \langle Z \rangle = 0$.

6. Let $X_1, X_2, \ldots$ be linearly independent subsets of a vector space satisfying $X_1 \subset X_2 \subset \cdots$. Then $X = \cup X_i$ is linearly independent. Given an example of linearly dependent subsets $Y_1 \supset Y_2 \supset \cdots$ in $k[X]$ such that their intersection is linearly independent.

4. BASES

(4.17) DEFINITION. A subset B of the vector space V is a **basis** if every vector $\mathbf{v} \in V$ is uniquely representable in the form

$$\mathbf{v} = a_1\mathbf{v}_1 + \cdots + a_r\mathbf{v}_r$$

for some $r \geqslant 0$, where the $\mathbf{v}_i$ are distinct elements of B and the a_i are nonzero scalars.

The wording is less cumbersome when B is finite, say if B consists of the r distinct elements $\mathbf{v}_1, \ldots, \mathbf{v}_r$. Then the condition is that each $\mathbf{v} \in V$ has a unique representation $\mathbf{v} = a_1\mathbf{v}_1 + \cdots + a_r\mathbf{v}_r$ where now possibly some of the **coordinates** a_i are 0.

The vector space $V = k^n$ of all n-tuples of elements of k has the **canonical basis** $B = \{\mathbf{u}_1 = (1,0,\ldots,0), \mathbf{u}_2 = (0,1,0,\ldots,0), \ldots, \mathbf{u}_n = (0,\ldots,0,1)\}$, as we now verify. If $\mathbf{v} = (a_1, \ldots, a_n)$ is any vector in V, then $\mathbf{v} = a_1\mathbf{u}_1 + \cdots + a_n\mathbf{u}_n$, so each $\mathbf{v}$ has at least one representation. If also $\mathbf{v} = a_1'\mathbf{u}_1 + \cdots + a_n'\mathbf{u}_n$, then we would have $(a_1, \ldots) = (a_1', \ldots)$, whence $a_1 = a_1'$, and so on, and therefore the representation is unique.

Of course, the canonical basis is not the only basis of k^n. For example $\{\mathbf{v}_1 = (1,1), \mathbf{v}_2 = (0,1)\}$ is another basis of k^2: If $\mathbf{v} = (a_1, a_2)$, then $\mathbf{v} = a_1\mathbf{v}_1 + (a_2 - a_1)\mathbf{v}_2$, and if also $\mathbf{v} = b_1\mathbf{v}_1 + b_2\mathbf{v}_2$, then $(a_1, a_2) = (b_1, b_1 + b_2)$, which implies that $b_1 = a_1$ and $b_2 = a_2 - a_1$.

Every $\mathbf{v}$ in $V = \{(x, y, z) \in \mathbb{Q}^3 : x + y + z = 0\}$ is uniquely a linear combination of $\mathbf{u}_1 = (1,0,0), \mathbf{u}_2 = (0,1,0), \mathbf{u}_3 = (0,0,1)$ but $B = \{\mathbf{u}_1, \mathbf{u}_2, \mathbf{u}_3\}$ is not a basis of V because $B \not\subset V$. It is a simple exercise to check that $\{(1,0,-1), (0,1,-1)\}$, for instance, is a basis of V.

$\{1, X, X^2, \ldots\}$ is a basis of $k[X]$; more generally, M is a basis of the monoid ring $k[M]$ regarded as a vector space$/k$.

(4.18) PROPOSITION. *A subset B of the vector space V is a basis iff*

(i) *B spans V, and*
(ii) *B is linearly independent.*

Proof. First assume that B is a basis. Then every $\mathbf{v} \in V$ is a linear combination of elements of B (indeed uniquely so), which proves (i). If $a_1\mathbf{v}_1 + \cdots + a_n\mathbf{v}_n = \mathbf{0}$, where $\mathbf{v}_i \in B$, then since also $0\mathbf{v}_1 + \cdots + 0\mathbf{v}_n = \mathbf{0}$ and the representation of the vector $\mathbf{0}$ as a linear combination of elements of B is unique, therefore $a_1 = \cdots = a_n = 0$; i.e., B is linearly independent.

Conversely let B satisfy (i) and (ii) and let $\mathbf{v} \in V$. We can write $\mathbf{v} = a_1\mathbf{v}_1 + \cdots + a_n\mathbf{v}_n$ for some $a_i \in k$ and some $\mathbf{v}_i \in B$ by (i). If we also had $\mathbf{v} = a_1'\mathbf{v}_1 + \cdots + a_n'\mathbf{v}_n$ (taking the list $\mathbf{v}_1, \ldots, \mathbf{v}_n$ large enough to accomodate both representations by inserting terms $0\mathbf{v}_i$ where necessary) then $(a_1 - a_1')\mathbf{v}_1 + \cdots + (a_n - a_n')\mathbf{v}_n = \mathbf{0}$, whence $a_i - a_i' = 0\ \forall i$ by (ii). ■

We now prove that every vector space has a basis. More precisely, we state

(4.19) THEOREM. *Let V be a vector space, I a linearly independent subset, and S a spanning set such that $I \subset S$. Then there exists a basis B of V satisfying*

$$I \subset B \subset S.$$

To deduce simply that V has a basis we can take $I = \varnothing$ and $S = V$.

The idea of the proof is straightforward. We keep enlarging I by adjoining elements of S such that the enlarged set is still linearly independent and prove that when we can enlarge I no further it must be a basis. This may involve the adjunction of infinitely many elements of S and a simple inductive argument will not do. The proof needs Zorn's lemma (3.30) and this introduces a distracting complication. So to understand the linear algebra part of the theorem, unencumbered by this set theoretic difficulty, we first give the proof when S is finite.

Proof of (4.19) when S is finite. If $\langle I \rangle = V$, we can take $B = I$. So we can suppose $\langle I \rangle \neq V$. Since $\langle S \rangle = V$, $S \not\subset \langle I \rangle$, and therefore we can choose $\mathbf{v}_1 \in S \setminus \langle I \rangle$. Putting $I_1 = I \cup \{\mathbf{v}_1\}$ we have $I \subset I_1 \subset S$. Now I_1 is linearly independent because if $a\mathbf{v}_1 + \Sigma b_i\mathbf{w}_i = 0$, where the $\mathbf{w}_i \in I$, then either $a \neq 0$, in which case we would have $\mathbf{v}_1 = -\Sigma(b_i/a)\mathbf{w}_i$, contrary to the fact that $\mathbf{v}_1 \notin \langle I \rangle$, or $a = 0$, and then $\Sigma b_i\mathbf{w}_i = 0$, whence every $b_i = 0$ because I is linearly independent. We can now repeat the argument: Either $\langle I_1 \rangle = V$, and then we can take $B = I_1$, or else $\exists \mathbf{v}_2 \in S \setminus \langle I_1 \rangle$ and then $I_2 = I_1 \cup \{\mathbf{v}_2\}$ is linearly independent. This process cannot be continued indefinitely because S is finite. Thus at some point we have $\langle I_n \rangle = V$ and we can take $B = I_n$.

Proof of (4.19) in the general case. Let C denote the collection of linearly independent subsets X of V that satisfy $I \subset X \subset S$. Thus $I \in C$, so C satisfies (3.30i), the first requisite of Zorn's lemma. Now let $\{X_i : i \in I\}$ be a nonempty chain in C and put $X = \cup X_i$. We claim that $X \in C$. Certainly $I \subset X \subset S$, so we must show that X is linearly independent. If $a_1\mathbf{v}_1 + \cdots + a_n\mathbf{v}_n = 0$, where each $\mathbf{v}_j \in X$, say $\mathbf{v}_j \in X_{i_j}$, then, since the X_i form a chain, one of $X_{i_1}, \ldots, X_{i_n}$, say X_{i_1}, contains the other $n-1$. Since X_{i_1} is linearly independent, $a_1\mathbf{v}_1 + \cdots a_n\mathbf{v}_n = 0 \Rightarrow$ each $a_j = 0$. This proves that X is linearly independent and consequently that Zorn's lemma applies to C.

Let B be a maximal member of C. By definition of C, B is linearly independent and the proof of (4.19) will be complete when we prove that B spans V. If it did not, then, as in the proof when S is finite, $\exists \mathbf{v} \in S \setminus \langle B \rangle$ and $B' = B \cup \{\mathbf{v}\}$ would be linearly independent. Then $B' \in C$, contradicting the maximality of B. ■

EXERCISES

1. Show that the vectors $(2,1,-1)$, $(1,3,-4)$, $(3,-3,6)$ form a basis of $\mathbf{Q}^3$. Relative to this basis find the coordinates of the vectors $(2,3,-4)$ and $(0,0,1)$.

2. Let $\mathbf{v}_1 = (1,2,\ldots,n)$, $\mathbf{v}_2 = (n+1,\ldots,2n)$, $\ldots$, $\mathbf{v}_n = (n^2-n+1,\ldots,n^2)$ be the n vectors in $\mathbf{Q}^n$ whose coordinates are the first n^2 natural numbers in sequence. Show that when $n \geqslant 2$, $\mathbf{v}_1,\mathbf{v}_2$ form a basis of the subspace V spanned by all the vs.

5. EXAMPLES OF BASES; PARTIAL FRACTIONS

Suppose W is the subspace of k^m spanned by the set $S = \{\mathbf{v}_1,\ldots,\mathbf{v}_n\}$ where

$$\mathbf{v}_i = (a_{1i},\ldots,a_{mi})$$

and it is required to find a basis B of W contained in S. An efficient numerical procedure is the following.

The vector equation

$$x_1\mathbf{v}_1 + \cdots + x_n\mathbf{v}_n = \mathbf{0}$$

is equivalent to the system

$$\begin{aligned} a_{11}x_1 + \cdots + a_{1n}x_n &= 0,\\ &\ \vdots \\ a_{m1}x_1 + \cdots + a_{mn}x_n &= 0. \end{aligned}$$

Solve this system so that the dependent x_i are either 0 or expressed as linear combinations of parameters x_j, with $j > i$. (That this is always possible, in fact uniquely so, will be proved in Section 15.) Then the $\mathbf{v}_i$ for which x_i is a dependent variable constitute a basis.

As a numerical example, let us complete

$$I = \{\mathbf{v}_1 = (1,1,1,1), \mathbf{v}_2 = (1,-3,-2,-2)\}$$

to a basis of $\mathbf{Q}^4$. Here $W = \mathbf{Q}^4$ and since S is not specified we can take any convenient one, say $S = I \cup \{\mathbf{u}_1,\ldots,\mathbf{u}_4\}$, where $\{\mathbf{u}_1,\ldots\}$ is the canonical basis. The system to be solved is

$$\begin{aligned}
x_1 + x_2 + x_3 \qquad\qquad\qquad &= 0,\\
x_1 - 3x_2 \qquad + x_4 \qquad\qquad &= 0,\\
x_1 - 2x_2 \qquad\qquad + x_5 \qquad &= 0,\\
x_1 - 2x_2 \qquad\qquad\qquad + x_6 &= 0.
\end{aligned}$$

Sequentially applying the elementary operations $E_{12}(-1)$, $E_{13}(-1)$, $E_{14}(-1)$, $E_{34}(-1)$, $E_{32}(-1)$, $E_{23}(-3)$, $E_{21}(1)$, $E_2(-1)$, $E_3(-1)$, $E_{31}(-1)$, $E_4(-1)$, $E_{41}(-3)$, $E_{42}(-1)$, $E_{43}(4)$ gives

$$\begin{aligned}
x_1 \qquad - 2x_4 \qquad + 3x_6 &= 0,\\
x_2 \quad - x_4 \qquad\quad + x_6 &= 0,\\
x_3 + 3x_4 \qquad - 4x_6 &= 0,\\
x_5 \quad - x_6 &= 0.
\end{aligned}$$

Since x_3 corresponds to $\mathbf{u}_1$, and so on $B = \{\mathbf{v}_1, \mathbf{v}_2, \mathbf{u}_1, \mathbf{u}_3\}$ is a basis as required. The detailed reasoning is as follows.

If $x_4 = x_5 = x_6 = 0$, then the above system tells us that all $x_i = 0$. This implies that $I_1 = \{\mathbf{v}_1, \mathbf{v}_2, \mathbf{u}_1\}$ is linearly independent. Next, by taking $x_4 = 1, x_6 = 0$ so that $x_1 = 2$, and so on, we see that $2\mathbf{v}_1 + \mathbf{v}_2 - 3\mathbf{u}_1 + \mathbf{u}_2 = \mathbf{0}$, so $\mathbf{u}_2$ is **linearly dependent on** I_1; i.e., $\mathbf{u}_2 \in \langle I_1 \rangle$. Therefore $\mathbf{u}_2$ is discarded in the sweep through S. Next, if $x_4 = x_6 = 0$, then all $x_i = 0$; hence $I_2 = I_1 \cup \{\mathbf{u}_3\}$ is linearly independent. Finally, taking $x_4 = 0$, $x_6 = 1$ shows that $\mathbf{u}_4 \in \langle I_2 \rangle$. Hence $\langle I_2 \rangle = \langle S \rangle$ and we can take $B = I_2$.

As another illustration of the theorem we take $V = k(X)$, the field of rational functions regarded as a vector space over k, and we complete the basis $\{1, X, X^2, \ldots\}$ of the subspace $k[X]$ to a basis of V. Our solution, as verified in (4.20) below, will be

$$B = \{X^i\} \cup \{X^j/p^e\},$$

where $i = 0, 1, 2, \ldots$; p runs through the set P of monic irreducible polynomials; $j = 0, 1, \ldots, \deg(p) - 1$; and $e = 1, 2, 3, \ldots$. Thus every rational function $f \in k(X)$ is uniquely representable in the form

$$f = a_n X^n + \cdots + a_1 X + a_0 + \Sigma a_{p,j,e} X^j/p^e,$$

where the various as are scalars. This is called the **partial fraction decom-**

position of f. For example,

$$\frac{1}{X^2-1}=\begin{cases}\dfrac{-\frac{1}{2}}{X+1}+\dfrac{\frac{1}{2}}{X-1} & \text{if} \quad \operatorname{char}(k)\neq 2,\\[2ex] \dfrac{1}{(X+1)^2} & \text{if} \quad \operatorname{char}(k)=2.\end{cases}$$

Let us work out the more complicated example

$$f=\frac{X^8+1}{X^3(X^2+X+1)^2}\in\mathbb{Q}(X).$$

$p=X^2+X+1$ is irreducible over $\mathbb{Q}$ by the rational roots test, as well as by the fact that its discriminant is negative. By the division algorithm,

$$f=X-2+r/X^3p^2,$$

where $r=X^6+4X^5+3X^4+2X^3+1$, and we can write

$$\frac{r}{X^3p^2}=\frac{c_1}{X}+\frac{c_2}{X^2}+\frac{c_3}{X^3}+\frac{c_4+c_5X}{p}+\frac{c_6+c_7X}{p^2},$$

where the scalars c_i can be determined in the following manner. It will be seen in the proof of (4.20) that we have allowed for sufficiently large es. Multiply this equation by X^3p^2:

$$r=c_1X^2p^2+c_2Xp^2+c_3p^2+(c_4+c_5X)X^3p+(c_6+c_7X)X^3.$$

Now expand the right side and compare its coefficients with those of the polynomial on the left, thereby obtaining a system of linear equations for the c_i:

$$\begin{array}{ll}(\text{coefficient of } X^0) & 1=c_3,\\ \vdots & \vdots\\ (\text{coefficient of } X^6) & 1=c_1+c_5.\end{array}$$

The final result is

$$f=X-2+\frac{1}{X}-\frac{2}{X^2}+\frac{1}{X^3}+\frac{4}{p}-\frac{X}{p^2}.$$

The amount of work can sometimes be lessened by substituting convenient values for X, as justified in (3.35). For instance here we could use

$$r(-1)=-1=c_1-c_2+c_3-c_4+c_5-c_6+c_7$$

(but in this case this is useful mainly as a check on the calculations).

Partial fraction decompositions exist for the quotient field of any P.I.D., so to prove the result in its natural setting we depart briefly from the realm of linear algebra.

Let A be a P.I.D., P a set of representatives of the irreducible elements, and for each $p \in P$ let S_p denote a set of representatives in A of the elements of A/pA, i.e., a complete residue system mod p. The expression "almost all x_i are zero" means that $\{i: x_i \neq 0\}$ is empty or finite.

(4.20) PROPOSITION. *Each $f \in Q(A)$ has a unique partial fraction decomposition*

$$f = a + \sum_{p \in P} \sum_{e \geq 1} r_{p,e}/p^e, \tag{4.21}$$

where $a \in A$, $r_{p,e} \in S_p$, and almost all $r_{p,e} = 0$.

Remark. In the case $A = k[X]$ we normally take P to be the set of monic irreducible polynomials and, for $p \in P$, S_p to be the set of all polynomials of degree $< n$, where $n = \deg(p)$, including the zero polynomial. If $r \in S_p$, then r/p^e can be written uniquely in the form

$$\sum_{i=0}^{n-1} a_i X^i/p^e,$$

from which it is clear that the B described earlier is a basis of $k(X)$.

Partial fraction decompositions for $\mathbb{Q}$ are perhaps not so familiar. For example, with $S_p = \{0, 1, \ldots, p-1\}$,

$$\frac{5}{12} = -1 + \frac{1}{2} + \frac{1}{2^2} + \frac{2}{3}.$$

Proof. We first consider the existence half of the proof. Let $f = s/t$, where s, t are relative prime elements of A and let $t = u \prod p^n$ be the unique factorization of t in A. We argue by induction on $N = \sum n$ that f has a decomposition (4.21) in which p ranges over the divisors of t and the corresponding e is subject to $1 \leq e \leq n = v_p(t)$.

First if $N = 0$ then we can take $a = f$ and all $r_{p,e} = 0$. Otherwise let q denote a particular one of the ps dividing t, say $v_q(t) = n > 0$, and put $w = t/q^n$. Then w is an element of A relatively prime to q. By (3.62), it represents a unit in A/qA. Thus $\exists r \in S_q \ni s \equiv rw \bmod q$. Put $s' = (s - rw)/q$ and $t' = t/q$ so that $s', t' \in A$ and, by induction, s'/t' has a partial fraction decomposition $s'/t' = a + \sum r_{p,e}/p^e$ in which $r_{p,e} \neq 0 \Rightarrow 1 \leq e \leq v_p(t')$. In particular, $r_{q,e} \neq 0 \Rightarrow e \leq n-1$. Now $s/t = a + r/q^n + \sum r_{p,e}/p^e$ and this completes the induction.

Second we prove uniqueness. Suppose some f has two decompositions, i.e., there is a relation of the form $g = 0$, where $g = a - a' + \sum (r_{p,e} - r'_{p,e})/p^e$. Suppose there is some $r_{p,e} - r'_{p,e} (= b$, say$) \neq 0$, where we can assume that e is maximal. Then by definition of S_p, $b \not\equiv 0 \bmod p$, so $v_p(b/p^e) = -e$. Every other term in g has p-adic value $> -e$; therefore $v_p(g) = -e$ (cf. the equality case of (3.58)), contradicting $v_p(g) = v_p(0) = \infty$. Thus we must have $r_{p,e} = r_{p,e}'$ in all cases and therefore also $a = a'$. ∎

EXERCISES

1. Find a basis of $\mathbf{Q}^4$ containing $\mathbf{v}_1=(2,1,4,-1)$, $\mathbf{v}_2=(2,-1,3,1)$, and $\mathbf{v}_3=(0,1,-1,1)$. Find a basis of the subspace of $\mathbf{Q}[X]$ consisting of all polynomials f of degree $\leqslant 4$ ($f=0$ included) satisfying $f(2)=0$ that includes $f_1=X^3+X-10$ and $f_2=2X^3-3X^2-2X$.

2. Let k be a field and for $i=0,1,2,\ldots$ let f_i be a polynomial/k of degree i. Then $\{f_0,f_1,\ldots\}$ is a basis of $k[X]$ as a vector space/k, and $\{f_0,\ldots,f_n\}$ is a basis of the subspace of all polynomials (0 included) of degree $\leqslant n$.

3. Verify the partial fraction expansions

$$\frac{n!}{X(X+1)\cdots(X+n)}=\sum_{m=0}^{n}(-1)^m\frac{\binom{n}{m}}{X+m},$$

$$\frac{n!}{X(X+1)\cdots(X+n)}\left(\frac{1}{X}+\frac{1}{X+1}+\cdots+\frac{1}{X+n}\right)=\sum_{m=0}^{n}(-1)^m\frac{\binom{n}{m}}{(X+m)^2};$$

hence deduce

$$\frac{1}{n+1}\left(1+\frac{1}{2}+\cdots+\frac{1}{n+1}\right)=\frac{1}{1^2}-\frac{1}{2^2}\binom{n}{1}+\frac{1}{3^2}\binom{n}{2}-\cdots+\frac{(-1)^n}{(n+1)^2}.$$

6. DIMENSION

As mentioned earlier, the subspaces of $\mathbf{Q}^3$ are the point $\mathbf{0}$, lines through $\mathbf{0}$, planes through $\mathbf{0}$, and $\mathbf{Q}^3$ itself. The intuitive concept of dimension is clear: Lines have dimension 1, planes have dimension 2, $\mathbf{Q}^3$ has dimension 3, and by extension $\mathbf{0}$ has dimension 0. Algebraically the dimension is "the number of elements" in a basis. Since a basis can be infinite, this requires elucidation. Moreover, for such a definition to have merit, two bases of the same space must have the "same number" of vectors. This is guaranteed by the following general result.

(4.22) THEOREM. *If B and B' are two bases of the vector space V then there exists a bijection $B\to B'$.*

As in the proof of the existence of bases in (4.19), the general case is complicated by set theoretic problems, this time rather more severe, and again it is worth going through the proof first in the finite case; for the infinite case see Section 9.

Proof of the finite case. The only basis of 0 is $\varnothing$, so we can suppose that $V\neq 0$.

Suppose then $B=\{\mathbf{v}_1,\ldots,\mathbf{v}_m\}$ and $B'=\{\mathbf{w}_1,\ldots,\mathbf{w}_n\}$ are both finite bases of V. Of course, it is understood that the $\mathbf{v}_i$ are distinct, so that $|B|=m$, and similarly $|B'| = n$. Removing $\mathbf{v}_1$ from B we are left with a linearly independent set $I = \{\mathbf{v}_2, \ldots, \mathbf{v}_m\}$ and this set is contained in the spanning set $I \cup B'$. By (4.19) there is a basis B_1 satisfying $I \subset B_1 \subset I \cup B'$. Since $\mathbf{v}_1 \notin \langle I \rangle$, $B_1 \neq I$, and therefore going from B to B_1 the one vector $\mathbf{v}_1$ of B is replaced by one or more vectors from B' (in reality exactly one, as we shall know when the proof is complete[1]). As a notational convenience let us renumber the elements of B' so that $B_1 = \{\mathbf{v}_2, \ldots, \mathbf{v}_m, \mathbf{w}_1, \ldots, \mathbf{w}_r\}$, with $r \geqslant 1$.

If $m \geqslant 2$, then $r < n$; that is, if the new basis still contains one or more of the **v**s, then it cannot contain all the **w**s. This is because $\mathbf{v}_m$ can be written as a linear combination of the elements $\mathbf{w}_1, \ldots, \mathbf{w}_n$ of the basis B', and if these elements were all in B_1, this would contradict the linear independence of B_1.

We repeat this procedure until all the **v**s have been replaced by **w**s. Thus, if $m \geqslant 2$, the next step is to insert a basis B_2 between the linearly independent set $I_1 = \{\mathbf{v}_3, \ldots, \mathbf{v}_m, \mathbf{w}_1, \ldots, \mathbf{w}_r\}$ and the spanning set $I_1 \cup \{\mathbf{w}_{r+1}, \ldots, \mathbf{w}_n\}$, say (renumbering $\mathbf{w}_{r+1}, \ldots, \mathbf{w}_n$ if necessary) $B_2 = \{\mathbf{v}_3, \ldots, \mathbf{v}_m, \mathbf{w}_1, \ldots, \mathbf{w}_s\}$. Since $\mathbf{v}_2 \notin \langle I_1 \rangle$, $s \geqslant r + 1$; if $m \geqslant 3$, then $s < n$ because B_2 is linearly independent.

Since at least one **w** replaces each **v**, we must have $m \leqslant n$ (cf. A1.1(iv)). Reversing the roles of B and B' we obtain $n \leqslant m$ and therefore $m = n$. ■

We draw some corollaries from this proof.

(4.23) COROLLARY. *Let V be a vector space possessing a finite basis B. Then every basis B' of V is finite and $|B'| = |B|$.*

We reason as follows: If B' were infinite and $|B| = n$, say, then we could choose a subset I of B' consisting of $n+1$ elements. (If $f: \mathbb{N} \to B'$ is an injection we can take $I = f(\{1, \ldots, n+1\})$.) By (4.19) there exists a basis $B'' \ni I \subset B'' \subset I \cup B$. Now the last set is finite, and therefore so is B'' and $|B''| \geqslant |I| = n + 1 > n = |B|$, contradicting the fact just proved that $|B''| = |B|$.

This corollary allows us to make the following definition. If V has a finite basis B then the **dimension** of V, abbreviated $\dim(V)$, is $|B|$. We extend this to $\dim(0) = 0$ and the phrase "V is finite dimensional" is understood to include the possibility $V = 0$.

Since the canonical basis of k^n consists of n elements, $\dim(k^n) = n$.

(4.24) COROLLARY. *Let V be a finite dimensional vector space and X a subspace. Then X is finite dimensional and*

$$\dim(X) \leqslant \dim(V)$$

with equality iff $X = V$. Equivalently, if $\dim(V) = n$ and I is a linearly

---

[1] The fact that some $\mathbf{w}_i$ can be exchanged for $\mathbf{v}_1$ to give a basis $\{\mathbf{w}_i, \mathbf{v}_2, \ldots, \mathbf{v}_m\}$ is known as the **Steinitz exchange theorem**.

independent subset of V, then I is finite (or empty) and $|I| \leqslant n$ with equality iff I is a basis of V.

We reason as follows: A basis I of X is a linearly independent subset of V, so by (4.19) can be extended to a basis B of V. Thus $I \subset B$, and hence $\dim(X) \leqslant \dim(V)$, and the final statement of the corollary is clear.

This result can now be applied to chains of subspaces, say,

$$X_1 \subset X_2 \subset \cdots \subset X_r \subset V.$$

Then $\dim(X_1) \leqslant \dim(X_2) \leqslant \cdots \leqslant \dim(X_r) \leqslant \dim(V)$, with a strict inclusion (i.e., $X_i \subsetneq X_{i+1}$) corresponding to a strict inequality. If all the inclusions are strict then this chain is said to have **length** $r+1$. Thus if $\dim(V)=n$, a chain of subspaces can have length at most $n+1$. This upper bound is actually attained: if $B=\{\mathbf{v}_1,\ldots,\mathbf{v}_n\}$ is any basis of V,

$$\mathbf{0} \subsetneq \langle \mathbf{v}_1 \rangle \subsetneq \langle \mathbf{v}_1, \mathbf{v}_2 \rangle \subsetneq \cdots \subsetneq \langle \mathbf{v}_1, \ldots, \mathbf{v}_{n-1} \rangle \subsetneq V$$

is such a maximal chain.

This justifies the claim made earlier that the subspaces of $\mathbf{Q}^3$ consist of $\mathbf{0}$, lines through $\mathbf{0}$, planes through $\mathbf{0}$, and $\mathbf{Q}^3$ itself. Since $\dim(\mathbf{Q}^3)=3$ there is no "room" for anything else.

We resume the proof of the general case of (4.22) in Section 9 after some necessary preliminaries in the next two sections.

EXERCISE

Let V and W denote the following subspaces of $\mathbf{Q}^5$:

$$V=\{(a,b,c,d,e): a=0 \text{ and } b+c+d=0\},$$

$$W=\{(p,q,r,s,t): p-q+2s=q+r+3t=0\}.$$

Find bases for $V, W, V+W$, and $V \cap W$ and verify that $\dim(V)+\dim(W)=\dim(V+W)+\dim(V \cap W)$.

Assignment 7

A7.1. In this question the ground field is $\mathbf{Q}$.

(a) Find all solutions of the systems

(i) $2x+2y+z=3,$ $3x+4z=5.$

(ii) $2x+2y+z=3,$ $3x+4z=5,$ $x-8y+8z=3.$

(iii) $2x+2y+z=3,$ $3x+4z=5,$ $x-8y+8z=0.$

(b) For each of the following systems determine for which $a \in \mathbb{Q}$ the system is consistent and find all solutions.

(i) $x+4y=2,$
$a^2x+y=a.$

(ii) $x+4y+az=2,$
$a^2x+y=a.$

(c) Determine the precise conditions on the scalars a, b, c in order that the system

$$x-y=a-b,$$

$$\frac{x}{a+c}+\frac{y}{b+c}=1,$$

$$\frac{x}{a-c}+\frac{y}{b-c}=1$$

be consistent.

A7.2. **(i)** Find a nontrivial equation of linear dependence among the following vectors in $\mathbb{Q}^3$: $\mathbf{v}_1=(2,-3,\frac{1}{2}), \mathbf{v}_2=(4,4,1), \mathbf{v}_3=(5,-1,2), \mathbf{v}_4=(\frac{2}{3},0,4)$.

(ii) Complete the set $\{\mathbf{v}_1=(0,1,1,0,0), \mathbf{v}_2=(2,3,4,-1,2)\}$ to a basis of $V=\{(x_1,x_2,x_3,x_4,x_5)\in\mathbb{Q}^5 : x_2-x_3+3x_4+2x_5=0\}$.

(iii) For which $a\in\mathbb{Q}$ is $\{\mathbf{v}_1=(1,a^2), \mathbf{v}_2=(4,1)\}$ a linearly independent subset of $\mathbb{Q}^2$?

(iv) Let $k=\mathbb{F}_q$ (finite field with q elements) and $V=k^n$. If $1\leqslant m\leqslant n$ show that the number of $(\mathbf{v}_1,\ldots,\mathbf{v}_m)\in V^m$, where the $\mathbf{v}_i$ are distinct and $\{\mathbf{v}_1,\ldots,\mathbf{v}_m\}$ is linearly independent, is

$$(q^n-1)(q^n-q)\cdots(q^n-q^{m-1}).$$

If $f(m)$ denotes the number of subspaces of V of dimension m, deduce that

$$f(m)=(q^n-1)(q^n-q)\cdots(q^n-q^{m-1})/(q^m-1)(q^m-q)\cdots$$
$$\times(q^m-q^{m-1}).$$

Then show that $f(n-m)=f(m)$.

A7.3. Let U and W be subspaces of a vector space, let $\mathfrak{T}=\{t_i : i\in I\}$ be a basis of $U\cap W$, and let

$$\mathfrak{U}=\mathfrak{T}\amalg\{u_r : r\in R\}, \qquad \mathfrak{W}=\mathfrak{T}\amalg\{w_s : s\in S\}$$

be bases of U, W respectively. Prove that

$$\mathfrak{T}\cup\{u_r\}\cup\{w_s\}$$

is a basis of $U+W$. Deduce that when $U+W$ is finite dimensional

$$\dim(U+W)=\dim U+\dim W-\dim(U\cap W).$$

A7.4. In the polynomial ring $k[X]$ we define the **symbolic powers** of X inductively by

$$X^{(0)} = 1,$$
$$X^{(n+1)} = X^{(n)}(X-n).$$

Thus

$$X^{(1)} = X^{(0)}(X-0) = X,$$
$$X^{(2)} = X(X-1),$$
$$X^{(3)} = X(X-1)(X-2) = X^3 - 3X^2 + 2X,$$
$$X^{(4)} = X^4 - 6X^3 + 11X^2 - 6X, \qquad \text{and so on.}$$

(i) Show that $\{X^{(n)}: n \in \mathbb{N}\}$ is a k-basis of $k[X]$.

(ii) When $k = \mathbb{Q}$ and $n \geqslant 1$, let

$$X^{(n)} = \sum_{m=1}^{n} s(n,m)X^m$$

and

$$X^n = \sum_{m=1}^{n} S(n,m)X^{(m)}.$$

The coefficients $s(n,m)$ and $S(n,m)$ are called **Stirling numbers** of the **first** and **second kinds**, respectively. By definition, $s(n,m) \in \mathbb{Z}$. Show that $S(n,m) \in \mathbb{Z}$ ($\forall n \geqslant 1$ and $1 \leqslant m \leqslant n$). (A "formula" for $S(n,m)$ is given in Supplementary Exercise 28.)

(iii) Let $f = \Sigma(a_n/n!)X^{(n)} \in \mathbb{Q}[X]$. Prove that $f(a) \in \mathbb{Z}\ \forall a \in \mathbb{Z}$ iff all $a_n \in \mathbb{Z}$.

A7.5. Let $K \subset L \subset M$ be fields with K a subfield of L and L a subfield of M. Let $\{x_i: i \in I\}$ be a basis of L as a vector space/K and $\{y_j: j \in J\}$ a basis of M as a vector space/L.

(i) Prove that

$$\{x_i y_j: (i,j) \in I \times J\}$$

is a basis of M as a vector space/K.

(ii) When I is finite, $|I|$ is called the **degree** of L over K and is denoted $[L:K]$. (When $[L:K] = 2$, L is called a **quadratic extension** of K. Similarly, extensions of degrees 3,4,... are called **cubic, quartic,...** extensions.) Show that when M is of finite dimension over K (this is indicated by $[M:K] < \infty$) then

$$[M:K] = [M:L][L:K].$$

Deduce that if $[M:K]$ is a prime number then either $L = K$ or $L = M$.

(iii) If $\mathbb{F}_q$ is a finite field with q elements and $\mathbb{F}_p$ is the prime subfield, show that $q = p^n$, where $n = [\mathbb{F}_q : \mathbb{F}_p]$. (Hence there is no field with six elements, for instance.)

A7.6. The three points (vectors)

$$\mathbf{P}=(p_1,\ldots,p_n),\mathbf{Q}=(q_1,\ldots,q_n),\mathbf{R}=(r_1,\ldots,r_n)$$

of k^n, where $\mathbf{P}\neq\mathbf{Q}$, are said to be **colinear** if $\mathbf{R}=\mathbf{P}$, or $\mathbf{R}=\mathbf{Q}$ or the subset

$$\{(p_1,\ldots,p_n,1),(q_1,\ldots,q_n,1),(r_1,\ldots,r_n,1)\}$$

of k^{n+1} is linearly dependent. The **line** L **determined by P** and **Q** is the set of **R** such that **P**,**Q**,**R** are colinear.

(i) Show that L is given by

$$\mathbf{R}=t\mathbf{P}+(1-t)\mathbf{Q}, \qquad t\in k.$$

(Hence if $\mathbf{Q}=\mathbf{0}$, then $L=\langle\mathbf{P}\rangle$ so the definition of L is consistent with the discussion in Section 2.)

(ii) Show that the line determined by any two distinct points of L is L.

(iii) Let L and M be distinct lines in k^n. Show that $L\cap M$ is either empty or consists of a single point. Now let **A**,**B** be distinct points on L and **C**,**D** distinct points on M. L and M are **parallel** if $\mathbf{A}-\mathbf{B}=a(\mathbf{C}-\mathbf{D})$ for some $a\in k$. Show that parallelism is well defined and that if L and M are parallel then $L\cap M=\varnothing$. If $L\cap M=\varnothing$ but L and M are not parallel, they are said to be **skew**. Show that this happens only if $n>2$.

(iv) State and prove analogs of (i)–(iii) for **planes**. Begin with a definition that four points **P**,**Q**,**R**,**S** (with **P**,**Q**,**R** distinct and not colinear) are **coplanar**. How large must n be to have two planes intersecting in a single point?

7. PARTIALLY ORDERED SETS AND ZORN'S LEMMA

In Section 8 of Chapter 3 we stated a special case of Zorn's lemma. The general (definitive) version involves the following notion.

(4.25) DEFINITION. A **partially ordered set** is a set X equipped with a relation $\leqslant$ between X and itself satisfying the axioms

(PO1) $x\leqslant x$: the relation is **reflexive**;
(PO2) $x\leqslant y$ and $y\leqslant x\Rightarrow x=y$: the relation is **antisymmetric**;
(PO3) $x\leqslant y$ and $y\leqslant z\Rightarrow x\leqslant z$: the relation is **transitive**.

One writes $x<y$ to mean $x\leqslant y$ and $x\neq y$. Thus (PO2) says that given $x, y\in X$ *at most one* of $x<y, x=y, y<x$ is true. A **totally ordered set** is a partially ordered set $(X,\leqslant)$ in which every two elements are comparable. Then the principle of trichotomy is valid: Given $x, y\in X$, exactly one of $x<y, x=y, y<x$ is true.

When $\leqslant$ is restricted to a subset Y then Y becomes a partially ordered set. An **upper bound** for Y is an element $x\in X\ni y\leqslant x\ \forall y\in Y$. The definition does not require $x\in Y$. A totally ordered subset is often called a **chain** in X. An element $x\in X$ is **maximal** if $y\in X, x\leqslant y\Rightarrow x=y$. This does not mean that x is a largest element: There may be other elements, even other maximal elements, that are not comparable with x.

Examples. 1. X is a set of subsets of the set S, i.e., $X \subset 2^S$ and $x \leqslant y$ means $x \subset y$. One says that X is **partially ordered by inclusion**. In this context we first encountered the notion of chain in (3.16) and that of maximal element in (3.29).

2. If X is a partially ordered set, then the chains in X themselves form a partially ordered set, ordered by inclusion. For example, if $X = 2^S$, where $S = \{1,2,3\}$, then $\{\varnothing\} \subset \{\varnothing,\{2\},\{1,2\}\} \subset \{\varnothing,\{2\},\{1,2\},S\}$ is a chain in the partially ordered set Y of chains in X. The last member of this chain, namely, $y = \{\varnothing,\{2\},\{1,2\},S\}$ is a maximal element of Y or, as one says, a **maximal chain** in X.

3. If X is the set of finite subsets of $\mathbb{N}$ partially ordered by inclusion, then $Y = \{\varnothing,\{1\},\{1,2\},\{1,2,3\},\dots\}$ is a chain with no upper bound in X.

4. If $(X, \leqslant)$ is a partially ordered set, then so is $(X, \leqslant')$, where $\leqslant'$ is defined by $x \leqslant' y \Leftrightarrow y \leqslant x$. When we thus reverse the sense of inequalities in the previous example, Y remains a chain but now has the unique upper bound $\varnothing$.

5. $\mathbb{N}$, $\mathbb{Z}$, and $\mathbb{Q}$ with the usual $\leqslant$ are totally ordered. Another partial ordering of $\mathbb{N}$ is given by $a \leqslant b$ iff $a|b$, but to avoid confusion with the usual meaning of $\leqslant$ we naturally use the $a|b$ notation. In this partial ordering 2 and 3 are incomparable; and if $A = \{a_1,\dots,a_n\}$ is a finite subset of $\mathbb{N}$ then, in terms of obviously defined concepts, l.c.m. (A) serves as a least upper bound for A, while g.c.d. (A) serves as a greatest lower bound.

(4.26) ZORN'S LEMMA. *Let $(X, \leqslant)$ be a partially ordered set satisfying the following two conditions: (i) $X \neq \varnothing$, and (ii) every nonempty chain in X has an upper bound in X. Then X contains a maximal element.*

(3.30) is a special case of this principle. (As explained there, in the interest of clarity we do not condense (i) and (ii) into the single requirement that every chain have an upper bound in X.) Conversely we can deduce this general principle from the special one. Given $(X, \leqslant)$, to an element $x \in X$ we associate the set $f(x) = \{y \in X: y \leqslant x\}$. We thus obtain a collection $C[\{f(x): x \in X\} \subset 2^X$ of subsets of X that we partially order by inclusion. Now $x \in f(x)$ by (PO1); hence $f(x) \leqslant f(x') \Rightarrow x \in f(x') \Rightarrow x \leqslant x'$. Conversely, if $x \leqslant x'$ and $y \in f(x)$, i.e., $y \leqslant x$, then $y \leqslant x'$ by (PO3). Thus

$$x \leqslant x' \Leftrightarrow f(x) \subset f(x'),$$

and hence by (PO2), $f(x) = f(x') \Rightarrow x = x'$. It follows that $f: X \to C$ is an order preserving bijection, and consequently

a. the subset Y of X is a chain iff $f(Y)$ is a chain in C, and
b. an element $x \in X$ is an upper bound of Y iff $f(x)$ is an upper bound of $f(Y)$.

Thus f translates the hypotheses for X in (4.26) into the hypotheses for C in (3.30). The conclusion for C then is translated back to that for X.

We have proved that (3.30) and (4.26) are **equivalent** in the sense that either statement can be deduced from the other. In the appendix to this chapter we prove that Zorn's lemma is equivalent to the axiom of choice and that therefore these two principles really amount to only one set theoretic axiom.

EXERCISE

Let S be a set and on the set 2^S define the relation $\sim$ by $a \sim b$ if $a \setminus b$ and $b \setminus a$ are finite or empty ("a and b are equal modulo finite subsets"). Then $\sim$ is an equivalence relation and a partial order is defined on the set of equivalence classes by $[a] \leqslant [b]$ if $a' \subset b'$ for some $a' \in [a]$ and $b' \in [b]$.

8. THE SCHROEDER–BERNSTEIN THEOREM

If X and Y are sets, we write $|X| \leqslant |Y|$ for the statement that there exists an injection $X \to Y$; similarly, $|X| = |Y|$ means that there exists a bijection $X \to Y$. This notation is consistent with that introduced in Section 6 of Chapter 1 for finite sets. Indeed, if X and Y are finite, say $|X| = m$ and $|Y| = n$, then there are bijections $f: \{1,\ldots,m\} \to X$ and $g: \{1,\ldots,n\} \to Y$. If there exists an injection $h: X \to Y$, then $g^{-1}hf$ is an injection, whence $m \leqslant n$ by (1.23). Conversely, if $m \leqslant n$ and if we define $k: \{1,\ldots,m\} \to \{1,\ldots,n\}$ by $i \mapsto i$, then $gkf^{-1}: X \to Y$ is injective. Thus $|X| \leqslant |Y| \Leftrightarrow m \leqslant n$ and similarly the notation $|X| = |Y|$ is consistent.

It is convenient to write $|\varnothing| = 0$. For each X there exists a unique injection $f: \varnothing \to X$ (the definition of f being vacuous). Hence $|\varnothing| \leqslant |X|$ is consistent with $0 \leqslant n$.

In general, the symbol $|X|$ is referred to as the **cardinality** of the set X, but we do not attempt to assign it an independent meaning. It will occur in comparative statements such as $|X| \leqslant |Y|$ or $|X| = |Y|$ and we shall never really use the symbol $|X|$ in isolation, except in the finite case (e.g., "by induction on $|X|$"). Card X is alternative standard notation for $|X|$.

Familiar properties of bijections and injections immediately imply the following facts:

$$|X| = |X|; \qquad |X| = |Y| \;\Rightarrow\; |Y| = |X|;$$
$$|X| = |Y| \text{ and } |Y| = |Z| \;\Rightarrow\; |X| = |Z|;$$
$$|X| \leqslant |Y| \text{ and } |Y| \leqslant |Z| \;\Rightarrow\; |X| \leqslant |Z|.$$

Not so obvious is the following principle of trichotomy. We write $|X| < |Y|$ to mean that $|X| \leqslant |Y|$ but $|X| \neq |Y|$; i.e., there does not exist a bijection $X \to Y$.

(4.27) THEOREM. *Given two sets X, Y, precisely one of the following is true:*

$$|X| < |Y|, \qquad |X| = |Y|, \qquad |Y| < |X|.$$

Proof. We first prove that at least one of the statements is true, or, in more colorful language, that "any two cardinal numbers are comparable." Let F be the set of pairs (Z, f), where $Z \subset X$ and f is an injection $Z \to Y$. We define $(Z, f) \leqslant (Z', f')$ to mean that $Z \subset Z'$ and $f(z) = f'(z)$ $\forall z \in Z$. Clearly (PO1)–(PO3) are satisfied and F is a partially ordered set.

$F \neq \varnothing$ since F contains $(\varnothing, f)$, where f is the unique map $\varnothing \to Y$. Second, if $C = \{(Z_i, f_i): i \in I\}$ is a chain in F, we define $Z = \cup Z_i$ and then define $f: Z \to Y$ as follows: If $z \in Z$, then $z \in Z_i$ for some i and we put $f(z) = f_i(z)$. We must check that f is well defined: If also $z \in Z_j$, then since C is a chain either $(Z_i, f_i) \leqslant (Z_j, f_j)$ or $(Z_j, f_j) \leqslant (Z_i, f_i)$. In either case, z is in the smaller domain and $f_i(z) = f_j(z)$ as required. Next we observe that f is injective: Suppose $f(z_i) = f(z_j)$, where $z_i \in Z_i, z_j \in Z_j$. Again, since C is a chain we have, say, $(Z_i, f_i) \leqslant (Z_j, f_j)$. Then $f_j(z_i) = f(z_i) = f(z_j) = f_j(z_j)$ and, since f_j is injective, $z_i = z_j$. Thus $(Z, f) \in F$ and since by construction $(Z_i, f_i) \leqslant (Z, f)$ $\forall i \in I$, (Z, f) is an upper bound for C in F.

We can apply Zorn's lemma. Let (Z, f) be a maximal element of F. If $Z = X$, then since f is injective we have $|X| \leqslant |Y|$.

There remains the case $Z \neq X$, say $x \in X \setminus Z$. If f were not surjective, say $y \notin \operatorname{Im}(f)$, then we could contradict the maximality of (Z, f) by extending f to $f': Z \amalg \{x\} \to Y$ by defining $f'(z) = f(z)$ for $z \in Z$ and $f'(x) = y$. Hence f must be surjective and therefore we have an injection $f^{-1}: Y \to X$, so $|Y| \leqslant |X|$.

There remains to prove the uniqueness aspect, which can be phrased

$$|X| \leqslant |Y| \quad \text{and} \quad |Y| \leqslant |X| \qquad \Rightarrow \qquad |X| = |Y|.$$

This result is known as the **Schroeder–Bernstein theorem**. The following elegant proof, due to Birkhoff and MacLane, does not use Zorn's lemma or the axiom of choice.

If $f: X \to Y$ and $g: Y \to X$ are injections, we wish to construct a bijection $X \to Y$. For each element $x \in X$ we trace back its "ancestry." We begin with $x_1 = x$. If there is a $y_1 \in Y$ such that $g(y_1) = x_1$ then that y_1 is unique because g is injective. If y_1 exists then because f is injective there is at most one $x_2 \in X$ such that $f(x_2) = y_1$. Applying g^{-1} and f^{-1} alternately in this manner yields the three possible outcomes for a given x. Either the lineage of x goes back to an ancestorless element of X (possibly x itself), the lineage stops at an element of Y, or the ancestral line in unending. (This last case includes the possibility that an ancestor appears in the line more than once. For instance if $x_5 = x_8$ then $f(x_5) = f(x_8)$, i.e., $y_4 = y_7$, whence $g(y_4) = g(y_7)$, i.e., $x_4 = x_7$, and so on down to $x_1 = x_4$. In this example the ancestral line consists of the cycle $x_1 y_1 x_2 y_2 x_3 y_3$ repeated ad infinitum.)

This classification partitions X correspondingly into three subsets that we denote by X_1, X_2, X_3. Similarly, we partition Y into the subsets Y_1, Y_2, Y_3, which consist of those y whose ancestral line, respectively, stops at an element of X, stops at an element of Y, is unending. We have bijections

$X_1 \to Y_1$, $X_2 \to Y_2$, $X_3 \to Y_3$ given by $x \mapsto f(x)$, $x \mapsto g^{-1}(x)$, $x \mapsto f(x)$ respectively; together they define a bijection $X \to Y$. ■

We can now divide infinite sets into two classes. X is **countable** or **denumerable** if $|\mathbb{N}| = |X|$ and **uncountable** if $|\mathbb{N}| < |X|$. An example of an uncountable set is the set $2^{\mathbb{N}}$ of all subsets of $\mathbb{N}$; cf. A8.7. To say that X is countable is to say that its members can be listed in a sequence thus: $X = \{x_1, x_2, x_3, \ldots\}$; the subscripts define a bijection $\mathbb{N} \to X$. When X is uncountable it is "too big" to be accommodated in a merely countable sequence.

The next lemma will be used in the proof of, and then superseded by, Proposition (4.30).

(4.28) LEMMA. $\mathbb{N} \times \mathbb{N}$ *is countable.*

Proof. Since $n \mapsto (n, 1)$ defines an injection, $|\mathbb{N}| \leqslant |\mathbb{N} \times \mathbb{N}|$. In the other direction, $(m, n) \mapsto 2^m 3^n$ defines an injection because of unique factorization. Hence $|\mathbb{N} \times \mathbb{N}| \leqslant |\mathbb{N}|$. ■

This result says that there exists a bijection $f: \mathbb{N} \to \mathbb{N} \times \mathbb{N}$, and it is not hard to exhibit one explicitly. We display the elements of $\mathbb{N} \times \mathbb{N}$ in an infinite matrix:

$$\begin{array}{ccccccc} (1,1) & (1,2) & (1,3) & (1,4) & (1,5) & \cdots \\ (2,1) & (2,2) & (2,3) & \cdots & & \\ (3,1) & (3,2) & (3,3) & \cdots & & \\ (4,1) & (4,2) & \cdots & & & \\ \vdots & & & & & \end{array}$$

The directed path is meant to indicate that $f(1) = (1,1)$, $f(2) = (2,1)$, $f(3) = (1,2)$, and so on. (*Exercise*: Show that $f^{-1}: \mathbb{N} \times \mathbb{N} \to \mathbb{N}$ is given by $(m, n) \mapsto ((m+n-1)^2 + 1 + (-1)^{m+n}(m-n))/2$.)

Each rational number is uniquely representable in the form a/b, where $b \in \mathbb{N}$, $a \in \mathbb{Z}$, and g.c.d.$(a, b) = 1$, and $a/b \mapsto [a^2 + b, a^2 + a + b]$ defines an injection $\mathbb{Q} \to \mathbb{N} \times \mathbb{N}$. Hence $|\mathbb{Q}| \leqslant |\mathbb{N}|$ and since $\mathbb{Q}$ is infinite we have

(4.29) COROLLARY. $|\mathbb{N}| = |\mathbb{Q}|$.

In other words, there are as many natural numbers as rational numbers, despite appearances to the contrary.

(4.30) PROPOSITION. *Let X be an infinite set. Then for every nonempty set Y such that $|Y| \leqslant |X|$ we have $|X \times Y| = |X|$. In particular, $|X \times \mathbb{N}| = |X|$ and $|X \times X| = |X|$.*

Remark. If $f\colon A \to A'$ and $g\colon B \to B'$ are maps of sets, then the map $A \times B \to A' \times B'$ given by $(a,b) \mapsto (f(a), g(b))$ is denoted $f \times g$. If f is injective (resp. bijective), then so obviously is $f \times 1_B$, whence

$$|A| \leqslant |A'| \quad \Rightarrow \quad |A \times B| \leqslant |A' \times B|, \quad \forall B,$$

and

$$|A| = |A'| \quad \Rightarrow \quad |A \times B| = |A' \times B|, \quad \forall B.$$

The notation may be suppressed when the meaning is clear. For example, in the following proof, from $Z \subset Z'$ we deduce $Z \times Z \subset Z' \times Z'$ without the formal explanation that if $h\colon Z \to Z'$ is injective then so is $h \times h\colon Z \times Z \to Z' \times Z'$.

Proof. (Adapted from Bourbaki [*Ensembles*, Chapter 3, page 71].) If $y \in Y$, then $x \mapsto (x, y)$ defines an injection $X \to X \times Y$. Hence $|X| \leqslant |X \times Y|$. On the other hand, since $|Y| \leqslant |X|$ we have $|X \times Y| \leqslant |X \times X|$. Thus the problem is reduced to proving the special case $|X \times X| = |X|$.

Since X is infinite we have an injection $i\colon \mathbb{N} \to X$; we write $J = \operatorname{Im}(i)$. Since J is in bijection with $\mathbb{N}$, by (4.28) (and the remark above) we have a bijection $j\colon J \to J \times J$.

Let F be the set of all pairs (Z, f), where $J \subset Z \subset X$ and f is a bijection $Z \to Z \times Z$ extending j (i.e., $f(x) = j(x)\ \forall x \in J$). Thus $(J, j) \in F$, so $F \neq \varnothing$. We partially order F by declaring that $(Z, f) \leqslant (Z', f')$ if $Z \subset Z'$ and $f(z) = f'(z)\ \forall z \in Z$.

As in the proof of (4.27), a chain $\{(Z_i, f_i) : i \in I\}$ in F is easily seen to have an upper bound $(Z, f) \in F$ defined by $Z = \cup Z_i$ and if $z \in Z$, say $z \in Z_i$, then $f(z) = f_i(z)$. Thus Zorn's lemma applies.

Let (Z, f) be a maximal element in F. Since $Z \subset X$, $|Z| \leqslant |X|$, and since f is a bijection, $|Z \times Z| = |Z|$. If $|Z| = |X|$ we have the result. We complete the proof by showing that the assumption $|Z| < |X|$ leads to a contradiction of the maximality of (Z, f).

Put $U = X \setminus Z$ and choose distinct elements $z_1, z_2 \in Z$. Suppose first that $|U| \leqslant |Z|$, say $g\colon U \to Z$ is an injection. Define $h\colon X \to Z \times Z$ by $h(z) = (z, z_1)$ for $z \in Z$ and $h(u) = (g(u), z_2)$ for $u \in U$. Since h is an injection we have the contradiction $|X| \leqslant |Z \times Z| = |Z|$.

Thus we must have $|Z| < |U|$ and therefore U contains a subset V such that $|V| = |Z|$; $s\colon V \to Z$, say, is a bijection. Put $Z' = Z \cup V\ (= Z \amalg V)$. Now the map $Z' \to Z \times Z$ defined by $z \mapsto (z, z_1)$, $v \mapsto (s(v), z_2)$ for z in Z, and v in V, respectively, is injective. Hence $|Z'| \leqslant |Z \times Z| = |Z|$; however, since $|Z| \leqslant |Z'|$, indeed $Z \subset Z'$, therefore $|Z'| = |Z|$.

Since $V \subset X \setminus Z$, we have $Z \cap V = \varnothing$ and therefore the four sets on the right side of $Z' \times Z' = (Z \times Z) \cup (Z \times V) \cup (V \times Z) \cup (V \times V)$ are mutually disjoint. We write $W = (Z \times V) \cup (V \times Z) \cup (V \times V)$. Since $W \subset Z' \times Z'$ we have $|W| \leqslant |Z' \times Z'| = |Z \times Z| = |Z| = |V|$ and since clearly $|V| \leqslant |W|$ we have a bijection $t\colon V \to W$.

Finally we define the bijection $f'\colon Z' \to Z' \times Z'$ by $f'(z) = f(z)$ for $z \in Z$ and $f'(v) = t(v)$ for $v \in V$. This gives us the desired contradiction $(Z, f) < (Z', f')$. ■

EXERCISES

1. A vector space V of countable dimension/$\mathbb{Q}$ is countable. The set of all finite dimensional subspaces of V is countable, while the set of all subspaces is uncountable.

2. For sets X, Y, X_i, Y_i, i running through some index set,
$$\left|\Pi(X^{Y_i})\right| = \left|X^{\amalg Y_i}\right| \quad \text{and} \quad \left|\Pi(X_i^{\,Y})\right| = \left|(\Pi X_i)^Y\right|.$$

3. (An alternative proof of the Schroeder–Bernstein theorem) Let $f\colon X_0 \to X_0$ be an injective map, define $X_1 = fX_0$, $X_2 = fX_1$, and so on, suppose $X_1 \subset Y_0 \subset X_0$, and define $Y_1 = fY_0$, $Y_2 = fY_1$, and so on. Then
$$g(x) = \begin{cases} f(x), & \text{if} \quad x \in X_n \setminus Y_n \quad \text{for some} \quad n \geqslant 0, \\ x, & \text{otherwise,} \end{cases}$$
defines a bijection $g\colon X_0 \to Y_0$.

9. INFINITE DIMENSION

We are now in a position to complete the proof of (4.22).

Proof of the infinite case of (4.22). Let B, B' be two bases of the vector space V. In view of (4.23) we can assume that both sets are infinite.

We express each $\mathbf{v} \in B'$ in terms of the basis B: $\mathbf{v} = a_1\mathbf{w}_1 + \cdots + a_n\mathbf{w}_n$, where $\mathbf{w}_i \in B$, $a_i \in k^*$. Thus to each $\mathbf{v} \in B'$ is associated a finite subset $B_\mathbf{v} = \{\mathbf{w}_1, \ldots, \mathbf{w}_n\}$ of B. Since B' is a basis and $\mathbf{v} \in \langle B_\mathbf{v} \rangle$, therefore $\cup B_\mathbf{v}$ spans V. Because B is a basis containing $\cup B_\mathbf{v}$, we have $B = \cup B_\mathbf{v}$.

Since the roles of B and B' can be interchanged, the result sought is a consequence of the following purely set theoretic corollary of (4.30).

(4.31) COROLLARY. *If B is an infinite set and $\{B_\mathbf{v} : \mathbf{v} \in B'\}$ is a collection of finite subsets such that $B = \cup B_\mathbf{v}$ then $|B| \leqslant |B'|$.*

Proof. By A3.3(ii), B' is infinite. We invoke the axiom of choice to choose for each $\mathbf{w} \in B$ a particular $\mathbf{v}$ for which $\mathbf{w} \in B_\mathbf{v}$; we denote this $\mathbf{v}$ by $f(\mathbf{w})$. By a second invocation of the axiom we choose for each $B_\mathbf{v}$ a definite ordering $\mathbf{w}_1, \ldots, \mathbf{w}_n$ of its elements so that to a given $\mathbf{w} \in B_\mathbf{v}$, say $\mathbf{w} = \mathbf{w}_i$, there is associated an integer $g_\mathbf{v}(\mathbf{w}) = i$. (In other words, for each $\mathbf{v}$ we choose an injection $g_\mathbf{v}\colon B_\mathbf{v} \to \mathbb{N}$ whose image is $\{n \in \mathbb{N} : n \leqslant |B_\mathbf{v}|\}$.)

The map $\mathbf{w} \mapsto (f(\mathbf{w}), g_{f(\mathbf{w})}(\mathbf{w}))$ defines an injection $B \to B' \times \mathbb{N}$; hence $|B| \leqslant |B' \times \mathbb{N}| = |B'|$. ■

10. LINEAR TRANSFORMATIONS

If $\{X_i: i \in I\}$ is a collection of rings or of semigroups or of monoids or of groups, then $X = \prod X_i$ with componentwise operations is an object of the same sort. The same is true of vector spaces.

Recall that an element f of X is a function defined on I such that, for each $i \in I$, $f(i) \in X_i$. It is often convenient to display f as a "vector":

$$f = (\ldots, x_i, \ldots),$$

where we have written x_i for $f(i)$. We use this notation even when I is uncountable; this is a harmless notational simplification. Now when the X_i are vector spaces we define

$$(f + f')(i) = f(i) + f'(i),$$

or

$$(\ldots, x_i, \ldots) + (\ldots, x_i', \ldots) = (\ldots, x_i + x_i', \ldots)$$

and for each scalar $a \in k$

$$(af)(i) = af(i)$$

or

$$a(\ldots, x_i, \ldots) = (\ldots, ax_i, \ldots).$$

We leave it as a simple exercise to check that X satisfies the vector space axioms. This construction includes the example k^n where each $X_i = k$. (k as a vector space over itself is one dimensional: Any $c \in k^*$ comprises a basis.)

In particular, if W is a vector space and V any set then the set W^V of all maps from V to W is a vector space. This remains true if V happens also to be a vector space.

(4.32) DEFINITION. If V and W are vector spaces, a map $f: V \to W$ is a **vector space homomorphism** or a **linear transformation** if $\forall \mathbf{v}, \mathbf{v}' \in V$ and $a \in k$

(L1) $f(\mathbf{v} + \mathbf{v}') = f(\mathbf{v}) + f(\mathbf{v}')$,
(L2) $f(a\mathbf{v}) = af(\mathbf{v})$.

It follows from (L2) (or (L1)) that $f(\mathbf{0}) = \mathbf{0}$ and $f(-\mathbf{v}) = -f(\mathbf{v})$. Since $(af)(\mathbf{v}) = a(f(\mathbf{v}))$, the right side of (L2) is unambiguous. The two statements (L1) and (L2) are equivalent to a single one involving finite linear combinations:

$$f\left(\sum a_i \mathbf{v}_i\right) = \sum a_i f(\mathbf{v}_i).$$

We say that $f: V \to W$ is linear.

Thus certain elements of W^V are linear transformations. The subset of these is denoted $\mathrm{Hom}(V, W)$, or $\mathrm{Hom}_k(V, W)$ when it is necessary to identify the ground field.

(4.33) PROPOSITION. $\operatorname{Hom}(V, W)$ *is a subspace of* W^V.

Proof. We must verify the three properties listed in (4.9).

First, the 0 element of W^V is the map $f: V \to W$ given by $f(\mathbf{v}) = \mathbf{0}\ \forall \mathbf{v} \in V$. This element is in the subset $\operatorname{Hom}(V, W)$ because

$$f(\mathbf{v} + \mathbf{v}') = \mathbf{0} = \mathbf{0} + \mathbf{0} = f(\mathbf{v}) + f(\mathbf{v}')$$

and

$$f(a\mathbf{v}) = \mathbf{0} = a\mathbf{0} = af(\mathbf{v})$$

for all $\mathbf{v}, \mathbf{v}' \in V$ and all $a \in k$.

Second, if $f, g \in \operatorname{Hom}(V, W)$ then $f + g \in \operatorname{Hom}(V, W)$ because

$$\begin{aligned}(f+g)(\mathbf{v}+\mathbf{v}') &= f(\mathbf{v}+\mathbf{v}') + g(\mathbf{v}+\mathbf{v}') && (\text{definition of } + \text{ in } W^V)\\ &= f(\mathbf{v}) + f(\mathbf{v}') + g(\mathbf{v}) + g(\mathbf{v}') && (f \text{ and } g \text{ are linear})\\ &= (f+g)(\mathbf{v}) + (f+g)(\mathbf{v}')\end{aligned}$$

and

$$\begin{aligned}(f+g)(a\mathbf{v}) &= f(a\mathbf{v}) + g(a\mathbf{v})\\ &= af(\mathbf{v}) + ag(\mathbf{v}) = a(f(\mathbf{v}) + g(\mathbf{v}))\\ &= a(f+g)(\mathbf{v}).\end{aligned}$$

Third, if $f \in \operatorname{Hom}(V, W)$ and $a, a' \in k$, then $af \in \operatorname{Hom}(V, W)$ because

$$\begin{aligned}(af)(\mathbf{v}+\mathbf{v}') &= f(a(\mathbf{v}+\mathbf{v}')) && (\text{definition of scalar multiplication in } W^V)\\ &= f(a\mathbf{v} + a\mathbf{v}')\\ &= f(a\mathbf{v}) + f(a\mathbf{v}')\\ &= (af)(\mathbf{v}) + (af)(\mathbf{v}')\end{aligned}$$

and

$$\begin{aligned}(af)(a'\mathbf{v}) &= f(a(a'(\mathbf{v})))\\ &= f((aa')\mathbf{v}) = f((a'a)\mathbf{v})\\ &= f(a'(a\mathbf{v})) = a'(f(a\mathbf{v}))\\ &= a'((af)(\mathbf{v})). \quad \blacksquare\end{aligned}$$

An example of a linear transformation is projection onto a subspace. For instance in $V = W = \mathbb{Q}^3$ the map $f: \mathbb{Q}^3 \to \mathbb{Q}^3$ given by $(x, y, z) \mapsto (x, y, 0)$ is obviously linear. So is the related map $\mathbb{Q}^3 \to \mathbb{Q}^2$ given by $(x, y, z) \mapsto (x, y)$ but it is the former map that is usually referred to as the projection onto the plane (or subspace) described by $z = 0$ (Figure 4.2). For the general definition of projection see A8.2.

To manufacture further examples the following result is most useful.

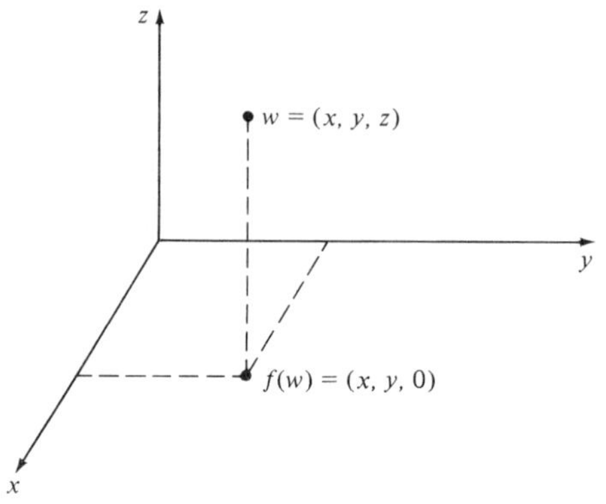

Figure 4.2 Projection onto the xy plane.

(4.34) PROPOSITION. *Let* $f \in \operatorname{Hom}(V, W)$ *and let* $B = \{\mathbf{v}_i : i \in I\}$ *be a basis of* V. *Then* f *is uniquely determined by its values* $f(\mathbf{v}_i) = \mathbf{w}_i$. *Conversely, for arbitrarily prescribed* $\mathbf{w}_i \in W$, *one for each* $i \in I$, $\exists! f \in \operatorname{Hom}(V, W)$ *such that* $f(\mathbf{v}_i) = \mathbf{w}_i$.

Remark. Put more formally, $f \mapsto f \,|\, B$ establishes a bijection $\operatorname{Hom}(V, W) \to W^I$.

Proof. Each element $\mathbf{v}$ of V can be written in the form $\Sigma a_i \mathbf{v}_i$. For any $f \in \operatorname{Hom}(V, W)$ we have $f(\mathbf{v}) = \Sigma a_i f(\mathbf{v}_i) = \Sigma a_i \mathbf{w}_i$, so f is completely determined by its values on B.

Conversely let $f(\mathbf{v}_i) = \mathbf{w}_i$ be prescribed. We define $f(\mathbf{v}) = \Sigma a_i \mathbf{w}_i$. Since B is a basis the a_i are uniquely determined by $\mathbf{v}$ and therefore f is well defined. It is obviously linear. ■

Thus $(x, y) \mapsto (0, x - 2y, x, -x/2)$ is seen at a glance to define a linear transformation $k^2 \to k^4$ (provided $\operatorname{char} k \neq 2$): It is the linear extension to all of k^2 of the map defined on the canonical basis of k^2 by $(1,0) \mapsto (0,1,1,-\frac{1}{2})$, $(0,1) \mapsto (0,-2,0,0)$.

(4.35) DEFINITION. (i) A bijective linear transformation $f: V \to W$ is a **vector space isomorphism**, or simply **isomorphism** when that is unambiguous.

(ii) A linear transformation $f: V \to V$ from a vector space to itself is an **endomorphism** of V. The set of these is denoted $\operatorname{End}(V)$ (or $\operatorname{End}_k(V)$ when necessary) as an alternative to $\operatorname{Hom}(V, V)$.

(iii) A bijective endomorphism is an **automorphism** (cf. (3.22)).

(iv) A subspace W of V is **invariant** with respect to the endomorphism f of V if $f(W) \subset W$.

Actually these terms are used quite generally for algebraic structures. Thus one speaks of an endomorphism of a group, an automorphism of a field, and so on.

The identity map $1 = 1_V$ on the vector space V is an automorphism. An automorphism that is not 1 is referred to as **nontrivial**. An example on k^2 is given by $(x, y) \mapsto (y, x)$; another is given by $(x, y) \mapsto (x+y, y)$, as is easily verified.

(4.36) PROPOSITION. *Let U, V, W be vector spaces and let $f, f' \in Hom(U, V)$, $g, g' \in Hom(V, W)$, and $a \in k$.*

$$U \xrightarrow{f} V \xrightarrow{g} W, \qquad gf: U \to W.$$

Then

(i) $gf \in \mathrm{Hom}(U, W)$;
(ii) $a(gf) = (ag)f = g(af)$;
(iii) $g(f+f') = gf + gf'$; and
(iv) $(g+g')f = gf + g'f$.

Proof. (i) We must show that gf satisfies the two conditions set out in (4.32). Let $\mathbf{u}, \mathbf{u}' \in U$ and $a \in k$.

$$\begin{aligned}(gf)(\mathbf{u}+\mathbf{u}') &= g(f(\mathbf{u}+\mathbf{u}')) \\ &= g(f(\mathbf{u}) + f(\mathbf{u}')) && \text{(since } f \text{ is linear)} \\ &= g(f(\mathbf{u})) + g(f(\mathbf{u}')) && \text{(since } g \text{ is linear)} \\ &= (gf)(\mathbf{u}) + (gf)(\mathbf{u}')\end{aligned}$$

and

$$\begin{aligned}(gf)(a\mathbf{u}) &= g(f(a\mathbf{u})) \\ &= g(af(\mathbf{u})) && \text{(since} f \text{ is linear)} \\ &= a(g(f(\mathbf{u}))) && \text{(since } g \text{ is linear)} \\ &= a((gf)(\mathbf{u})).\end{aligned}$$

(ii) Each of the three functions maps an element $\mathbf{u}$ of U onto $ag(f(\mathbf{u}))$.

(iii) For any $\mathbf{u} \in U$,

$$\begin{aligned}(g(f+f'))(\mathbf{u}) &= g((f+f')(\mathbf{u})) \\ &= g(f(\mathbf{u}) + f'(\mathbf{u})) && \text{(definition of + in Hom)} \\ &= g(f(\mathbf{u})) + g(f'(\mathbf{u})) && \text{(since } g \text{ is linear)} \\ &= (gf)(\mathbf{u}) + (gf')(\mathbf{u}) \\ &= (gf + gf')(\mathbf{u}) && \text{(definition of + in Hom).}\end{aligned}$$

This being true for all $\mathbf{u} \in U$, (iii) is proved; (iv) is proved in a similar way. ■

(4.37) COROLLARY. End(V) *is a ring. The group* (End V)*, *which is denoted* GL(V) *and called the* **general linear group** *of* V, *consists of the automorphisms.*

Proof. End(V) is a vector space by (4.33), *a fortiori* an abelian group with respect to the binary operation $+$. The remaining ring axioms follow from the proposition and the general set theoretic facts

$$f1 = f = 1f, \qquad h(gf) = (hg)f. \quad \blacksquare$$

EXERCISES

1. If $f: V \to W$ is a vector space isomorphism, so is f^{-1}.

2. If $\mathbf{0}$ denotes the 0 element of the appropriate Hom, $f\mathbf{0} = \mathbf{0}$ and $\mathbf{0}f = \mathbf{0}$.

The map

$$F: \mathrm{Hom}(U,V) \times \mathrm{Hom}(V,W) \to \mathrm{Hom}(U,W)$$

given by $(f,g) \mapsto gf$ is *not* linear because

$$\begin{aligned} F((f,g)+(f',g')) &= F((f+f', g+g')) \\ &= (g+g')(f+f') = gf + gf' + g'f + g'f' \end{aligned}$$

does not (usually) coincide with

$$F((f,g)) + F((f',g')) = gf + g'f'.$$

What the preceding proposition says is that F is linear in its arguments individually. That is, if we fix g, then

$$f \mapsto F(f,g) = gf$$

defines a linear transformation $\mathrm{Hom}(U,V) \to \mathrm{Hom}(U,W)$. Similarly, for each f, $g \mapsto gf$ defines a linear transformation $\mathrm{Hom}(V,W) \to \mathrm{Hom}(U,W)$. Thus F is bilinear according to the following general definition.

(4.38) DEFINITION. If $V_1, V_2, \ldots, V_n, W$ are vector spaces then a map $F: V_1 \times V_2 \times \cdots \times V_n \to W$ is **multilinear** (more precisely, ***k*-multilinear**) if for each $i, 1 \leqslant i \leqslant n$,

(ML1) $F(\mathbf{v}_1, \ldots, \mathbf{v}_i + \mathbf{v}_i', \ldots, \mathbf{v}_n) = F(\mathbf{v}_1, \ldots, \mathbf{v}_i, \ldots, \mathbf{v}_n) + F(\mathbf{v}_1, \ldots, \mathbf{v}_i', \ldots, \mathbf{v}_n)$,
(ML2) $F(\mathbf{v}_1, \ldots, a\mathbf{v}_i, \ldots, \mathbf{v}_n) = aF(\mathbf{v}_1, \ldots, \mathbf{v}_i, \ldots, \mathbf{v}_n)$, $\forall a \in k$.

When $W = k$, F is called a multilinear **form**. When $n = 2$, F is called **bilinear**. A bilinear form $V_1 \times V_2 \to k$ is also known as a **bilinear pairing**.

When $n = 1$ this reduces to the notion of a linear transformation. Multilinear maps will be encountered later in connection with determinants.

EXERCISES

1. Let $f \in \text{Hom}(\mathbb{Q}^3, \mathbb{Q})$ and suppose $f(4,-1,3)=2$, $f(2,1,0)=-1$. Find $f(2,-5,6)$.

2. Find a linear transformation $f: \mathbb{Q}^3 \to \mathbb{Q}^2$ such that $f(1,1,-1)=(2,0)$ and $f(3,-1,2)=(1,2)$. Show that there is no such f that also satisfies $f(-3,5,-7) = (0,0)$.

3. Find $f \in \text{End}(\mathbb{Q}^3) \ni \text{Ker}(f) = \langle (1,0,2) \rangle$ and $\text{Im}(f) = \langle (1,1,-1),(1,0,2) \rangle$.

4. Let the automorphism f of the vector space $\mathbb{Q}^3$ be given by $f(x,y,z) = (3x-z, 2x+y+z, 3z)$. Express f^2 and f^{-1} similarly.

5. Let $V = V_1 \times \cdots \times V_n$, where V_i is a vector space of finite dimension d_i. Then $\dim(V) = d_1 + \cdots + d_n$.

6. Let k be a field and k^k the vector space of k-valued functions on k. Then the polynomial functions (i.e., functions given by $x \mapsto f(x)$ for some $f \in k[X]$) form a subspace W of k^k. When k is finite, $W = k^k$.

7. Let V be a vector space and $W = \text{End}(V)$. For $f \in W$ define $T_f: W \to W$ by $T_f(g) = fg - gf$. Then $T_f \in \text{End}(W)$ and $f \mapsto T_f$ defines an element of $\text{Hom}(W, \text{End}(W))$.

8. Let $f, g \in V = \text{Hom}(\mathbb{Q}^2, \mathbb{Q}^3)$ be given by $f(x,y) = (x+2y, -x, 3x+y)$, $g(x,y) = (y, x, 0)$. Show that $\{f, g\}$ is linearly independent and complete this set to a basis of V.

9. Let V, W be nonzero vector spaces and $\mathbf{v}, \mathbf{v}'$ distinct elements of V. Then $\exists f \in \text{Hom}(V, W) \ni f(\mathbf{v}) \neq f(\mathbf{v}')$.

10. Let $f \in \text{End}(k^2)$ be defined by $f(1,0) = (a,b)$, $f(0,1) = (c,d)$. Then $f^2 - (a+d)f + (ad-bc) = 0$.

11. Let $V = k^2, \mathbf{v} = (a,b), \mathbf{w} = (c,d)$, and let $f_i: V \times V \to k$ be given by $f_1(\mathbf{v},\mathbf{w}) = a+c$, $f_2(\mathbf{v},\mathbf{w}) = 2a - 3c + 4d$, $f_3(\mathbf{v},\mathbf{w}) = ad$, $f_4(\mathbf{v},\mathbf{w}) = 2ac + 3bd$, $f_5(\mathbf{v},\mathbf{w}) = a^2$. Determine which are linear and which are bilinear.

12. Let f and g be commuting endomorphisms ($fg = gf$) of the vector space V. Then $\text{Ker}(f)$ and $\text{Im}(f)$ are g-invariant subspaces.

13. Let V be a vector space over k, $f \in \text{End}(V)$, $\mathbf{v} \in V$, and W an f-invariant subspace of V. Then $\{g \in k[X]: g(f)(\mathbf{v}) \in W\}$ is an ideal in $k[X]$, and is proper iff $v \notin W$.

14. For $f \in \text{End}(V)$, every subspace of V is f-invariant iff f is a scalar multiple of the identity endomorphism.

11. NULLITY AND RANK

As with ring homomorphisms, the **kernel** of a vector space homomorphism $f: V \to W$ is

$$\mathrm{Ker}(f) = \{\mathbf{v}: f(\mathbf{v}) = \mathbf{0}\}.$$

Ker(f) is also called the **null space** of f.

(4.39) PROPOSITION. (i) *If $f: V \to W$ is a linear transformation, then* Ker(f) *is a subspace of V and* Im(f) *is a subspace of W.*

(ii) *f is injective iff* $\mathrm{Ker}(f) = 0$.

(iii) *If V' is a subspace of V, then $f(V') = \{f(\mathbf{v}): \mathbf{v} \in V'\}$ is a subspace of W contained in* Im(f).

(iv) *If W' is a subspace of W, then $f^{-1}W' = \{\mathbf{v} \in V: f(\mathbf{v}) \in W'\}$ is a subspace of V containing* Ker(f).

Proof. (i)

$$f(\mathbf{0}) = \mathbf{0} \Rightarrow \mathbf{0} \in \mathrm{Ker}(f);$$

$$\mathbf{v},\mathbf{v}' \in \mathrm{Ker}(f) \quad \Rightarrow \quad f(\mathbf{v}+\mathbf{v}') = f(\mathbf{v}) + f(\mathbf{v}') = \mathbf{0} + \mathbf{0} = \mathbf{0}$$

$$\Rightarrow \quad \mathbf{v}+\mathbf{v}' \in \mathrm{Ker}(f);$$

$$\mathbf{v} \in \mathrm{Ker}(f), \quad a \in k \quad \Rightarrow \quad f(a\mathbf{v}) = af(\mathbf{v}) = a\mathbf{0} = \mathbf{0}$$

$$\Rightarrow \quad a\mathbf{v} \in \mathrm{Ker}(f).$$

Thus Ker(f) is a subspace. Second,

$$f(\mathbf{0}) = \mathbf{0} \quad \Rightarrow \quad \mathbf{0} \in \mathrm{Im}(f);$$

$$\mathbf{w},\mathbf{w}' \in \mathrm{Im}(f), \quad \text{say } f(\mathbf{v}) = \mathbf{w}, \quad f(\mathbf{v}') = \mathbf{w}' \quad \Rightarrow \quad f(\mathbf{v}+\mathbf{v}') = \mathbf{w}+\mathbf{w}'$$

$$\Rightarrow \quad \mathbf{w}+\mathbf{w}' \in \mathrm{Im}(f);$$

$$\mathbf{w} \in \mathrm{Im}(f), \quad \text{say } f(\mathbf{v}) = \mathbf{w}, \quad \text{and} \quad a \in k \quad \Rightarrow \quad f(a\mathbf{v}) = a\mathbf{w}$$

$$\Rightarrow \quad a\mathbf{w} \in \mathrm{Im}(f).$$

Thus Im(f) is a subspace of W.

(ii)

$$f(\mathbf{v}) = f(\mathbf{v}') \quad \Leftrightarrow \quad f(\mathbf{v}-\mathbf{v}') = \mathbf{0} \quad \Leftrightarrow \quad \mathbf{v}-\mathbf{v}' \in \mathrm{Ker}(f).$$

(iii) The restriction of f to V', that is, the map g(say): $V' \to W$ given by $g(\mathbf{v}) = f(\mathbf{v})$ for $\mathbf{v} \in V'$ is a linear transformation and therefore $\mathrm{Im}(g) = g(V') = f(V')$ is a subspace of W; it obviously is contained in Im(f).

(iv) $\mathbf{0} \in f^{-1}W'$ since $f(\mathbf{0}) = \mathbf{0} \in W'$. More generally, $\mathrm{Ker}(f) \subset f^{-1}W'$ since $\mathbf{v} \in \mathrm{Ker}(f) \Rightarrow f(\mathbf{v}) = \mathbf{0} \in W'$. If $\mathbf{v},\mathbf{v}' \in f^{-1}W'$, then $f(\mathbf{v})$ and $f(\mathbf{v}')$ are in W'. Hence $f(\mathbf{v}+\mathbf{v}') = f(\mathbf{v}) + f(\mathbf{v}') \in W'$ and therefore $\mathbf{v}+\mathbf{v}' \in f^{-1}W'$. Also, for any scalar c, $f(c\mathbf{v}) = cf(\mathbf{v}) \in W'$, so $c\mathbf{v} \in f^{-1}W'$. ■

(4.40) DEFINITION. When finite, $\dim \mathrm{Ker}(f)$ is the **nullity** of f and $\dim \mathrm{Im}(f)$ is the **rank** of f.

Example. The projection $f:\mathbb{Q}^3 \to \mathbb{Q}^3$ given by $(x,y,z) \mapsto (x,y,0)$. Here

$$\mathrm{Ker}(f) = \{(x,y,z):(x,y,0)=\mathbf{0}\}$$

consists of all vectors of the form $(0,0,z)$ where z is arbitrary. Since $(0,0,z) = z(0,0,1)$, this space is 1-dimensional, the single vector $(0,0,1)$ comprising a basis. Thus

$$\text{nullity of } f = 1.$$

Second, $\mathrm{Im}(f)$ consists of vectors of the form $(x,y,0) = x(1,0,0) + y(0,1,0)$ where x and y are arbitrary. An obvious basis for this space is $\{(1,0,0),(0,1,0)\}$ and

$$\text{rank of } f = 2.$$

(4.41) DEFINITION. If V is a vector space and U is a subspace of V, a **complement**, or **complementary subspace**, of U in V is a subspace W of V such that $U \cap W = 0$ and $U + W = V$. One then writes $V = U \dotplus W$.

Recall from Section 2 that $U + W = V$ means that every vector in V can be written in the form $\mathbf{u}+\mathbf{w}$, where $\mathbf{u} \in U$ and $\mathbf{w} \in W$. The other condition that $U \cap W = 0$ means that this representation is unique: If $\mathbf{u}+\mathbf{w} = \mathbf{u}'+\mathbf{w}'$, then $\mathbf{u}-\mathbf{u}' = \mathbf{w}'-\mathbf{w} \in U \cap W = 0$, which implies that $\mathbf{u}=\mathbf{u}'$ and $\mathbf{w}=\mathbf{w}'$. The symbol $\dotplus$ is used in a novel way; one cannot form $U \dotplus W$ for any subspaces since this notation carries with it the implication that $U \cap W = 0$.

(4.42) PROPOSITION. *Every subspace has a complement.*

Proof. Given a subspace U of the vector space V, choose a basis B of U and complete it to a basis $B' \supset B$ of V. Then $W = \langle B' \setminus B \rangle$ is a complement of U in V. ■

Notice that every complement of the given subspace U of V is obtained in the manner of the proof: if $V = U \dotplus W$ and $\mathfrak{U}, \mathfrak{W}$ are bases for U, W respectively, then applying A7.3 with $\mathfrak{T} = \mathfrak{U} \cap \mathfrak{W} = \varnothing$ we see that $\mathfrak{U} \cup \mathfrak{W}$ is a basis of $U \dotplus W = V$.

As an example, consider $V = \mathbb{Q}^3$ and the subspace U of vectors (x,y,z) satisfying the system

$$\begin{aligned} x + \quad\;\; z &= 0, \\ y - 2z &= 0. \end{aligned}$$

The typical vector in U is $(-z, 2z, z)$ with z arbitrary. Thus $\dim(U) = 1$, $B = \{(-1,2,1)\}$ being a basis. Geometrically, U is the line through $\mathbf{0}$ and the point $(-1,2,1)$, and a complement of U in $\mathbb{Q}^3$ is any plane through $\mathbf{0}$

not containing U. For instance, the ***xy*-plane**, consisting of all points with $z=0$, is such a complement; this is obtained as in the proof above by taking $B'=\{(-1,2,1),(1,0,0),(0,1,0)\}$. Other complements in this case are the ***xz*-plane**, which consists of all points $(x,0,z)$ with y-coordinate 0, and the ***yz*-plane**, which consists of all points $(0,y,z)$.

(4.43) PROPOSITION. *Let* $f\colon V\to W$ *be a linear transformation and let* U *be a complement of* $\mathrm{Ker}(f)$ *in* V. *Then* $\mathbf{u}\mapsto f(\mathbf{u})$ *defines an isomorphism* $\bar{f}\colon U\to \mathrm{Im}(f)$. (*See Figure* 4.3.)

Proof. By definition $\bar{f}$ is linear. The typical element of V can be written as $\mathbf{u}+\mathbf{x}$, where $\mathbf{x}\in\mathrm{Ker}(f)$. Since $f(\mathbf{u}+\mathbf{x})=f(\mathbf{u})+f(\mathbf{x})=f(\mathbf{u})$, $\bar{f}$ is surjective. Moreover, since $\bar{f}(\mathbf{v})=\mathbf{0}\Rightarrow\mathbf{v}\in U\cap\mathrm{Ker}(f)=\mathbf{0}$, $\mathrm{Ker}(\bar{f})=\mathbf{0}$, i.e., $\bar{f}$ is injective. ■

(4.44) COROLLARY. *Let* $f\colon V\to W$ *be a linear transformation and let* $\dim(V)$ *be finite, say* $\dim(V)=n$. *Then the nullity and rank of* f *are finite and*

$$\text{nullity}+\text{rank}=n.$$

Proof. A complement U of $\mathrm{Ker}(f)$ is isomorphic with $\mathrm{Im}(f)$; hence $\mathrm{rank}(f)=\dim(U)$ (cf. A8.1). Since $V=U\dot{+}\mathrm{Ker}(f)$, by A7.3, $n=\dim(U)+\dim\mathrm{Ker}(f)$. ■

(4.45) COROLLARY. *Let* V *be finite dimensional and* $f,g\in\mathrm{End}(V)$. *Then*

$$fg=1 \quad\Rightarrow\quad gf=1.$$

Proof. Let $\dim(V)=n$. Now $fg=1\Rightarrow f$ is surjective $\Rightarrow$ rank of $f=n\Rightarrow$ nullity of $f=0\Rightarrow\mathrm{Ker}(f)=0\Rightarrow f$ is also injective. Thus $f\in(\mathrm{End}\,V)^*$ and $f^{-1}=g$; f and g are mutually inverse automorphisms. ■

We can generalize (4.44) in the following way.

Figure 4.3

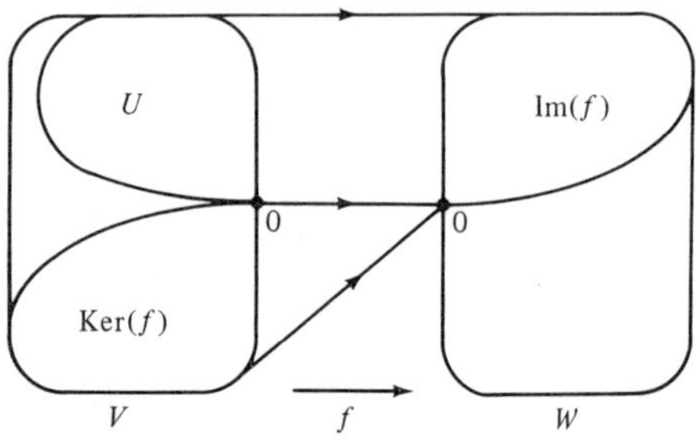

(4.46) COROLLARY. *Let $f: V \to W$ be a linear transformation where V is finite dimensional, let ν denote the nullity of f, and let W' be a subspace of W. Then*

$$(4.47) \qquad \dim(f^{-1}W') = \dim(W' \cap \operatorname{Im}(f)) + \nu \leqslant \dim(W') + \nu.$$

Proof. If we let g denote the linear transformation $f^{-1}W' \to W' \cap \operatorname{Im}(f)$ given by $\mathbf{v} \mapsto f(\mathbf{v})$, then g is surjective; hence $\operatorname{rank}(g) = \dim(W' \cap \operatorname{Im}(f))$. Because $\operatorname{Ker}(g) = \operatorname{Ker}(f)$ by (4.39(iv)), the nullity of g is ν. The result follows by applying (4.44) to g. ■

Here is an example showing that the assumption of finite dimensionality is essential in (4.45). Let k be a field of characteristic 0 and let V denote the vector space of polynomials over k. **Differentiation** on V is the endomorphism $D \in \operatorname{End}(V)$ defined on the basis $\{1, X, X^2, \ldots\}$ by $D(1) = 0$ and $D(X^n) = nX^{n-1}$ for $n \geqslant 1$ and extended linearly as explained in (4.34). What might be called "integration from 0 to X" is the element $S \in \operatorname{End}(V)$ defined by $S(X^n) = X^{n+1}/(n+1)$ for $n \geqslant 0$. Then $DS = 1$ but $SD \neq 1$. Since $\operatorname{char}(k) = 0$, $\operatorname{Ker}(D)$ consists of the constant polynomials.

Let V be a vector space and λ a scalar. The endomorphism $V \to V$ given by $\mathbf{v} \mapsto \lambda\mathbf{v}$ is denoted simply by λ. For instance, if $f \in \operatorname{End}(V)$, then $f - 1$ means the endomorphism given by $(f-1)\mathbf{v} = f(\mathbf{v}) - \mathbf{v}$.

EXERCISES

1. Find the rank and nullity of $f \in \operatorname{Hom}(\mathbb{Q}^3, \mathbb{Q}^4)$ where $f(1,0,0) = (0,1,0,2)$, $f(0,1,0) = (0,1,1,0)$, $f(0,0,1) = (0,1,-1,4)$.

2. For $f \in \operatorname{End}(V)$, where $\dim(V) < \infty$, the following are equivalent:
   a. f is singular, i.e., $f \notin (\operatorname{End} V)^*$;
   b. f is a left divisor of zero: $fg = 0$ for some nonzero g in $\operatorname{End}(V)$;
   c. f is a right divisor of zero.

3. Let f, g be linear transformations

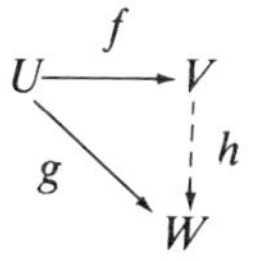

   such that $\operatorname{Ker}(f) \subset \operatorname{Ker}(g)$. Then $\exists h \in \operatorname{Hom}(V, W)$ so that the diagram commutes.

4. Let V and W be finite dimensional vector spaces, and for $f \in \operatorname{Hom}(V, W)$ let $|f|$ denote the rank of f. Then

$$(4.48) \qquad |f| - |g| \leqslant |f + g| \leqslant |f| + |g|,$$

   and, if $c \in k^*$,

$$|cf| = |f|.$$

12. DIRECT SUMS

We extend the notion of linear independence and at the same time that of complementary subspaces in the following way. Let $\{W_i : i \in I\}$ be a collection of subspaces of the vector space V and let $W = \Sigma W_i$. Thus every element $\mathbf{w}$ of W can be written $\mathbf{w} = \Sigma \mathbf{w}_i$, where $\mathbf{w}_i \in W_i$ and almost all $\mathbf{w}_i = \mathbf{0}$. We say that this sum of subspaces is **direct** and we write $W = \dot{\Sigma} W_i$ when the representation of each $\mathbf{w}$ is unique, that is, if also $\mathbf{w} = \Sigma \mathbf{w}_i'$, then $\mathbf{w}_i = \mathbf{w}_i'$, $\forall i$. (*Exercise*: If $\mathbf{w}_i$ (for $i \in I$) are nonzero elements of V, then the sum of the one-dimensional subspaces $W_i = \langle \mathbf{w}_i \rangle$ is direct iff the $\mathbf{w}_i$ are distinct and $\{\mathbf{w}_i\}$ is linearly independent.)

In the case of finitely many subspaces we also write $W = W_1 \dot{+} W_2 \dot{+} \cdots \dot{+} W_n$ to indicate that their sum is direct. ($\dot{+}$ is not an "operation" that can be carried out between any two subspaces.) Notice that the present meaning of $W = W_1 \dot{+} W_2$ coincides with the earlier one that W_1 and W_2 are complementary subspaces in W.

(4.49) PROPOSITION. *The sum of the subspaces W_i $(i \in I)$ is direct iff, $\forall s \in I$,*

(4.50) $$W_s \cap \sum W_t = 0,$$

where the sum is extended over all $t \neq s$ in I.

Proof. Suppose first that ΣW_i is direct and let $\mathbf{v} \in W_s \cap \Sigma W_t$. The fact that $\mathbf{v} \in W_s$ can be emphasized by writing $\mathbf{v} = \mathbf{w}_s \in W_s$. Since $\mathbf{v} \in \Sigma W_t$ we can also write $\mathbf{v}$ in the form $\mathbf{w}_{t_1} + \cdots + \mathbf{w}_{t_n}$, where $\mathbf{w}_{t_r} \in W_{t_r}$ and no $t_r = s$. Thus in ΣW_i, $\mathbf{v}$ has the two representations $\mathbf{w}_s = \mathbf{w}_{t_1} + \cdots + \mathbf{w}_{t_n}$. Since the sum is direct this obliges $\mathbf{w}_s = \mathbf{w}_{t_1} = \cdots = \mathbf{0}$, thus proving (4.50).

Conversely assume (4.50) and suppose we have two representations

$$\mathbf{v} = \mathbf{w}_{t_1} + \cdots + \mathbf{w}_{t_n} = \mathbf{w}_{t_1}' + \cdots + \mathbf{w}_{t_n}',$$

where $\mathbf{w}_{t_r}$ and $\mathbf{w}_{t_r}'$ are elements of W_{t_r}, possibly $\mathbf{0}$ since we have taken the list $t_1, \ldots$ large enough to accommodate both representations. For each r between 1 and n we have

$$\mathbf{w}_{t_r} - \mathbf{w}_{t_r}' = \sum \{\mathbf{w}_{t_q}' - \mathbf{w}_{t_q} : 1 \leqslant q \leqslant n, q \neq r\}$$

$$\in W_{t_r} \cap \sum \{W_j : j \in I, j \neq t_r\} = 0,$$

whence $\mathbf{w}_{t_r} - \mathbf{w}_{t_r}' = \mathbf{0}$, so the representations are identical after all. ■

The sum of subspaces ΣW_i can be likened to the set theoretic operation $\cup X_i$ of the union of subsets. $W = \dot{\Sigma} W_i$ is the vector space analog of the set theoretical situation in which the X_i are mutually disjoint: Subspaces have to overlap at least at the element $\mathbf{0}$ and (4.50) is as close, so to speak, to mutual disjointness as subspaces come.

The vector space analog of $\amalg$ is the construction $\oplus$, which we now describe. Just as $\amalg X_i$ is a set containing mutually disjoint copies of the sets X_i, and is as small as possible in the sense that no proper subset contains all these copies, so $\oplus W_i$ is a vector space containing copies of the W_i as subspaces whose sum is direct and such that no proper subspace of $\oplus W_i$ contains all the copies of the W_i. The construction is easy: $\oplus W_i$ consists of all $\mathbf{w} = (\ldots, \mathbf{w}_i, \ldots) \in \prod W_i$ for which almost all $\mathbf{w}_i = 0$. Of course if I is finite then $\oplus W_i = \prod W_i$.

For instance, if $I = \mathbb{N}$ and each $W_i = k$, then the typical element of $\prod W_i = k^{\mathbb{N}}$ looks like $(a_1, a_2, a_3, \ldots)$, where each $a_i \in k$. The elements $(1,1,1,\ldots)$ of $\prod W_i$, which has all its entries 1, is not in $\oplus W_i$. An example of an element in $\oplus W_i$ is $(0,0,-1,0,2,5,0,0,\ldots)$, where $a_i = 0$ for all $i > 6$. This element qualifies for membership in $\oplus W_i$ since $\{i : a_i \neq 0\} = \{3,5,6\}$ is finite.

Returning to the general case, if $\mathbf{w} = (\ldots, \mathbf{w}_i, \ldots)$ and $\mathbf{w}' = (\ldots, \mathbf{w}_i', \ldots)$ are two elements of $\oplus W_i$, then by definition their **supports**

$$\operatorname{Supp}(\mathbf{w}) = \{i : \mathbf{w}_i \neq \mathbf{0}\}$$

and

$$\operatorname{Supp}(\mathbf{w}') = \{i : \mathbf{w}_i' \neq 0\}$$

are empty or finite. Since $\operatorname{Supp}(\mathbf{w} + \mathbf{w}') \subset \operatorname{Supp}(\mathbf{w}) \cup \operatorname{Supp}(\mathbf{w}')$, $\operatorname{Supp}(a\mathbf{w}) \subset \operatorname{Supp}(\mathbf{w})$ (with equality if $a \neq 0$), and $\operatorname{Supp}(\mathbf{0}) = \varnothing$, it follows that $\oplus W_i$ is a subspace of $\prod W_i$ and is therefore itself a vector space.

The vector space $\oplus W_i$ is called the **direct sum** of the vector spaces W_i. When the W_i are subspaces of some space and their sum $W = \dot{\Sigma} W_i$ is direct, one sometimes calls $\oplus W_i$ the **external** direct sum to emphasize the distinction between it and the **internal** direct sum $\dot{\Sigma} W_i$. The connection between the two is spelled out in the following proposition.

(4.51) PROPOSITION. (i) *For each $j \in I$, the map $\mathbf{x} \mapsto (\ldots, \mathbf{0}, \mathbf{x}, \mathbf{0}, \ldots)$ (an $\mathbf{x}$ in position j, $\mathbf{0}$s elsewhere) defines an injective vector space homomorphism $W_j \to \oplus W_i$. Hence W_j is isomorphic with a subspace W_j' of $\oplus W_i$;*

(ii) *$\oplus W_i$ is internally the direct sum of its subspaces W_i';*

(iii) *if W_i are subspaces of a vector space V then $(\ldots, \mathbf{w}_i, \ldots) \mapsto \Sigma \mathbf{w}_i$ defines a surjective vector space homomorphism $\oplus W_i \to \Sigma W_i$. This is an isomorphism iff ΣW_i is direct.*

Proof. The proofs of (i) and (ii) are left to the reader. Let f denote the map in (iii). Since

$$\begin{aligned} f((\ldots, \mathbf{w}_i, \ldots) + (\ldots, \mathbf{w}_i', \ldots)) &= f((\ldots, \mathbf{w}_i + \mathbf{w}_i', \ldots)) \\ &= \sum (\mathbf{w}_i + \mathbf{w}_i') = \sum \mathbf{w}_i + \sum \mathbf{w}_i' \\ &= f((\ldots, \mathbf{w}_i, \ldots)) + f((\ldots, \mathbf{w}_i', \ldots)), \end{aligned}$$

and

$$f(a(\ldots,\mathbf{w}_i,\ldots))=f((\ldots,a\mathbf{w}_i,\ldots))$$

$$=\sum a\mathbf{w}_i=a\sum \mathbf{w}_i=af((\ldots,\mathbf{w}_i,\ldots)),$$

f is linear. Now any element $\mathbf{w}\in\Sigma W_i$ can be written, not necessarily uniquely, in the form $\mathbf{w}_{i_1}+\cdots+\mathbf{w}_{i_n}$ and if we define $\mathbf{x}=(\ldots,\mathbf{x}_i,\ldots)$ by $\mathbf{x}_i=\mathbf{w}_{i_r}$ if $i=i_r$ and $\mathbf{x}_i=0$ if i is not one of $i_1,\ldots,i_n$, then $\mathbf{x}\in\oplus W_i$ and $f(\mathbf{x})=\mathbf{w}$. Thus $\operatorname{Im}(f)=\Sigma W_i$.

If $\mathbf{w}$ has another such representation $\Sigma\mathbf{w}_i'$, then this gives another element $\mathbf{x}'\in\oplus W_i$ sent onto $\mathbf{w}$ by f. It follows that if ΣW_i is not direct then f is not injective.

Conversely, if f is not injective, say $\mathbf{w}=(\ldots,\mathbf{w}_i,\ldots)\in\operatorname{Ker}(f)$, then the element $\mathbf{0}$ has the distinct representations $\Sigma_\varnothing=\Sigma\mathbf{w}_i$ and hence ΣW_i is not direct. ■

Let $\lambda_j\colon W_j\to\oplus W_i$ denote the **canonical injection** described in (i). Since each $\mathbf{w}\in\oplus W_i$ is uniquely of the form $\Sigma\lambda_i\mathbf{w}_i$, $\mathbf{w}_i\in W_i$, if B_i is a basis of W_i then $\cup\lambda_i(B_i)$ is a basis of $\oplus W_i$. (When there are infinitely many $W_i\neq 0$ it is not feasible to write out a basis of ΠW_i explicitly; one must rely on Zorn's lemma to prove that a basis does exist.) When the W_i are all the same, say each $W_i=W$, we have been writing W^I for ΠW_i. For $\oplus W_i$ we shall use the notation $\oplus_I W$.

Thus a basis of $\oplus_I k$ is $\{\mathbf{u}_i : i\in I\}$, where $\mathbf{u}_i=(\ldots,0,1,0,\ldots)=\lambda_i(1)$. This is called the **canonical basis**, generalizing the case when I is finite. The vector spaces $\oplus_I k$ command respect because, up to isomorphism, there are no others!

(4.52) THEOREM. (i) *Let V be a vector space, $B=\{\mathbf{v}_i : i\in I\}$ a basis of V and let $\{\mathbf{u}_i : i\in I\}$ denote the canonical basis of $\oplus_I k$. Then $\Sigma a_i\mathbf{v}_i\mapsto\Sigma a_i\mathbf{u}_i$ defines a vector space isomorphism $V\xrightarrow{\sim}\oplus_I k$.*

(ii) *The vector spaces V,V' with bases B, B' are isomorphic iff $|B|=|B'|$. In particular, $\oplus_I k$ and $\oplus_J k$ are isomorphic iff $|I|=|J|$.*

Proof. Since representation of vectors in terms of a basis is unique, the map is a bijection. It is linear since it is the linear extension of the map $B\to\oplus_I k$ given by $\mathbf{v}_i\mapsto\mathbf{u}_i$ (cf. (4.34)).

(ii) If $f\colon V\to V'$ is an isomorphism then, by A8.1, $f(B)$ is a basis of V'. Since f is bijective, $|B|=|f(B)|$ and, by (4.22), $|f(B)|=|B'|$, so $|B|=|B'|$. Conversely, suppose $g\colon B\to B'$ is a bijection. Then we can write $B=\{\mathbf{v}_i : i\in I\}$, $B'=\{g(\mathbf{v}_i) : i\in I\}$ and we have isomorphisms $f\colon V\to\oplus_I k$, $h\colon V'\to\oplus_I k$; hence an isomorphism $h^{-1}f\colon V\to V'$. ■

Theorem (4.52) is what is known as a **structure theorem**. All the objects under consideration, in this case vector spaces/k, are described and classified up to isomorphism.

Of course one does not always want to rewrite a vector space in the form $\oplus_I k$. For instance, if B is a basis of k^I, then $k^I = \oplus_B k$, but normally we prefer to write the vectors of this space as I-tuples (with unrestricted support). Similarly we usually prefer to think of the elements of Hom(U,V) as homomorphisms, not as members of some $\oplus_I k$. (*Exercise*: If $V_1,\ldots,V_r$ are finite dimensional subspaces, then

$$\dim \sum V_i \leqslant \sum \dim V_i,$$

with equality iff the sum is direct.)

Assignment 8

A8.1. Let $f: V \to W$ be a linear transformation and X a subset of V. Show that (i) X spans V and f surjective $\Rightarrow f(X)$ spans W; and (ii) X linearly independent and f injective $\Rightarrow f(X)$ linearly independent.

Hence if B is a basis of V and f is an isomorphism, then $f(B)$ is a basis of W.

A8.2. An endomorphism p of the vector space V is called a **projection** if, as an element of the ring End(V), it is idempotent, i.e., $p^2 = p$.

(i) Suppose $V = U \dotplus W$ (cf. Section 12) and let $\mathbf{v} = \mathbf{u} + \mathbf{w}$, where $\mathbf{u} \in U$, and so on. Show that $p(\mathbf{v}) = \mathbf{u}$ defines a projection with $\mathrm{Im}(p) = U$ and $\mathrm{Ker}(p) = W$; similarly the map $1 - p$ given by $\mathbf{v} \mapsto \mathbf{w}$ is a projection whose kernel is U and whose image is W.

(ii) Conversely, if p is a projection, show that

$$V = \mathrm{Im}(p) \dotplus \mathrm{Ker}(p).$$

More generally, show that if $p_1,\ldots,p_r \in \mathrm{End}(V)$ are **orthogonal idempotents** i.e., $p_i p_j = \delta_{ij} p_i$, satisfying $p_1 + \cdots + p_r = 1$, then

$$V = \mathrm{Im}(p_1) \dotplus \cdots \dotplus \mathrm{Im}(p_r).$$

(iii) With $V = U \dotplus W$ and p as in (i) and $f \in \mathrm{End}(V)$, show that $fp = pf$ iff U and W are both f-invariant.

Remarks. The term "projection" has a slightly different meaning when used in the sense of canonical projection $\pi_i: \prod V_i \to V_i$ where $\pi_i(\ldots,\mathbf{v}_i,\ldots) = \mathbf{v}_i$ (as in A5.4 in the ring case). When the V_i are vector spaces the restrictions π_i': $\oplus V_i \to V_i$ of π_i to the subspace $\oplus V_i$ of $\prod V_i$ are also called canonical projections. In (4.51) we defined the canonical injections $\lambda_i: V_i \to \oplus V_i$, and this term is similarly extended to $\lambda_i': V_i \to \prod V_i$, where λ_i' is characterized by

$$\pi_j \lambda_i'(\mathbf{x}) = \delta_{ji}\mathbf{x}.$$

Notice that $\lambda_i'\pi_i$ and $\lambda_i\pi_i'$ are projections in the sense of this question: They are idempotent endomorphisms.

A8.3. **(i)** Let V and W be finite dimensional vector spaces with bases $\{\mathbf{v}_1,\ldots,\mathbf{v}_n\},\{\mathbf{w}_1,\ldots,\mathbf{w}_m\}$, respectively, and let $f_{ij}\in\mathrm{Hom}(V,W)$ for $1\leqslant i\leqslant n, 1\leqslant j\leqslant m$ be defined (with the aid of (4.34)) by

$$f_{ij}(\mathbf{v}_r)=\begin{cases}\mathbf{0} & \text{if } r\neq i,\\ \mathbf{w}_j & \text{if } r=i.\end{cases}$$

Show that $\{f_{ij}\}$ is a basis of $\mathrm{Hom}(V,W)$, and therefore

$$\dim\mathrm{Hom}(V,W)=\dim(V)\cdot\dim(W).$$

(ii) Generalize (4.33) as follows: the set $\mathrm{Mult}(V_1,\ldots,V_n;W)$ of all multilinear maps $V_1\times\cdots\times V_n\to W$ is a subspace of $W^{V_1\times\cdots\times V_n}$. (The vector space of all bilinear maps is also denoted $\mathrm{Bil}(V_1,V_2;W)$ or $\mathrm{Bil}(V_1\times V_2\to W)$.)

A8.4. **(i)** Let V be a vector space of countable dimension with basis $\{\mathbf{v}_0,\mathbf{v}_1,\mathbf{v}_2,\ldots\}$ and let $f\in\mathrm{End}(V)$ be the **right shift operator** determined by

$$f\mathbf{v}_i=\mathbf{v}_{i+1}.$$

Show that f has infinitely many left inverses but is not an automorphism.

(ii) Let W be another vector space of countable dimension with basis $\{\mathbf{w}_0,\mathbf{w}_1,\ldots\}$ and right shift operator g. Show that

$$H=\{h\in\mathrm{Hom}(V,W): hf=(1-g)h\}$$

is a subspace of $\mathrm{Hom}(V,W)$ and that $h\mapsto h(\mathbf{v}_0)$ defines a vector space isomorphism $H\to W$.

(iii) If $h\in H$, show that $h(1-f)^n=g^nh$ for $n\geqslant 1$.

(iv) Let h_0 be the unique element of H such that $h_0(\mathbf{v}_0)=\mathbf{w}_0$. Show that

$$h_0(\mathbf{v}_n)=\sum_{m=0}^{n}(-1)^m\binom{n}{m}\mathbf{w}_m,$$

and that h_0 is an isomorphism (hence $(1-f)^nh_0^{-1}=h_0^{-1}g^n$).

(v) Let $a_0,a_1,\ldots$ be a sequence of elements in k and define the sequence $b_0,b_1,\ldots$ by

$$(*)\qquad b_n=\sum_{m=0}^{n}(-1)^m\binom{n}{m}a_m.$$

Using $\alpha\in\mathrm{Hom}(W,k)$, defined by $\alpha\mathbf{w}_n=a_n$ and $\beta=\alpha h_0\in\mathrm{Hom}(V,k)$, justify the following argument.

Write $(*)$ "symbolically" as $b^n=(1-a)^n$, with the understanding that exponents are to be debased to subscripts. Taking $n=1$ we solve $b=1-a$ symbolically for a: $a=1-b$. Hence $a^n=(1-b)^n$, i.e.,

$$a_n=\sum_{m=0}^{n}(-1)^m\binom{n}{m}b_m.$$

(The body of technique of symbolic abbreviations for arguments involving linear transformations (and induction) was at one time known as the *umbral calculus*. We hope that this example, which was first mentioned to me by N. S. Mendelsohn, has shed some light.)

A8.5. Let X be an infinite set and Y a finite set. Show that $|X \setminus Y| = |X|$.

A8.6. If X and Y are sets, define $|X| \geqslant |Y|$ to mean that either $Y = \varnothing$ or $\exists$ surjection $X \to Y$. (Recall that $|Y| \leqslant |X|$ was defined in Section 8 to mean that there exists an injection $Y \to X$.) Using the axiom of choice, show that $|X| \geqslant |Y|$ iff $|Y| \leqslant |X|$.

A8.7. **(i)** Let X be a set and 2^X the set of subsets of X (as in A3.4). Show that

$$|X| < |2^X|.$$

(*Hint*: If $f\colon X \to 2^X = (\mathbb{Z}/2\mathbb{Z})^X$ is any injection show that f cannot be surjective by the following device, known as **Cantor's diagonal method**. Define $g\colon X \to \mathbb{Z}/2\mathbb{Z}$ by $g(x) = 1 - f(x)(x)$. Then $g \notin \mathrm{Im}(f)$.)

(ii) Deduce that if Y is a set containing at least two distinct elements and X is any set, then

$$|X| < |Y^X|,$$

and, in particular, the ring $\mathbb{Q}^{\mathbb{N}}$ of all sequences $(a_1, a_2, \ldots)$ of rational numbers is uncountable.

(iii) Suppose that the sets X, Y satisfy the conditions: $X \neq \varnothing$, Y is infinite, and there exist sets A, B such that $|Y| = |A^B|$ and $|X| \leqslant |B|$. Using A3.2(ii) prove that

$$|Y^X| = |Y|.$$

(iv) Let I be an infinite set and k a field satisfying $|k| \leqslant |I|$. Show that

$$|\oplus_I k| = |I|.$$

(Hence $|\oplus_I k| < |k^I|$, so under these circumstances the vector spaces $\oplus_I k$ and k^I are not isomorphic.)

13. MATRICES

Let V and W be a vector spaces with bases $\mathcal{V} = \{\mathbf{v}_j\colon j \in J\}$ and $\mathcal{W} = \{\mathbf{w}_i\colon i \in I\}$, respectively, and let $f \in \mathrm{Hom}(V, W)$. As observed in (4.34), f is uniquely determined by the scalars a_{ij} in the equations

(4.53) $$f(\mathbf{v}_j) = \sum_i a_{ij}\mathbf{w}_i.$$

N.B.: The order of the subscripts on a_{ij} will always be chosen this way: The first subscript is the summation variable and the second is the subscript of the vector on the left.

Consider the example $V = W = \mathbb{Q}^3$, $\mathcal{V} = \mathcal{W} = \{\mathbf{v}_1 = \mathbf{w}_1 = (1,0,0), \mathbf{v}_2 = \mathbf{w}_2 = (0,1,0), \mathbf{v}_3 = \mathbf{w}_3 = (0,0,1)\}$, and f is the projection $(x, y, z) \mapsto (x, y, 0)$. Then $f(\mathbf{v}_1) = f((1,0,0)) = (1,0,0) = \mathbf{w}_1$ so $a_{11} = 1$, $a_{21} = 0$, $a_{31} = 0$; $f(\mathbf{v}_2) = \mathbf{w}_2$ so $a_{12} = 0$, $a_{22} = 1$, $a_{32} = 0$; and $f(\mathbf{v}_3) = \mathbf{0}$ so $a_{13} = a_{23} = a_{33} = 0$. We display these nine scalars in a matrix:

$$\mathbf{A}=\begin{pmatrix}1&0&0\\0&1&0\\0&0&0\end{pmatrix}=\begin{pmatrix}a_{11}&a_{12}&a_{13}\\a_{21}&a_{22}&a_{23}\\a_{31}&a_{32}&a_{33}\end{pmatrix}. \tag{4.54}$$

The arrangement in general is

$$\begin{array}{r}\\ \text{row } i\\ \\ \end{array}\begin{pmatrix} & \vdots & \\ \cdots & a_{ij} & \cdots \\ & \vdots & \end{pmatrix}.$$
$$\text{column } j$$

This labeling of positions is consistent with that introduced in (4.7).

If instead we consider the linear transformation $g\colon V=\mathbf{Q}^3\to\mathbf{Q}^2=W$ given by $(x,y,z)\mapsto(x,y)$ with the same $\mathcal{V}$ but now with $\mathcal{W}=\{\mathbf{w}_1=(1,0),\ \mathbf{w}_2=(0,1)\}$, the matrix representing g is

$$\begin{pmatrix}1&0&0\\0&1&0\end{pmatrix}.$$

When $\mathcal{V}$ is finite, say $|\mathcal{V}|=m$, it is always tacitly assumed that the elements of $\mathcal{V}$ have been assigned subscripts $1,2,\ldots,m$ and that the row positions begin with 1 at the top and increase to the bottom, mth row. Similarly, when $|\mathcal{W}|=n$, the column numbers begin with 1 on the left and increase to the rightmost, nth column. This is a useful convention since then, for example, when $\mathbf{A}$ is given by its numerical value in (4.54) we know exactly what that means (once the $\mathbf{v}_j$ and $\mathbf{w}_i$ have been chosen) and there is no need for the second literal matrix in (4.54). In this context it is useful to remember

$f(\mathbf{v}_j)$ is described by the jth column.

In the case of an infinite index set the situation is similar to that of products $\prod_{i\in I}X_i$, where we visualize the elements as one-rowed matrices $(\ldots,\mathbf{x}_i,\ldots)$ with one position for each $i\in I$. I is not usually explicitly totally ordered. (When it is, one can say when one subscript's position is to the left or right of another.) Similarly in the general matrix for each $(i,j)\in I\times J$ there is one position, called the ijth position, but again I and J need not be explicitly totally ordered. The matrix is referred to as an I by J (or $I\times J$) matrix. In the finite case this becomes m by n (or $m\times n$), and the terminology extends to expressions such as "finite by countable."

If we change one or both the bases, or the labeling of the elements within a basis, then usually the matrix will change. For instance, if we keep $g\colon\mathbf{Q}^3\to\mathbf{Q}^2$ and $\mathcal{V}$ as above but change $\mathcal{W}$ to $\{w_1=(0,1), w_2=(1,0)\}$, then the corresponding 2 by 3 matrix is

$$\begin{pmatrix} 0 & 1 & 0 \\ 1 & 0 & 0 \end{pmatrix}.$$

It need hardly be said that an array such as

$$\begin{pmatrix} 1 & 2 & \\ & 3 & 4 \end{pmatrix}$$

is not a matrix (unless one makes the convention that a blank means 0). We shall normally denote matrices by capital letters **A**, **B**, and so on.

In the general situation $f: V \to W$ with chosen bases $\mathcal{V}, \mathcal{W}$ we use the notation $R_{\mathcal{V},\mathcal{W}}(f)$ to designate the matrix representing f. When $V = W$ and $\mathcal{V} = \mathcal{W}$, this is shortened to $R_{\mathcal{V}}(f)$. The jth column of this matrix has the entries a_{ij} given in (4.53), where i runs through I and therefore there are at most finitely many nonzero entries in each column. Such a matrix is said to be **column finite**. If there are infinitely many columns, the number of nonzero entries in the various columns may be unbounded, that is, there may exist columns with more than N nonzero entries for every $N \in \mathbb{N}$.

If V or W is 0, then $\operatorname{Hom}(V, W)$ consists of the single element 0 defined by $0(\mathbf{v}) = \mathbf{0}\ \forall \mathbf{v} \in V$. Since $I \times J = \varnothing$, $R_{\mathcal{V},\mathcal{W}}(0)$ is the "empty matrix." This extreme case is of little interest; nonetheless the statements and results of this section are true when properly interpreted. For instance, in (4.58), if either **A** or **B** is the empty matrix, then all the sums are empty, and hence all $c_{ir} = 0$. However, there is no real loss in assuming throughout that the vector spaces involved are nonzero.

For an infinite dimensional example take $V = k[X]$ with basis $\mathcal{V} = \{\mathbf{v}_1 = 1, \mathbf{v}_2 = X, \mathbf{v}_3 = X^2, \ldots\}$ and the endomorphism $p(X) \mapsto Xp(X)$. Then $\mathbf{v}_i \mapsto \mathbf{v}_{i+1}$ and

(4.55)
$$R_{\mathcal{V}}(f) = \begin{pmatrix} 0 & 0 & 0 & \cdots \\ 1 & 0 & 0 & \cdots \\ 0 & 1 & 0 & \cdots \\ 0 & 0 & 1 & \cdots \\ 0 & 0 & 0 & \cdots \\ \vdots & \vdots & \vdots & \end{pmatrix}.$$

We sometimes write $\mathbf{A} = (a_{ij})$ to describe a matrix by a typical entry when there is no danger of this being misconstrued as a 1×1 matrix.

(4.56) PROPOSITION. *Let U, V, W be vector spaces with bases $\mathcal{U} = \{\mathbf{u}_r : r \in R\}, \mathcal{V} = \{\mathbf{v}_j : j \in J\}, \mathcal{W} = \{\mathbf{w}_i : i \in I\}$; let $\alpha, \alpha' \in \operatorname{Hom}(V, W)$ and $\beta \in \operatorname{Hom}(U, V)$; put $\alpha'' = \alpha + \alpha'$ and $\gamma = \alpha\beta$;*

$$U \xrightarrow{\beta} V \xrightarrow{\alpha} W. \qquad (\alpha\beta = \gamma : U \to W)$$

In terms of these bases let $\alpha, \alpha', \alpha'', \beta, \gamma$ have the matrix representations $\mathbf{A} = (a_{ij})$, $\mathbf{A}' = (a_{ij}')$, $\mathbf{A}'' = (a_{ij}'')$, $\mathbf{B} = (b_{jr})$, $\mathbf{C} = (c_{ir})$, respectively. Then

$$a_{ij}'' = a_{ij} + a_{ij}', \tag{4.57}$$

$$c_{ir} = \sum_j a_{ij} b_{jr}. \tag{4.58}$$

*(Each of these sums involves only finitely many nonzero terms since **B** is column finite.) Moreover, if $a \in k$ then the matrix representing $a\alpha$ has ijth entry $a\alpha_{ij}$.*

Proof

$$\begin{aligned}\alpha''(\mathbf{v}_j) &= (\alpha + \alpha')(\mathbf{v}_j) = \alpha(\mathbf{v}_j) + \alpha'(\mathbf{v}_j)\\ &= \sum_i a_{ij}\mathbf{w}_i + \sum_i a_{ij}'\mathbf{w}_i\\ &= \sum_i (a_{ij} + a_{ij}')\mathbf{w}_i;\end{aligned}$$

$$\begin{aligned}\gamma(\mathbf{u}_r) &= \alpha\beta(\mathbf{u}_r) = \alpha\sum_j b_{jr}\mathbf{v}_j = \sum_j b_{jr}\alpha(\mathbf{v}_j)\\ &= \sum_j b_{jr}\sum_i a_{ij}\mathbf{w}_i\\ &= \sum_i \left(\sum_j a_{ij}b_{jr}\right)\mathbf{w}_i;\end{aligned}$$

and finally

$$(a\alpha)(\mathbf{v}_j) = a\alpha(\mathbf{v}_j) = a\sum_i a_{ij}\mathbf{w}_i = \sum_i (aa_{ij})\mathbf{w}_i. \quad \blacksquare$$

Let us look at some explicit numerical examples. Suppose that $\dim(U) = 3$, $\dim(V) = 3$, $\dim(W) = 2$, and

$$\mathbf{A} = \begin{pmatrix} 1 & 2 & 3 \\ 0 & -4 & 5 \end{pmatrix}, \quad \mathbf{A}' = \begin{pmatrix} 6 & 0 & -7 \\ 0 & 4 & -5 \end{pmatrix}, \quad \mathbf{B} = \begin{pmatrix} -1 & 6 & -7 \\ 8 & -2 & 4 \\ -5 & 3 & 9 \end{pmatrix}.$$

Then $a_{11}'' = a_{11} + a_{11}' = 1 + 6 = 7$, and so on, whence

$$\mathbf{A}'' = \begin{pmatrix} 7 & 2 & -4 \\ 0 & 0 & 0 \end{pmatrix}.$$

Next,

$$\begin{aligned}c_{11} &= \sum_j a_{1j}b_{j1} = a_{11}b_{11} + a_{12}b_{21} + a_{13}b_{31}\\ &= 1\cdot(-1) + 2\cdot 8 + 3\cdot(-5) = 0,\\ c_{12} &= \sum_j a_{1j}b_{j2} = a_{11}b_{12} + a_{12}b_{22} + a_{13}b_{32}\\ &= 1\cdot 6 + 2\cdot(-2) + 3\cdot 3 = 11,\end{aligned}$$

and so on for the other elements of **C**:

$$\mathbf{C}=\begin{pmatrix} 0 & 11 & 28 \\ -57 & 23 & 29 \end{pmatrix}.$$

As will be explained in general in a moment, we use (4.57) and (4.58) to define addition and multiplication of matrices. The present examples of $\mathbf{A}+\mathbf{A}'=\mathbf{A}''$ and $\mathbf{AB}=\mathbf{C}$ are

$$\begin{pmatrix} 1 & 2 & 3 \\ 0 & -4 & 5 \end{pmatrix}+\begin{pmatrix} 6 & 0 & -7 \\ 0 & 4 & -5 \end{pmatrix}=\begin{pmatrix} 7 & 2 & -4 \\ 0 & 0 & 0 \end{pmatrix},$$

$$\begin{pmatrix} 1 & 2 & 3 \\ 0 & -4 & 5 \end{pmatrix}\begin{pmatrix} -1 & 6 & -7 \\ 8 & -2 & 4 \\ -5 & 3 & 9 \end{pmatrix}=\begin{pmatrix} 0 & 11 & 28 \\ -57 & 23 & 29 \end{pmatrix}.$$

To paraphrase (4.58), to obtain the irth entry of the product work across the ith row of the left-hand factor at the same time working down the rth column of the right-hand factor and accumulate the products of the corresponding entries. The catch phrase to remember is

matrix multiplication is row by column.

If we had chosen the subscripts on a_{ij} the opposite way in (4.53), then linear transformations would be represented by row finite matrices and matrix multiplication would be "column by row." However, this notational decision was made long ago and is standard.

Similarly, the last statement of the proposition is used to define a scalar multiple of a matrix. For instance,

$$-\tfrac{1}{2}\begin{pmatrix} 1 & 2 & 3 \\ 0 & -4 & 5 \end{pmatrix}=\begin{pmatrix} -\tfrac{1}{2} & -1 & -\tfrac{3}{2} \\ 0 & 2 & -\tfrac{5}{2} \end{pmatrix}.$$

Here is another example. If the linear transformation η is represented by the countable by countable column finite matrix

$$\begin{pmatrix} 1 & 2 & 3 & 4 & \cdots \\ 0 & 1 & 2 & 3 & \cdots \\ 0 & 0 & 1 & 2 & \cdots \\ \vdots & \vdots & \vdots & \vdots & \end{pmatrix}$$

then 2η and η^2 are represented by

$$\begin{pmatrix} 2 & 4 & 6 & 8 & \cdots \\ 0 & 2 & 4 & 6 & \cdots \\ 0 & 0 & 2 & 4 & \cdots \\ \vdots & \vdots & \vdots & \vdots & \end{pmatrix} \quad \text{and} \quad \begin{pmatrix} 1 & 4 & 10 & 20 & \cdots \\ 0 & 1 & 4 & 10 & \cdots \\ 0 & 0 & 1 & 4 & \cdots \\ \vdots & \vdots & \vdots & \vdots & \end{pmatrix},$$

respectively.

If I, J are any two nonempty sets, we let $\mathrm{Mat}_{I,J}(k)$ denote the set of all I by J column finite matrices. When $I=J$ this is abbreviated to $\mathrm{Mat}_I(k)$ and the matrices are said to be **square**. When I and J are finite, say $|I|=m$ and $|J|=n$, we also write $\mathrm{Mat}_{m,n}(k)$; when $m=n$ this is shortened to $\mathrm{Mat}_n(k)$.

We let $\mathbf{0}$ denote the element of $\mathrm{Mat}_{I,J}(k)$, all of whose entries are 0. When it is necessary to make explicit the dimensions of the matrix, we write $\mathbf{0}_{I,J}$. For example in the context of $\mathrm{Mat}_2(k)$,

$$\mathbf{0}=\begin{pmatrix} 0 & 0 \\ 0 & 0 \end{pmatrix},$$

while in the context of $\mathrm{Mat}_{1,3}(k)$, $\mathbf{0}=(0,0,0)$. (In the case of a 1 by J matrix one usually inserts commas.)

The element of $\mathrm{Mat}_I(k)$ whose entries are δ_{ij} (Kronecker δ) is called the **identity matrix** and has the standard notation $\mathbf{I}$. Thus, if $V=k^3$, then the identity matrix of $\mathrm{Mat}_k(k)$, which represents $1 \in \mathrm{End}(V)$, is

$$\mathbf{I}=\begin{pmatrix} 1 & 0 & 0 \\ 0 & 1 & 0 \\ 0 & 0 & 1 \end{pmatrix}.$$

Again one can attach a subscript, in this case $\mathbf{I}_3$, to exhibit the dimension.

Notice that a zero matrix can be "rectangular" but an identity matrix is always square.

(4.59) COROLLARY. *Let* $\mathbf{A},\mathbf{A}' \in \mathrm{Mat}_{I,J}(k)$, $\mathbf{B},\mathbf{B}' \in \mathrm{Mat}_{J,R}(k)$, $a \in k$, *and define* $\mathbf{A}''=\mathbf{A}+\mathbf{A}'$, $\mathbf{C}=\mathbf{AB}$, *and* $a\mathbf{A}$ *by means of* (4.57), (4.58), *and the final statement of the proposition. Then* $\mathrm{Mat}_{I,J}(k)$ *is a vector space over* k,

$$a(\mathbf{AB})=(a\mathbf{A})\mathbf{B}=\mathbf{A}(a\mathbf{B}),$$

$$(\mathbf{A}+\mathbf{A}')\mathbf{B}=\mathbf{AB}+\mathbf{A}'\mathbf{B},$$

and

$$\mathbf{A}(\mathbf{B}+\mathbf{B}')=\mathbf{AB}+\mathbf{AB}'.$$

Moreover, if $\mathbf{M} \in \mathrm{Mat}_{R,S}(k)$, *then*

$$(\mathbf{AB})\mathbf{M}=\mathbf{A}(\mathbf{BM}).$$

In particular, $\mathrm{Mat}_I(k)$ *is a ring whose* 0 *and* 1 *are the matrices* $\mathbf{0}$ *and* $\mathbf{I}$.

Proof

$$\alpha \mapsto R_{\mathcal{V},\mathcal{W}}(\alpha)$$

defines a bijection $\mathrm{Hom}(V,W) \to \mathrm{Mat}_{I,J}(k)$; this is just (4.34) in a nutshell. (4.57) and (4.58) are translations, via this bijection, of the vector space structure of $\mathrm{Hom}(V,W)$ into matrix notation. In other words, this bijection makes $\mathrm{Mat}_{I,J}(k)$ into a copy of the vector space $\mathrm{Hom}(V,W)$. The remaining statements of the corollary similarly are translations into matrix notation of familiar facts about linear transformations first proved in (4.36). ■

Given any two nonempty sets I, J, we can take $V=\oplus_J k, W=\oplus_I k$ with canonical bases and then obtain a bijection

$$R_{\mathcal{V},\mathcal{W}}:\mathrm{Hom}(V,W)\to \mathrm{Mat}_{I,J}(k).$$

In general, many other such bijections are possible, but they all endow $\mathrm{Mat}_{I,J}(k)$ with the same vector space structure. This is clear from (4.57) and the definition of $a\mathbf{A}$ since these definitions do not depend on which linear transformations one regards the matrices as representing. Similarly, matrix multiplication can be defined without reference to linear transformations. From this point of view one can regard $R_{\mathcal{V},\mathcal{W}}$ as a labor-saving device to give a quick proof of (4.59) and to permit us to carry out matrix calculations without necessarily thinking in terms of linear transformations.

Indeed there are many situations involving matrices where it would be quite artificial to force the matrices into the mold of representations of linear transformations. This is usually true for instance of the coefficient and augmented matrices attached to a system of linear equations, as defined in (4.7). Similarly, one may wish to discuss properties of the ring of $n\times n$ matrices over k without explicitly identifying its elements as endomorphisms of some n-dimensional space.

However, when matrices are thus divorced from linear transformations, certain points deserve clarification. If $\mathbf{A}\in\mathrm{Mat}_{I,J}(k)$ and $\mathbf{A}'\in\mathrm{Mat}_{I',J'}(k)$, then $\mathbf{A}=\mathbf{A}'$ iff $I=I'$, $J=J'$, and, with the usual notation, $a_{ij}=a_{ij}{}'$ $\forall i, j$. Also, the limitations inherent in (4.57) and (4.58) must be spelled out:

i. if $\mathbf{A}\in\mathrm{Mat}_{I,J}(k)$ and $\mathbf{A}'\in\mathrm{Mat}_{I',J'}(k)$, then $\mathbf{A}+\mathbf{A}'$ is defined iff $I=I'$ and $J=J'$, and then $\mathbf{A}+\mathbf{A}'\in\mathrm{Mat}_{I,J}(k)$; and
ii. if $\mathbf{A}\in\mathrm{Mat}_{I,J}(k)$ and $\mathbf{B}\in\mathrm{Mat}_{J',R}(k)$, then $\mathbf{AB}$ is defined iff $J=J'$, and then $\mathbf{AB}\in\mathrm{Mat}_{I,R}(k)$.

It is worth restating these restrictions for finite matrices:

> If $\mathbf{A},\mathbf{A}'$ are matrices and $\mathbf{A}$ is m by n, then $\mathbf{A}+\mathbf{A}'$ is defined iff $\mathbf{A}'$ is also m by n, and then $\mathbf{A}+\mathbf{A}'$ is again m by n.

> If $\mathbf{A}$ and $\mathbf{B}$ are finite matrices, say, $\mathbf{A}$ is m by n and $\mathbf{B}$ is q by r, then $\mathbf{AB}$ is defined iff $n=q$ and then $\mathbf{AB}$ is m by r: $\mathbf{A}_{m\times n}\mathbf{B}_{n\times r}$.
>
> inner dimensions must agree
> outer dimensions are those of the product

For instance, if

$$\mathbf{A}=(1,0)\qquad\text{and}\qquad \mathbf{B}=\begin{pmatrix}0\\1\end{pmatrix},$$

then $\mathbf{A}+\mathbf{B}$ is not defined while both $\mathbf{AB}$ and $\mathbf{BA}$ are defined. In fact, $\mathbf{AB}$ is the 1 by 1 matrix $\mathbf{0}$, and

$$\mathbf{BA}=\begin{pmatrix}0\\1\end{pmatrix}(1,0)=\begin{pmatrix}0&0\\1&0\end{pmatrix}.$$

If $\mathbf{A}$ is the m by n coefficient matrix of a system of linear equations as described in (4.7) and we define the n by 1 and m by 1 matrices

$$\mathbf{X}=\begin{pmatrix}x_1\\\vdots\\x_n\end{pmatrix},\qquad \mathbf{B}=\begin{pmatrix}b_1\\\vdots\\b_m\end{pmatrix},$$

then $\mathbf{AX}$ is defined and is the m by 1 matrix whose ith entry is $a_{i1}x_1+a_{i2}x_2+\cdots+a_{in}x_n$. Therefore, the system (4.4) can be written compactly in matrix notation as $\mathbf{AX}=\mathbf{B}$, and the associated homogeneous system (4.5) is $\mathbf{AY}=0$, where $\mathbf{Y}=(y_1,\ldots,y_n)^T$ (the T denotes **transpose**; see A9.2).

Let J be any nonempty set. A simple calculation shows that $a\mapsto a\mathbf{I}$ defines an injective ring homomorphism $k\to \mathrm{Mat}_J(k)$, and therefore matrices of the form $a\mathbf{I}$, which are known as **scalar matrices**, comprise a subring of $\mathrm{Mat}_J(k)$ that is isomorphic to k. For instance, when $J=\{1,2,3\}$,

$$a\mapsto a\mathbf{I}=\begin{pmatrix}a&0&0\\0&a&0\\0&0&a\end{pmatrix}$$

gives an isomorphism of k with the subring of scalar matrices of $\mathrm{Mat}_3(k)$.

A scalar matrix is a special kind of **diagonal matrix**, i.e., a matrix $\mathbf{D}=(d_{ij})$ with $d_{ij}=0$ whenever $i\neq j$. Thus

$$\mathbf{D}=\begin{pmatrix}0&0\\0&-2\end{pmatrix}$$

is a diagonal (but not a scalar) matrix in $\mathrm{Mat}_2(k)$. As a notational convenience one writes $\mathbf{D}=\mathrm{diag}(0,-2)$. While we are on the subject, $\mathbf{A}=(a_{ij})$ is **upper** (resp. **lower**) **triangular** if $a_{ij}=0$ whenever $i>j$ (resp. $i<j$). For example,

$$\mathbf{A}=\begin{pmatrix}0&2&3\\0&1&0\\0&0&4\end{pmatrix}$$

is upper triangular.

EXERCISES

1. Show that the set R of matrices of the form

$$\begin{pmatrix}a&b\\4a&b\end{pmatrix},\qquad a,b\in\mathbf{Q}$$

is a commutative subring of $\mathrm{Mat}_2(\mathbf{Q})$, that the number of roots of $X^2-4=0$ in R is 4, and consequently that R is not an integral domain.

2. In each of the following cases prove that the map $T: V \to W$ is a linear transformation and determine the matrix $R_{\mathcal{V},\mathcal{W}}(T)$.

(i) $V = \mathbf{Q}^3, W = \mathbf{Q}^4$, $\mathcal{V}$ and $\mathcal{W}$ canonical,

$$T(x,y,z) = (2y - 3z, 0, x, x+y+z).$$

(ii) $V = W$ is the vector space of polynomials of degree $\leqslant 3$, $\mathcal{V} = \mathcal{W} = \{1, X, X^2, X^3\}$ and $T = 5 + 3D - XD + 2D^2$, where D denotes differentiation; i.e., $T(f) = 5f + (3 - X)f' + 2f''$, where the primes indicate derivatives.

(iii) $V = \operatorname{Mat}_{2,3}(k), W = \operatorname{Mat}_2(k)$ (k any field), $T(\mathbf{M}) = \mathbf{AMB}$, where

$$\mathbf{A} = \begin{pmatrix} 0 & 1 \\ 0 & 1 \end{pmatrix}, \qquad \mathbf{B} = \begin{pmatrix} 1 & 0 \\ 1 & 0 \\ 0 & 1 \end{pmatrix},$$

and, letting $\mathbf{F}_{ij}$ denote the matrix (of appropriate dimensions) with a 1 in the ijth position and 0s elsewhere, $\mathcal{V} = \{\mathbf{F}_{11}, \mathbf{F}_{12}, \mathbf{F}_{21}, \mathbf{F}_{22}\}$ and similarly $\mathcal{W} = \{\mathbf{F}_{11}, \ldots, \mathbf{F}_{23}\}$.

(iv) $V = W = \operatorname{Mat}_2(k), \mathcal{V} = \mathcal{W} = \{\mathbf{F}_{11}, \ldots, \mathbf{F}_{22}\}$, and $T(\mathbf{M}) = \mathbf{M} + \mathbf{M}^T$ (the last T denoting transpose; see A9.2.).

(v) $V = k^4$, $W = k$, $T(\mathbf{v}) = \mathbf{v}\mathbf{u}^T$, where $\mathbf{u} = (0, 2, -3, 1)$, $\mathcal{V}$ is canonical, and $\mathcal{W} = \{1\}$.

3. **(i)** If $\mathbf{A} \in \operatorname{Mat}_n(k)$, then the centralizer of $\mathbf{A}$,

$$Z(\mathbf{A}) = \{\mathbf{B} \in \operatorname{Mat}_n(k) : \mathbf{AB} = \mathbf{BA}\},$$

is a subspace.

(ii) Determine $Z(\mathbf{A})$ in $\operatorname{Mat}_2(\mathbf{Q})$ in each of the following cases:

$$\mathbf{A} = \begin{pmatrix} 1 & 0 \\ 0 & 0 \end{pmatrix}, \begin{pmatrix} 0 & 1 \\ 0 & 0 \end{pmatrix}, \begin{pmatrix} 1 & 1 \\ 0 & 1 \end{pmatrix}, \begin{pmatrix} 1 & 0 \\ 0 & 2 \end{pmatrix}.$$

4.

$$a \mapsto \begin{pmatrix} 1 & a \\ 0 & 1 \end{pmatrix}$$

defines an isomorphism between the the additive group of k and the multiplicative subgroup of $\operatorname{Mat}_2(k)$ consisting of unipotent matrices of the indicated form.

14. ELEMENTARY MATRICES

The elementary row operations, defined in Section 3, are of three types: E_{ij}, where $i \neq j$; $E_{ij}(c)$, where $i \neq j$ and $c \in k$; and $E_i(c)$, where $c \in k^*$. They can be interpreted as acting on any matrix, as we now explain, except that we shall confine our discussion to finite matrices.

Let $\mathbf{A} \in \operatorname{Mat}_{m,n}$. The ith row of $\mathbf{A}$, denoted

$$\operatorname{row}_i(\mathbf{A}) = (a_{i1}, a_{i2}, \ldots, a_{in}),$$

can be regarded as an element of the vector space k^n. In each of the following cases $\mathbf{A}'$ denotes the matrix obtained by performing the elementary row operation on $\mathbf{A}$.

(α) The effect of E_{ij} on $\mathbf{A}$ is to interchange the ith and jth rows. Thus $\mathrm{row}_i(\mathbf{A}') = \mathrm{row}_j(\mathbf{A}), \mathrm{row}_j(\mathbf{A}') = \mathrm{row}_i(\mathbf{A})$, and otherwise $\mathrm{row}_t(\mathbf{A}') = \mathrm{row}_t(\mathbf{A})$.

(β) The effect of $E_{ij}(c)$ is to add c times the ith row to the jth. Thus

$$\mathrm{row}_j(\mathbf{A}') = \mathrm{row}_j(\mathbf{A}) + c\cdot \mathrm{row}_i(\mathbf{A}),$$

and otherwise $\mathrm{row}_t(\mathbf{A}') = \mathrm{row}_t(\mathbf{A})$, including $t = i$.

(γ) The effect of $E_i(c)$ is to multiply the ith row by c:

$$\mathrm{row}_i(\mathbf{A}') = c\cdot \mathrm{row}_i(\mathbf{A})$$

and $\mathrm{row}_t(\mathbf{A}') = \mathrm{row}_t(\mathbf{A})$ for $t \neq i$.

Thus $E_2(\frac{1}{2})$ followed by $E_{21}(-1)$ acting on

(4.60) $$\mathbf{A} = \begin{pmatrix} 1 & 3 & 5 \\ 2 & 4 & 6 \end{pmatrix}$$

results in the matrix

(4.61) $$\begin{pmatrix} 0 & 1 & 2 \\ 1 & 2 & 3 \end{pmatrix}.$$

If E denotes any one of these elementary row operations we use the symbol $\mathbf{E}$ to denote the matrix obtained by applying E to the identity matrix $\mathbf{I} \in \mathrm{Mat}_m(k)$. For instance, when $m = 3$, $\mathbf{E}_{23}$ ($=\mathbf{E}_{32}$) denotes the matrix obtained by carrying out on $\mathbf{I}_3$ the elementary row operation of interchanging the second and third rows:

$$\mathbf{E}_{23} = \begin{pmatrix} 1 & 0 & 0 \\ 0 & 0 & 1 \\ 0 & 1 & 0 \end{pmatrix}.$$

Similarly,

$$\mathbf{E}_{21}(-1) = \begin{pmatrix} 1 & -1 & 0 \\ 0 & 1 & 0 \\ 0 & 0 & 1 \end{pmatrix}, \qquad \mathbf{E}_3(\tfrac{2}{3}) = \begin{pmatrix} 1 & 0 & 0 \\ 0 & 1 & 0 \\ 0 & 0 & \frac{2}{3} \end{pmatrix}.$$

The various m by m matrices thus obtained (where m is determined by the context in any particular instance) are called **elementary matrices**. We now justify this notation.

(4.62) PROPOSITION. *Let E denote an elementary row operation, of any of the three types, and let $\mathbf{A} \in Mat_{m,n}(k)$. Then the matrix obtained by applying E to $\mathbf{A}$ coincides with $\mathbf{EA}$, where $\mathbf{E}$ denotes the corresponding elementary matrix.*

Proof. We write $\mathbf{EA}=\mathbf{B}=(b_{ij})$. First let $\mathbf{E}=\mathbf{E}_{st}$. If i is neither s nor t, then $\text{row}_i(\mathbf{E})=\text{row}_i(\mathbf{I})$; hence

$$b_{ij}=\sum_r \delta_{ir}a_{rj}=a_{ij},$$

i.e., $\text{row}_i(\mathbf{B})=\text{row}_i(\mathbf{A})$. Next, $\text{row}_s(\mathbf{E})$ has entries $e_{sr}=0$, except for $e_{st}=1$, and therefore

$$b_{sj}=\sum_r e_{sr}a_{rj}=a_{tj},$$

i.e., $\text{row}_s(\mathbf{B})=\text{row}_t(\mathbf{A})$. By the same token, $\text{row}_t(\mathbf{B})=\text{row}_s(\mathbf{A})$.

The other two types of E can be treated in a similar way; the details are left to the reader. ■

Strictly speaking, $\mathbf{E}_{ij}$ is not elementary because it is a product of "truly elementary" matrices:

(4.63) $$\mathbf{E}_{ij}=\mathbf{E}_i(-1)\mathbf{E}_{ij}(1)\mathbf{E}_{ji}(-1)\mathbf{E}_{ij}(1),$$

as is easily verified (especially in view of (4.62), which allows us to regard the products as a right-to-left succession of elementary row operations). However, we continue as a technical convenience to include the matrices $\mathbf{E}_{ij}$ among the elementary matrices.

As a numerical example, the transition form (4.60) to (4.61) amounts to the matrix product

(4.64) $$\mathbf{E}_{21}(-1)\mathbf{E}_2(\tfrac{1}{2})\mathbf{A}=\begin{pmatrix}1 & -1\\ 0 & 1\end{pmatrix}\begin{pmatrix}1 & 0\\ 0 & \frac{1}{2}\end{pmatrix}\begin{pmatrix}1 & 3 & 5\\ 2 & 4 & 6\end{pmatrix}=\begin{pmatrix}0 & 1 & 2\\ 1 & 2 & 3\end{pmatrix}.$$

The group of units $(\text{Mat}_n(k))^*$ of the ring $\text{Mat}_n(k)$ is called the **general linear group** (of dimension n) and is usually denoted $\text{GL}_n(k)$, or sometimes $\text{GL}(n,k)$. A member $\mathbf{A}$ of this group is called an **invertible matrix** and its inverse is written $\mathbf{A}^{-1}$ as usual. Another term frequently used is **nonsingular**: To say that a matrix $\mathbf{A}$ is nonsingular is to say, first, that $\mathbf{A}$ is square and, second, that $\mathbf{A}^{-1}$ exists. Put the other way, $\mathbf{A}$ is **singular** if either $\mathbf{A}$ is not square or is square but has no inverse.

Recall from (4.45) that to prove that the $n\times n$ matrix $\mathbf{A}$ is nonsingular it is sufficient to exhibit an $n\times n$ matrix $\mathbf{B}$ such that $\mathbf{AB}=\mathbf{I}$ because then necessarily $\mathbf{BA}=\mathbf{I}$ also. Alternatively, it is enough to verify $\mathbf{BA}=\mathbf{I}$. However, as we saw in A8.4(i) and the example (4.55), when I is infinite the proposed inverse of a matrix $\mathbf{A}\in\text{Mat}_I(k)$ has to be checked on both sides.

A simple but useful observation is the following.

(4.65) PROPOSITION. *If* $\mathbf{A},\mathbf{B}\in\text{Mat}_n(k)$, *then* $\mathbf{AB}$ *is nonsingular iff* $\mathbf{A}$ *and* $\mathbf{B}$ *are both nonsingular.*

Proof. If $\mathbf{A}$ and $\mathbf{B}$ are nonsingular, then so is $\mathbf{AB}$, because the nonsingular matrices form a group. Conversely, if $\mathbf{AB}$ is nonsingular, say $(\mathbf{AB})\mathbf{C}=\mathbf{I}$, then $\mathbf{A}(\mathbf{BC})=\mathbf{I}$ shows that $\mathbf{A}$ is nonsingular and $\mathbf{CAB}=\mathbf{I}$ shows that $\mathbf{B}$ is nonsingular. ■

(4.66) PROPOSITION. *The elementary matrices are nonsingular and their inverses are again elementary.*

Proof. It is clear by (4.62) that $\mathbf{E}_{ij}\mathbf{E}_{ij}=\mathbf{I}$, $\mathbf{E}_{ij}(a)\mathbf{E}_{ij}(-a)=\mathbf{I}$, and $\mathbf{E}_i(a)\mathbf{E}_i(1/a)=\mathbf{I}$. ■

(4.67) COROLLARY. *If a system of linear equations undergoes a sequence of elementary row operations, then the new system has the same set of solutions as the original system.*

Proof. As explained at the end of the last section, the system can be written in matrix form $\mathbf{AX}=\mathbf{B}$. Now if $E_1,\dots, E_t$ is the sequence of elementary row operations, the new system is $\mathbf{E}_t\cdots\mathbf{E}_1\mathbf{AX}=\mathbf{E}_t\cdots\mathbf{E}_1\mathbf{B}$. Thus, if

$$\mathbf{X}=\mathbf{C}=\begin{pmatrix} c_1 \\ c_2 \\ \vdots \\ c_n \end{pmatrix}$$

is a solution of $\mathbf{AX}=\mathbf{B}$, i.e., if $\mathbf{AC}=\mathbf{B}$, then $\mathbf{E}_t\cdots\mathbf{E}_1\mathbf{AC}=\mathbf{E}_t\cdots\mathbf{E}_1\mathbf{B}$, which shows that $\mathbf{C}$ is also a solution of the new system.

Conversely, if $\mathbf{X}=\mathbf{C}$ is a solution of the new system, then multiplying $\mathbf{E}_t\cdots\mathbf{E}_1\mathbf{AC}=\mathbf{E}_t\cdots\mathbf{E}_1\mathbf{B}$ on the left by

$$(\mathbf{E}_t\cdots\mathbf{E}_1)^{-1}=\mathbf{E}_1^{-1}\mathbf{E}_2^{-1}\cdots\mathbf{E}_t^{-1}$$

shows that $\mathbf{C}$ is also a solution of the original system. ■

15. ROW EQUIVALENCE AND ECHELON FORM

The $m\times n$ matrix $\mathbf{A}$ is **row equivalent** to the $m\times n$ matrix $\mathbf{A}'$ if there exist elementary matrices $\mathbf{E}_1,\dots,\mathbf{E}_t$ such that $\mathbf{A}'=\mathbf{E}_t\cdots\mathbf{E}_1\mathbf{A}$.

(4.68) PROPOSITION. *Row equivalence is an equivalence relation on the set* $\mathrm{Mat}_{m,n}(k)$.

Proof. When $t=0$, $\mathbf{E}_t\cdots\mathbf{E}_1=\mathbf{I}$ and $\mathbf{A}=\mathbf{IA}$, so the relation is reflexive. (Or, if one insists on $t>0$, $\mathbf{A}=\mathbf{E}_1(1)\mathbf{A}$.) If $\mathbf{A}'=\mathbf{E}_t\cdots\mathbf{E}_1\mathbf{A}$, then $\mathbf{A}=\mathbf{E}_1^{-1}\cdots\mathbf{E}_t^{-1}\mathbf{A}'$ and the $\mathbf{E}_i^{-1}$ are again elementary; hence the relation is symmetric. The relation is also transitive since $\mathbf{A}'=\mathbf{E}_s\cdots\mathbf{E}_1\mathbf{A}$ and $\mathbf{A}''=\mathbf{E}_t\cdots\mathbf{E}_{s+1}\mathbf{A}'\Rightarrow\mathbf{A}''=\mathbf{E}_t\cdots\mathbf{E}_{s+1}\mathbf{E}_s\cdots\mathbf{E}_1\mathbf{A}$. ■

In this section we shall find canonical representatives for the **row classes**, as we may as well call the equivalence classes for this relation. Thus a given matrix **A** falls into a particular row class and therefore determines a unique representative, called the **echelon form** of **A**. Of course this representative is also the echelon form of every matrix row equivalent to **A**.

If we multiply (4.64) on the left by $\mathbf{E}_{21}(-2)\mathbf{E}_{12}$ we obtain

$$\mathbf{A}' = \begin{pmatrix} 1 & 0 & -1 \\ 0 & 1 & 2 \end{pmatrix},$$

and this matrix is therefore row equivalent to the matrix **A** given in (4.60). As will be explained, $\mathbf{A}'$ is the echelon form of **A**. If we interpret **A** as the augmented matrix of the system (say over $k = \mathbb{Q}$)

$$x + 3y = 5,$$

$$2x + 4y = 6,$$

then $\mathbf{A}'$ represents the solution of this system:

$$x = -1,$$

$$y = 2.$$

We have simply recast the elementary row operations that we perform to solve the system as left multiplications by the corresponding elementary matrices.

(4.69) DEFINITION. The **row space** of the m by n matrix **A** is the subspace of k^n spanned by the m rows of **A**.

(4.70) PROPOSITION. row space$(\mathbf{BA}) \subset$ row space$(\mathbf{A})$, $\forall \mathbf{B} \ni \mathbf{BA}$, *is defined. Hence when* **P** *is invertible*, **PA** *and* **A** *have the same row space.*

Proof. $\text{row}_i(\mathbf{BA}) = b_{i1}\text{row}_1(\mathbf{A}) + b_{i2}\text{row}_2(\mathbf{A}) + \cdots + b_{im}\text{row}_m(\mathbf{A})$. ■

We let $\text{col}_j(\mathbf{A})$ stand for the jth column of **A**; this is an $m \times 1$ matrix.

(4.71) DEFINITION. The m by n matrix $\mathbf{A} = (a_{ij})$ is in **echelon form** if

(α) for some r with $0 \leqslant r \leqslant m$, $\text{row}_i(\mathbf{A}) \neq 0$ for $1 \leqslant i \leqslant r$ and $\text{row}_i(\mathbf{A}) = 0$ for $r < i \leqslant m$;

(β) for $1 \leqslant i \leqslant r$, if κ_i denotes the smallest j such that $a_{ij} \neq 0$ then $\kappa_1 < \kappa_2 < \cdots < \kappa_r$; and

(γ) for $1 \leqslant i \leqslant r$, $\text{col}_{\kappa_i}(\mathbf{A})$ has entries all 0 except for a 1 in the ith row.

Thus $a_{i\kappa_i} = 1$ for $i = 1, \ldots, r$. We call these entries **pivots**. In some books the definition of echelon form does not require (γ), the idea being that if the augmented matrix of a system of linear equations is reduced to a form satisfying only (α) and (β), then the system is almost solved. Then another term such as *row canonical form* is used to describe what we call echelon form.

Here is an example of a matrix in echelon form. The pivots are encircled.

$$\mathbf{A}=\begin{pmatrix} 0 & \textcircled{1} & 0 & 2 & -3 & 0 & 0 & 4 & 7 & 0 & 1 \\ 0 & 0 & 0 & 0 & 0 & \textcircled{1} & 0 & 5 & 0 & 0 & 8 \\ 0 & 0 & 0 & 0 & 0 & 0 & \textcircled{1} & 4 & 9 & 0 & -1 \\ 0 & 0 & 0 & 0 & 0 & 0 & 0 & 0 & 0 & \textcircled{1} & 1 \\ 0 & 0 & 0 & 0 & 0 & 0 & 0 & 0 & 0 & 0 & 0 \end{pmatrix}.$$

$$\uparrow \kappa_1=2 \qquad \uparrow \kappa_2=6 \qquad \uparrow \kappa_3=7 \qquad \uparrow \kappa_4=10$$

In this case $r=4$. The entries a_{13} and a_{29} happen to be 0, but echelon form does not require this.

We can reword this definition more informally as follows. The 0 rows, if any, are grouped at the bottom. For the nonzero rows, as one reads from left to right the first nonzero entry encountered is a 1; that 1, called a pivot, is the only nonzero entry in its column. The pivotal 1s move off steadily to the right as one moves down the nonzero rows. Thus all entries to the south and west of a pivot are 0. (*Exercise*: $\mathbf{0}$ and $\mathbf{I}$ are in echelon form.)

(4.72) PROPOSITION. *Each row class of* $\mathrm{Mat}_{m,n}(k)$ *contains precisely one matrix in echelon form. Thus each matrix* $\mathbf{A}$ *is row equivalent to a unique matrix in echelon form.*

Letting $\mathbf{A}_{\mathrm{ech}}$ denote the matrix in echelon form determined by $\mathbf{A}$, we see that two $m\times n$ matrices $\mathbf{A}$ and $\mathbf{B}$ are row equivalent iff $\mathbf{A}_{\mathrm{ech}}=\mathbf{B}_{\mathrm{ech}}$. Before going to the proof we work through the example

$$\mathbf{A}=\begin{pmatrix} 0 & 0 & 0 & 1 & 0 & 3 \\ 1 & 1 & 0 & -1 & 2 & 1 \\ 2 & 2 & 0 & 0 & 4 & 8 \\ -3 & -3 & 0 & 5 & -6 & 3 \end{pmatrix}.$$

By means of this example we shall explain the algorithm, called **Gauss elimination**,[2] by which any matrix is converted into its echelon form. That is, we shall find elementary row operations $E_1,\ldots,E_t$ such that $\mathbf{A}_{\mathrm{ech}}=\mathbf{E}_t\cdots\mathbf{E}_1\mathbf{A}$ is in echelon form. The number t and the various Es that accomplish this are by no means unique, but the final outcome $\mathbf{A}_{\mathrm{ech}}$ is unique.

[2] Some writers call this Gauss–Jordan elimination and use the term Gauss elimination for a shorter algorithm that leads to a matrix satisfying (α) and (β) of (4.71) but not necessarily (γ).

The calculations proceed from left to right, dealing with one column at a time. For this first column the procedure is as in Figure 4.4. Notice that, as in a computer program, a_{ij} denotes the *current* value of the ijth entry, after whatever elementary operations may have preceded.

In the present example this gives (we encircle the pivots as they appear)

$$\mathbf{E}_{14}(3)\mathbf{E}_{13}(-2)\mathbf{E}_{12}\mathbf{A}=\begin{pmatrix} \textcircled{1} & 1 & 0 & -1 & 2 & 1 \\ 0 & 0 & 0 & 1 & 0 & 3 \\ 0 & 0 & 0 & 2 & 0 & 6 \\ 0 & 0 & 0 & 2 & 0 & 6 \end{pmatrix}$$

$=\mathbf{A}'$, say. In the flow chart in Figure 4.4, taking the smallest i such that $a_{i1}\neq 0$ is an arbitrary choice and any i (with $a_{i1}\neq 0$) will do. For instance, here we could deal with the first column as follows:

$$\mathbf{E}_{13}(-2)\mathbf{E}_{12}(-1)\mathbf{E}_{1}(-1/3)\mathbf{E}_{14}\mathbf{A}=\begin{pmatrix} 1 & 1 & 0 & -\frac{5}{3} & 2 & 1 \\ 0 & 0 & 0 & \frac{2}{3} & 0 & 2 \\ 0 & 0 & 0 & \frac{10}{3} & 0 & 10 \\ 0 & 0 & 0 & 1 & 0 & 3 \end{pmatrix}$$

$=\mathbf{A}''$, say. The matrices $\mathbf{A},\mathbf{A}',\mathbf{A}''$ are all row equivalent and have the same echelon form. As a practical matter it is sometimes important to allow flexibility in the procedure since the numerical entries may be approximations to their correct values and the calculations themselves may introduce further "round off errors." For instance, an entry may appear as $-3/10^6$ while its correct value is 0.

However, we continue our description of Gauss elimination as a strict algorithm with no choices and with no elaborations to deal with "errors."

Figure 4.4 Gauss elimination (first column).

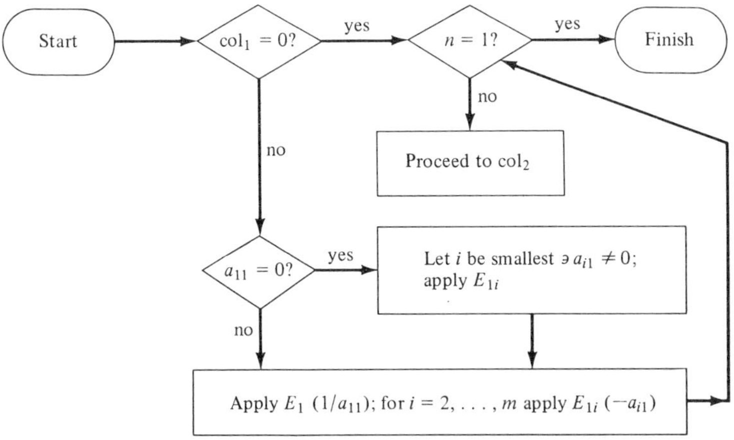

Inductively, having dealt with col_{j-1}, suppose the last pivot determined is $a_{st}=1$. (See Figure 4.5.) In the case $\mathbf{A}'$ above we have $j=2$, $s=t=1$. Since $a_{12}=0$ for all $i>1$ we pass to $j=3$, and then since $a_{i3}=0$ for all $i>1$ we pass to $j=4$. Now we find $a_{24}=1$. No adjustments are necessary; we are ready to clear out the rest of col_4:

$$\mathbf{E}_{24}(-2)\mathbf{E}_{23}(-2)\mathbf{E}_{21}(1)\mathbf{A}'=\begin{pmatrix} 1 & 1 & 0 & 0 & 2 & 4 \\ 0 & 0 & 0 & 1 & 0 & 3 \\ 0 & 0 & 0 & 0 & 0 & 0 \\ 0 & 0 & 0 & 0 & 0 & 0 \end{pmatrix}.$$

This matrix is $\mathbf{A}_{\text{ech}}$.

Proof of (4.72). Let $\mathbf{A}\in\text{Mat}_{m,n}(k)$. We deal first with the existence of $\mathbf{A}_{\text{ech}}$. We proceed by induction on n, m being arbitrary.

First let $n=1$. Since $\mathbf{0}$ is already in echelon form, we can suppose that some $a_{i1}\neq 0$. Applying $\mathbf{E}_{i1}$ if $i>1$, we see that $\mathbf{A}$ is row equivalent to a matrix with $a_{11}\neq 0$. Next we apply $\mathbf{E}_1(a_{11}{}^{-1})$ and then $\mathbf{E}_{1j}(-a_{j1})$ for $j=2,\ldots,m$. The resulting matrix $(1,0,\ldots,0)^T$ is in echelon form and is row equivalent to $\mathbf{A}$.

Now let $n>1$ and let $\mathbf{B}$ be the m by $n-1$ matrix obtained from $\mathbf{A}$ by deleting $\text{col}_n(\mathbf{A})$. By inductive hypothesis, there exist elementary matrices $\mathbf{E}_1,\ldots,\mathbf{E}_t$ such that $\mathbf{B}'=\mathbf{E}_t\cdots\mathbf{E}_1\mathbf{B}$ is in echelon form. Let r_B denote the number of nonzero rows in $\mathbf{B}'$ and put $\mathbf{A}'=(a'_{ij})=\mathbf{E}_t\cdots\mathbf{E}_1\mathbf{A}$. If $a'_{in}=0$ for all $i>r_B$, then $\mathbf{A}'$ is in echelon form and we are finished. Otherwise let $a_{sn}\neq 0$, where $s>r_B$. Then it only remains to convert this element to 1, put it in row number $r=r_B+1$, and then use it to clear out the rest of the nth

Figure 4.5 Gauss elimination (with previous pivot a_{st}).

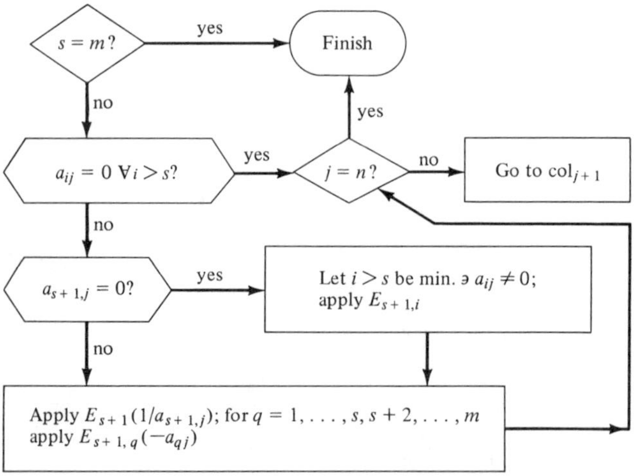

column:

$$\left[\prod_{\substack{j=1\\ j\neq r}}^{m} \mathbf{E}_{rj}(-a_{jn})\right]\mathbf{E}_{rs}\mathbf{E}_{s}(1/a_{sn})\mathbf{A}', \tag{4.73}$$

where $\mathbf{E}_{rs}=\mathbf{I}$ when $r=s$, is the required matrix in echelon form.

Note that the row operations in (4.73) do not disturb the echelon form of the first $n-1$ columns of $\mathbf{A}'$.

It remains to show that the echelon form is unique.

(4.74) LEMMA. *If the matrix* $\mathbf{A}$ *is in echelon form and has* $r \geqslant 0$ *nonzero rows, then* r *is the dimension of the row space of* $\mathbf{A}$.

Proof. By definition, the row space is spanned by the r rows of $\mathbf{A}$, so we wish to prove that these rows are linearly independent. Consider

$$\mathbf{v}=c_1\text{row}_1(\mathbf{A})+\cdots+c_r\text{row}_r(\mathbf{A})=(b_1,\dots,b_n), \qquad \text{say.}$$

Then for $i=1,\dots,r$, $b_{\kappa_i}=c_i$; hence $\mathbf{v}=0 \Rightarrow c_1=\cdots c_r=0$, as required. ■

Thus if $\mathbf{A}$ and $\mathbf{A}'$ are row equivalent, say $\mathbf{A}=\mathbf{P}\mathbf{A}'$, where $\mathbf{P}$ is a product of elementary matrices, and both are in echelon form, then by (4.70) and (4.74) at least they have a common value of r. We prove that $\mathbf{A}=\mathbf{A}'$ by induction on n, the number of columns.

The result is clear if $n=1$: either $r=0$, and then $\mathbf{A}=\mathbf{A}'=\mathbf{0}$, or $r=1$, and then $\mathbf{A}=\mathbf{A}'=(1,0,\dots,0)^T$. Thus let $n>1$ and let $\mathbf{B}$ (resp. $\mathbf{B}'$) denote the m by $(n-1)$ matrix obtained from $\mathbf{A}$ (resp. $\mathbf{A}'$) by deleting col_n. Clearly $\mathbf{B}$ and $\mathbf{B}'$ are in echelon form and $\mathbf{B}=\mathbf{P}\mathbf{B}'$. Therefore by induction $\mathbf{B}=\mathbf{B}'$ and it remains to show that $\text{col}_n(\mathbf{A})=\text{col}_n(\mathbf{A}')$.

Let the pivots of $\mathbf{A}$ occur in columns $\kappa_1,\dots,\kappa_r$. If $\kappa_r=n$, then, since $\mathbf{B}=\mathbf{B}'$, the first $r-1$ pivots of $\mathbf{A}'$ occur in columns $\kappa_1,\dots,\kappa_{r-1}$ and the rth pivot of $\mathbf{A}'$ is obliged to fall in column n. In this case $\text{col}_n(\mathbf{A})=\text{col}_n(\mathbf{A}')$ consists of 0 entries except for a 1 in row r.

There remains the case $\kappa_r<n$. From $\mathbf{A}=\mathbf{P}\mathbf{A}'$ we have

$$\text{row}_i(\mathbf{A})=p_{i1}\text{row}_1(\mathbf{A}')+\cdots+p_{ir}\text{row}_r(\mathbf{A}')$$

for $i=1,\dots,r$. Since $a_{i\kappa_i}=1$ and $a'_{t\kappa_i}=\delta_{ti}$, we have $p_{ii}=1$ and for $i\neq j$, $a_{i\kappa_j}=0$; hence $p_{ij}=0$. Thus $a_{in}=a'_{in}$. ■

EXERCISES

1. Show that $\langle S\rangle=\langle T\rangle$ in $\mathbf{Q}^5$, where

$$S=\{(0,1-1,2,4),(-2,3,1,0,4),(-5,9,1,3,16)\},$$

$$T=\{(3,-1,-5,7,8),(4,-3,-5,6,4)\}$$

by the following method. Define $\mathbf{A} \in \mathrm{Mat}_{3,5}(\mathbb{Q})$ by taking the vectors in S as its rows, and similarly use T to construct $\mathbf{B} \in \mathrm{Mat}_{2,5}(\mathbb{Q})$; reduce $\mathbf{A}$ and $\mathbf{B}$ to echelon form and discover that $\mathbf{A}$ and $\mathbf{B}$ have the same row space.

2. If the matrix $\mathbf{A}$ is in echelon form, then so is any matrix obtained by deleting a row or a nonpivotal column.

3. Find a basis for the subspace of $\mathrm{Mat}_{m,n}(k)$ spanned by the set of all $m \times n$ matrices in echelon form.

16. APPLICATIONS OF ECHELON FORM

If $\mathbf{A} \in \mathrm{Mat}_{m,n}(k)$, then the columns of $\mathbf{A}$ are the rows of the transposed matrix $\mathbf{A}^T$ (see A9.2), so

$$\mathrm{col}_j(\mathbf{A})^T \in k^m.$$

Alternatively, we have $\mathrm{col}_j(\mathbf{A}) \in k^m$ if we regard the elements of k^m as written vertically, and then they are called **column vectors**. Of course this is not a new type of vector but simply another way of writing a "row vector." However one writes the vectors, the subspace of k^m spanned by the columns of $\mathbf{A}$ is the **column space** of $\mathbf{A}$. Notice that if $\mathbf{AX} = \mathbf{B}$, where $\mathbf{X} = (x_1, \ldots, x_n)^T$ and $\mathbf{B} = (b_1, \ldots, b_m)^T$, then

$$\mathbf{B} = x_1 \mathrm{col}_1(\mathbf{A}) + \cdots + x_n \mathrm{col}_n(\mathbf{A}).$$

Hence the system $\mathbf{AX} = \mathbf{B}$ is consistent iff $\mathbf{B} \in$ the column space of $\mathbf{A}$.

One defines elementary column operations analogously to those for rows and an inspection of the equations

$$(4.75) \qquad (\mathbf{EA}^T)^T = \mathbf{AE}^T, \qquad \mathbf{E}_{ij}{}^T = \mathbf{E}_{ij},$$

$$\mathbf{E}_{ij}(c)^T = \mathbf{E}_{ji}(c), \qquad \mathbf{E}_i(c)^T = \mathbf{E}_i(c),$$

shows that elementary column operations are effected by right multiplication by the appropriate elementary matrices:

$$(4.76) \qquad \begin{gathered} \mathbf{AE}_{ij} \text{ interchanges columns } i \text{ and } j, \\ \mathbf{AE}_{ij}(c) \text{ adds } c \text{ times } \mathrm{col}_j \text{ to } \mathrm{col}_i, \\ \mathbf{AE}_i(c) \text{ multiplies } \mathrm{col}_i \text{ by } c. \end{gathered}$$

Notice that, in the case of $\mathbf{E}_{ij}(c)$, the roles of the subscripts are opposite to what they were for row operations.

Thus one has the equivalence relation of **column equivalence**, and $((\mathbf{A}^T)_{\mathrm{ech}})^T$ is the column version of the echelon form. One tends to become more accustomed to row operations and when it is necessary to put the columns of a matrix in echelon form it is usually worth transposing, then putting the rows in echelon form, and then transposing back again.

Row equivalent matrices do not necessarily have the same column space. For example,

$$\mathbf{A}=\begin{pmatrix}1 & 0\\ 0 & 0\end{pmatrix},\qquad \mathbf{E}_{12}\mathbf{A}=\begin{pmatrix}0 & 0\\ 1 & 0\end{pmatrix}.$$

However, the dimension of the column space is an invariant:

(4.77) PROPOSITION. *If* $\mathbf{A}$ *and* $\mathbf{A}'$ *are row equivalent* $m\times n$ *matrices, then any linear relation*

$$c_1\operatorname{col}_1(\mathbf{A})+\cdots+c_n\operatorname{col}_n(\mathbf{A})=0 \tag{4.78}$$

among the columns of $\mathbf{A}$ *also obtains among those of* $\mathbf{A}'$:

$$c_1\operatorname{col}_1(\mathbf{A}')+\cdots+c_n\operatorname{col}_n(\mathbf{A}')=0. \tag{4.78$'$}$$

Hence if $\{\operatorname{col}_{t_1}(\mathbf{A}),\ldots,\operatorname{col}_{t_r}(\mathbf{A})\}$ *is a basis of the column space of* $\mathbf{A}$, *then* $\{\operatorname{col}_{t_1}(\mathbf{A}'),\ldots,\operatorname{col}_{t_r}(\mathbf{A}')\}$ *is a basis of the column space of* $\mathbf{A}'$.

Proof. (4.78) is the same as the matrix equation $\mathbf{AC}=\mathbf{0}$, where $\mathbf{C}=(c_1,\ldots,c_n)^T$. If $\mathbf{A}'=\mathbf{PA}$ this implies $\mathbf{A}'\mathbf{C}=\mathbf{0}$, i.e., (4.78′). The statement concerning bases is a direct application of this and the symmetry of the relation of row equivalence. ■

(4.79) COROLLARY. *If the pivots of* $\mathbf{A}_{\text{ech}}$ *occur in columns* $\kappa_1<\kappa_2<\cdots<\kappa_r$ *(in the notation of* (4.71)), *then* $\{\operatorname{col}_{\kappa_1}(\mathbf{A}),\ldots,\operatorname{col}_{\kappa_r}(\mathbf{A})\}$ *is a basis of the column space of* $\mathbf{A}$.

Proof. The equation

$$c_1\operatorname{col}_{\kappa_1}(\mathbf{A}_{\text{ech}})+\cdots+c_r\operatorname{col}_{\kappa_r}(\mathbf{A}_{\text{ech}})=(c_1,\ldots,c_r,0,\ldots,0)^T$$

makes it clear that $\{\operatorname{col}_{\kappa_1}(\mathbf{A}_{\text{ech}}),\ldots,\operatorname{col}_{\kappa_r}(\mathbf{A}_{\text{ech}})\}$ is a basis of the column space of $\mathbf{A}_{\text{ech}}$ (not of $\mathbf{A}$), and the result follows from the proposition. ■

This gives an efficient numerical procedure for obtaining a basis as a subset of a given spanning set. For instance, let V be the subspace of k^4 spanned by $\mathbf{w}_1=(1,2,3,4)$, $\mathbf{w}_2=(0,1,1,0)$, and $\mathbf{w}_3=(2,1,3,8)$. With $\operatorname{col}_j(\mathbf{A})=\mathbf{w}_j$ written vertically,

$$\mathbf{A}=\begin{pmatrix}1 & 0 & 2\\ 2 & 1 & 1\\ 3 & 1 & 3\\ 4 & 0 & 8\end{pmatrix},$$

and we find that

$$\mathbf{A}_{\text{ech}}=\begin{pmatrix}\textcircled{1} & 0 & 2\\ 0 & \textcircled{1} & -3\\ 0 & 0 & 0\\ 0 & 0 & 0\end{pmatrix}.$$

Hence $\{\mathbf{w}_1,\mathbf{w}_2\}$ (the original $\mathbf{w}_i$, not the columns of $\mathbf{A}_{\text{ech}}$) is a basis of V.

(4.80) PROPOSITION. *The following integers coincide*:

(i) *the dimension of the row space of* **A**,
(ii) *the dimension of the column space of* **A**, *and*
(iii) *the rank of any linear transformation f represented by* **A**.

Proof. The equality of the integers in (i) and (ii) is a consequence of (4.74) and (4.79). Now suppose $\mathbf{A}=R_{\mathcal{V},\mathcal{W}}(f)$, where $f\in \mathrm{Hom}(V,W)$ and $\mathcal{V}=\{\mathbf{v}_1,\ldots,\mathbf{v}_n\}$, $\mathcal{W}=\{\mathbf{w}_1,\ldots,\mathbf{w}_m\}$. Then $f(x_1\mathbf{v}_1+\cdots+x_n\mathbf{v}_n)=y_1\mathbf{w}_1+\cdots+y_m\mathbf{w}_m$, where $y_i=a_{i1}x_1+\cdots+a_{in}x_n$. This can be written in terms of the column vectors $\mathbf{X}=(x_1,\ldots,x_n)^T$ and $\mathbf{Y}=(y_1,\ldots,y_m)^T$ as $\mathbf{AX}=\mathbf{Y}$, or

$$x_1\,\mathrm{col}_1(\mathbf{A})+\cdots+x_n\mathrm{col}_n(\mathbf{A})=\mathbf{Y}.$$

Thus $\mathbf{Y}\mapsto y_1\mathbf{w}_1+\cdots+y_m\mathbf{w}_m$ is an isomorphism from the column space of **A** to $\mathrm{Im}(f)$, and since $\dim(\mathrm{Im}(f))$ is the rank of f the result follows. ■

This integer is called the **rank** of **A** and is denoted rank(**A**). Since the m rows of **A** span the row space, $\mathrm{rank}(\mathbf{A})\leqslant m$, and similarly for the columns:

$$\mathrm{rank}(\mathbf{A})\leqslant \min\{m,n\}. \tag{4.81}$$

Continuing with the same notation, the kernel of f consists of those **X** such that $\mathbf{AX}=0$. Once again this leads to a definition independent of linear transformations: the **null space** of the m by n matrix **A** is the subspace of (column) vectors $\mathbf{X}\in k^n$ for which $\mathbf{AX}=0$. (The term kernel is not common here.) The **nullity** of **A** is the dimension of the null space. We restate (4.44):

$$\text{rank}+\text{nullity}=\text{number of columns}. \tag{4.82}$$

Since the row space of **A** is the column space of $\mathbf{A}^T$,

(4.83) COROLLARY. **A** *and* $\mathbf{A}^T$ *have the same rank*.

By (4.82), **A** and $\mathbf{A}^T$ have the same nullity iff **A** is square. The following generalizes (4.65).

(4.84) PROPOSITION. *If* $\mathbf{A}\in \mathrm{Mat}_{m,n}(k)$ *and* $\mathbf{B}\in \mathrm{Mat}_{n,q}(k)$, *then* $\mathrm{rank}(\mathbf{A})+\mathrm{rank}(\mathbf{B})-n\leqslant \mathrm{rank}(\mathbf{AB})\leqslant \min\{\mathrm{rank}(\mathbf{A}),\mathrm{rank}(\mathbf{B})\}$.

Proof. (4.70) implies that $\mathrm{rank}(\mathbf{AB})\leqslant \mathrm{rank}(\mathbf{B})$ and, in conjunction with (4.83), that $\mathrm{rank}(\mathbf{AB})=\mathrm{rank}((\mathbf{AB})^T)\leqslant \mathrm{rank}(\mathbf{A}^T)=\mathrm{rank}(\mathbf{A})$.

Now let $\alpha\colon k^n\to k^m$ and $\beta\colon k^q\to k^n$ be the linear transformations represented by **A** and **B** in terms of the canonical bases; thus $\alpha(\mathrm{col}_i(\mathbf{I}))=\mathrm{col}_i(\mathbf{A})\in k^m$. Since $(\alpha\beta)(\mathbf{v})=0$ iff $\beta(\mathbf{v})\in \mathrm{Ker}(\alpha)$, by (4.46)

$$\dim(\mathrm{Ker}(\alpha\beta))=\dim\big(\beta^{-1}\mathrm{Ker}(\alpha)\big)\leqslant \text{nullity of }(\alpha)+\text{nullity of }(\beta);$$

i.e.,

$$q-\mathrm{rank}(\mathbf{AB})\leqslant n-\mathrm{rank}(\mathbf{A})+q-\mathrm{rank}(\mathbf{B}). \quad ■$$

(4.85) PROPOSITION. *The following are equivalent for* $\mathbf{A} \in \mathrm{Mat}_n(k)$:

(α) $\mathbf{A}$ *is nonsingular*;
(β) *the nullity of* $\mathbf{A}$ *is* 0;
(γ) *the rank of* $\mathbf{A}$ *is* n;
(δ) $\mathbf{A}_{\text{ech}} = \mathbf{I}$;
(ε) $\mathbf{A}$ *can be written as a product of elementary matrices.*

Remark. We shall prove the five implications $(\alpha) \Rightarrow (\beta) \Rightarrow (\gamma) \Rightarrow (\delta) \Rightarrow (\varepsilon) \Rightarrow (\alpha)$. Then all of the 20 $(x) \Rightarrow (y)$ are consequences. For instance, $(\varepsilon) \Rightarrow (\beta)$ because if (ε) is true for $\mathbf{A}$ then so is (α), which in turn implies that (β) is true for $\mathbf{A}$. For obvious reasons such a proof is called a **cyclic proof**. A judicious choice of the order of the statements to be proved in a cyclic proof can save work.

Proof. $(\alpha) \Rightarrow (\beta)$: $\mathbf{AX} = \mathbf{0} \Rightarrow \mathbf{A}^{-1}\mathbf{AX} = \mathbf{0} \Rightarrow \mathbf{X} = \mathbf{0}$.

$(\beta) \Rightarrow (\gamma)$: $\mathrm{rank}(\mathbf{A}) = n - \mathrm{nullity}(\mathbf{A}) = n$.

$(\gamma) \Rightarrow (\delta)$: $\mathbf{A}_{\text{ech}}$ has n pivots, and since there are only n columns, $\kappa_1 = 1, \ldots, \kappa_n = n$. The definition of echelon form implies that $\mathbf{A}_{\text{ech}} = \mathbf{I}$.

$(\delta) \Rightarrow (\varepsilon)$: We have $\mathbf{E}_t \cdots \mathbf{E}_1 \mathbf{A} = \mathbf{I}$ for appropriate elementary matrices $\mathbf{E}_i$; hence $\mathbf{A} = \mathbf{E}_1^{-1} \cdots \mathbf{E}_t^{-1}$ is a product of elementary matrices.

$(\varepsilon) \Rightarrow (\alpha)$: The nonsingular matrices form a group. Elementary matrices are nonsingular, and therefore so is any product of them. ■

If $\mathbf{A}$ is a $n \times n$ matrix the numerical calculation of $\mathbf{A}^{-1}$, or the discovery that $\mathbf{A}$ is singular, can be conveniently arranged as follows: Form the $n \times (2n)$ matrix $(\mathbf{A}|\mathbf{I})$ by writing $\mathbf{A}$ and the $n \times n$ identity matrix side by side and then put this matrix in echelon form. When $\mathbf{A}$ is nonsingular,

$$(\mathbf{A}|\mathbf{I})_{\text{ech}} = (\mathbf{I}|\mathbf{A}^{-1}).$$

We leave the proof of this as an exercise. Here is a numerical example.

$$(\mathbf{A}|\mathbf{I}) = \begin{pmatrix} 1 & 2 & 1 & 0 \\ 3 & 4 & 0 & 1 \end{pmatrix},$$

$$\mathbf{E}_{12}(-3)(\mathbf{A}|\mathbf{I}) = \begin{pmatrix} 1 & 2 & 1 & 0 \\ 0 & -2 & -3 & 1 \end{pmatrix},$$

$$\mathbf{E}_{21}(1)\mathbf{E}_{12}(-3)(\mathbf{A}|\mathbf{I}) = \begin{pmatrix} 1 & 0 & -2 & 1 \\ 0 & -2 & -3 & 1 \end{pmatrix},$$

$$\mathbf{E}_2(-\tfrac{1}{2})\mathbf{E}_{21}(1)\mathbf{E}_{12}(-3)(\mathbf{A}|\mathbf{I}) = \begin{pmatrix} 1 & 0 & -2 & 1 \\ 0 & 1 & \frac{3}{2} & -\frac{1}{2} \end{pmatrix}.$$

Hence

$$\begin{pmatrix} 1 & 2 \\ 3 & 4 \end{pmatrix}^{-1} = \begin{pmatrix} -2 & 1 \\ \frac{3}{2} & -\frac{1}{2} \end{pmatrix}.$$

After such a calculation it is a good idea to check that in fact

$$\begin{pmatrix} 1 & 2 \\ 3 & 4 \end{pmatrix}\begin{pmatrix} -2 & 1 \\ \frac{3}{2} & -\frac{1}{2} \end{pmatrix} = \begin{pmatrix} 1 & 0 \\ 0 & 1 \end{pmatrix}.$$

In general,

$$(\mathbf{A}|\mathbf{I})_{\text{ech}} = (\mathbf{A}_{\text{ech}}|\mathbf{C})$$

for a certain matrix **C**, and a case where **A** is singular is immediately apparent from $\mathbf{A}_{\text{ech}} \neq \mathbf{I}$. Even in this case **C** contains meaningful information; see Exercise 8 at the end of this section.

If $\mathbf{AX} = \mathbf{B}$ is the matrix representation of a system of equations and **A** is nonsingular then the system has the unique solution $\mathbf{X} = \mathbf{A}^{-1}\mathbf{B}$. Moreover, once $\mathbf{A}^{-1}$ has been calculated, different **B** can be fed into this formula for **X**. This situation, of course, is very special and in particular requires the number of equation to agree with the number of unknowns.

Let us now apply our results to the general system $\mathbf{AX} = \mathbf{B}$ of m linear equations in n unknowns. Let $\mathbf{A}'$ denote the m by $n+1$ augmented matrix and let $\mathbf{A}_{\text{ech}}' = \mathbf{PA}'$, where **P** is nonsingular. Since the first n columns of $\mathbf{A}'$ also comprise a matrix in echelon form, we have $\mathbf{PA} = \mathbf{A}_{\text{ech}}$. We denote the common rank of **A** and $\mathbf{A}_{\text{ech}}$ by r, and that of $\mathbf{A}'$ and $\mathbf{A}_{\text{ech}}'$ by r'. As observed in (4.67), the set of solutions of $\mathbf{AX} = \mathbf{B}$ is the same as that of $\mathbf{A}_{\text{ech}}\mathbf{X} = \mathbf{PB}$. Let us denote the elements of $\mathbf{A}_{\text{ech}}$ by e_{ij} and let $\mathbf{PB} = (c_1, \ldots, c_m)^T$. When written in echelon form the first r equations are as follows:

$$x_{\kappa_i} + e_{i,\kappa_i+1}x_{\kappa_i+1} + \cdots + e_{in}x_n = c_i,$$

where $e_{ij} = 0$ whenever $j = \kappa_t$ for some $t > i$.

Now the augmented matrix has just one column more than the coefficient matrix and therefore has room for at most one more pivot; i.e., $r' = r$ or $r+1$. In the latter case the $(n+1)$th column of $\mathbf{A}_{\text{ech}}'$ consists of a 1 in row $r+1$ and 0s elsewhere; hence the $(r+1)$th equation is $0 = 1$: The system is inconsistent. In the former case $r = r'$, the ith equation for $i = r+1, \ldots, m$ is simply $0 = 0$, and the system is consistent. In fact, the first r equations, as described a moment ago, display the r pivotal x_{κ_i} as dependent variables and the nonpivotal x_j as parameters. Thus

the number of parameters in the solution of a consistent system is the nullity of the coefficient matrix.

For instance the system

$$\begin{aligned} x + y + z + w &= 1, \\ 2x - y + z - 4w &= 2, \\ 3x \quad + 2z - 3w &= 2 \end{aligned}$$

has augmented matrix

$$\mathbf{A}' = \begin{pmatrix} 1 & 1 & 1 & 1 & 1 \\ 2 & -1 & 1 & -4 & 2 \\ 3 & 0 & 2 & -3 & 2 \end{pmatrix}$$

whose echelon form is

$$\mathbf{A}_{\text{ech}}' = \begin{cases} \begin{pmatrix} 1 & 0 & \frac{2}{3} & -1 & 0 \\ 0 & 1 & \frac{1}{3} & 2 & 0 \\ 0 & 0 & 0 & 0 & 1 \end{pmatrix} & \text{if} \quad \operatorname{char}(k) \neq 3, \\ \begin{pmatrix} 1 & 1 & 0 & 1 & 0 \\ 0 & 0 & 1 & 0 & 0 \\ 0 & 0 & 0 & 0 & 1 \end{pmatrix} & \text{if} \quad \operatorname{char}(k) = 3. \end{cases}$$

In either case the last equation is inconsistent. If the third equation is changed to $3x + 2z - 3w = 3$, then

$$\mathbf{A}_{\text{ech}}' = \begin{pmatrix} 1 & 0 & \frac{2}{3} & -1 & 1 \\ 0 & 1 & \frac{1}{3} & 2 & 0 \\ 0 & 0 & 0 & 0 & 0 \end{pmatrix} \quad \text{or} \quad \begin{pmatrix} 1 & 1 & 0 & 1 & 1 \\ 0 & 0 & 1 & 0 & 0 \\ 0 & 0 & 0 & 0 & 0 \end{pmatrix}$$

for characteristic $\neq 3$ or 3, respectively. In the former case, x and y are dependent variables given in terms of the parameters z and w:

$$x \quad + \tfrac{2}{3}z - \ w = 1,$$

$$y + \tfrac{1}{3}z + 2w = 0.$$

If $\operatorname{char}(k) = 3$, then x and z are dependent while y and w are parameters:

$$x + y + w = 1,$$

$$z = 0.$$

It can be worthwhile to carry out the echelon reduction of the augmented matrix with a generalized last column. We explain this by means of the previous example in the generalized form

$$\mathbf{A}' = \begin{pmatrix} 1 & 1 & 1 & 1 & b_1 \\ 2 & -1 & 1 & -4 & b_2 \\ 3 & 0 & 2 & -3 & b_3 \end{pmatrix}.$$

The echelon form of this for the first four columns is

$$\begin{pmatrix} 1 & 0 & \frac{2}{3} & -1 & (b_1 + b_2)/3 \\ 0 & 1 & \frac{1}{3} & 2 & (2b_1 - b_2)/3 \\ 0 & 0 & 0 & 0 & b_3 - b_1 - b_2 \end{pmatrix}$$

or

$$\begin{pmatrix} 1 & 1 & 0 & 1 & b_2 - b_1 \\ 0 & 0 & 1 & 0 & -b_1 - b_2 \\ 0 & 0 & 0 & 0 & b_3 - b_1 - b_2 \end{pmatrix}$$

when the characteristic is $\neq 3$ or 3, respectively. In any case the system is consistent iff $b_3 - b_1 - b_2 = 0$, and when this condition is met we can read off the general solution immediately. The reader will have no difficulty in constructing examples in which several or no conditions are imposed on the bs.[3]

We use the above echelon form of $\mathbf{A}'$ in the char $\neq 3$ case to illustrate three further points. The simple proofs of the corresponding general statements are left to the reader.

1. The nonzero rows of $\mathbf{A}_{\text{ech}}$, namely, $\mathbf{v}_1 = (1, 0, \frac{2}{3}, -1)$ and $\mathbf{v}_2 = (0, 1, \frac{1}{3}, 2)$, form a basis of the row space of $\mathbf{A}_{\text{ech}}$ and also that of $\mathbf{A}$. The (1,5) entry $\frac{1}{3}(b_1 + b_2)$ tells us how to write $\mathbf{v}_1$ as a linear combination of the rows of the original coefficient matrix $\mathbf{A}$:
$$\mathbf{v}_1 = \tfrac{1}{3}(1,1,1,1) + \tfrac{1}{3}(2,-1,1,-4)$$
and similarly the entry $\frac{1}{3}(2b_1 - b_2)$ informs us that
$$\mathbf{v}_2 = \tfrac{2}{3}(1,1,1,1) - \tfrac{1}{3}(2,-1,1,-4).$$
2. The pivotal columns of $\mathbf{A}_{\text{ech}}$ form a basis of the column space and the entires in $\mathbf{A}_{\text{ech}}$ tell us how to write the nonpivotal columns as linear combinations of them. For instance,
$$\begin{pmatrix} \frac{2}{3} \\ \frac{1}{3} \\ 0 \end{pmatrix} = \tfrac{2}{3}\begin{pmatrix} 1 \\ 0 \\ 0 \end{pmatrix} + \tfrac{1}{3}\begin{pmatrix} 0 \\ 1 \\ 0 \end{pmatrix};$$
i.e., $\text{col}_3 = \frac{2}{3}\,\text{col}_1 + \frac{1}{3}\,\text{col}_2$. By (4.77) the same relation holds among the columns of $\mathbf{A}$:
$$\begin{pmatrix} 1 \\ 1 \\ 2 \end{pmatrix} = \tfrac{2}{3}\begin{pmatrix} 1 \\ 2 \\ 3 \end{pmatrix} + \tfrac{1}{3}\begin{pmatrix} 1 \\ -1 \\ 0 \end{pmatrix}.$$
3. We obtain the associated homogeneous system by setting all the $b_i = 0$. In this case the general solution is
$$x \quad + \tfrac{2}{3}z - \ w = 0,$$
$$y + \tfrac{1}{3}z + 2w = 0,$$

[3]See Exercise 8 at the end of this section for an alternative way of recording the information contained in the "generalized column."

where z and w are parameters. As a general rule,

> to obtain a basis of the null space take each parameter in turn, set it = 1, and set all the other parameters = 0. The solutions of the homogeneous system thus obtained form the required basis.

In this example we first set $z=1$, $w=0$, and second set $z=0$, $w=1$. The two vectors $(x, y, z, w)=(-\frac{2}{3}, -\frac{1}{3}, 1, 0), (1, -2, 0, 1)$ (written as column vectors if desired) form a basis of the null space of $\mathbf{A}$.

We restate some of the foregoing in a proposition.

(4.86) PROPOSITION. *Let the coefficient matrix* $\mathbf{A}$ *of the system of linear equations* $\mathbf{AX}=\mathbf{B}$ *have rank* r, *nullity* s, *and let the augmented matrix* $\mathbf{A}'$ *have rank* r'. *Then*

(i) *the system is consistent iff* $r=r'$;

(ii) *the dimension of the solution space of the associated homogeneous system* $\mathbf{AX}=\mathbf{0}$ *is* s;

(iii) *the system has a unique solution iff* $r=r'$ *and* $s=0$ (*cf.* (4.6)); *in particular, a homogeneous system has a nonzero solution iff* $s>0$;

(iv) *if the system is inconsistent, then* $r'=r+1$.

(v) *A homogeneous system with fewer equations than unknowns has a nontrivial solution.*

For (v), in the usual notation, $\operatorname{rank}(\mathbf{A}) \leqslant \min\{m, n\} = m < n$ so $\operatorname{nullity}(\mathbf{A}) = n - \operatorname{rank}(\mathbf{A}) > 0$. Of course the analogous statement for nonhomogeneous systems is not true. For example, the system

$$x_1 + x_2 + \cdots + x_{40} = 0,$$
$$x_1 + x_2 + \cdots + x_{40} = 1$$

is inconsistent.

In Section 2 of this chapter we alluded to the geometric objects lines and planes through $\mathbf{0}$ and stated that, for instance, a plane through $\mathbf{0}$ in $\mathbb{Q}^3$ is given by a single equation. Here is the explanation.

A **line through 0** in k^n is a one-dimensional subspace V. The next proposition shows that V can be described by a homogeneous system of $n-1$ linear equations, but not by one of fewer equations. Similarly, a **plane through 0** is a subspace of dimension 2 (the existence of such a plane of course implies that $n \geqslant 2$), and is describable by $n-2$, but not fewer, linear equations. A **hyperplane through 0** is a subspace of dimension $n-1$ and is describable by one equation; when $n=3$ this is the same as a plane through $\mathbf{0}$.

(4.87) PROPOSITION. *Let* $\{\mathbf{v}_1,\ldots,\mathbf{v}_n\}$ *be a basis of the vector space* V *and let* W *be a subspace of dimension* m. *Then there exists an* $n-m$ *by* n *matrix* $\mathbf{M}$ *such that the map* $x_1\mathbf{v}_1+\cdots\mapsto(x_1,\ldots)^T$ *restricted to* W *defines an isomorphism from* W *to the null space of* $\mathbf{M}$. *Thus* W *is described by* $n-m$ *linear homogeneous equations*:

$$W=\{x_1\mathbf{v}_1+\cdots+x_n\mathbf{v}_n:\mathbf{M}(x_1,\ldots,x_n)^T=\mathbf{0}\}.$$

W cannot be described by fewer than $n-m$ equations.

Remark. When $V=k^n$ and $\{\mathbf{v}_1,\ldots\}$ is the canonical basis, the description of W takes the familiar coordinate form. For example, a plane through $\mathbf{0}$ in $k^3=\{(x,y,z)\}$ is describable by a single equation of the form $ax+by+cz=0$.

Proof. Let $\{\mathbf{w}_1,\ldots,\mathbf{w}_m\}$ be a basis of W, $\{\mathbf{w}_1,\ldots,\mathbf{w}_m,\ldots,\mathbf{w}_n\}$ a basis of V, and

$$\mathbf{v}_j=\sum_i a_{ij}\mathbf{w}_i.$$

Then $\mathbf{v}=z_1\mathbf{w}_1+\cdots+z_n\mathbf{w}_n\in W\Leftrightarrow z_{m+1}=\cdots=z_n=0$; hence

$$\mathbf{v}=\sum_j x_j\mathbf{v}_j=\sum_j\Big(\sum_i x_j a_{ij}\Big)\mathbf{w}_j\in W$$

iff $\mathbf{M}(x_1,\ldots,x_n)^T=0$, where $\mathbf{M}$ is the $(n-m)\times n$ matrix defined by $\text{row}_i(\mathbf{M})=\text{row}_{i+m}(\mathbf{A})$, $1\leqslant i\leqslant n-m$. Hence $x_1\mathbf{v}_1+\cdots\mapsto(x_1,\ldots)^T$ gives an isomorphism $W\to$ the null space of $\mathbf{M}$, and nullity$(\mathbf{M})=m$. It is not possible to describe W by fewer equations, say $\mathbf{M}'(x_1,\ldots,x_n)^T=0$, since nullity $(\mathbf{M}')<m$. ■

(4.88) PROPOSITION. *Let* K *be a field containing* k *as a subfield and let* $\mathbf{A}$ *be a finite matrix over* k *of rank* r. *When* $\mathbf{A}$ *is regarded as a matrix over* K, *the rank of* $\mathbf{A}$ *remains* r. *The nullity of* $\mathbf{A}$ *is similarly invariant with respect to base field extension.*

Proof. The k-echelon form of $\mathbf{A}$ satisfies all the requirements of the K-echelon form and is row equivalent to $\mathbf{A}$ as a K-matrix since elementary matrices in $\text{Mat}_m(k)$ are elementary in $\text{Mat}_m(K)$. Therefore the two echelon forms are the same. Hence the rank, which is equal to the number of nonzero rows in the echelon form, is the same. It follows that the nullity, which is the number of columns minus the rank, also does not change. ■

(4.89) COROLLARY. *With* $K\supset k$ *as in the proposition, if* $\{\mathbf{v}_1,\ldots,\mathbf{v}_m\}$ *is a linearly independent set of vectors in* k^n, *then it remains linearly independent in* K^n.

For the matrix with rows $\mathbf{v}_1,\ldots,\mathbf{v}_m$ has rank m.

EXERCISES

1. Determine the rank and nullity of each of the linear transformations in Exercise 2 after Section 13.

2. Find a matrix whose null space is the subspace of $\mathbb{Q}^4$ spanned by $(2,-1,1,3),(1,0,-2,2),(1,-2,8,0)$.

3. The $n\times n$ matrix whose ijth entry is $i-j$ has rank 2 when $n\geq 2$.

4. Find examples of 3×4 matrices $\mathbf{A}$ and 4×2 matrices $\mathbf{B}$ over $\mathbb{Q}$ for which $r(\mathbf{A})$ (the rank of $\mathbf{A}$) $=2$, $r(\mathbf{B})=2$, and $r(\mathbf{AB})$ takes on each of the values allowed by (4.84).

5. Find a 2×3 matrix $\mathbf{A}$ such that $\mathbf{AA}^T=\mathbf{I}$. Give the theoretical reason why $\mathbf{A}^T\mathbf{A}\neq\mathbf{I}$.

6. Let $\mathbf{v}_1,\ldots,\mathbf{v}_m$ be vectors in a vector space over k, $\mathbf{A}=(a_{ij}),\mathbf{B}=(b_{ij})$ column equivalent matrices in $\mathrm{Mat}_{m,n}(k)$ and

$$\mathbf{u}_j=\sum_i a_{ij}\mathbf{v}_i,\qquad \mathbf{w}_j=\sum_i b_{ij}\mathbf{v}_i.$$

Then $\langle\mathbf{u}_1,\ldots,\mathbf{u}_n\rangle=\langle\mathbf{w}_1,\ldots,\mathbf{w}_n\rangle$. Thus when $m=n$ and $\mathbf{v}_1,\ldots,\mathbf{v}_n$ are linearly independent, $\mathbf{A}$ is nonsingular iff $\mathbf{u}_1,\ldots,\mathbf{u}_n$ are linearly independent.

7. Let $V=\mathrm{Mat}_n(k)$, $\mathbf{A},\mathbf{B}\in V$, and define $f\in\mathrm{End}(V)$ by $f(\mathbf{M})=\mathbf{AMB}$. Then f is nonsingular iff $\mathbf{A}$ and $\mathbf{B}$ are both nonsingular.

8. Let $\mathbf{A}$ be an $m\times n$ matrix and let $\mathbf{I}$ be the $m\times m$ identity matrix so the partitioned matrix $(\mathbf{A}|\mathbf{I})$ is $m\times(n+m)$. Show that for a $p\times m$ matrix $\mathbf{P}$,

$$\mathbf{P}(\mathbf{A}|\mathbf{I})=(\mathbf{PA}|\mathbf{P}).$$

Verify the example

$$\mathbf{A}=\begin{pmatrix}1&1&1&1\\2&-1&1&-4\\3&0&2&-3\end{pmatrix},$$

$$\mathbf{E}_{21}(-1)\mathbf{E}_2(-\tfrac{1}{3})\mathbf{E}_{23}(-1)\mathbf{E}_{13}(-3)\mathbf{E}_{12}(-2)(\mathbf{A}|\mathbf{I})$$

$$=\left(\begin{array}{cccc|ccc}1&0&\frac{2}{3}&-1&\frac{1}{3}&\frac{1}{3}&0\\0&1&\frac{1}{3}&2&\frac{2}{3}&-\frac{1}{3}&0\\0&0&0&0&-1&-1&1\end{array}\right)$$

$$=(\mathbf{A}_{\mathrm{ech}}|\mathbf{B}),\qquad\text{say,}$$

and give a general explanation of the fact that the rows of $\mathbf{B}$ describe how to write the rows of $\mathbf{A}_{\mathrm{ech}}$ as linear combinations of the rows of $\mathbf{A}$:

$$\mathrm{row}_1(\mathbf{A}_{\mathrm{ech}})=\tfrac{1}{3}\mathrm{row}_1(\mathbf{A})+\tfrac{1}{3}\mathrm{row}_2(\mathbf{A}),$$

$$\mathrm{row}_2(\mathbf{A}_{\mathrm{ech}})=\tfrac{2}{3}\mathrm{row}_1(\mathbf{A})-\tfrac{1}{3}\mathrm{row}_2(\mathbf{A}),$$

$$0=-\mathrm{row}_1(\mathbf{A})-\mathrm{row}_2(\mathbf{A})+\mathrm{row}_3(\mathbf{A}).$$

(In fact **B** amounts to a convenient bookkeeping method for carrying along a "generalized extra column" $(\frac{1}{3}(b_1+b_2), \frac{1}{3}(2b_1-b_2), b_3-b_1-b_2)^T$; cf. the example **A**′ discussed before (4.86).) Show that in general

$$(\mathbf{A}|\mathbf{I})_{\text{ech}} = (\mathbf{A}_{\text{ech}}|\mathbf{C})$$

for a certain matrix **C**. For the present example,

$$(\mathbf{A}|\mathbf{I})_{\text{ech}} = \mathbf{E}_3(-1)\mathbf{E}_{32}(\tfrac{2}{3})\mathbf{E}_{31}(\tfrac{1}{3})(\mathbf{A}_{\text{ech}}|\mathbf{B})$$

$$= \left(\begin{array}{cccc|ccc} \textcircled{1} & 0 & \frac{2}{3} & -1 & 0 & 0 & \frac{1}{3} \\ 0 & \textcircled{1} & \frac{1}{3} & 2 & 0 & -1 & \frac{2}{3} \\ 0 & 0 & 0 & 0 & \textcircled{1} & 1 & -1 \end{array}\right) = (\mathbf{A}_{\text{ech}}|\mathbf{C})$$

(hence we also have $\text{row}_1(\mathbf{A}_{\text{ech}}) = \frac{1}{3}\text{row}_3(\mathbf{A})$, and so on).

17. DETERMINANTS

If k is a field and **A** is a finite square matrix over k, there is a scalar associated to **A** called the determinant of **A**, denoted

$$|\mathbf{A}| \qquad \text{or} \qquad \det(\mathbf{A}).$$

Before stating the precise definition we discuss the idea informally.

Consider two linearly independent vectors $\mathbf{u} = (a, b)$ and $\mathbf{v} = (c, d)$ in the plane $\mathbb{Q}^2$ as shown in Figure 4.6. According to what we were taught in school, we would say that the areas of triangles α and β are $ab/2$ and $cd/2$, respectively; the area of rectangle γ is bc; and therefore the area of the parallelogram δ determined by **u** and **v** is

(4.90) $$(a+c)(b+d) - 2\cdot ab/2 - 2\cdot cd/2 - 2\cdot bc = ad - bc.$$

Figure 4.6

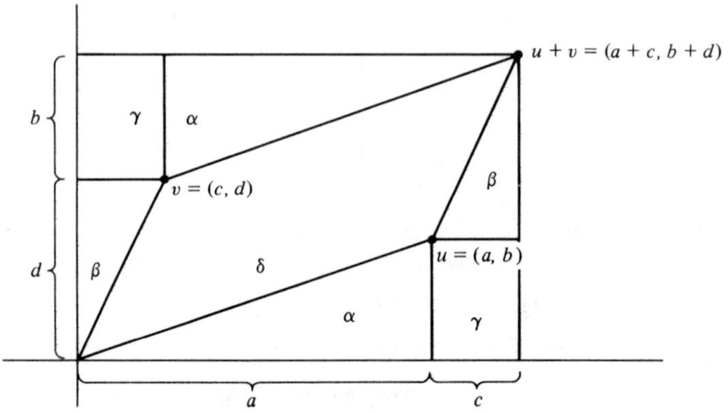

This scalar is the determinant of the matrix

$$\mathbf{A}=\begin{pmatrix} a & b \\ c & d \end{pmatrix} \tag{4.91}$$

whose rows are $\mathbf{u}$ and $\mathbf{v}$.

It is possible to perform the analogous calculation for the volume of the parallelepiped determined by three vectors $\mathbf{v}_i=(a_{i1},a_{i2},a_{i3})$ $(1\leqslant i\leqslant 3)$ in $\mathbf{Q}^3$. Assuming that all $a_{ij}>0$ and that the three $\mathbf{v}_i$ are positioned suitably (so that the calculations are not complicated by negative volumes), the result turns out to be

(4.92)

$$a_{11}a_{22}a_{33}-a_{11}a_{23}a_{32}-a_{13}a_{22}a_{31}-a_{12}a_{21}a_{33}+a_{12}a_{23}a_{31}+a_{13}a_{21}a_{32}.$$

This scalar will turn out to be the determinant of the 3×3 matrix $\mathbf{A}=(a_{ij})$.

Our intuition concerning these areas and volumes (and even higher dimensional "hypervolumes") suggests the following rules, which we state for convenience in the volume case:

(i) If $\mathbf{A}=\mathbf{I}$ then the volume is 1. (The parallelepiped "spanned" by the three vectors of the canonical basis is called the **unit cube**.)
(ii) If one of the vectors is multiplied by a (positive) scalar factor t, and the other vectors are left unchanged, then the volume is multiplied by t. This is also true when $t=0$, since then the parallelepiped is collapsed into a plane and the volume is 0.
(iii) If a multiple of one of the vectors is added to another the volume is unchanged.

We illustrate the last rule geometrically in two dimensions by replacing $\mathbf{u}$ by $\mathbf{u}'=\mathbf{u}+t\mathbf{v}$. Figure 4.7 indicates a value $t<0$. The reason that the areas of the two parallelograms are the same is that they have the same "base" $\mathbf{v}$ and the same "height," i.e., the sides parallel to the base lie in the same line passing through the points $\mathbf{u}$ and $\mathbf{u}'$.

Figure 4.7

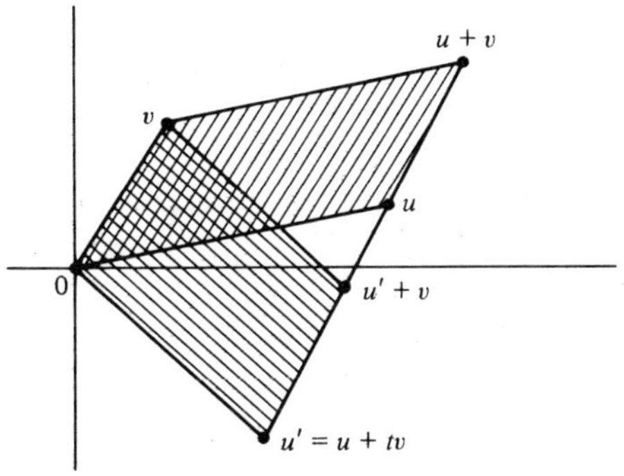

This is easy to prove algebraically: $\mathbf{u}' = (a + tc, b + td)$ and

$$(a + tc)d - (b + td)c = ad - bc,$$

which is the old value.

When arbitrary vectors are allowed, the areas and volumes calculated according to these formulas will sometimes be negative. In the definition of determinant about to be given one might consider replacing any negative value of a determinant by the corresponding positive value. But there are two reasons for not doing this. First, we wish the definition to apply to square matrices over any field, and in this generality there is no notion of positiveness. Second, even if we restricted the definition to fields like $\mathbb{Q}$ with a $\leqslant$ relation, discarding negative signs would actually complicate many of the results (for instance, (4.120)).

(4.93) DEFINITION. For a given $n \in \mathbb{N}$ and field k, a **determinant function** is a map $\mathrm{Mat}_n(k) \to k$ satisfying the following three axioms for all n by n matrices as indicated; the image of $\mathbf{A}$ under the map is denoted $|\mathbf{A}|$ and called the **determinant** of $\mathbf{A}$:

(D1) $|\mathbf{I}| = 1$;
(D2) $|\mathbf{E}_i(c)\mathbf{A}| = c|\mathbf{A}|$ for all $c \in k$, including $c = 0$; and
(D3) $|\mathbf{E}_{ij}(c)\mathbf{A}| = |\mathbf{A}|$.

When $c = 0$, $\mathbf{E}_i(c)$ is singular and not an elementary matrix, but this case is included in (D2) because we want the axioms to include the statement that $|\mathbf{A}| = 0$ when one of the rows of $\mathbf{A}$ is $\mathbf{0}$.

(4.94) THEOREM. (i) *For each $n \in \mathbb{N}$ and each field k there exists a unique determinant function.*

(ii) *The determinants of the elementary matrices have the following values:*

$$|\mathbf{E}_{ij}| = -1, \qquad |\mathbf{E}_i(c)| = c, \qquad |\mathbf{E}_{ij}(c)| = 1.$$

(iii) $|\mathbf{A}| = 0$ *iff* $\mathbf{A}$ *is singular; otherwise* $|\mathbf{A}^{-1}| = |\mathbf{A}|^{-1}$.
(iv) *For* $\mathbf{A}$ *and* $\mathbf{B}$ *both n by n,*

$$|\mathbf{AB}| = |\mathbf{A}||\mathbf{B}|.$$

(v) $|\mathbf{A}^T| = |\mathbf{A}|$.

Proof. We first prove (ii), assuming the existence of a determinant function. By (D1) and (D2), $|\mathbf{E}_i(c)| = |\mathbf{E}_i(c)\mathbf{I}| = c|\mathbf{I}| = c$, and similarly, by (D1) and (D3), we have $|\mathbf{E}_{ij}(c)| = 1$. Next, by (4.63) and several applications of (D2) and (D3), $|\mathbf{E}_{ij}\mathbf{A}| = -|\mathbf{A}|$ and therefore $|\mathbf{E}_{ij}| = -|\mathbf{I}| = -1$. Thus if $\mathbf{E}$ is an elementary matrix of any of the three types,

$$|\mathbf{EA}| = |\mathbf{E}||\mathbf{A}|. \tag{4.95}$$

We now prove the uniqueness of the determinant function. That is, if $\mathbf{A} \mapsto |\mathbf{A}|$ and $\mathbf{A} \mapsto |\mathbf{A}|'$ are both determinant functions we shall prove that $|\mathbf{A}| = |\mathbf{A}|'$ $\forall \mathbf{A} \in \mathrm{Mat}_n(k)$. For a given $\mathbf{A}$ choose elementary matrices $\mathbf{E}_i$ so that

$$\mathbf{E}_t \cdots \mathbf{E}_1 \mathbf{A} = \mathbf{A}_{\mathrm{ech}}.$$

Repeated application of (4.95) gives

$$|\mathbf{E}_t| \cdots |\mathbf{E}_1||\mathbf{A}| = |\mathbf{A}_{\mathrm{ech}}|.$$

Since $\prod |\mathbf{E}_i| = d$, say, is nonzero by (ii),

$$|\mathbf{A}| = d^{-1}|\mathbf{A}_{\mathrm{ech}}|.$$

The values $|\mathbf{E}|'$ for $\mathbf{E}$ elementary, as we proved a moment ago, must be as tabulated in (ii); hence $|\mathbf{E}_i|' = |\mathbf{E}_i|$ for each i, and therefore the value of d in

$$|\mathbf{A}|' = d^{-1}|\mathbf{A}_{\mathrm{ech}}|'$$

is the same as before. Thus we wish to show that $|\mathbf{A}_{\mathrm{ech}}| = |\mathbf{A}_{\mathrm{ech}}|'$. (The situation is perhaps slightly confused by the nonuniqueness of the **E**s. If we choose another sequence of elementary matrices $\mathbf{F}_1, \ldots, \mathbf{F}_q$ such that $\mathbf{F}_q \cdots \mathbf{F}_1 \mathbf{A} = \mathbf{A}_{\mathrm{ech}}$, then it is possible (when $\mathbf{A}$ is singular) that $\prod |\mathbf{F}_i| \neq d$. However, this is not at issue here: We choose one sequence $\mathbf{E}_1, \ldots, \mathbf{E}_t$ and use it for both $|\mathbf{A}|$ and $|\mathbf{A}|'$.)

If $\mathrm{rank}(\mathbf{A}) < n$, then $\mathbf{A}_{\mathrm{ech}}$ has a zero row and then, by (D2), $|\mathbf{A}_{\mathrm{ech}}|$ and $|\mathbf{A}_{\mathrm{ech}}|'$ are both 0. On the other hand, if $\mathrm{rank}(\mathbf{A}) = n$ then, since $\mathbf{A}$ is square, $\mathbf{A}_{\mathrm{ech}} = \mathbf{I}$; hence $|\mathbf{A}| = |\mathbf{A}|' = d^{-1}$. This completes the proof of uniqueness, as well as the first part of (iii).

The second part of (iii) will follow from (iv) since then $1 = |\mathbf{I}| = |\mathbf{A}\mathbf{A}^{-1}| = |\mathbf{A}||\mathbf{A}^{-1}|$. To prove (iv) (still assuming that a determinant function exists) we first note that, if either $\mathbf{A}$ or $\mathbf{B}$ is singular, then so is $\mathbf{AB}$ by (4.65), and then $|\mathbf{AB}| = 0 = |\mathbf{A}||\mathbf{B}|$. Otherwise, let $\mathbf{E}_i$ and $\mathbf{F}_i$ be elementary matrices such that $\mathbf{E}_t \cdots \mathbf{E}_1 \mathbf{A} = \mathbf{I}$ and $\mathbf{F}_q \cdots \mathbf{F}_i \mathbf{B} = \mathbf{I}$. By what has already been proved,

$$|\mathbf{A}| = \prod |\mathbf{E}_i|^{-1} \qquad \text{and} \qquad |\mathbf{B}| = \prod |\mathbf{F}_i|^{-1}.$$

Since $\mathbf{F}_q \cdots \mathbf{F}_1 \mathbf{E}_t \cdots \mathbf{E}_1 \mathbf{AB} = \mathbf{I} = (\mathbf{AB})_{\mathrm{ech}}$, we have

$$|\mathbf{AB}| = \prod |\mathbf{F}_i|^{-1} \cdot \prod |\mathbf{E}_i|^{-1} = |\mathbf{B}||\mathbf{A}| = |\mathbf{A}||\mathbf{B}|.$$

It is interesting to note that $|\mathbf{AB}| = |\mathbf{BA}|$ even when $\mathbf{AB} \neq \mathbf{BA}$.

We now prove (v). If $\mathbf{A}$ is singular, then so is $\mathbf{A}^T$ (cf. 4.83) and then $|\mathbf{A}| = |\mathbf{A}^T| = 0$. Next by going through the three cases we see by (ii) and (4.75) that $|\mathbf{E}^T| = |\mathbf{E}|$ for $\mathbf{E}$ elementary. Finally, if $\mathbf{A}$ is nonsingular, say $\mathbf{E}_t \cdots \mathbf{E}_1 \mathbf{A} = \mathbf{I}$, then $\mathbf{A}^T \mathbf{E}_1{}^T \cdots \mathbf{E}_t{}^T = \mathbf{I}^T = \mathbf{I}$. Hence, by (iv), $|\mathbf{A}^T||\mathbf{E}_1{}^T| \cdots |\mathbf{E}_t{}^T| = 1$ and therefore

$$|\mathbf{A}^T| = \prod |\mathbf{E}_i{}^T|^{-1} = \prod |\mathbf{E}_i|^{-1} = |\mathbf{A}|.$$

To complete the proof of the theorem it remains to exhibit a determinant function. A definition as suggested by the foregoing, $|\mathbf{A}|=0$ if $\mathbf{A}$ is singular and $|\mathbf{A}|=\Pi|\mathbf{E}_i|^{-1}$ otherwise, where the $|\mathbf{E}_i|$ have values defined as in (ii), would be most awkward to work with. Instead we define $|\mathbf{A}|$ for $\mathbf{A}\in \mathrm{Mat}_n(k)$ by induction on n, after we explain some notation. When we wish to display the elements of $\mathbf{A}=(a_{ij})$ in $|\mathbf{A}|$ we omit the matrix parentheses:

$$|\mathbf{A}|=\begin{vmatrix} a_{11} & \cdots & a_{1n} \\ \vdots & & \vdots \\ a_{n1} & \cdots & a_{nn} \end{vmatrix},$$

and we refer to this as an ***n* by *n* determinant**. But it must be remembered that the object on the right is not an array but a single scalar (which is calculated in terms of the displayed a_{ij}).

For integers i, j between 1 and n, $\mathbf{A}_{ij}$ denotes the $n-1$ by $n-1$ matrix obtained from $\mathbf{A}$ by deleting its ith row and jth column. For instance, if

$$\mathbf{A}=\begin{pmatrix} 1 & 2 & 3 \\ 0 & -3 & -2 \\ -1 & 4 & -4 \end{pmatrix}, \tag{4.96}$$

then

(4.97)

$$\mathbf{A}_{11}=\begin{pmatrix} -3 & -2 \\ 4 & -4 \end{pmatrix}, \quad \mathbf{A}_{12}=\begin{pmatrix} 0 & -2 \\ -1 & -4 \end{pmatrix}, \quad \mathbf{A}_{13}=\begin{pmatrix} 0 & -3 \\ -1 & 4 \end{pmatrix},$$

and so on.

When $n=1$ we define

$$|a_{11}|=a_{11}. \tag{4.98}$$

(In this exceptional case we would tend to write $\det(a_{11})=a_{11}$ to avoid confusion with the absolute value of a_{11}, which is discussed in Chapter 5.) Inductively, for $n>1$ we choose an i between 1 and n and define

$$|\mathbf{A}|=\sum_{j=1}^{n}(-1)^{i+j}a_{ij}|\mathbf{A}_{ij}|. \tag{4.99}$$

There is one term in the sum for each element in the ith row and accordingly this formula for $|\mathbf{A}|$ is referred to as **expansion** of the determinant **along the *i*th row**.

Actually this gives $n!$ different definitions of $|\mathbf{A}|$ since each step in the induction involves a choice of i. Let us denote the successive choices by $i_2, i_3,\ldots$ up to the present $i=i_n$, where $1\leqslant i_r\leqslant r$. Thus the total number of choices is $2\cdot 3\cdots n=n!$. We are going to show that each defines a determinant function and therefore, by (i), that these maps must all be the same. Thus for a given n by n $\mathbf{A}$, these $n!$ ways of calculating $|\mathbf{A}|$ must all yield the same value. $|\mathbf{A}_{ij}|$ is called the ijth **minor** of $\mathbf{A}$ and the signed minor $(-1)^{i+j}|\mathbf{A}_{ij}|$ is called the ijth **cofactor**.

Before continuing with the proof let us look at some examples. The general 2×2 determinant by expansion along the top row is

$$\text{(4.100)}\qquad \begin{vmatrix} a_{11} & a_{12} \\ a_{21} & a_{22} \end{vmatrix} = \sum_{j=1,2} (-1)^{1+j} a_{1j} |\mathbf{A}_{1j}|$$
$$= (-1)^2 a_{11} |\mathbf{A}_{11}| + (-1)^3 a_{12} |\mathbf{A}_{12}|$$
$$= a_{11}a_{22} - a_{12}a_{21}.$$

Expansion along the bottom row gives the same result:

$$\sum_{j=1,2} (-1)^{2+j} a_{2j} |\mathbf{A}_{2j}| = (-1)^3 a_{21}a_{12} + (-1)^4 a_{22}a_{11}$$
$$= a_{11}a_{22} - a_{12}a_{21}.$$

Thus the three numerical examples in (4.97) have the values

$$\text{(4.101)}\qquad |\mathbf{A}_{11}| = 12 - (-8) = 20, \qquad |\mathbf{A}_{12}| = -2, \qquad |\mathbf{A}_{13}| = -3,$$

and therefore the matrix in (4.96) by expansion along the top row has the determinant

$$(-1)^2 \cdot 1 \cdot 20 + (-1)^3 \cdot 2 \cdot (-2) + (-1)^4 \cdot 3 \cdot (-3) = 15.$$

The reader is invited to verify that expansions along the second and third rows also give the value 15.

We now prove by induction on n that determinants as defined by (4.98) and (4.99) satisfy (D1)–(D3). This is clear for $n=1$ and 2 by direct inspection of (4.98) and (4.100). ((D3) is vacuously true when $n=1$.) Now assume that $n \geqslant 3$ and $|A|$ is given by (4.99) for some fixed i.

Proof of (D1). Let $\mathbf{A} = \mathbf{I}_n$. Then $a_{ij} = \delta_{ij}$ and

$$|\mathbf{A}| = (-1)^{i+i} |\mathbf{A}_{ii}| = |\mathbf{I}_{n-1}| = 1$$

by (D1) in the case $n-1$.

Proof of (D2). We wish to prove that $|\mathbf{E}_s(c)\mathbf{A}| = c|\mathbf{A}|$. We must distinguish the cases $s=i$, $s \neq i$. In the former case $(\mathbf{E}_i(c)\mathbf{A})_{ij} = \mathbf{A}_{ij}$ and

$$|\mathbf{E}_i(c)\mathbf{A}| = \sum_j (-1)^{i+j} c a_{ij} |\mathbf{A}_{ij}| = c|\mathbf{A}|,$$

while in the latter case

$$(\mathbf{E}_s(c)\mathbf{A})_{ij} = \mathbf{E}_s(c)\mathbf{A}_{ij},$$

the second $\mathbf{E}_s(c)$ being $n-1$ by $n-1$; hence by induction $|\mathbf{E}_s(c)\mathbf{A}_{ij}| = c|\mathbf{A}_{ij}|$ and

$$|\mathbf{E}_s(c)\mathbf{A}| = \sum_j (-1)^{i+j} a_{ij} c |\mathbf{A}_{ij}| = c|\mathbf{A}|.$$

Proof of (D3). We wish to prove that $|\mathbf{E}_{st}(c)\mathbf{A}| = |\mathbf{A}|$. If $i \neq s$ or t then $(\mathbf{E}_{st}(c)\mathbf{A})_{ij}$ is obtained from $\mathbf{A}_{ij}$ by adding a multiple of one row to another.

Therefore by induction they have the same determinant and, by (4.99), $|\mathbf{E}_{st}(c)\mathbf{A}| = |\mathbf{A}|$. There remain two cases: $i = s$ and $i = t$.

(4.102) LEMMA. *If* $\mathbf{B} = (b_{ij})$ *is* $n \times n$ *and* $\text{row}_r(\mathbf{B}) = \text{row}_i(\mathbf{B})$ *for some* $r \neq i$, *then* $|\mathbf{B}|$, *as defined by* (4.99), *is* 0.

Proof. Define q to be $r-1$ if $i < r$ or r if $i > r$. Thus $\text{row}_q(\mathbf{B}_{ij})$ is obtained from $\text{row}_r(\mathbf{B})$ by deleting b_{rj}. By induction we can evaluate each $|\mathbf{B}_{ij}|$ by (4.99)-type expansion along its qth row:

$$|\mathbf{B}| = \sum_{j=1}^{n} (-1)^{i+j} b_{ij} \left[\sum_{\substack{h=1 \\ h \neq j}}^{n} (-1)^{q+h'} b_{ih} |(\mathbf{B}_{ij})_{qh'}| \right],$$

where $h' = h$ or $h-1$, depending on whether $h < j$ or $h > j$. As we now explain, the terms cancel in pairs, leaving $|\mathbf{B}| = 0$.

For any pair of integers $e < f$ between 1 and n, the combination $b_{ie} b_{if}$ occurs twice, once with $j = e, t = f$, and again with $j = f, t = e$. Their contribution to the sum for $|\mathbf{B}|$ is

$$b_{ie} b_{if} \left[(-1)^{i+e+q+f-1} |(\mathbf{B}_{ie})_{q,f-1}| + (-1)^{i+f+q+e} |(\mathbf{B}_{if})_{qe}| \right] = 0,$$

since $(\mathbf{B}_{ie})_{q,f-1} = (\mathbf{B}_{if})_{qe}$, these $n-2$ by $n-2$ matrices both being obtained from $\mathbf{B}$ by deleting, in the original numbering of $\mathbf{B}$, rows i and r and columns e and f. (We use here $n \geqslant 3$, but by (4.100) the lemma is also true when $n = 2$.) ■

We return to the case $i = s$ of (D3).

Let $t' = t-1$ or t, according to whether $i < t$ or $i > t$. By induction, in the (4.99) expansion of $|\mathbf{E}_{it}(c)\mathbf{A}|$ we can expand each minor along its t'th row:

$$\begin{aligned} |\mathbf{E}_{it}(c)\mathbf{A}| &= \sum_{j=1}^{n} (-1)^{i+j} a_{ij} \left[\sum_{h=1, h \neq j}^{n} (-1)^{t'+h'} (a_{th} + c a_{ih}) |(\mathbf{A}_{ij})_{t'h'}| \right] \\ &= S_1 + S_2, \qquad \text{say,} \end{aligned}$$

where S_1 contains the terms involving a_{th} and

$$S_2 = c \sum_{j=1}^{n} (-1)^{i+j} a_{ij} \left[\sum_{h=1, h \neq j}^{n} (-1)^{t'+h'} a_{ih} |(\mathbf{A}_{ij})_{t'h'}| \right].$$

Clearly $S_1 = |\mathbf{A}|$ (take $c = 0$ in the above) and we recognize S_2 as c times the (4.99) expansion of the determinant of the matrix obtained from $\mathbf{A}$ by replacing row t by a duplicate of row i. By the lemma, $S_2 = 0$.

Finally let $i = t$:

$$|\mathbf{E}_{si}(c)\mathbf{A}| = \sum_{j=1}^{n} (-1)^{i+j}(a_{ij} + ca_{sj})|\mathbf{A}_{ij}|$$

$$= |\mathbf{A}| + c\sum_{j=1}^{n} (-1)^{i+j} a_{sj}|\mathbf{A}_{ij}|.$$

The sum in the second term is the (4.99) expansion of the matrix obtained from **A** by replacing row i by a duplicate of row s and is therefore 0 by the lemma. Thus $|\mathbf{E}_{si}(c)\mathbf{A}| = |\mathbf{A}|$. This completes the proof of the theorem. ■

From part (v) we have

(4.103) COROLLARY. *Determinants can be evaluated by expansion along any column: for any j between 1 and n,*

$$\mathbf{A} = \sum_{i=1}^{n} (-1)^{i+j} a_{ij}|\mathbf{A}_{ij}|.$$

For instance, the matrix of (4.96) by expansion along the first column has determinant

$$1\begin{vmatrix} -3 & -2 \\ 4 & -4 \end{vmatrix} + 0 + (-1)\begin{vmatrix} 2 & 3 \\ -3 & -2 \end{vmatrix} = 20 + 0 - 5 = 15.$$

EXERCISES

1. Verify that the determinants

$$\begin{vmatrix} 1 & -2 \\ 3 & -5 \end{vmatrix}, \quad \begin{vmatrix} 1 & 2 & 3 \\ 4 & 5 & 6 \\ 7 & 8 & 9 \end{vmatrix}, \quad \begin{vmatrix} \frac{1}{2} & \frac{1}{2} & \frac{1}{2} & \frac{1}{2} \\ \frac{1}{2} & \frac{1}{2} & -\frac{1}{2} & -\frac{1}{2} \\ \frac{1}{2} & -\frac{1}{2} & \frac{1}{2} & -\frac{1}{2} \\ \frac{1}{2} & -\frac{1}{2} & -\frac{1}{2} & \frac{1}{2} \end{vmatrix},$$

have the values $1, 0, -1$ respectively.

2. The list $\mathbf{v}_1, \ldots, \mathbf{v}_n$ of vectors $\mathbf{v}_i = (a_{i1}, \ldots, a_{in})$ is linearly dependent iff $\det(a_{ij}) = 0$. In particular, the two vectors (a, b) and (c, d) are linearly dependent iff $ad - bc = 0$.

3. Verify (4.92) and the following *memoria technica* (in plain English, mnemonic device) for the evaluation of 3×3 determinants: write the first and second columns a second time, compute the products along the indicated diagonal lines, attach the indicated signs, and then sum the results, as shown in Figure 4.8. (Note that the analogous procedure for 4×4 determinants, where the first three columns are written a second time, cannot possibly work since there are $4! = 24$ terms in the expansion given in (4.120).)

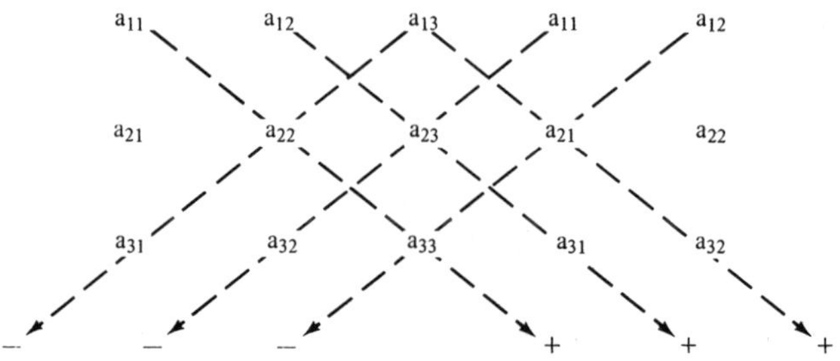

Figure 4.8 Calculating a 3×3 determinant.

4. If a_i are scalars and $a_{ij} = a_{\max\{i,j\}}$ for $1 \leqslant i, j \leqslant n$, then $\det(a_{ij}) = a_n \prod_{i=1}^{n-1}(a_i - a_{i+1})$.

5. The line joining (a_1, a_2) and (b_1, b_2) (in the sense of A7.6) consists of those (x, y) satisfying

$$\begin{vmatrix} x & y & 1 \\ a_1 & a_2 & 1 \\ b_1 & b_2 & 1 \end{vmatrix} = 0.$$

6. Let $\mathbf{A} = -\mathbf{A}^T$ be an $n \times n$ skew symmetric matrix over a field of characteristic $\neq 2$. If n is odd, then $|\mathbf{A}| = 0$.

7. Let $\mathbf{A} \in \mathrm{Mat}_{m,n}(k)$, k a field. Then the rank of $\mathbf{A}$ is the largest integer r for which $\mathbf{A}$ contains a nonsingular $r \times r$ submatrix obtained by intersecting any r rows of $\mathbf{A}$ with any r columns. (Of course, $r = 0$ if $\mathbf{A} = 0$. This version of r is sometimes called the **determinantal rank** since it is the size of the largest nonzero "subdeterminant.")

8. Let $\mathbf{M} = \begin{pmatrix} \mathbf{A} & \mathbf{B} \\ \mathbf{C} & \mathbf{D} \end{pmatrix} \in \mathrm{Mat}_N(k)$, where $\mathbf{A}$ is $m \times m$, $\mathbf{D}$ is $n \times n$, $m + n = N$, and $\mathbf{B}, \mathbf{C}$ are $m \times n$, $n \times m$ respectively.
   (i) If $\mathbf{D}$ is nonsingular, then $|\mathbf{M}| = |\mathbf{A} - \mathbf{B}\mathbf{D}^{-1}\mathbf{C}||\mathbf{D}|$.
   (ii) If $\mathbf{D}$ commutes with $\mathbf{C}$, then $|\mathbf{M}| = |\mathbf{A}\mathbf{D} - \mathbf{B}\mathbf{C}|$. (*Hint*: Replace $\mathbf{D}$ by $\mathbf{D} - X\mathbf{I}$, which is nonsingular and commutes with $\mathbf{C}$. Then substitute $X \mapsto 0$.)

18. THE ADJUGATE AND CRAMER'S RULE

Let $\mathbf{A} \in \mathrm{Mat}_n(k)$ and, as in the last section, when $n > 1$ let $\mathbf{A}_{ij} \in \mathrm{Mat}_{n-1}(k)$ be obtained from $\mathbf{A}$ by striking out the ith row and jth column. The **adjugate** of $\mathbf{A}$ is the $n \times n$ matrix $\mathrm{adj}(\mathbf{A}) = (a_{ij}{}')$ with entries

(4.104) $$a_{ij}{}' = (-1)^{j+i}|\mathbf{A}_{ji}|.$$

Note the transposition of the subscripts. To complete the definition, when $n = 1$ we define $\mathrm{adj}(\mathbf{A}) = (1)$, the 1×1 identity matrix. The adjugate is often called the **adjoint** matrix, but we reserve the latter term for another (standard) meaning; see A12.10. We have the rule

(4.105) $$\operatorname{adj}(\mathbf{A}^T) = (\operatorname{adj}(\mathbf{A}))^T.$$

Thus if $\mathbf{A}$ is the matrix in (4.96) then, by (4.101),

$$a_{11}' = +|\mathbf{A}_{11}| = 20,$$

$$a_{21}' = -|\mathbf{A}_{12}| = 2,$$

$$a_{31}' = +|\mathbf{A}_{13}| = -3,$$

and so on for the second and third columns. The following illustrates the next proposition.

$$\mathbf{A}\cdot\operatorname{adj}(\mathbf{A}) = \begin{pmatrix} 1 & 2 & 3 \\ 0 & -3 & -2 \\ -1 & 4 & -4 \end{pmatrix}\begin{pmatrix} 20 & 20 & 5 \\ 2 & -1 & 2 \\ -3 & -6 & -3 \end{pmatrix} = \begin{pmatrix} 15 & 0 & 0 \\ 0 & 15 & 0 \\ 0 & 0 & 15 \end{pmatrix}.$$

(4.106) PROPOSITION. *If* $\mathbf{A} \in \operatorname{Mat}_n(k)$, *then* $\mathbf{A}\cdot\operatorname{adj}(\mathbf{A}) = \operatorname{adj}(\mathbf{A})\cdot\mathbf{A} = |\mathbf{A}|\mathbf{I}$ *and therefore, if* $\mathbf{A}$ *is nonsingular,*

(4.107) $$\mathbf{A}^{-1} = |\mathbf{A}|^{-1}\operatorname{adj}(\mathbf{A}).$$

Proof. The ijth entry of $\mathbf{A}\cdot\operatorname{adj}(\mathbf{A})$ is

$$\sum_{r=1}^{n} a_{ir}(-1)^{j+r}|\mathbf{A}_{jr}|.$$

If $j = i$, this is the expansion of $|\mathbf{A}|$ along the ith row and therefore has the value $|\mathbf{A}|$. If $j \neq i$, we can interpret this as the expansion along the ith row of $|\mathbf{B}|$ where the matrix $\mathbf{B}$ is obtained from $\mathbf{A}$ by replacing the jth row by a copy of $\operatorname{row}_i(\mathbf{A})$, since then $\mathbf{B}_{ir} = \mathbf{B}_{jr} = \mathbf{A}_{jr}$. Because $\mathbf{B}$ has two rows the same, $|\mathbf{B}| = 0$, thus proving that $\mathbf{A}\cdot\operatorname{adj}(\mathbf{A}) = |\mathbf{A}|\mathbf{I}$. We obtain $\operatorname{adj}(\mathbf{A})\cdot\mathbf{A} = |\mathbf{A}|\mathbf{I}$ either by column expansions or, more simply, by transposing:

$$\operatorname{adj}(\mathbf{A})\cdot\mathbf{A} = \left(\mathbf{A}^T\cdot\operatorname{adj}(\mathbf{A}^T)\right)^T = \left(|\mathbf{A}^T|\mathbf{I}\right)^T = |\mathbf{A}|\mathbf{I}. \quad \blacksquare$$

Referring to the numerical example above, when $\operatorname{char}(k)$ is neither 3 nor 5,

$$\begin{pmatrix} 1 & 2 & 3 \\ 0 & -3 & -2 \\ -1 & 4 & -4 \end{pmatrix}^{-1} = \frac{1}{15}\begin{pmatrix} 20 & 20 & 5 \\ 2 & -1 & 2 \\ -3 & -6 & -3 \end{pmatrix} = \begin{pmatrix} \frac{4}{3} & \frac{4}{3} & \frac{1}{3} \\ \frac{2}{15} & -\frac{1}{15} & \frac{2}{15} \\ -\frac{1}{5} & -\frac{2}{5} & -\frac{1}{5} \end{pmatrix}.$$

It is usually easier, and less liable to error, to calculate the inverse of a matrix by the method of reduction to echelon form as explained in the last section. Generally speaking, one seeks to replace the evaluation of a large determinant by a less arduous calculation. Of course this is not always possible, and we offer a few practical hints on simplifying such calculations.

In the following let $k=\mathbb{Q}$ for definiteness. To evaluate

$$|\mathbf{A}|=\begin{vmatrix}1 & 0 & -1 & -2\\ 2 & 0 & -2 & 4\\ 3 & 5 & 7 & 11\\ 4 & 0 & 5 & 6\end{vmatrix}$$

we choose expansion along the second column since there is only one nonzero term:

(4.108) $$|\mathbf{A}|=-5\begin{vmatrix}1 & -1 & -2\\ 2 & -2 & 4\\ 4 & 5 & 6\end{vmatrix}.$$

The sign $(-1)^{i+j}$ attached to a particular minor to give the cofactor is quickly determined by keeping in mind the checkerboard

$$\begin{matrix}+ & - & + & - & + & \cdots\\ - & + & - & + & - & \cdots\\ + & - & + & - & + & \cdots\\ \vdots & & & & & \end{matrix}$$

taken as large as necessary for the matrix at hand.

The determinants of the various elementary matrices are easily remembered and the rules $|\mathbf{A}|=|\mathbf{E}|^{-1}|\mathbf{EA}|=|\mathbf{E}|^{-1}|\mathbf{AE}|$ are most useful. In other words, it is often a good idea to apply row and column operations to simplify the determinant before evaluating. For instance, in (4.108) we can remove a factor 2 from the second row by applying $\mathbf{E}_2(\frac{1}{2})$:

$$|\mathbf{A}|=-10\begin{vmatrix}1 & -1 & -2\\ 1 & -1 & 2\\ 4 & 5 & 6\end{vmatrix}.$$

Applying $\mathbf{E}_{12}(-1)$ gives

$$|\mathbf{A}|=-10\begin{vmatrix}1 & -1 & -2\\ 0 & 0 & 4\\ 4 & 5 & 6\end{vmatrix}.$$

Finally by expansion along the second row,

$$|\mathbf{A}|=-10\cdot 4\cdot(-1)\begin{vmatrix}1 & -1\\ 4 & 5\end{vmatrix}=360.$$

Next we consider a system $\mathbf{AX}=\mathbf{B}$ of n linear equations in n unknowns, where $\mathbf{X}=(x_1,\ldots,x_n)^T$, $\mathbf{B}=(b_1,\ldots,b_n)^T$, and $\mathbf{A}$ is nonsingular. The unique solution $\mathbf{X}=\mathbf{A}^{-1}\mathbf{B}$ of this system is given by the following formula, known as **Cramer's rule**. As a temporary notation we let $\mathbf{A}_i$ denote the $n\times n$ matrix obtained from $\mathbf{A}$ by replacing its ith column by $\mathbf{B}$. Then

(4.109) $$x_i=|\mathbf{A}_i|/|\mathbf{A}|.$$

Proof. By the previous proposition, $\mathbf{X} = |\mathbf{A}|^{-1}\mathrm{adj}(\mathbf{A})\mathbf{B}$. Hence

$$x_i = |\mathbf{A}|^{-1}\left[(-1)^{1+i}|\mathbf{A}_{1i}|b_1 + (-1)^{2+i}|\mathbf{A}_{2i}|b_2 + \cdots\right],$$

which we recognize as $|\mathbf{A}|^{-1}$ times the expansion along the ith row of $|\mathbf{A}_i|$. ∎

For instance, the coefficient matrix of

$$x + 2y = 3,$$
$$4x + 5y = 6$$

has determinant

$$\begin{vmatrix} 1 & 2 \\ 4 & 5 \end{vmatrix} = -3$$

and, when $\mathrm{char}(k) \neq 3$, the system has the unique solution

$$x = \begin{vmatrix} 3 & 2 \\ 6 & 5 \end{vmatrix} \Big/ (-3) = 3/(-3) = -1,$$

$$y = \begin{vmatrix} 1 & 3 \\ 4 & 6 \end{vmatrix} \Big/ (-3) = -6/(-3) = 2.$$

EXERCISES

1. Calculate A, adj(A), and $\mathbf{A}^{-1}$ when $k = \mathbb{Q}$ and

$$\mathbf{A} = \begin{pmatrix} 1 & 2 & 3 \\ 2 & 3 & 1 \\ 3 & 1 & 2 \end{pmatrix}, \quad \begin{pmatrix} 1 & 1 & 1 & 1 \\ 1 & 0 & 0 & 1 \\ 1 & 0 & 1 & 0 \\ 1 & 1 & 0 & 0 \end{pmatrix}.$$

2. If $\mathbf{A} \in \mathrm{Mat}_n(k)$, then $\mathrm{rank}(\mathrm{adj}(\mathbf{A})) = 0, 1$, or n.

3. Solve the following systems by Cramer's rule:
   (i) $x + y + z = 1,$
   $2x - 3y + 4z = 0,$
   $3x - 2y + z = 0.$
   (ii) As in (i) but with the right-hand sides 1,2,3.
   (iii) $2x + 3y \equiv 4 \mod 13.$
   $-5x + 2y \equiv 2 \mod 13.$

19. PERMUTATIONS

Let E be a set. As explained in Section 6 of Chapter 3, the group of units $(E^E)^*$ in the monoid E^E of all maps $E \to E$ consists of the bijections. This group is called the **symmetric group** and is denoted $\mathrm{Sym}(E)$. These self-bijections are also called **permutations** of E. There is a connection between permutations and determinants that will be explained later in this section.

We first give some basic *combinatorial* (or counting) results and then describe the cyclic notation for permutations.

When E is the finite set $\{1,2,\ldots,n\}$ we write Sym(n) for the symmetric group.

(4.110) PROPOSITION. $|\text{Sym}(n)| = n!$. *More generally, if* $|X| = |Y| = n$ *then the number of bijections* $\sigma\colon X \to Y$ *is* $n!$.

Proof by induction on n. The statement is obviously true when $n = 1$. (We could even start the induction at $n = 0$ since there is exactly $0! = 1$ map $\varnothing \to \varnothing$ and that map is a bijection!) Assuming the result for $n-1$, we pick an $x \in X$ and partition the set S of bijections $\sigma\colon X \to Y$ into the mutually disjoint subsets $S_y = \{\sigma : \sigma(x) = y\}$, one for each $y \in Y$. Now, for $\sigma \in S_y$, $x' \mapsto \sigma(x')$ defines a bijection $\bar{\sigma}\colon X\backslash\{x\} \to Y\backslash\{y\}$ and $\sigma \mapsto \bar{\sigma}$ sets up a bijection between S_y and the set S' of bijections $X\backslash\{x\} \to Y\backslash\{y\}$. By induction, $|S_y| = |S'| = (n-1)!$, $\forall y \in Y$. Since there are n ys, by A3.3, $|S| = |\amalg S_y| = n\cdot(n-1)! = n!$ ■

The term *permutation* is also used in the following slightly different sense. If E is a set of n elements and k is a natural number $\leqslant n$, then a **permutation on E, k elements at a time** is an injection $f\colon\{1,\ldots,k\} \to E$. We can regard $f = (f(1),\ldots,f(k)) \in E^k$ and the number of such f is denoted ${}_nP_k$. We define ${}_nP_0 = 1$. (There is exactly one $f\colon \varnothing \to E$.)

A subset of k elements of E in certain contexts is called a **combination of E, k elements at a time**, and the number of these is denoted ${}_nC_k$. Thus ${}_nC_0 = 1$.

(4.111) PROPOSITION.

$$ {}_nP_k = k!\binom{n}{k} = n(n-1)\cdots(n-k+1) \qquad \textit{and} \qquad {}_nC_k = \binom{n}{k}. $$

Proof. The formulas are correct when $k = 0$, so we can assume that $k > 0$. To count the number of $f = (f(1),\ldots,f(k))$ we count the number of ways of choosing successively $f(1), f(2),\ldots$. There are n choices for $f(1)$: any one of the n elements of E. Having chosen $f(1)$, there are $n-1$ possibilities left for $f(2)$ and so on down to $f(k)$, for which there are $n-k+1$ possibilities. Therefore the total number of possibilities is ${}_nP_k = n(n-1)\cdots(n-k+1)$.

To each permutation (k at a time) $f = (f(1),\ldots,f(k))$ we can associate the combination $F = \{f(1),\ldots,f(k)\}$. It remains to show that if X is the set of such f associated to a given F, then $|X| = k!$. Let us choose a particular $f_1 = (f_1(1),\ldots) \in X$ and let $f \in X$. Then $f_1(i) \mapsto f(i)$ defines a permutation σ_f on F. Conversely, if $\sigma \in \text{Sym}(F)$, then $(\sigma(f_1(1)),\ldots,\sigma(f_1(k))) \in X$ and $f \mapsto \sigma_f$ defines a bijection $X \to \text{Sym}(F)$. Hence $|X| = |\text{Sym}(F)| = k!$. ■

For another combinatorial interpretation of the binomial coefficient $\binom{n}{k}$, see (5.173).

There is a special compact notation used for elements $\sigma \in \mathrm{Sym}(n)$ that we explain by means of the example

$$\sigma = (3428)(57) \in \mathrm{Sym}(8).$$

Reading from left to right, the fact that 3 is followed by 4 means, by definition, that $\sigma(4) = 3$. Next, since 2 follows 4 we have $\sigma(2) = 4$, and similarly $\sigma(8) = 2$. The parentheses tell us that $\sigma(3) = 8$, as we now explain.

Each set of symbols enclosed in parentheses is called a **cycle** and is to be read cyclically as though it were wrapped around and the ends joined to make a loop. Thus (3428) becomes

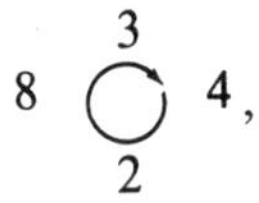

which is to be read clockwise. Thus (3428) = (4283) = (2834) = (8342), but this cycle is *not* the same as (3482).

The second cycle (57) in σ carries the information $\sigma(7) = 5$ and $\sigma(5) = 7$. Again, (57) = (75). The remaining symbols 1 and 6 are not explicitly mentioned and the interpretation of their absence is $\sigma(1) = 1$ and $\sigma(6) = 6$. If it is necessary to make clear what symbols are involved, one can write

$$\sigma = (1)(3428)(57)(6).$$

The order in which the cycles are written does not matter since they are *disjoint*, i.e., do not have symbols in common. For instance,

$$\sigma = (57)(3428),$$

since this carries the same information as before.

Let us take an example where we are given the bijection and wish to write it in cyclic notation, say $\tau \in \mathrm{Sym}(8)$, as in the accompanying table. We begin by choosing any symbol, say 1, and then build up the cycle until it closes on itself. The cycle begins (13 since $\tau(3) = 1$. Next we have (132 since $\tau(2) = 3$. Now the cycle closes because $\tau(1) = 2$. We start the next cycle with any symbol not yet accounted for, say 4: (132) (4 leads to (132)(46). Finally, (132)(46)(5 leads to

$$\tau = (132)(46)(578).$$

x	1	2	3	4	5	6	7	8
$\tau(x)$	2	3	1	6	8	4	5	7

In view of the way we have defined cyclic notation and the fact that in the composition of maps we read the factors right to left (e.g., if $\tau(c) = b$ and $\sigma(b) = a$, then $(\sigma\tau)(c) = a$), we multiply permutations according to the following scheme:

$$\overbrace{\cdots(\cdots ab\cdots)\cdots}^{\sigma}\ \overbrace{\cdots(\cdots bc\cdots)\cdots}^{\tau} = \overbrace{\cdots(\cdots ac\cdots)\cdots}^{\sigma\tau}.$$

Let us write "$a \leftarrow b \leftarrow c$ so $a \leftarrow c$" as short for "$\sigma(b)=a$ and $\tau(c)=b$ so $\sigma\tau(c)=a$." For example, to write

$$\sigma\tau=(3428)(57)(132)(46)(578)$$

as a product of disjoint cycles, we can begin with the symbol 1 and follow it through from left to right as indicated in the scheme above: $1 \leftarrow 1 \leftarrow 3$ so $1 \leftarrow 3$; next, $3 \leftarrow 4 \leftarrow 6$ so $3 \leftarrow 6$; next, $6 \leftarrow 6 \leftarrow 4$ so $6 \leftarrow 4$; then $4 \leftarrow 2 \leftarrow 1$ so $4 \leftarrow 1$; and this signals the end of the cycle (1364). Starting with another symbol, say 2, we have

$$\begin{aligned} 2 \leftarrow 8 \leftarrow 5 \quad &\text{so} \quad 2 \leftarrow 5; \\ 5 \leftarrow 7 \leftarrow 8 \quad &\text{so} \quad 5 \leftarrow 8; \\ 8 \leftarrow 3 \leftarrow 2 \quad &\text{so} \quad 8 \leftarrow 2; \end{aligned}$$

and end of cycle. The only symbol not yet accounted for is 7, which must therefore occur in the "unicycle" (7). (Indeed, $7 \leftarrow 5 \leftarrow 7$; hence $7 \leftarrow 7$.) Thus

$$\sigma\tau=(1364)(258).$$

Notice that the juxtaposition of the cycles is actually multiplication: If $\eta=(1364)$ and $\xi=(258)$, then the above permutation is $\eta\xi$. It is also $\xi\eta$, exemplifying the general rule that *disjoint cycles commute*. (*Exercise*: $\tau\sigma=(1462)(387)$.)

More generally, to write a product of several permutations as a product of disjoint cycles, for instance,

$$\psi=(12)(13)(432)(5231)(12),$$

follow through the combined effect of the various maps, reading left to right, as follows (for clarity we write an arrow for each cycle): $1 \leftarrow 2 \leftarrow 2 \leftarrow 4 \leftarrow 4 \leftarrow 4$, so $1 \leftarrow 4$; $4 \leftarrow 4 \leftarrow 4 \leftarrow 3 \leftarrow 1 \leftarrow 2$, so $4 \leftarrow 2$; and so on. The final result is

$$\psi=(14235).$$

A permutation such as ψ that can be written as a single cycle is called a **cyclic permutation**, and one of length 2 such as (25) is also called a **transposition.**

Since the group inverse of a permutation is just the inverse map, we have, for instance,

$$(3428)^{-1}=(8243),$$

and in general, using (3.18),

$$[(a_1\cdots a_s)\cdots(b_1\cdots b_t)]^{-1}=(b_t\cdots b_1)\cdots(a_s\cdots a_1).$$

Notice that a transposition $(ab)=(ba)$ is its own inverse.

The factorization of a given $\sigma\in\mathrm{Sym}(n)$ into disjoint cycles is unique apart from trivial variations (order of the factors, presence or absence of cycles of length 1, and the different ways of writing each cycle). This is so because each symbol a, such that $a \neq \sigma(a)$, is preceded, in the cyclic sense, by $\sigma(a)$ (alternatively, is followed by $\sigma^{-1}(a)$). If we had two truly different factorizations of some σ there would be a symbol a followed by b in one factorization and by $c \neq b$ in the other. However, this is not possible because $\sigma^{-1}(a)$ has only one value.

Every cycle of length >1 can be written as a product of transpositions:

$$(a_1 a_2 \cdots a_m) = (a_1 a_2)(a_1 a_3) \cdots (a_1 a_m).$$

For instance, $(123) = (12)(13)$ and $(4567) = (45)(46)(47)$. Thus every permutation can be written as a product of transpositions. For example,

$$\rho = (123)(4567)(89) = (12)(13)(45)(46)(47)(89).$$

This factorization is by no means unique; even the number of transpositions is not fixed:

$$\rho = (14)(24)(34)(18)(58)(68)(78)(19)(18)(14),$$

and it is easy to devise many other factorizations of ρ into transpositions. However, among all such factorizations of a given permutation there is an invariant: the **parity** (the evenness or oddness) of the number of transpositions. The factorizations of ρ above involve six and ten transpositions. Both these numbers are even, and the following proposition guarantees that we can never succeed in writing this particular ρ as a product of an odd number of transpositions.

(4.112) PROPOSITION. *If the permutation $\rho \in \mathrm{Sym}(n)$ is written as a product of s transpositions and also as a product of t transpositions then* $s \equiv t \bmod 2$.

Proof. We let the permutations in $\mathrm{Sym}(n)$ act on the identity matrix $\mathbf{I} \in \mathrm{Mat}_n(\mathbf{Q})$ by permuting its rows. Thus (12) interchanges rows 1 and 2, while (123) replaces row 1 by row 2 (since $1 \leftarrow 2$), row 2 by row 3, and row 3 by row 1. When $n = 3$ the result of (123) acting on $\mathbf{I}$ is the matrix

$$\tilde{\sigma} = \begin{pmatrix} 0 & 1 & 0 \\ 0 & 0 & 1 \\ 1 & 0 & 0 \end{pmatrix}. \tag{4.113}$$

The proper explanation of this is the following.

We define $\mathrm{Sym}(n) \to \mathrm{GL}_n(\mathbf{Q})$, using the notation $\sigma \mapsto \tilde{\sigma} = (\tilde{\sigma}_{ij})$, by

$$\tilde{\sigma}_{ij} = \begin{cases} 0 & \text{if } \sigma(j) \neq i, \\ 1 & \text{if } \sigma(j) = i. \end{cases} \tag{4.114}$$

If σ is a transposition, say (rs), then $\tilde{\sigma} = \mathbf{E}_{rs}$; hence $|\tilde{\sigma}| = -1$. This map is a group homomorphism; i.e.,

$$\widetilde{\sigma\tau} = \tilde{\sigma}\tilde{\tau}$$

for all σ, $\tau \in \mathrm{Sym}(n)$. This is because the ijth entry of $\tilde{\sigma}\tilde{\tau}$ is

$$\sum_{r=1}^{n} \tilde{\sigma}_{ir}\tilde{\tau}_{rj},$$

which is 1 if $\sigma(r)=1$ and $\tau(j)=r$ for some r, i.e., if $\sigma\tau(j)=i$, and 0 otherwise. This coincides with the ijth entry of $\widetilde{\sigma\tau}$.

Hence if $\rho=\tau_1\cdots\tau_s$, where the τ_i are transpositions, then

$$|\tilde{\rho}|=|\tilde{\tau}_1\cdots\tilde{\tau}_s|=|\tilde{\tau}_1|\cdots|\tilde{\tau}_s|=(-1)^s.$$

If also $\rho=\tau_1'\cdots\tau_t'$ so that $|\tilde{\rho}|=(-1)^t$, then $(-1)^s=(-1)^t$; hence $s\equiv t \bmod 2$. ■

It is clear from (4.114) that the permuation σ can be recovered from the matrix $\tilde{\sigma}$; in other words, the homomorphism $\sigma\mapsto\tilde{\sigma}$ is injective. It is also clear that for every field k the same formula serves to define an injective group homomorphism

$$\mathrm{Sym}(n)\to \mathrm{GL}_n(k).$$

(For the purpose of proving the proposition, we need the implication $(-1)^s=(-1)^t \Rightarrow s\equiv t \bmod 2$, so we can use any field of characteristic $\neq 2$. We took $k=\mathbf{Q}$ for definiteness.)

Matrices of the form $\tilde{\sigma}$ are called **permutation matrices**. They are easily recognized by the property that each row and each column contains precisely one 1, the other entries being 0. They form a subgroup of $\mathrm{GL}_n(k)$ isomorphic to $\mathrm{Sym}(n)$. An easy consequence of (4.114) is

$$\widetilde{\sigma^{-1}}=\tilde{\sigma}^{-1}=\tilde{\sigma}^T. \tag{4.115}$$

For instance, for the matrix of (4.113),

$$\widetilde{(123)^{-1}}=\widetilde{(132)}=\widetilde{(123)}^T=\begin{pmatrix}0&0&1\\1&0&0\\0&1&0\end{pmatrix}.$$

Permutation matrices are orthogonal according to the

(4.116) DEFINITION. A nonsingular matrix $\mathbf{A}$ is **orthogonal** if $\mathbf{A}^{-1}=\mathbf{A}^T$.

If $\mathbf{A}$ and $\mathbf{B}$ are orthogonal then

$$(\mathbf{AB})(\mathbf{AB})^T=\mathbf{ABB}^T\mathbf{A}^T=\mathbf{ABB}^{-1}\mathbf{A}^{-1}=\mathbf{I},$$

so $\mathbf{AB}$ is also orthogonal; also $\mathbf{A}^{-1}(\mathbf{A}^{-1})^T=\mathbf{A}^{-1}(\mathbf{A}^T)^{-1}=\mathbf{A}^{-1}\mathbf{A}=\mathbf{I}$, and of course $\mathbf{I}^{-1}=\mathbf{I}^T$. Thus the orthogonal matrices form a subgroup of $\mathrm{GL}_n(k)$, which we denote $\mathrm{OG}_n(k)$, in turn containing the permutation matrices as a subgroup.

$$\begin{pmatrix} \frac{3}{5} & \frac{4}{5} \\ -\frac{4}{5} & \frac{3}{5} \end{pmatrix}$$

is an example of an orthogonal matrix that is not a permutation matrix.

If $\mathbf{A}$ is orthogonal, then $1=|\mathbf{I}|=|\mathbf{A}\mathbf{A}^T|=|\mathbf{A}||\mathbf{A}^T|=|\mathbf{A}|^2$, so $|\mathbf{A}|=\pm 1$. (± 1 are the only roots of the polynomial $X^2-1=(X-1)(X+1)$ in any field; in characteristic 2 they coincide.)

We define the **sign** of a permutation σ to be the determinant

(4.117) $$\operatorname{sgn}(\sigma)=|\tilde{\sigma}|=\pm 1.$$

(For definiteness we regard $\tilde{\sigma}\in \mathrm{GL}_n(\mathbb{Q})$.) Thus $\operatorname{sgn}(\sigma)=1$ means that whenever σ is written as a product of transpositions there will always be an even number of them; we then call σ an **even** permutation. The identity permutation is even. Similarly σ is **odd** when $\operatorname{sgn}(\sigma)=-1$. Every transposition is odd. Since both maps $\sigma\mapsto\tilde{\sigma}$ and $\tilde{\sigma}\mapsto|\tilde{\sigma}|$ preserve products, we have

$$\operatorname{sgn}(\sigma\tau)=\operatorname{sgn}(\sigma)\operatorname{sgn}(\tau), \qquad \operatorname{sgn}(\sigma^{-1})=\operatorname{sgn}(\sigma).$$

Thus the even permutations form a subgroup of $\mathrm{Sym}(n)$. It is called the **alternating group** and is denoted $\mathrm{Alt}(n)$. The first four cases are as in the accompanying table.

n	$\mathrm{Alt}(n)$	Odd permutations in $\mathrm{Sym}(n)$
1	1	none
2	1	(12)
3	1,(123),(132)	(12),(13),(23)
4	1,(123),(132),(124),(142) (134),(143),(234),(243), (12)(34),(13)(24),(14)(23)	(12),(13),(14),(23),(24), (34),(1234),(1243),(1324), (1342),(1423),(1432)

If σ is an even permutation, say $\sigma=(a_1b_1)(a_2b_2)\cdots(a_{2m}b_{2m})$, then $\sigma(12)=(a_1b_1)\cdots(a_{2m}b_{2m})(12)$ is odd. Conversely (when $n\geqslant 2$), every odd permutation $\tau\in\mathrm{Sym}(n)$ can be written in the form $\tau=\tau(12)(12)$, where $\tau(12)$ is even. Thus, when $n\geqslant 2$ there are $n!/2$ even permutations and the same number of odd permutations. In the notation of A6.1,

(4.118) $$(\mathrm{Sym}(n)\colon \mathrm{Alt}(n))=2 \qquad (n\geqslant 2).$$

Plainly (12) can be replaced by any other transposition:

(4.119) $$\mathrm{Sym}(n)=\mathrm{Alt}(n)\amalg\mathrm{Alt}(n)(ij) \qquad (n\geqslant 2).$$

There is one more group we should define: the **special linear group** $\mathrm{SL}_n(k)$, which is the subgroup of $\mathrm{GL}_n(k)$ consisting of those $\mathbf{A}$ with $|\mathbf{A}|=1$. To summarize, we have the arrangement of subgroups shown in Figure 4.9. In characteristic 2, SL slips into a position between OG and GL.

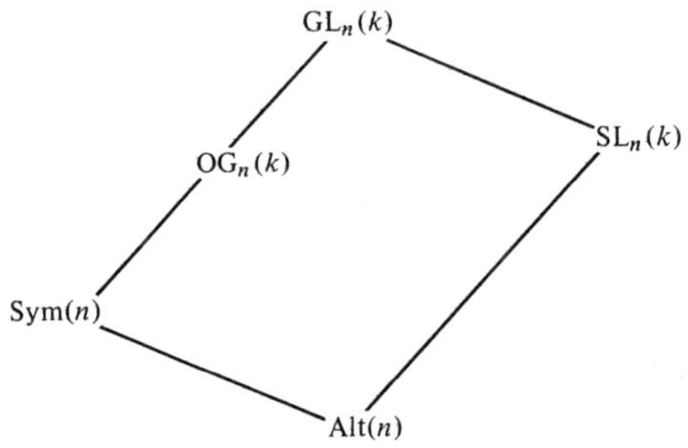

Figure 4.9

We come now to the main connection between permutations and determinants.

(4.120) PROPOSITION. *If* $\mathbf{A} \in \mathrm{Mat}_n(k)$, *then*

$$|\mathbf{A}| = \sum_{\sigma \in \mathrm{Sym}(n)} \mathrm{sgn}(\sigma) a_{1\sigma(1)} a_{2\sigma(2)} \cdots a_{n\sigma(n)}.$$

Before beginning the proof let us look at a few cases. When $n = 1$, the formula reduces to $|\mathbf{A}| = \mathrm{sgn}(1)a_{11} = a_{11}$, which is correct. When $n = 2$, the formula gives

$$\mathrm{sgn}(1)a_{11}a_{22} + \mathrm{sgn}((12))a_{12}a_{21} = a_{11}a_{22} - a_{12}a_{21},$$

which is again correct. Similarly we see that it gives the correct value as in (4.92) for 3×3 determinants.

Proof. The simplest approach is to prove that $|\mathbf{A}|$ as defined by the formula in the proposition satisfies the determinant axioms.

Proof of (D1). Since the ijth entry of $\mathbf{I}$ is δ_{ij}, the only nonzero term in the sum is $\mathrm{sgn}(1)a_{11} \cdots a_{nn} = 1$.

Proof of (D2). Each *summand* (i.e., term in the sum) contains exactly one element from each row (and exactly one from each column). Thus if the ith row is multiplied by c then so is each summand.

Proof of (D3). According to the formula,

$$|\mathbf{E}_{ij}(c)\mathbf{A}| = \sum_{\sigma \in \mathrm{Sym}} \mathrm{sgn}(\sigma) a_{1\sigma(1)} \cdots (a_{j\sigma(j)} + c a_{i\sigma(j)}) \cdots$$

$$= |\mathbf{A}| + c \sum_{\sigma \in \mathrm{Sym}} \mathrm{sgn}(\sigma) a_{1\sigma(1)} \cdots a_{i\sigma(j)} \cdots a_{n\sigma(n)}$$

and it remains to show that the last sum, call it S, is 0. We write the typical summand of S as $\mathrm{sgn}(\sigma)a(\sigma)$, where in $a(\sigma) = a_{1\sigma(1)} \cdots$ the ith factor is

$a_{i\sigma(i)}$ while the jth is $a_{i\sigma(j)}$. Using (4.119) we can group these summands in pairs corresponding to $\sigma \in \text{Alt}(n)$ and $\sigma(ij)$. In the latter case the subscripts can be simplified as follows.

$$\sigma(ij)(r) = \begin{cases} \sigma(r) & \text{if} \quad r \text{ is neither } i \text{ nor } j, \\ \sigma(j) & \text{if} \quad r = i, \\ \sigma(i) & \text{if} \quad r = j. \end{cases}$$

Thus the ith factor in $a(\sigma(ij))$ is $a_{i\sigma(j)}$ while the jth is $a_{i\sigma(i)}$. Hence $a(\sigma(ij)) = a(\sigma)$. Since $\text{sgn}(\sigma) = 1$ and $\text{sgn}(\sigma(ij)) = -1$, the terms cancel in pairs and we have $S = 0$. ■

EXERCISES

1. Let $\sigma = (12)(345) \in \text{Sym}(5)$. Write $\sigma^{-1}\tau\sigma$ as a product of disjoint cycles for the following τ: (123), (1234), (12)(34), (12345), (123)(45). From these examples conjecture and prove a rule to determine $\sigma^{-1}\tau\sigma$ without actually multiplying.

2. If $\sigma = (a_1 \cdots a_p) \cdots (z_1 \cdots z_q)$ is a product of disjoint cycles, the order of σ in the symmetric group is l.c.m.$(p, \ldots, q)$.

3. Alt(4) has no subgroup of order 6 (hence the obvious converse of Lagrange's theorem is false).

4. If $\sigma \in \text{Sym}(n)$ and ν denotes the number of pairs of integers i, j satisfying $1 \leqslant i < j \leqslant n$ and $\sigma(i) > j$, then $\text{sgn}(\sigma) = (-1)^\nu$.

5. The smallest subgroup of $\text{Sym}(n)$ containing (12) and $(12 \ldots n)$ is the whole group: $\text{Sym}(n) = \langle (12), (12 \ldots n) \rangle$. Also, $\text{Sym}(n) = \langle (12), (13), \ldots, (1n) \rangle$, and, when $n \geqslant 3$, $\text{Alt}(n) = \langle (123), (124), \ldots, (12n) \rangle$.

6. If **A** is a permutation matrix, then so is one of $\pm \text{adj}(\mathbf{A})$.

7. Let k be field, let L (resp. U) denote the subspace of $\text{Mat}_n(k)$ of lower (resp. upper) triangular matrices, and let L_1 (resp. U_1) denote the set of those $\mathbf{P} \in L$ (resp. $\mathbf{P} \in U$) with diagonal $(1, \ldots, 1)$.
   (a) L_1 is a subgroup of $\text{SL}_n(k)$; $\mathbf{P} \in L_1$ iff **P** can be written as a product of elementary matrices of the form $\mathbf{E}_{ij}(c)$ with $i < j$. Proceed analogously for U_1.
   (b) If $\mathbf{A} \in \text{Mat}_n(k)$, the **leading principal minors** of **A** are the n scalars

$$\Delta_r(\mathbf{A}) = \begin{vmatrix} a_{11} & \cdots & a_{1r} \\ \vdots & & \vdots \\ a_{r1} & \cdots & a_{rr} \end{vmatrix}, \qquad 1 \leqslant r \leqslant n.$$

   Then for $P \in L_1, Q \in U_1$ we have $\Delta_r(\mathbf{PAQ}) = \Delta_r(\mathbf{A})$.

(c) For $\mathbf{A} \in GL_n(k)$, $\exists \mathbf{P} \in L_1 \ni \mathbf{PA} \in U \Leftrightarrow$ all $\Delta_r(\mathbf{A}) \neq 0$; then by (a), $\mathbf{A} = \mathbf{P}^{-1}\mathbf{PA} \in L_1U$. Hence, if all principal minors of $\mathbf{A}$ are nonzero, then $\mathbf{A}$ can be factored as $\mathbf{BC}$, where $\mathbf{B} \in L_1$ and $\mathbf{C} \in U$.

8. Generalize (4.118) as follows. If G is a subgroup of Sym(n) and H is the subset of even permutations in G, then H is a subgroup of index 1 or 2 in G. Hence a group of permutations consists either entirely of even permutations, or exactly half are even and half are odd.

Assignment 9

A9.1. (i) Suppose the $m \times n$ matrix $\mathbf{A}$ and the $n \times r$ matrix $\mathbf{B}$ are partitioned into submatrices

$$\mathbf{A} = \begin{pmatrix} \mathbf{A}_{11} & \cdots & \mathbf{A}_{1t} \\ \vdots & & \vdots \\ \mathbf{A}_{s1} & \cdots & \mathbf{A}_{st} \end{pmatrix}, \qquad \mathbf{B} = \begin{pmatrix} \mathbf{B}_{11} & \cdots & \mathbf{B}_{1u} \\ \vdots & & \vdots \\ \mathbf{B}_{t1} & \cdots & \mathbf{B}_{tu} \end{pmatrix}$$

in such a way that all the following sums of products of matrices are defined:

$$\mathbf{C}_{pq} = \sum_{j=1}^{t} \mathbf{A}_{pj}\mathbf{B}_{jq}.$$

Show that $\mathbf{AB} = \mathbf{C}$, where

$$\mathbf{C} = \begin{pmatrix} \mathbf{C}_{11} & \cdots & \mathbf{C}_{1u} \\ \vdots & & \vdots \\ \mathbf{C}_{s1} & \cdots & \mathbf{C}_{su} \end{pmatrix}.$$

(This manner of calculating a matrix product is known as **block multiplication.**)

(ii) Deduce that if $\mathbf{A}$ is $n \times n$ and has the **block diagonal form**

$$\mathbf{A} = \begin{pmatrix} \mathbf{A}_1 & & & \\ & \mathbf{A}_2 & & \\ & & \ddots & \\ & & & \mathbf{A}_s \end{pmatrix} = \operatorname{diag}(\mathbf{A}_1, \ldots, \mathbf{A}_s),$$

where each $\mathbf{A}_i$ is square (say $n_i \times n_i$, so $n_1 + \cdots + n_s = n$) and outside these square blocks all entries of $\mathbf{A}$ are 0, then if each $\mathbf{A}_i$ is idempotent (resp. nilpotent of index ν_i), then $\mathbf{A}$ is idempotent (resp. nilpotent of index $\max\{\nu_1, \ldots, \nu_s\}$).

Remarks. If $V = V_1 \oplus \cdots \oplus V_s$ and $f_i \in \operatorname{End}(V_i)$, then $\mathbf{v} = (\mathbf{v}_1, \ldots, \mathbf{v}_s) \mapsto (f_1\mathbf{v}_1, \ldots, f_s\mathbf{v}_s)$ defines an endomorphism f of V called the **direct sum** of the f_i and denoted $f_1 \oplus \cdots \oplus f_s$. If $\mathcal{V}_i$ is a basis of V_i, canonically identified as a subset of V so that $\mathcal{V} = \mathcal{V}_1 \cup \cdots \cup \mathcal{V}_s$ is a basis of V, and if $R_{\mathcal{V}_i}(f_i) = A_i$,

then

$$R_{\mathcal{V}}(f) = \mathbf{A} = \operatorname{diag}(\mathbf{A}_1, \ldots, \mathbf{A}_s)$$

as above, and for this reason $\mathbf{A}$ is often called the **direct sum of** the **matrices** $\mathbf{A}_i$.

(iii) Let $\mathcal{V} = \{\mathbf{v}_1, \ldots, \mathbf{v}_s\}$, $\mathcal{W} = \{\mathbf{w}_1, \ldots, \mathbf{w}_t\}$ be two lists of vectors in k^n, say $s \leqslant t$, let $\mathbf{A}$ be the $s \times n$ matrix defined by $\text{row}_i\, \mathbf{A} = \mathbf{v}_i$, and similarly let $\mathbf{B}$ be the $t \times n$ matrix whose rows are the $\mathbf{w}_i$. Prove that $\langle \mathcal{V} \rangle = \langle \mathcal{W} \rangle$ iff $\mathbf{A}_{\text{ech}}$ and $\mathbf{B}_{\text{ech}}$ have the same nonzero rows. (Hence each subspace V of k^n has a **canonical basis**, which can be computed as the nonzero rows in $\mathbf{A}_{\text{ech}}$, starting with any spanning set $\mathcal{V}$ of V. In the case $V = k^n$ this gives the canonical basis as defined before.) Use this to show that in $\mathbf{Q}^5$, $\langle \mathcal{V} \rangle = \langle \mathcal{W} \rangle$, where

$$\mathcal{V} = \{(2,5,4,1,0), (-10,12,-7,-16,25), (8,-10,1,4,-17)\},$$

$$\mathcal{W} = \{(1,2,0,-3,1), (-1,2,1,1,2), (3,-1,2,2,-5),$$
$$(-1,1,-3,-6,4), (3,1,10,16,-9)\}.$$

A9.2. Let $\mathbf{A}, \mathbf{B} \in \operatorname{Mat}_{m,n}(k)$ and let $\mathbf{A}^T \in \operatorname{Mat}_{n,m}(k)$ denote the **transpose** of $\mathbf{A}$: The ijth entry of $\mathbf{A}^T$ is the jith entry a_{ji} of $\mathbf{A}$. The matrix $\mathbf{A}$ is **symmetric** if $\mathbf{A} = \mathbf{A}^T$; this requires $\mathbf{A}$ to be square.

(i) Show that $\mathbf{A} \mapsto \mathbf{A}^T$ defines a vector space isomorphism $\operatorname{Mat}_{m,n}(k) \to \operatorname{Mat}_{n,m}(k)$.

(ii) Show that $(\mathbf{AB})^T = \mathbf{B}^T\mathbf{A}^T$ and that $\mathbf{AA}^T$ is symmetric $\forall \mathbf{A}$.

(iii) If $\mathbf{A}^T\mathbf{A}$ is nonsingular, show that $\mathbf{C} = \mathbf{A}(\mathbf{A}^T\mathbf{A})^{-1}\mathbf{A}^T$ is idempotent.

(iv) If $m = n$ and $\mathbf{A}$ is nonsingular, show that $\mathbf{A}^T$ is nonsingular and $(\mathbf{A}^T)^{-1} = (\mathbf{A}^{-1})^T$.

(v) Give an example of $\operatorname{rank}(\mathbf{A}^T\mathbf{A}) < \operatorname{rank}(\mathbf{A})$. (*Hint*: Try $\operatorname{char}(k) > 0$.)

A9.3. Let $\mathbf{A}, \mathbf{B} \in \operatorname{Mat}_n(k)$.

(i) Suppose that $\mathbf{A}$ is upper triangular of **level** s for some $s \geqslant 0$, i.e., $a_{ij} = 0$ if $j - i < s$. (Then, by definition, $\mathbf{A}$ is upper triangular of level s', $\forall s' \leqslant s$. When $s = 0$ this just means that $\mathbf{A}$ is upper triangular.) Suppose also that $\mathbf{B}$ is upper triangular of level $t \geqslant 0$. Prove that $\mathbf{AB}$ is upper triangular of level $s + t$ and deduce that if $s > 0$ then $\mathbf{A}$ is nilpotent of index $\leqslant \lceil n/s \rceil$ (the least integer $\geqslant n/s$, i.e., $-\lfloor -n/s \rfloor$).

(ii) An element x of a ring R is **unipotent** if $y = 1 - x$ is nilpotent. If $y^r = 0$, show that $x \in R^*$ with inverse

$$1 + y + y^2 + \cdots + y^{r-1}.$$

Use this to calculate

$$\begin{pmatrix} 1 & 2 & 3 \\ 0 & 1 & 4 \\ 0 & 0 & 1 \end{pmatrix}^{-1}.$$

Show that the inverse of a unipotent element, in particular of a unipotent matrix, is again unipotent; and that when R is commutative the unipotent elements form a subgroup of R^*.

(iii) Let R be a ring, S a subset of R, and put

$$Z(S)=\{r \in R: rs=sr, \forall s \in S\}.$$

Prove that $Z(S)$ is a subring of R and that

$$S \subset Z(Z(S)).$$

($Z(S)$ is called the **centralizer** of S in R, and the subring $Z(R)$ is called the **center** of R.)

(iv) Show that the center of $\text{Mat}_n(k)$ consists of the scalar matrices. (*Hint*: Consider the condition $\mathbf{AF}_{st}=\mathbf{F}_{st}\mathbf{A}$, where $\mathbf{F}_{st}=(f_{ij})$ is the so-called **matrix unit** defined by $f_{ij}=0\ \forall i,j$ except for $f_{st}=1$. Of course $\mathbf{F}_{st}$ is not a unit in the sense of having an inverse.)

A9.4. (i) Let $\mathcal{V}=\{\mathbf{v}_j: j \in J\}$ and $\mathcal{V}'=\{\mathbf{v}_j': j \in J\}$ be two bases of the vector space V and define the matrix $\mathbf{P} \in \text{Mat}_J(k)$ by

$$\mathbf{v}_j'=\sum p_{rj}\mathbf{v}_r.$$

$\mathbf{P}$ is called the **transition matrix** from $\mathcal{V}$ to $\mathcal{V}'$. Show that $\mathbf{P}$ is invertible and that $\mathbf{P}^{-1}$ is the transition matrix from $\mathcal{V}'$ to $\mathcal{V}$. Verify the following rule for **change of coordinates** (let us say, in a finite dimensional space): If $\mathbf{v}=a_1\mathbf{v}_1+\cdots+a_n\mathbf{v}_n=a_1'\mathbf{v}_1'+\cdots+a_n'\mathbf{v}_n'$, then

$$(a_1,\dots,a_n)^T=\mathbf{P}(a_1',\dots,a_n')^T.$$

(ii) Similarly, let $\mathcal{W}=\{\mathbf{w}_i; i \in I\}$ and $\mathcal{W}'=\{\mathbf{w}_i'\}$ be bases of W with transition matrix $\mathbf{Q} \in \text{Mat}_I(k)$. Show that, for $f \in \text{Hom}(V,W)$,

$$\mathbf{R}_{\mathcal{V}',\mathcal{W}'}(f)=\mathbf{Q}^{-1}\mathbf{R}_{\mathcal{V},\mathcal{W}}(f)\mathbf{P}.$$

(iii) Two $I \times J$ matrices $\mathbf{A}$ and $\mathbf{B}$ are **equivalent** if $\exists \mathbf{M} \in \text{Mat}_I(k)^*$ and $\mathbf{P} \in \text{Mat}_J(k)^* \ni \mathbf{B}=\mathbf{MAP}$. Show that this is an equivalence relation on $\text{Mat}_{I,J}(k)$.

(iv) Now let I and J be finite, say $|I|=m$, $|J|=n$. Show that equivalent $m \times n$ matrices have the same rank and nullity. Show that $\mathbf{A} \in \text{Mat}_{m,n}(k)$ is equivalent to exactly one matrix of the form $\text{diag}(I_r,0)$ (the matrix whose first r diagonal entries are 1, and all other entries are 0; r is the rank of $\mathbf{A}$).

(v) For $f \in \text{End}(V)$ the formula in (ii) becomes

$$\mathbf{R}_{\mathcal{V}'}(f)=\mathbf{P}^{-1}\mathbf{R}_{\mathcal{V}}(f)\mathbf{P},$$

which leads to a definition: Two $J \times J$ matrices are **similar** if $\exists \mathbf{P} \in \text{Mat}_J(k)^* \ni$

$$\mathbf{B}=\mathbf{P}^{-1}\mathbf{AP}.$$

Prove that similarity is an equivalence relation on $\text{Mat}_J(k)$.

(vi) The **trace** of the finite square matrix $\mathbf{A}=(a_{ij})$ is the sum $a_{11}+a_{22}+\cdots$ of the diagonal elements, denoted $\text{Tr}(\mathbf{A})$. Show that similar matrices have the same trace and same determinant.

A9.5. Let $\sigma \in \text{Sym}(n)$ have the (essentially) unique factorization into disjoint cycles

$$\sigma=\sigma_1\cdots\sigma_r=(a_{11}\cdots)\cdots(a_{r1}\cdots),$$

where cycles of length 1 are included so that each of the symbols $1,2,\ldots,n$ appears exactly once among the a_{ij}. Let $\sim$ denote the equivalence relation on $\{1,\ldots,n\}$ given by $a\sim b$ iff a and b occur in the same cycle σ_i, and define $l(\sigma)=n-r$. For example, $l(1)=0$.

(i) If τ denotes the transposition (ab), prove that

$$l(\sigma\tau)=\begin{cases} l(\sigma)-1 & \text{if } a\sim b,\\ l(\sigma)+1 & \text{otherwise.}\end{cases}$$

(ii) Use (i) to give an alternate proof of (4.112).

(iii) Show that $a\sim b$ iff $a=\sigma^m(b)$ for some $m\in\mathbb{Z}$.

A9.6. Let V be a vector space over the field k. A multilinear form

$$F\colon V^n=V\times V\times\cdots\times V\to k$$

is **alternating** if $F(\mathbf{v}_1,\ldots,\mathbf{v}_n)=0$ whenever two of the $\mathbf{v}$s are equal.

(i) Let $V=k^n$ and define det: $V^n\to k$ by $\det(\mathbf{v}_1,\ldots,\mathbf{v}_n)=$ the determinant of the matrix whose ith row is $\mathbf{v}_i$. Show that det is an alternating multilinear form.

(ii) Prove that if $F\colon V^n\to k$ is an alternating multilinear form and $\sigma\in\mathrm{Sym}(n)$, then

$$(*)\qquad F(\mathbf{v}_{\sigma(1)},\ldots,\mathbf{v}_{\sigma(n)})=\mathrm{sgn}(\sigma)F(\mathbf{v}_1,\ldots,\mathbf{v}_n).$$

(An F satisfying $(*)$ is called **skew symmetric** (whereas an F satisfying $F(\mathbf{v}_{\sigma(1)},\ldots)=F(\mathbf{v}_1,\ldots)$ $\forall\sigma\in\mathrm{Sym}(n)$ is called **symmetric**). Thus every alternating form is skew symmetric. (*Hint*: first let σ be a transposition.)

A9.7. Let K be a commutative ring and for $m,n\in\mathbb{N}$ let $\mathrm{Mat}_{m,n}(K)$ denote the set of $m\times n$ arrays of elements of K, with matrix operations defined as in the case when K is a field. $\mathrm{Mat}_{m,n}$ is shortened to Mat_n when $m=n$. Prove the following facts.

(i) $\mathrm{Mat}_{m,n}(K)$ is an abelian group and the displayed formulas of (4.59) remain valid. Hence $\mathrm{Mat}_n(K)$ is a ring containing K as a subring if we identify $a\in K$ with $\mathrm{diag}(a,a,\ldots)$.

(ii) For $\mathbf{A}\in\mathrm{Mat}_n(K)$, $|\mathbf{A}|$ defined inductively on n by row expansion (4.99) is well defined and satisfies (4.94) (ii), (iv), and (v), (4.103), and (4.120).

(iii) $\mathbf{A}\in\mathrm{Mat}_n(K)$ is invertible iff $|\mathbf{A}|\in K^*$, and then

$$\mathbf{A}^{-1}=|\mathbf{A}|^{-1}\mathrm{adj}(\mathbf{A}),$$

the adjugate being defined in the usual way. Then the system of equations $\mathbf{AX}=\mathbf{B}$ has the unique solution $\mathbf{X}=\mathbf{A}^{-1}\mathbf{B}$, which can be computed according to Cramer's rule. (However, it must be borne in mind that in this generality the concepts of linear independence, dimension, rank, row space, and echelon form are lacking.)

A9.8. A **euclidean algorithm ring** (EA ring for short) is a commutative ring K equipped with a map $\rho\colon K\to\mathbb{N}$ satisfying the following three axioms:

(EA0) $\rho(a)=0\Leftrightarrow a=0$;

(EA1) $\rho(a)=1\Leftrightarrow a\in K^*$; and

(EA2) $\forall a, b \in K$ with $b \neq 0$, $\exists q, r \in K \ni$

$$a = bq + r \qquad \text{and} \qquad \rho(r) < \rho(b).$$

(*Remarks.* This is not the standard definition of "euclidean ring"—usually a requirement of the form $\rho(ab) \geqslant \rho(a)$ for $b \neq 0$ or $\rho(ab) = \rho(a)\rho(b)$ is included to force K to be an integral domain. There is no need to impose any such restriction for the results of this question. Axiom (EA1) has been included for "cosmetic" reasons: It makes certain statements neater, e.g., the description below of matrices over K in echelon form. Repeated application of (EA2) as in (3.66) gives K a Euclidean algorithm. (EA2) does not require that q and r be unique for a given pair a and b, but to have an algorithm, strictly speaking, particular q and r must be assigned to each division. $\mathbb{Z}$ is EA if we take $\rho(a) = \pm a$, whichever is $\geqslant 0$; another possibility is $\rho(a) = a^2$. If F is a field then $F[X]$ is EA with respect to

$$\rho(a) = \begin{cases} 0 & \text{if} \quad a = 0, \\ 2^{\deg(a)} & \text{if} \quad a \neq 0. \end{cases}$$

A field is EA if we define $\rho(a) = 1$, $\forall a \neq 0$.)

(i) Show that in an EA ring every ideal is principal. (*Hint*: Copy the proof of (3.31).)

(ii) Suppose K is a commutative ring and ρ': $K \to \mathbb{N}$ satisfies (EA0), (EA2), and (EA1^{b}): $\rho(1) = 1$. Prove that K is EA if we define

$$\rho(a) = \min\{\rho'(au) : u \in K^*\}.$$

(iii) If I is a proper ideal in the EA ring K prove that K/I is EA if we define

$$\rho'(a + I) = \min\{\rho(x) : x \in a + I\}$$

(and then apply (ii) with K replaced by K/I).

(iv) Let K be an EA ring. The set of $m \times m$ **elementary matrices**

$$\{\mathbf{E}_{ij}\} \cup \{\mathbf{E}_{ij}(a) : a \in K\} \cup \{\mathbf{E}_i(u) : u \in K^*\}$$

$= S_m$, say, is defined as in the field case. Establish the following (straightforward) generalization of echelon form:

For $\mathbf{B} \in \operatorname{Mat}_{m,n}(K), \exists \mathbf{E}_1, \ldots, \mathbf{E}_t \in S_m \ni \mathbf{A} = \mathbf{E}_1 \cdots \mathbf{E}_t \mathbf{B}$ satisfies the conditions of (4.71) except that (γ) is modified to read as follows. For $1 \leqslant t < i \leqslant r$, $\rho(a_{t\kappa_i}) < \rho(a_{i\kappa_i})$ (i.e., the entries directly above a pivot are "smaller" than the pivot and can be nonzero). Find echelon forms for

$$\mathbf{B} = \begin{pmatrix} 6 & -3 & 0 \\ -2 & 1 & 1 \\ 2 & -1 & 2 \end{pmatrix},$$

when $K = \mathbb{Z}$ and when $K = \mathbb{Z}/4\mathbb{Z}$.

(v) Deduce from (iv) that an $n \times n$ matrix/an EA ring K is invertible iff it can be written as a product of elementary matrices. (Hence S_n is a set of generators for $\mathrm{GL}_n(K)$ according to the following definition: A subset S **generates** the group G if every $g \in G$ can be written, in at least one way, as $g = x_1 \cdots x_t$, where x_i or x_i^{-1} is in S. In other words, the smallest subgroup containing S is G itself. As in the case of ideals and vector spaces, this is indicated notationally by $G=\langle S\rangle$. As a generating set S_n contains many redundant elements. A more frugal generating set is given for SL_n in the next part.)

(vi) Show that for an EA ring K,

$$\mathrm{SL}_n(K)=\langle \mathbf{E}_{ij}(a):1\leqslant i,j\leqslant n, a\in K\rangle.$$

(*Hint*, stated in the case $n=2$: For $u\in K^*$,

$$\begin{pmatrix} u^{-1} & 0\\ 0 & u\end{pmatrix}=\begin{pmatrix} 1 & u^{-1}\\ 0 & 1\end{pmatrix}\begin{pmatrix} 1 & 0\\ -u & 1\end{pmatrix}\begin{pmatrix} 1 & u^{-1}\\ 0 & 1\end{pmatrix}\begin{pmatrix} 0 & -1\\ 1 & 0\end{pmatrix}.\Bigg)$$

20. ALGEBRAS

We have seen that $n\times n$ scalar matrices over the field k add and multiply as the corresponding scalars:

$$\mathrm{diag}(a,a,\ldots)+\mathrm{diag}(b,b,\ldots)=\mathrm{diag}(a+b,a+b,\ldots),$$
$$\mathrm{diag}(a,a,\ldots)\mathrm{diag}(b,b,\ldots)=\mathrm{diag}(ab,ab,\ldots).$$

The other ring operations also correspond exactly:

$$0=\mathrm{diag}(0,0,\ldots),\qquad 1=\mathrm{diag}(1,1,\ldots),$$
$$-\mathrm{diag}(a,a,\ldots)=\mathrm{diag}(-a,-a,\ldots).$$

Thus the set of scalar matrices form a copy of k as a subring in $\mathrm{Mat}_n(k)$. More formally, the map

$$\rho\colon k\to \mathrm{Mat}_n(k)$$

defined by $\rho(a)=\mathrm{diag}(a,a,\ldots)$ is an injective ring homomorphism.

The polynomial ring is another instance where we start with a ground field k, or more generally a ground ring R, and again we have a ring homomorphism

$$\rho\colon k\to k[X],$$

where $\rho(a)$ is the constant polynomial $a+0X+0X^2+\cdots$. This example generalizes to the monoid ring $\rho\colon R\to R[M]$, as we explained in Chapter 2.

Before stating the general definition we describe one more example.

If V is a vector space over k, then for each scalar a we have the map $\rho(a)$: $V\to V$ given by $\mathbf{v}\mapsto a\mathbf{v}$. The vector space axiom (V1) gives $\rho(a)(\mathbf{v}+\mathbf{v}')=a\mathbf{v}+a\mathbf{v}'=\rho(a)\mathbf{v}+\rho(a)\mathbf{v}'$. If also $a'\in k$, then axiom (V3), together with the commutativity of k, give $\rho(a)(a'\mathbf{v})=a'(a\mathbf{v})=a'\rho(a)(\mathbf{v})$. These two facts mean that $\rho(a)\in\mathrm{End}(V)$, and therefore we have a map $\rho\colon k\to\mathrm{End}(V)$. Axioms (V2)–(V4) can be restated

$$\rho(a+b)=\rho(a)+\rho(b),\qquad \rho(ab)=\rho(a)\rho(b),\qquad \rho(1)=1.$$

In other words, ρ is a ring homomorphism. (By A5.1, ρ is injective except when $V=0$, the only instance of $\mathrm{End}(V)=\not{1}$.) When $\dim V=n$ and we choose a basis, then End(V) can be identified with $\mathrm{Mat}_n(k)$, and $\rho(a)$ becomes diag$(a, a, \ldots)$, as in our first example.

$\mathrm{Mat}_n(k)$, $k[X]$, $k[M]$, and End(V) are central k-algebras:

(4.121) DEFINITION. If R is a ring, an ***R*-algebra** is a ring S equipped with a ring homomorphism $\rho: R \to S$, called the **structure homomorphism**. The product $\rho(r)s$ in S is usually abbreviated as rs. The R-algebra S is **central** if $\rho(r)s = s\rho(r)$ for all $r \in R$ and $s \in S$ (i.e., $\rho(R) \subset Z(S)$ in the notation of A9.3).

Notice that ρ is not required to be injective. According to (3.5), every ring S is a $\mathbb{Z}$-algebra in a unique way, and obviously S is a central $\mathbb{Z}$-algebra.

Another example is the **Boolean algebra** of subsets of a set X which we encountered already in A3.4. This is the ring $\mathbb{F}_2^X$ (direct product of copies of the two element field), of characteristic 2, equipped with the unique ring homomorphism $\mathbb{F}_2 \to \mathbb{F}_2^X$ as explained in (3.34). Thus $\mathbb{F}_2^X$ is an $\mathbb{F}_2$-algebra.

Notice that in the case of a field k, a k-algebra S has the "substructure" of a vector space over k; scalar multiplication $a\mathbf{v} = \rho(a)\mathbf{v}$ is obtained by "forgetting" part of the multiplication table $S \times S \to S$. Thus $\mathrm{Mat}_n(k)$ is a vector space of dimension n^2.

If $\rho: R \to S$ and $\rho': R \to S'$ are R-algebras, an ***R*-algebra homomorphism** from the first to the second is a ring homomorphism $f: S \to S'$ such that the diagram

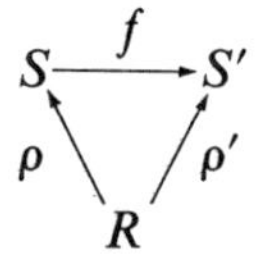

is commutative, that is, such that $f\rho = \rho'$. (In general, a diagram of maps is said to be *commutative* if for each pair of objects A_1, A_2 in the diagram all maps $A_1 \to A_2$ (if any) obtained by composing maps in the diagram agree. This includes "loops" from an object back to itself.)

A **subalgebra** of the R-algebra S is a subring S' containing $\rho(R)$. Since $r \mapsto \rho(r)$ defines a ring homomorphism $\rho': R \to S'$, S' is itself an R-algebra, and obviously the inclusion map $x \mapsto x$ is an R-algebra homomorphism $S' \to S$.

If S_i are R-subalgebras of S, so is $\cap S_i$. Hence if E is any subset of S, there is a unique smallest subalgebra containing E, often denoted $R[E]$ (especially when Ker$(\rho) = 0$, so we can regard $R \subset S$). This consists of all polynomial-like expressions

$$\sum r x_1^{n_1} \cdots x_t^{n_t},$$

with various $r \in R$ and $x_i \in E$ (including single terms of the form $r \cdot 1 = \rho(r)$), and is called the subalgebra **generated** by E. When $E = \{x_1, x_2, \ldots\}$ this is also written as $R[x_1, x_2, \ldots]$. For instance, in $\mathbb{Q}$, $\mathbb{Z}[\frac{1}{2}]$ consists of all sums of the form $r_0 + r_1/2 + \cdots + r_t/2^t$, $r_i \in \mathbb{Z}$, that is, all fractions of the form $r/2^t, r \in \mathbb{Z}$. (Hence $\mathbb{Z}[\frac{1}{2}] = T^{-1}\mathbb{Z}$, where $T = \{1,2,4,\ldots\}$.) In $R[X]$, $R[X^2]$ denotes the subalgebra of all polynomials $a_0 + a_2X^2 + a_4X^4 + \cdots$ in the variable X^2.

EXERCISE

Prove the following statements concerning the R-algebra homomorphisms $f: S \to T$ and $g: T \to U$.

1. $gf: S \to U$ is an R-algebra homomorphism.
2. The structure homomorphism $\rho: R \to S$ is an R-algebra homomorphism. (R is always understood to have 1_R as structure homomorphism.)
3. The identity map 1_S is an R-algebra homomorphism.
4. If f is an R-algebra isomorphism, i.e., is bijective, then so is f^{-1}.
5. The set $\mathrm{Aut}_{R\text{-alg}}(S)$ of R-algebra automorphisms of S is a subgroup of $\mathrm{Sym}(S)$.
6. $f(S)$ is a subalgebra of T.
7. $f(R[x_1,\ldots]) = R[f(x_1),\ldots]$.
8. Every ring homomorphism is a $\mathbb{Z}$-algebra homomorphism.

21. THE RESULTANT

(4.122) DEFINITION. If $f = a_mX^m + \cdots + a_0$ and $g = b_nX^n + \cdots + b_0$ are polynomials over the field k, of positive degrees m and n, respectively, their **resultant** is the determinant $R = R(f, g) = |\mathbf{A}|$, where $\mathbf{A} \in \mathrm{Mat}_{m+n}(k)$ is defined as follows. For $1 \leqslant i \leqslant n$,

$$\mathrm{row}_i(\mathbf{A}) = (0,\ldots,0, a_m, a_{m-1},\ldots, a_0, 0,\ldots,0)$$

consists of $i-1$ zeros, followed by the coefficients of f, then followed by zeros to fill up the rest of the row. For $n+1 \leqslant i \leqslant m+n$, $\mathrm{row}_i(\mathbf{A})$ consists of $i-n-1$ zeros followed by $b_n,\ldots, b_0$, then zeros.

For instance, if $f = 2X^2 - 3$ and $g = 4X^3 + 5X^2 + 6X$, then

$$R(f,g) = \begin{vmatrix} 2 & 0 & -3 & 0 & 0 \\ 0 & 2 & 0 & -3 & 0 \\ 0 & 0 & 2 & 0 & -3 \\ 4 & 5 & 6 & 0 & 0 \\ 0 & 4 & 5 & 6 & 0 \end{vmatrix} = -1278.$$

One way to motivate this definition is to look at the problem of calculating r and s in $rf+sg=h=\text{g.c.d.}(f,g)$. First we note that we can choose r so that $\deg(r)<n$ (or $r=0$); for if $h=r'f+s'g$ and $r'=gq+r$, then $h=rf+sg$, where $s=s'+fq$. Then since $\deg(h)\leqslant\min\{m,n\},\deg(s)<m$ (or $s=0$). If

$$r=z_1X^{n-1}+\cdots+z_n,\qquad s=z_{n+1}X^{m-1}+\cdots+z_{m+n},$$

then

$$\mathbf{A}(z_1,\ldots,z_{m+n})^T=(h_1,\ldots,h_{m+n})^T=\mathbf{H},$$

say, where $h=h_1X^{m+n-1}+\cdots+h_{m+n}$. Thus $\mathbf{A}$ puts $rf+sg=h$ in matrix notation.

If $R\neq 0$, so that $\mathbf{A}$ is nonsingular, we can solve the system $\mathbf{AZ}=\mathbf{H}$ for any $\mathbf{H}$, not just $(h_1,\ldots)^T$, and in particular for $\mathbf{H}=(0,\ldots,0,1)^T$. This gives r and s such that $rf+sg=1$ and therefore $h=\text{g.c.d.}(f,g)$ must be 1. Conversely, suppose $h=1$. Then the r,s satisfying $rf+sg=1$ and $\deg(r)<n,\deg(s)<m$ are unique: If r_1,s_1 were another pair, we would have $(r-r_1)f=(s_1-s)g$, and if $r\neq r_1$, then since $\text{g.c.d.}(f,g)=1$, $f\,|\,(s_1-s)$, which contradicts $m>\deg(s_1-s)$. This means that $\mathbf{AZ}=(0,\ldots,0,1)^T$ has a unique solution. The nullity of $\mathbf{A}$ is thus 0. We have proved

(4.123) PROPOSITION. *If f and g are nonconstant polynomials over the field k, then* $\text{g.c.d.}(f,g)=1$ *iff* $R(f,g)\neq 0$.

For example, when $f=X^3-XY^2+X-Y$ and $g=X^3Y+X^2Y^2-X^2-1$ are regarded as polynomials in X over the field $k(Y)$, we find $R(f,g)=0$, which predicts a common factor. In fact, both are divisible by X^2+XY+1. Of course a common factor is also predicted by regarding f and g as polynomials in Y over $k(X)$.

If we replace f by af, where $a\in k^*$ then the first n rows of $\mathbf{A}$ are multiplied by a. Thus with a similar change in g we have

$$R(af,bg)=a^nb^mR(f,g). \tag{4.124}$$

(4.125) PROPOSITION. *Let f and g be polynomials of positive degree over the field k and let $R=R(f,g)$ denote their resultant. Then there exist $\lambda,\mu\in k[X]$ such that $R=\lambda f+\mu g$.*

Proof. The system $\mathbf{AY}=\mathbf{B}$, with $\mathbf{A}$ as defined in (4.122) and $\mathbf{B}=(X^{n-1}f,X^{n-2}f,\ldots,f,X^{m-1}g,\ldots,g)^T$ has the solution $\mathbf{Y}=(X^{m+n-1},\ldots,X,1)^T$. Comparing the $(m+n)$th entries in the vectors

$$R\mathbf{Y}=\operatorname{adj}(\mathbf{A})\cdot\mathbf{B}$$

as in the proof of Cramer's rule gives

$$
(4.126) \qquad R = \begin{vmatrix}
a_m & \cdots & a_0 & & & & X^{n-1}f \\
& a_m & \cdots & a_0 & & & X^{n-2}f \\
& & \ddots & & \ddots & & \vdots \\
& & a_m & \cdots & & a_0 & Xf \\
& & & a_m & \cdots & a_1 & f \\
b_n & \cdots & b_0 & & & & X^{m-1}g \\
& \ddots & & \ddots & & & \vdots \\
& & b_n & \cdots & & b_0 & Xg \\
& & & b_n & \cdots & b_1 & g
\end{vmatrix},
$$

where the blank areas are filled with zeros. Expansion along the last column gives the result. ■

For the numerical example following (4.122), (4.126) gives

$$-1278 = (192X^2 + 120X + 426)f - (96X - 60)g.$$

In (5.126) we shall derive a convenient formula for R when one of the polynomials factors into linear factors.

EXERCISES

1. $R(g, f) = (-1)^{mn} R(f, g)$ where m, n are the degrees of f, g.

2. $X^3 + aX + b$ and $X^3 + cX + d$ have a common factor iff $(ad - bc)(a - c)^2 = (b - d)^3$.

APPENDIX: THE EQUIVALENCE OF ZORN'S LEMMA AND THE AXIOM OF CHOICE

We preface the theorem with a few remarks concerning set theory.

"The set of all sets" is not a valid concept, for if there were such a set X, then the set 2^X of all subsets of X would satisfy (by A8.7)

$$|X| < |2^X|.$$

However, each member of 2^X is a set, and therefore a member of X. This implies

$$|2^X| \leqslant |X|,$$

and we have contradicted the Schroeder–Bernstein theorem (the uniqueness half of (4.27), whose proof used neither Zorn's lemma nor the axiom of choice). The fact that no such set exists is expressed "X is a class," the intuitive idea being that X is "too big" to be a set. Similarly we speak of the class of all groups, the class of all isomorphism types of fields, and so on. (However, this use of the word "class" is not strictly adhered to: An equivalence class is a set.)

Bona fide sets are defined in terms of existing sets:

If Y is a set then

$$Z = \{y \in Y: y \text{ satisfies conditions} \ldots\}$$

is a set.

If Y and Z are sets, there is a set $Y \times Z$ (used to define maps, as in Chapter 1).

If Y and Z are sets, Z^Y (all maps $Y \to Z$) is a set.

If I is a set and for each $i \in I$ X_i is a set, then there exists a set $\amalg X_i$, as described in (1.25). (The construction ΠX_i uses a combination of the above.)

The starting point in this book was, in effect, the axiom

$$\mathbb{N} \text{ is a set.}$$

When set theory is axiomatized one naturally seeks a list of axioms as short and uncluttered as possible; in particular, one asks which axioms in a given list are consequences of the others and can therefore be dropped. Those that cannot be dropped are called **independent**.

Recently P. Cohen solved a long outstanding problem: The axiom of choice is independent of the "elementary" axioms of set theory (those concerned with basic properties of $\in, \subset, \amalg$). He constructed a mathematical system (model) that satisfies the elementary axioms but not the axiom of choice.[4]

It is therefore of some interest to keep track of which proofs depend on the axiom of choice and which do not. In algebra, the axiom tends to be involved in such blanket statements as "for all rings" or "for all vector spaces." For instance, the theorems

every vector space has a basis,

every proper ideal is contained in a maximal ideal, and

every saturated multiplicative set is the complement of a union of prime ideals

all depend in an essential way on the axiom. It frequently happens that the axiom can be circumvented when the theorem is restricted.

---

[4]The reader who wishes to pursue further the matters touched on in this appendix should see T. J. Jech, *The Axiom of Choice*, North Holland, New York, 1973.

In the next chapter we indicate where the axiom is used and we adhere to the following principle: *The results explicitly pertaining to locally compact fields* (the fields $\mathbb{F}_q$, $\mathbb{R}$, $\mathbb{C}$, $\mathbb{F}_q((X))$, $\mathbb{Q}_p$, and extensions of the $\mathbb{Q}_p$ of finite degree) *do not depend on the axiom*. For example, the following are proved without using the axiom:

the Weierstrass Nullstellensatz for $\mathbb{R}$,

the fundamental theorem for $\mathbb{C}$, and

the convergence of Newton's method (in the form of Hensel's lemma) for $\mathbb{Q}_p$ and $F((X))$.

In fact, results concerning these fields that depend on the axiom would usually be classified as belonging to analysis (e.g., the existence of nonmeasurable sets and the Hahn–Banach theorem).

However, avoiding the use of the axiom often complicates proofs. For instance, the proofs of the Bolzano–Weierstrass theorem (5.291) and its corollaries are considerably shortened by quoting some general (axiom of choice dependent) results on metric spaces.

We turn now to the theorem of this appendix. For the definitions of partially ordered set, totally ordered set, chain and maximal chain, see Section 7. A **well-ordered set** is a totally ordered set in which every nonempty subset S contains a least element s, i.e., $s \in S$ and $s \leqslant s'$, $\forall s' \in S$. Thus $\mathbb{N}$ with the usual $\leqslant$ is well ordered, but $\mathbb{Z}$ is not since $S = \mathbb{Z}$ does not contain a least element. $\{q \in \mathbb{Q} : q \geqslant 0\}$ is not well ordered since the subset $S = \{q \in \mathbb{Q} : q > 0\}$ does not contain g.l.b.$(S) = 0$.

THEOREM. *The following statements are logically equivalent (any one implies the others):*

(1) *The axiom of choice (cf.* 1.26);
(2) *Kuratowski's lemma—every chain in a partially ordered set is contained in a maximal chain*;
(3) *Zorn's lemma (cf.* 4.26); *and*
(4) *the well-ordering theorem—every set can be well ordered.*

Proof. We give a cyclic proof. To prove that (1) ⇒ (2) we require a

LEMMA. *Let A be a nonempty partially ordered set in which every nonempty chain has a least upper bound. Let $f: A \to A$ be a map with the property*

$$x \leqslant f(x), \qquad \forall x \in A.$$

Then f has a **fixed point** *x_0: $f(x_0) = x_0$ for some $x_0 \in A$.*

Proof of the lemma. (This proof does not use the axiom of choice.) Let a be any element of A; it will remain fixed throughout the discussion. Let M be the collection of all subsets B of A with the three properties

(α) $a \in B$;
(β) $x \in B \Rightarrow f(x) \in B$; and
(γ) any nonempty chain C in B has its (unique) least upper in B.

Now $M \neq \varnothing$ since $A \in M$. Also, it is clear that $D \in M$, where

$$D = \bigcap_{B \in M} B.$$

We shall show that D is a chain. The proof will then be complete for, by (γ), D as a chain in D has an upper bound $d \in D$. By (β), $d \leqslant f(d) \in D$, and therefore $d = f(d)$.

Let $D_1 = \{x \in D : a \leqslant x\}$. We show that $D_1 = D$ by showing that $D_1 \in M$:

(α) $a \leqslant a$, so $a \in D_1$.
(β) $x \in D_1 \Rightarrow a \leqslant x \leqslant f(x) \Rightarrow f(x) \in D_1$.
(γ) Let C be a chain in D_1. Since it is also a chain in D, its least upper bound u is in D. Clearly $a \leqslant u$, so $u \in D_1$.

Now define

$$D_2 = \{x \in D : y \in D \text{ and } y < x \Rightarrow f(y) \leqslant x\},$$

where $y < x$ means $y \leqslant x$ and $y \neq x$. We show that $D_2 = D$ again by showing that $D_2 \in M$. In order to do this we define for each $x \in D_2$

$$D_3 = D_3(x) = \{y \in D : \text{either } y \leqslant x \text{ or } f(x) \leqslant y\}.$$

Notice that $x \in D_3$. Now $D_3 \in M$ (hence $D_3 = D$, $\forall x$) by the following reasoning:

(α) $a \leqslant x$ since $x \in D = D_1$, and therefore $a \in D_3$.
(β) Let $y \in D_3$. Either $y < x$, $y = x$, or $f(x) \leqslant y$. If $y < x$, then $f(y) \leqslant x$ since $x \in D_2$ and therefore $f(y) \in D_3$. If $y = x$, then $f(y) = f(x)$ and $f(y) \in D_3$. If $f(x) \leqslant y$, then $f(x) \leqslant y \leqslant f(y)$ and $f(y) \in D_3$. Thus, in any case, $f(y) \in D_3$.
(γ) Let C be a chain in D_3. Since each element c_i of C is in D_3, either (i) $c_i \leqslant x$, $\forall i$, or (ii) $\exists i \ni c_i \geqslant f(x)$. C is a chain in D and therefore its least upper bound u is in D. In case (i), x is an upper bound of C; hence $u \leqslant x$ so $u \in D_3$. In case (ii), $u \geqslant c_i \geqslant f(x)$, which again implies that $u \in D_3$.

We can now prove that $D_2 \in M$:

(α) $a \in D_2$ since $D = D_1$.
(β) Let $x \in D_2$ and let y be an element of D such that $y < f(x)$. To show that $f(x) \in D_2$ we must prove that $f(y) \leqslant f(x)$. Since $y \in D_3 = D$, $y < f(x)$ implies that $y \leqslant x$. If $y = x$, then $f(y) \leqslant f(x)$ trivially. If $y < x$, then $f(y) \leqslant x \leqslant f(x)$ since $x \in D_2$.

(γ) Let $C=\{c_i\}$ be a chain in D_2 with least upper bound $u \in D$. We must show that $u \in D_2$, i.e., $y \in D$, $y<u \Rightarrow f(y) \leqslant u$. Now $c_i \leqslant y$, $\forall i$, is impossible since this would imply $u \leqslant y$. Since $y \in D = D_3(c_i)$, $\forall i$, either $y \leqslant c_i$ or $c_i \leqslant f(c_i) \leqslant y$. In the present case we can conclude that $\exists i \ni y < c_i$. Since $c_i \in D_2$. we have $f(y) \leqslant c_i \leqslant u$. Hence $u \in D_2$.

Thus $D_2 = D_3 = D$ and, for any x and y in D, either $y \leqslant x$ or $x \leqslant f(x) \leqslant y$. Hence D is a chain and this completes the proof of the lemma.

We can now prove Kuratowski's lemma. Let A be a partially ordered set and let M be the set of all chains in A partially ordered by inclusion. $M \neq \varnothing$ since $\varnothing \in M$: The empty subset of A is a chain. Let $K=\{C_i\}$ be a chain in M and put $C = \cup C_i$. Then $C \in M$ because if $x, y \in C$, say $x \in C_i$ and $y \in C_j$, then since K is a chain we have, say, $C_i \leqslant C_j$. Then x and y are both in the chain C_j and are hence comparable, which proves that C is a chain. It follows that C is a least upper bound of K, and we can apply the lemma to M and appropriate f.

Suppose (2) is false for A. Then

$$S(C)=\{C' \in M : C < C'\} \neq \varnothing, \qquad \forall C \in M.$$

From each $S(C)$ choose, by the axiom of choice, a representative $f(C) \in S(C)$. Thus $f(C) > C$ for every C, but the previous lemma says that $f(C) = C$ for some C. This contradiction proves (2).

Proof that (2) ⇒ (3). Let A be a set in which every chain has an upper bound. By (2), A has a maximal chain C. An upper bound u of C must be a maximal element since, if $u<v$, then $C \cup \{v\}$ is a chain $>C$, contradicting the maximality of C.

Proof that (3) ⇒ (4). Let A be a set and W the set of well orderings w on subsets B_w of A; for $x, y \in B_w$, the relation xwy stands for $x \leqslant y$ in the well ordering w on B_w. Included in W is the well ordering (with empty graph) on the subset $\varnothing$ of A, so $W \neq \varnothing$. For $v, w \in W$ define $v \leqslant w$ to mean that v is an "initial segment" of w: $B_v \subset B_w$ and

$$(*) \qquad x \in B_v, \quad y \in B_w, \quad ywx \quad \Rightarrow \quad y \in B_v \text{ and } yvx.$$

Plainly this is a partial order on W. For $w \in W$, let w also denote the graph of w regarded as a subset of $A \times A$. Thus $v \leqslant w \Rightarrow v \subset w$. If $\{w_i\}$ is a chain in W, let w denote the relation on $B = \cup B_{w_i}$ with graph $w = \cup w_i$. The straightforward verification that w is a total order on B is left to the reader. If S is a nonempty subset of B, say $S' = S \cap B_{w_i} \neq \varnothing$, then it follows from $(*)$ that the w_i-least element of S' is a w-least element of S. Hence $w \in W$ and w serves as an upper bound for the chain $\{w_i\}$. Thus Zorn's lemma is applicable to W.

Now if w is any member of W, say w is a well ordering on B, and if $B \neq A$, say $a \in A \setminus B$, then

$$w' = w \cup \{(a,a)\} \cup \{(x,a) : x \in B\}$$

is a well ordering on $B \cup \{a\}$ and $w < w'$. Thus if w is a maximal element of W, and Zorn's lemma guarantees the existence of such, then $B = A$ and w is the required well ordering of A.

Proof that (4) ⇒ (1). Let $\{A_i\}$ be the set of sets for which we require a choice function, and put $A = \amalg A_i$. Now A can be well ordered and this well ordering restricts to a well ordering of A_i regarded as a subset of A. Setting

$$f(A_i) = \text{the least member of } A_i$$

proves the axiom of choice. ■

SUPPLEMENTARY EXERCISES

1. [Section 1] Let $a_{ij} \in \mathbb{Q}$ form an m by n matrix as in (4.7). Then

$$\max_j \min_i a_{ij} \leqslant \min_i \max_j a_{ij}.$$

2. [Section 6] Let F be a field and $K = F(X)$.

(i) The rational functions in X^2 form a subfield $F(X^2) = k$ (say) of K that is isomorphic to K. If $f = f(X) \in K$, then $f(X)f(-X) \in k$; hence K, as a vector space over k, has dimension 2 with basis $\{1, X\}$.

(ii) The additive group V of K becomes a vector space over K of dimension 2 if we define scalar multiplication $K \times V \to V$ by $(f, g) \mapsto f(X^2)g(X)$ (multiplication in K).

3. [A7.5] Let the field K contain the field k as a subfield and let V be a vector space over K. Explain how V can be regarded as a vector space over k and that if $\dim_K V$ and $[K:k]$ are finite then

$$\dim_k V = [K:k] \dim_K V.$$

In the situation $k \subsetneq K \subset k(X)$, show that $[k(X):K] < \infty$.

4. [Section 10] (**Dedekind's theorem**) Let k be a field, M a monoid, and $\rho_1, \dots, \rho_n$: $M \to k$ distinct homomorphisms into the multiplicative monoid of k. Then $\{\rho_1, \dots, \rho_n\}$ is a linearly independent subset of k^M. (This applies in particular when M is a ring and the ρ_i are ring homomorphisms. Conversely, the monoid case is a consequence of the ring case by means of the universal property of the monoid ring $\mathbb{Z}[M]$ (q.v.). *Hint*: Use $\rho_i(xy) = \rho_i(x)\rho_i(y)$ to reduce to the case $n - 1$.)

5. [Section 10] Let V be a vector space, $v \in V$, and $f \in \mathrm{GL}(V)$. ($\mathrm{GL}(V)$ is the standard notation for the group of automorphisms $(\mathrm{End}\, V)^*$.) Then the map $\sigma_{f,v}$: $V \to V$ defined by $w \mapsto f(w) + v$ is bijective, the set of all such $\sigma_{f,v}$ form a subgroup G of $\mathrm{Sym}(V)$, and $\sigma_{f,v} \mapsto f$ defines a group homomorphism $G \to \mathrm{GL}(V)$.

6. [Section 10] Let V, W be vector spaces over F and let σ be an automorphism of the field F. A map f: $V \to W$ is **σ-linear** if $f(\mathbf{v} + \mathbf{v}') = f(\mathbf{v}) + f(\mathbf{v}')$ and $f(a\mathbf{v}) =$

$\sigma(a)f(\mathbf{v})$, $\forall \mathbf{v},\mathbf{v}' \in V$ and $a \in F$. (In this terminology, *linear* is *1-linear*.) Prove

(i) the analog of (4.34);

(ii) $E=\{a \in F; \sigma(a)=a\}$ is a subfield of F;

(iii) if $f: V \to V$ is σ-linear, then $U=\{\mathbf{v}: f(\mathbf{v})=\mathbf{v}\}$ is an E-subspace of V.

7. [Section 10] Let k be a field, V the vector space $k[X]$, and, for $f \in V$, define $\delta(f)=f(X+1)-f(X)$. Then in the notation of A7.4, $\delta(a_0+a_1X+a_2X^{(2)}+\cdots)=a_1+2a_2X+3a_3X^{(2)}+\cdots$; hence $\delta \in \mathrm{End}(V)$. When the characteristic of k is 0, for a given g $\exists! f \ni \delta(f)=g$ and $f(0)=0$. Find f in the case $g=X^3-5X^2+X+1$.

8. [Section 11] Let f_i: $V_i \to V_{i+1}(1 \leqslant i \leqslant n)$ be homomorphisms of finite dimensional vector spaces such that $\mathrm{Ker}(f_{i+1})=\mathrm{Im}(f_i)$ $(1 \leqslant i \leqslant n-1)$ and $V_1=V_{n+1}=0$. Then $\Sigma(-1)^i\dim(V_i)=0$.

9. [Section 12] For subspaces X, Y, Z of a vector space,

$$(X \cap Y)+(X \cap Z) \subset X \cap (Y+Z),$$

$$(X+Y) \cap (X+Z) \supset X+(Y \cap Z).$$

Give examples of inequality in the two cases.

10. [Section 12] Let $f \in \mathrm{End}(V)$, where $\dim(V)<\infty$, and define $I_i=\mathrm{Im}(f^i)$, $K_i=\mathrm{Ker}(f^i)$. Then $I_1 \supset I_2 \supset \cdots$ and $K_1 \subset K_2 \subset \cdots$ and both sequences become stationary. If $I_r=I_{r+1}=\cdots$ and $K_s=K_{s+1}=\cdots$, where r and s are minimal, then $r=s$ and $V=I_r \dotplus K_r$.

11. [A8.2] If $p=p^2 \in \mathrm{End}(V)$, so that $V=I \dotplus N$, where $I=\mathrm{Im}(p)$ and $N=\mathrm{Ker}(p)$, one calls p the projection of V **onto** I **along** N. Find the projection of k^2 onto $\langle(1,2)\rangle$ along $\langle(3,4)\rangle$ (i.e., determine $p(x,y)$ $\forall x,y$). Now find the projection of k^2 onto $\langle(3,4)\rangle$ along $\langle(1,2)\rangle$.

12. [A8.2]

(i) If $p_1,\ldots,p_r$ are orthogonal idempotents, then so are $p_1,\ldots,p_r, 1-p_1-\cdots-p_r$.

(ii) If $p_1,\ldots,p_r \in \mathrm{End}(V)$ satisfy $p_ip_j=0$ for $i \neq j$ and $p_1+\cdots+p_r=1$, then they are idempotents.

(iii) If $p=p^2 \in \mathrm{End}_k V$ and $\mathrm{char}(k) \neq 2$, then $1+p$ is invertible, i.e., $1+p \in \mathrm{GL}(V)$.

13. [A8.3] Let $F \subset E$ be an extension of fields of finite degree and let $f,g \in \mathrm{Hom}_F(E,F)$ with $f \neq 0$. Then $\exists! e \in E \ni g(x)=f(ex)$ $\forall x \in E$.

14. [Section 13]

(i) Let I be an abelian group written additively and k a field. Then the set of **odd functions** $\{f \in k^I: f(-x)=-f(x), \forall x \in I\}$ and the set of **even functions** $\{f: f(-x)=f(x), \forall x \in I\}$ are subspaces of k^I.

(ii) Generalize (i) as follows. Let I be a set, σ: $I \to I$ any map, and c a scalar. Then $V(c)=\{f \in k^I: f(x)-cf(\sigma x)=0, \forall x \in I\}$ is a subspace of k^I.

(iii) If $\mathrm{char}(k)\neq 2$ and σ is an **involution**, i.e., a permutation of I satisfying $\sigma^2=1$, then $k^I=V(1)\dot{+}V(-1)$. Hence deduce

every function $\mathbf{Q}\to\mathbf{Q}$ (for instance) is uniquely the sum of an even function and an odd function;

every $\mathbf{A}\in\mathrm{Mat}_n(k)$, where $\mathrm{char}(k)\neq 2$, is uniquely the sum of a symmetric matrix $\mathbf{A}_+(\mathbf{A}_+{}^T=\mathbf{A}_+)$ and a skew symmetric matrix $\mathbf{A}_-(\mathbf{A}_-{}^T=-\mathbf{A}_-)$.

Determine the dimension of the subspace of all $\mathbf{A}_+$(resp. $\mathbf{A}_-$).

15. [Section 13] Let $\mathbf{s}\in\mathrm{Mat}_{\mathbf{N}}(\mathbf{Z})$ have mnth entry $s(n,m)$ (cf. A7.4) and similarly let $\mathbf{S}$ be the matrix of Stirling numbers of the second kind. Then $\mathbf{sS}=\mathbf{Ss}=\mathbf{I}$.

16. [Section 16] Let f,g,h be linear transformations between finite dimensional vector spaces, or finite matrices, such that hgf is defined, and let r denote rank. Then $r(gf)+r(hg)\leqslant r(g)+r(hgf)$.

17. [Section 16] Let $\mathbf{A}\in\mathrm{Mat}_m(k)$, $\mathbf{B}\in\mathrm{Mat}_n(k)$, and let V denote $\mathrm{Mat}_{m,n}(k)$. Then $\mathbf{X}\mapsto\mathbf{AX}-\mathbf{XB}$ defines a map $f\in\mathrm{End}(V)$ and $(\mathbf{A},\mathbf{B})\mapsto f$ defines a vector space homomorphism

$$\psi\colon \mathrm{Mat}_m(k)\times\mathrm{Mat}_n(k)\to\mathrm{End}(V)$$

whose kernel is one dimensional with basis $(\mathbf{I}_m,\mathbf{I}_n)$. Hence $\dim\mathrm{Im}(\psi)=m^2+n^2-1$ and therefore ψ is not surjective unless $\min\{m,n\}=1$. When $m=2$, $n=3$, and

$$\mathbf{A}=\begin{pmatrix}0 & 2\\ 0 & -1\end{pmatrix},\qquad \mathbf{B}=\begin{pmatrix}2 & 2 & 1\\ 3 & 2 & 1\\ 0 & 0 & 0\end{pmatrix},$$

find bases for $\mathrm{Ker}(f)$ and $\mathrm{Im}(f)$. When $m=2$ and $n=3$ prove (and generalize) that $\mathrm{rank}(f)=1$ is not possible for any $\mathbf{A},\mathbf{B}$.

18. [Section 16] Let $a,\ldots,s$ be scalars such that $D=dp+eq+fr\neq 0$ and $def\neq 0$. Show that the system $px+qy+rz=s,(x-a)/d=(y-b)/e=(z-c)/f$ has the solution with $x=(q(ae-bd)+r(af-cd)+ds)/D$, etc., and interpret geometrically.

19. [Section 17] If

$$\mathbf{A}=\begin{pmatrix}1 & a & a^2 & & \cdots & a^{n-1}\\ a & 1 & a & & \cdots & a^{n-2}\\ a^2 & a & 1 & a & \cdots & \\ \vdots & & & & & \\ a^{n-1} & & \cdots & & & 1\end{pmatrix},$$

then $|\mathbf{A}| = (1-a^2)^{n-1}$ and, when $a^2 \neq 1$,

$$\mathbf{A}^{-1} = \begin{pmatrix} b & c & 0 & & \cdots & 0 \\ c & d & c & 0 & \cdots & 0 \\ 0 & c & d & & \cdots & \\ \vdots & & & & & c \\ 0 & & & 0 & c & b \end{pmatrix}$$

for certain b, c, d (a "band matrix" whose diagonal entries, except for the first and last, are the same). This example was given to me by A. Evans.

20. [Section 17] Let $\mathbf{A} = (a_{ij})$ be an $n \times n$ matrix whose entries can be written $a_{ij} = 1/(b_i + c_j)$. Then (this may prove to be a difficult question)

$$\det(\mathbf{A}) = \prod_{i<j} (b_j - b_i)(c_j - c_i) / \prod_{i,j} (b_i + c_j).$$

In particular, the **Hilbert matrix**

$$\mathbf{A}_n = \begin{pmatrix} 1 & \frac{1}{2} & \cdots & 1/n \\ \frac{1}{2} & \frac{1}{3} & \cdots & \\ & & \cdots & 1/(2n-1) \end{pmatrix}$$

has determinant

$$\left(\prod_{i=1}^{n-1} i! \right)^3 \Big/ \prod_{i=n}^{2n-1} i!.$$

Calculate $\mathbf{A}_n^{-1}$. (*Hint*: $\mathbf{A}_n^{-1} \in \operatorname{Mat}_n(\mathbb{Z})$.)

21. [Section 17] Over a field the system $(a+b)x+(b+c)y+(c+a)=0$, $(b+c)x+(c+a)y+(a+b)=0$, $(c+a)x+(a+b)y+(b+c)=0$ is consistent iff

$$2\begin{vmatrix} a & b & c \\ c & a & b \\ b & c & a \end{vmatrix} = 2(a^3+b^3+c^3-3abc) = 0.$$

22. [Section 18] If $D = ad - bc \neq 0$, then the set of solutions of the nonlinear system $ax+by+exy=0$, $cx+dy+fxy=0$ is $(x,y)=(0,0)$ and $(D/(ce-af), D/(bf-de))$, when the latter is defined.

23. [Section 19] The cyclic permutation $(12\cdots n)$ cannot be written as a product of fewer than $n-1$ transpositions.

24. [Section 19] For $n > 3$, the product (in any order) of the elements of order 2 in $\operatorname{Sym}(n)$ is an even permutation.

25. [Section 19] The number of cyclic permutations of length n in $\operatorname{Sym}(n)$ is $(n-1)!$.

26. [Section 19] An element of a group is a **commutator** if it can be written in the form $ghg^{-1}h^{-1}$. Show that the inverse of a commutator is a commutator, and, if $n \geqslant 5$, every cyclic permutation of length 3 is a commutator in $\mathrm{Sym}(n)$.

27. [Section 19] There are $2(2^{n-1}-1)$ ways of dealing n cards to two persons. (They may be dealt unequal numbers of cards.)

28. [Section 19]

(i) For $m,k \in \mathbb{N}$, let $g(m,k)$ denote the number of surjections from a set with m elements to a set with k elements (thus $g(m,k)=0$ when $m<k$), and let X,Y be sets with m and n elements, respectively. Then the number of $f\colon X \to Y$ with $|\mathrm{Im}(f)|=k$ is $\binom{n}{k}g(m,k)$; hence the total number is

$$|Y^X| = n^m = g(m,0) + \binom{n}{1}g(m,1) + \cdots + \binom{n}{n}g(m,n).$$

Now use the inversion formula of A8.4(v) to obtain

$$g(m,n) = n^m - \binom{n}{1}(n-1)^m + \binom{n}{2}(n-2)^m - \cdots.$$

Deduce by (4.110) that

$$n! = n^n - \binom{n}{1}(n-1)^n + \binom{n}{2}(n-2)^n - \cdots.$$

(ii) A formula for Stirling numbers of the second kind (A7.4):

$$S(n,m) = \frac{1}{(m-1)!}\left(m^{n-1} - \binom{m-1}{1}(m-1)^{n-1} + \binom{m-1}{2}(m-2)^{n-1} - \cdots + (-1)^{m-1}\right).$$

(iii) For integers j,n satisfying $0 \leqslant j < n$, $\sum_{k=0}^{n}(-1)^k\binom{n}{k}k^j = 0$. (*Hint*: The linear operator $X\,d/dX$ must be applied at least n times to

$$(1-X)^n = \sum (-1)^k \binom{n}{k} X^k$$

to get a term not containing the factor $1-X$.) Hence if $0 \leqslant m < n$,

$$\sum_{k=0}^{n} (-1)^k \binom{n}{k}(n+kX)^m = 0.$$

What if $m=n$?

29. [Section 19] Let $\mathbf{A} \in \mathrm{Mat}_n(k)$ and let $\mathbf{A}^{r_1 \cdots r_s}_{c_1 \cdots c_t}$ denote the $s \times t$ submatrix obtained by intersecting rows $r_1,\ldots,r_s$ with columns $c_1,\ldots,c_t$. Thus

$$\mathbf{A}^{31}_{14} = \begin{pmatrix} a_{31} & a_{34} \\ a_{11} & a_{14} \end{pmatrix}.$$

Then, given an integer k between 1 and n and a fixed permutation $(r_1,\ldots,r_n)$ of $(1,\ldots,n)$,

$$|\mathbf{A}| = \sum \mathrm{sgn}(\sigma)\left|\mathbf{A}^{r_1 \cdots r_k}_{c_1 \cdots c_k}\right|\left|\mathbf{A}^{r_{k+1} \cdots r_n}_{c_{k+1} \cdots c_n}\right|,$$

where $\sigma \in \mathrm{Sym}(n)$ is defined by $\sigma(r_i) = c_i$, and there are $\binom{n}{k}$ terms in the sum, one for each combination $\{c_1, \dots, c_k\}$ of $\{1, \dots, n\}$ k at a time, and a particular permutation $(c_1, \dots, c_k)$ is chosen to represent each combination. (*Hint*: All permutations of $(1, \dots, n)$ are obtained by separating $\{1, \dots, n\}$ into two sets $\{c_1, \dots, c_k\}$ and $\{c_{k+1}, \dots, c_n\}$ in all possible ways and then permuting each of these sets in all possible ways.) This generalization of (4.120) is known as the **Laplace expansion** of $|\mathbf{A}|$.

30. [A9.3] Find unipotent matrices $\mathbf{A}, \mathbf{B}$ for which $\mathbf{AB}$ is not unipotent.

31. [A9.3] For $\mathbf{A} \in \mathrm{Mat}_n(k), \mathbf{P} \in \mathrm{GL}_n(k)$, the centralizer $Z(\mathbf{P}^{-1}\mathbf{A}\mathbf{P}) = \mathbf{P}^{-1}Z(\mathbf{A})\mathbf{P}$. Second, if $\mathbf{A}$ is similar to $\mathrm{diag}(\mu_1 \mathbf{I}_{e_1}, \dots, \mu_r \mathbf{I}_{e_r})$, where the μ_i are distinct (i.e., $\mathrm{diag}(\lambda_1, \dots, \lambda_n)$, where e_i of the λs have the value μ_i), then $\dim Z(\mathbf{A}) = e_1^2 + \cdots + e_r^2$.

32. [Section 20] Let k be a field.

(i) If Y is a transcendental element of $k(X)$, as defined in Section 10 of Chapter 3, prove there is a unique k-algebra endomorphism of $k(X)$ in which $X \mapsto Y$. (This combines the universal property of the polynomial ring $k[X]$ and the universal property of localization in the case $S^{-1}k[X] = k(X)$; cf. A4.4.)

(ii) Show that k is algebraically closed in $k(X)$, i.e., that every $Y \in k(X) \setminus k$ is transcendental over k.

(iii) If

$$\sigma = \begin{pmatrix} a & b \\ c & d \end{pmatrix} \in \mathrm{GL}_2(k),$$

let $\bar{\sigma}$ denote the endomorphism (as in (i)) given by

$$X \mapsto Y = \frac{aX + c}{bX + d}.$$

Show that $\bar{\sigma}$ is an automorphism (so $k(Y) = k(X)$) and that $\sigma \mapsto \bar{\sigma}$ defines a group homomorphism

$$\mathrm{GL}_2(k) \to \mathrm{Aut}_{k\text{-alg}}(k(X)).$$

(An automorphism of $k(X)$ of the form $\bar{\sigma}$ is called a **fractional linear transformation**. It can be shown that every k-algebra automorphism of $k(X)$ is of this type, in other words, that the above group homomorphism is surjective.) Show that the subgroup generated by the two automorphisms $X \mapsto 1/X$ and $X \mapsto 1 - X$ is isomorphic with Sym(3).

33. [Section 20] The number of monomials $X_1^{r_1} X_2^{r_2} \cdots X_m^{r_m}$ in m variables of total degree $n = r_1 + \cdots + r_m$ is

$$\binom{n+m-1}{m-1} = \binom{n+m-1}{n}.$$

34. [Section 20] The coefficient of $X_1^{r_1}\cdots X_m^{r_m}$ in $(X_1+\cdots+X_m)^n$, where $\Sigma r_i=n$, is the **multinomial coefficient**

$$\binom{n}{r_1,\ldots,r_m}=\frac{n!}{r_1!\ldots r_m!}.$$

This number also admits the following combinatorial interpretations:

(i) It is the number of words (strings of letters) that can be formed from a bag of n letters consisting of r_1 copies of the first letter of the alphabet,..., r_m copies of the mth letter.

(ii) It is the number of ways of distributing n letters in m pigeonholes, such that for $1\leqslant i\leqslant m$, r_i of the letters go into the ith pigeonhole.

Next, if $n=mq+r, 0\leqslant r<m$, then the maximum multinomial coefficient for a given n occurs when r of the r_i have the value $q+1$ and the remaining $m-r$ of the r_i have the value q. The maximum value is $n!/(((q+1)!)^r(q!)^{n-r})$.

35. [Section 21] Every n-variable function $f\colon \mathbb{F}_q^{\,n}\to\mathbb{F}_q$ is given by a polynomial $p\in\mathbb{F}_q[X_1,\ldots,X_n]$. (The case $n=1$ occurs in Exercise 6 after Section 10.)

36. [A9.7] Let K be a commutative ring and $\mathbf{A}\in \mathrm{GL}_n(K)$ (i.e., $\mathbf{A}\in\mathrm{Mat}_n(K)$ and $\det(\mathbf{A})\in K^*$). If the elements $x_1,\ldots,x_n$ in K generate the ideal I and $(x_1,\ldots,x_n)\mathbf{A}=(y_1,\ldots,y_n)$ then the ys also generate I.

37. [A9.7] If R is any ring (possibly noncommutative), the usual definitions make $\mathrm{Mat}_n(R)$ into a ring.

(i) $I\mapsto \mathrm{Mat}_n(I)=$ the set of $(a_{ij})\in\mathrm{Mat}_n(R)$ with all $a_{ij}\in I$ gives a bijection between the set of all ideals of R and that of $\mathrm{Mat}_n(R)$; $\mathrm{Mat}_n(R)/\mathrm{Mat}_n(I)\approx\mathrm{Mat}_n(R/I)$.

(ii) The set $\mathrm{Upp}_n(R)$ of upper triangular matrices is an R-subalgebra of $\mathrm{Mat}_n(R)$. (See Section 20.)

(iii) Find the ideals of $\mathrm{Upp}_2(\mathbb{Q})$ and $\mathrm{Upp}_2(\mathbb{Z})$.

(iv) By block multiplication, $\mathrm{Mat}_m(\mathrm{Mat}_n(R))\approx\mathrm{Mat}_{mn}(R)$.

(v) If k is a field and I is an infinite set, the set of $\mathbf{A}\in\mathrm{Mat}_I(k)$ of finite rank is a proper ideal.

38. [A9.8]

(i) If m is a square free integer $\neq 1$, the ideal I generated by X^2-m in $\mathbb{Z}[X]$ is prime, and hence $R=\mathbb{Z}[X]/I$ is an integral domain.

Let K denote $Q(R)$. As in A6.4, the elements of R (resp. K) are uniquely of the form $x+y\sqrt{m}$ where $x,y\in\mathbb{Z}$ (resp. $x,y\in\mathbb{Q}$). The **norm** $N\colon K\to\mathbb{Q}$ is defined by

$$N(x+y\sqrt{m})=(x+y\sqrt{m})(x-y\sqrt{m})=x^2-my^2=N(x-y\sqrt{m}).$$

Notice that N restricts to $R\to\mathbb{Z}$.

(ii) With the notation of A9.8, R is EA with respect to $\rho(\alpha)=\pm N(\alpha)$, whichever is $\geqslant 0$, when $m=-1,-2,2,3$. Consequently each of these $\mathbb{Z}[\sqrt{m}]$ is a P.I.D. (*Hint*: To satisfy (EA2), write a/b in the form $s_1+s_2\sqrt{m}, s_i\in\mathbb{Q}$, and choose $q=q_1+q_2\sqrt{m}$ with $q_i\in\mathbb{Z}\ni -\frac{1}{2}\leqslant q_i-s_i\leqslant\frac{1}{2}$.)

(iii) When $R=\mathbb{Z}[\sqrt{-1}]$, $R^*=\{\pm 1, \pm\sqrt{-1}\}$, and the following are the factorizations into irreducible factors:

$$2=\sqrt{-1}\left(1-\sqrt{-1}\right)^2, \qquad 5=\left(2+\sqrt{-1}\right)\left(2-\sqrt{-1}\right), \qquad 9=3\cdot 3.$$

(The elements of this P.I.D. are known as **Gauss integers**.)

(iv) $Z[\sqrt{-1}]/3\mathbb{Z}[\sqrt{-1}]$ is a nine-element field.

(v) $Z[\sqrt{2}]^*=\{\pm(1-\sqrt{2})^n : n\in\mathbb{Z}\}$.

(vi) Let $m\equiv 1 \bmod 4$ and let σ denote the element $(\sqrt{m}-1)/2$ of K. Then $R'=\{x+y\sigma : x, y\in\mathbb{Z}\}$ is a subring of K and $N(x+y\sigma)=x^2-xy-m'y^2$, where $m'=\frac{1}{4}(m-1)$. Also show that R' is EA as in (ii) when $m=-3$ and 5; and in these cases, R'^* is $\{\pm 1, \pm\sigma, \pm\sigma^2\}$ (resp. $\{\pm\sigma^n : n\in\mathbb{Z}\}$).

39. Let $a_1,\ldots,a_q$ denote the elements of $\mathbb{F}_q$ and let $\mathbf{A}\in \mathrm{Mat}_q(\mathbb{F}_q)$ have ijth entry a_i^{j-1}. Then

$$|\mathbf{A}|^2=(-1)^{(q+1)(q+2)/2}.$$

Use the nonsingularity of $\mathbf{A}$ to prove that if E is any specified set of points in $\mathbb{F}_q{}^m$, then there exists $f\in\mathbb{F}_q[X_1,\ldots,X_m]$ such that $f(x_1,\ldots,x_m)=0 \Leftrightarrow (x_1,\ldots,x_m)\in E$. (For instance, any set of points of the plane $\mathbb{F}_q{}^2$ can be the points of an "algebraic curve/$\mathbb{F}_q$.") Find $f\in\mathbb{F}_3[X,Y]\ni f(x,y)=0\Leftrightarrow(x,y)\in\{(0,0),(0,1),(0,2),(1,1),(1,2),(2,2)\}$.

The Real, Complex, and p-adic Numbers

5

1. INTRODUCTION

In this chapter we explain what is meant by a real number, give explicit definitions of certain particular real numbers, including $\sqrt{2}$, e, $\log 2$, π, and prove the following statements. *Every real number can be written as an integer followed by a decimal expansion. For instance,*

$$-\tfrac{3}{2} = -1.5, \qquad \tfrac{1}{11} = 0.090909\ldots, \qquad \sqrt{2} = 1.41421\ldots, \qquad \pi = 3.14159\ldots.$$

The real numbers form a field, denoted $\mathbb{R}$, which contains $\mathbb{Q}$ as a subfield. The elements of $\mathbb{R} \setminus \mathbb{Q}$ are called irrational numbers and "most" real numbers are irrational.

It is possible to define $\mathbb{R}$ as the set of such decimal expansions, then define $+$ and so on, and ultimately verify the field axioms. However, this approach is complicated and not very illuminating. The procedure we adopt is, in a nutshell,

$$\mathbb{R} = R/M,$$

where R is the ring of cauchy sequences and M is the ideal of null sequences. We can convey the basic ideas here by a numerical example.

The number $\sqrt{2}$ is irrational since $X^2 - 2$ has no root in $\mathbb{Q}$. We could construct this "missing" number by forming $\mathbb{Q}[X]/(X^2-2)\mathbb{Q}[X]$, but such an approach is piecemeal and in any case "most" real numbers are transcendental, that is, are not roots of any polynomial over $\mathbb{Q}$.

We shall construct real numbers by means of sequences of approximations by rationals. For instance the sequence

$$(a_1, a_2, \ldots) = \left(1, \tfrac{14}{10}, \tfrac{141}{100}, \tfrac{1414}{1000}, \ldots\right)$$

represents $\sqrt{2}$ in the sense that ${a_n}^2$ *approaches 2 as n approaches* ∞. In other words, the distance $\pm(a_n^2-2)$ (whichever is positive) between a_n^2 and 2 can be made smaller than any given positive number (e.g., $\frac{1}{10}, \frac{1}{100}, \frac{1}{1000}, \ldots$) provided n is taken sufficiently large. However, we must avoid reference to the polynomial X^2-2. The way around this is to consider distances $\pm(a_i-a_j)$ between pairs of members of the sequence.

This leads to the idea of a cauchy sequence $(a_1, a_2, \ldots)$, whose members become closer together as one goes farther out in the sequence. An example is the sequence

$$a_1=1, \quad a_2=2, \quad a_3=\tfrac{5}{2}, \quad \ldots, \quad a_{n+1}=a_n+1/n!,$$

which serves to define the real number $e=2.71828\ldots$. (See Proposition (5.228).) Cauchy sequences form a ring.

If we modify the earlier sequence for $\sqrt{2}$, say, by adding 1 to the numerators, we obtain a different sequence:

$$2, \quad \tfrac{15}{10}, \quad \tfrac{142}{100}, \quad \tfrac{1415}{1000}, \quad \ldots,$$

but clearly we want this sequence also to define $\sqrt{2}$. This leads to the idea of regarding two cauchy sequences as equivalent if they differ by a null sequence, that is, a sequence that *approaches 0*. This is a congruence relation on the ring R of cauchy sequences: the null sequences form an ideal M. In fact, M is maximal and R/M is a field.

All this can be carried out with surprisingly little effort and depends at bottom on the simple notion of the absolute value $|a|=\pm a$, whichever is $\geqslant 0$. Indeed we do rather more. By the identical construction R/M in one stroke we obtain the *completion* of any field with respect to any *absolute value*, and in this way we obtain not only the real field $\mathbb{R}$, but also the various p-adic fields $\mathbb{Q}_2, \mathbb{Q}_3, \ldots$ and fields of formal power series. Of course, all these terms will be explained as they arise in this chapter.

2. ABSOLUTE VALUES

If $a \in \mathbb{Q}$, we define its absolute value to be

(5.1)
$$|a|=\begin{cases} a & \text{if} \quad a\geqslant 0,\\ -a & \text{if} \quad a<0.\end{cases}$$

Thus $|-\frac{3}{2}|=|\frac{3}{2}|=\frac{3}{2}$. This function has the following four properties:

(AV0) $\forall a$, $|a|\geqslant 0$ and $|a|=0$ iff $a=0$;
(AV1) $\forall n \in \mathbb{N}$, if $|n|>1$, then $|n|=n$;
(AV2) $|ab|=|a||b|$; and
(AV3) $|a+b|\leqslant |a|+|b|$.

The first three are obvious; to prove the fourth we add the inequalities

$$-|a|\leqslant a\leqslant |a|, \qquad -|b|\leqslant b\leqslant |b|$$

to obtain

$$-(|a|+|b|)\leqslant a+b\leqslant |a|+|b|,$$

which implies (AV3).

(AV3) is known as the **triangle inequality** because of the following geometrical interpretation (see Figure 5.1). Anticipating the definition of *normed vector space*, to be given in Section 23, in that context $|\mathbf{a}|$ denotes the length of the vector $\mathbf{a}$, and (AV3) states the familiar fact that one side of a triangle has length at most the sum of the lengths of the other two sides. In the present one-dimensional situation the "triangles" collapse into line segments, which explains the rather trivial proof of (AV3) in this case.

There are other functions arising naturally that have the properties (AV0)–(AV3). We refer to $|a|$ as defined in (5.1) as the **ordinary absolute value on $\mathbf{Q}$**. For instance, if v_2 is the usual 2-adic valuation on $\mathbf{Q}$, then the map $|\ |:\mathbf{Q}\to\mathbf{Q}$ given by $|0|=0$ and for $a\in\mathbf{Q}^*$ by

$$|a|=2^{-v_2(a)}$$

satisfies (AV0)–(AV3), as will be verified in a moment. Here are some numerical examples. Since $v_2(12)=2$ and $v_2(-\frac{4}{3})=2$, therefore $|12|=|-\frac{4}{3}|=2^{-2}=\frac{1}{4}$. Now $v_2(12-\frac{4}{3})=v_2(\frac{32}{3})=5$; hence $|12-\frac{4}{3}|=2^{-5}$, which is less than $|12|+|-\frac{4}{3}|=\frac{1}{2}$, an illustration of the triangle inequality. Since $v_2(\frac{25}{4})=-2$, therefore $|\frac{25}{4}|=4$ and $|(-\frac{4}{3})(\frac{25}{4})|=|-\frac{25}{3}|=|-\frac{4}{3}||\frac{25}{4}|=1$.

More generally, let B be a U.F.D. and $k=Q(B)$ its field of quotients. Let $a\in k^*$ have the unique factorization

$$a=u\prod p^{v_p(a)},\qquad u\in B^*.$$

As explained in Section 11 of Chapter 3, the integers $v_p(a)$ are intrinsic invariants of a, independent of the particular irreducible elements p chosen to represent their classes; that is, if $p'=pw$, where $w\in B^*$, then $v_{pw}(a)=v_p(a)$. We choose p and a rational number c satisfying $0<c<1$ and define $|\ |:k\to\mathbf{Q}$ by

$$(5.2)\qquad |a|=\begin{cases} c^{v_p(a)} & \text{if}\quad a\neq 0,\\ 0 & \text{if}\quad a=0.\end{cases}$$

Figure 5.1

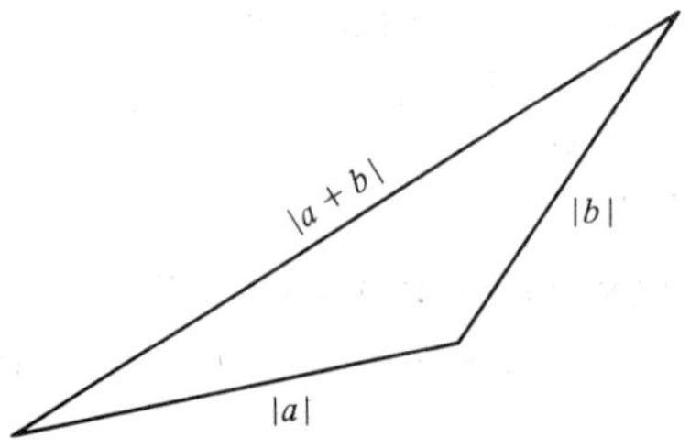

We now verify that this satisfies (AV0)–(AV3). It is convenient to adopt the convention

$$c^{\infty}=0$$

so that $|a|=c^{v_p(a)}$ is now true for all $a\in k$.

(AV0) is obviously true, and (AV1) follows from the fact that each natural number, regarded as an element of k, lies in the subring B and

$$b\in B \quad\Rightarrow\quad v_p(b)\geqslant 0 \quad\Leftrightarrow\quad |b|\leqslant 1.$$

From Chapter 3 we recall

(3.55) $$v_p(ab)=v_p(a)+v_p(b),$$

and this implies (AV2):

$$|ab|=c^{v_p(ab)}=c^{v_p(a)+v_p(b)}=c^{v_p(a)}c^{v_p(b)}=|a||b|,$$

including cases in which $ab=0$. Second, we recall

(3.56) $$v_p(a+b)\geqslant \min\{v_p(a),v_p(b)\}.$$

If $v_p(a)\leqslant v_p(b)$ so that $v_p(a+b)\geqslant v_p(a)$, then, since $0<c<1$,

$$c^{v_p(a)}\geqslant c^{v_p(b)} \qquad\text{and}\qquad c^{v_p(a+b)}\leqslant c^{v_p(a)},$$

again including cases involving $c^{\infty}=0$. Hence $|a+b|\leqslant|a|$ and therefore $|a+b|\leqslant|a|+|b|$, which proves (AV3). In fact we have proved that this $|\ |$ satisfies the **strong triangle inequality**

(AV3$^{\#}$) $|a+b|\leqslant\max\{|a|,|b|\}$.

For example take the quotient field $k=\mathbb{F}_2(X)$ of the P.I.D. $B=\mathbb{F}_2[X]$. (Since $1+1=0$ precludes any sensible definition of $\leqslant$ on this field, we see that such maps $|\ |: k\to\mathbb{Q}$ need not be related to any notion of positiveness.) If we pick $c=\frac{1}{3}$ and for p the irreducible polynomial X, we have

$$v_X((1+X)/X^2)=v_X(1+X)-v_X(X^2)=0-2=-2$$

so $|(1+X)/X^2|_X=(\frac{1}{3})^{-2}=9$. (We sometimes attach an identifying subscript on $|\ |$.)

Taking a different value for c in $|a|=c^{v(a)}$ of course alters the function $|\ |$, but not in an essential way; this matter will be clarified in (5.48). In the case of $\mathbb{Q}$, the standard choice for v_p is $c=1/p$, and then

$$|a|_p=p^{-v_p(a)}.$$

If we let $|a|_{\infty}$ denote the ordinary absolute value as given in (5.1), known as the *infinite prime* in this context, one has the following **product formula**:

(5.3) $$\prod |a|_p=1 \qquad \forall a\in\mathbb{Q}^*$$

where the product is extended over all primes including the one "at infinity." For instance, when $a=-\frac{3}{4}$, $|a|_2=2^2=4$, $|a|_3=\frac{1}{3}$, $|a|_{\infty}=\frac{3}{4}$, and all other $|a|_p=1$. In analogy with an infinite sum in which almost all terms are 0, here the infinite product is meant to be the product of the $|a|_p\neq 1$ and an empty product is 1. Thus $\Pi|a|_p=|-\frac{3}{4}|_2|-\frac{3}{4}|_3|-\frac{3}{4}|_\infty=1$.

Here is another example. On the field $k(X)$ of rational functions over the field k we define $|\ |$ by $|0|=0$ and for a nonzero element a, say $a=s/t$, where $s,t\in k[X]$,

$$|a|=c^{\deg(t)-\deg(s)}.$$

As before, c is a rational number satisfying $0<c<1$. One can check that this is well defined and satisfies (AV0)–(AV3), indeed (AV3$^\#$). However, this is not necessary since this $|\ |$ is actually one of our previous examples in disguise, as we now explain. The bijection $\psi: k(X)\to k(X)$ that leaves the elements of k fixed and replaces X by $1/X$ (so $(a_0+a_1X+\cdots)/(b_0+b_1X+\cdots)\mapsto(a_0+a_1/X+a_2/X^2+\cdots)/(b_0+b_1/X+\cdots)$) clearly preserves sums and products: it is an automorphism of the field. (In the terminology of Section 20 of Chapter 4, it is a k-algebra automorphism.) This means that $1/X$ can be treated like X, so we have $v_{1/X}$ (arising from the U.F.D. $k[1/X]$ of polynomials in the variable $1/X$), where

$$v_{1/X}(a)=v_X(\psi(a)),$$

and the above absolute value is given by

$$|a|=|\psi(a)|_X.$$

Since ψ is a ring homomorphism and $|\ |_X$ satisfies (AV0)–(AV3$^\#$), $|\ |$ does as well.

These examples point to the desirability of having a general definition.

(5.4) DEFINITION. A (rational valued) **absolute value** on the field k is a map $|\ |: k\to\mathbb{Q}$ satisfying (AV0)–(AV3). An absolute value satisfying the strong triangle inequality (AV3$^\#$) is called **ultrametric**. A nonultrametric $|\ |$ is called **archimedean**.

It is possible to prove (AV1) on the basis of the remaining three axioms, but we do not take the trouble to do so. The proof uses the fact that the values are rational numbers and is no longer valid when we generalize this definition to real numbers in (5.23).

In mathematics the notation $|a|$ is ordinarily understood to mean the ordinary absolute value of a rational number a as defined in (5.1) (or the extension of this to real and complex numbers as defined later in this chapter). When some other absolute value is needed, another notation such as $|a|_p$ or $|a|'$ is used. However for the purpose of this general discussion it is convenient to use $|\ |$ abstractly:

Until the end of Section 3, $|\ |$ will denote an absolute value as defined in (5.4).

This allows $|\ |$ to denote even the **trivial absolute value** defined by

(5.5) $$|a| = 1 - \delta_{0a} = 1 \qquad \forall a \quad \text{except } |0| = 0.$$

An absolute value arising as in (5.2) is called a ***p*-adic absolute value**. For instance with $c = \frac{1}{2}$, $|-\frac{3}{4}|_2 = 4$ and $|5X + 2/3X|_X = 2$ are examples of the 2-adic absolute value on $\mathbb{Q}$ and the X-adic absolute value on $\mathbb{Q}(X)$.

Here are some simple deductions from the axioms.

(5.6) LEMMA

(i) $|1| = 1$;
(ii) $|a^{-1}| = |a|^{-1}\ \forall a \in k^*$;
(iii) $|-a| = |a|\ \forall a \in k$;
(iv) $|a - b| \geqslant |a| - |b|\ \forall a, b \in k$;
(v) *if* $|\ |$ *is ultrametric and* $a_1, \ldots, a_n \in k$, *then*

$$|a_1 + \cdots + a_n| \leqslant \max\{|a_1|, \ldots, |a_n|\}$$

with equality if the maximum is attained just once, i.e.,

$$|a_1 + \cdots + a_n| = |a_i|$$

if $|a_j| < |a_i|$ *for all* $j \neq i$.

Proof. $|1||1| = |1 \cdot 1| = |1|$ by (AV2) and $|1| \neq 0$ by (AV0). Hence we can cancel to get $|1| = 1$ and therefore $1 = |1| = |aa^{-1}| = |a||a^{-1}|$ so $|a^{-1}| = |a|^{-1}$ for $a \neq 0$. Next, $|-1|^2 = |(-1)^2| = |1| = 1$ and, since the only roots of $X^2 = 1$ in $\mathbb{Q}$ are ± 1, we have $|-1| = 1$ by (AV0). Hence $|-a| = |(-1)a| = |a|$.

We obtain (iv) by replacing $a + b$ by a in (AV3):

$$|a| = |a - b + b| \leqslant |a - b| + |b|.$$

Of course we also have $|a + b| \geqslant |a| - |b|$ (since $|-b| = |b|$).

The inequality in (v) is obtained by repeated application of (AV3$^\sharp$): $|a_1 + \cdots + a_n| \leqslant \max\{|a_1|, |a_2 + \cdots + a_n|\} \leqslant \max\{|a_1|, \max\{|a_2|, \ldots, |a_n|\}\} = \max\{|a_1|, \ldots, |a_n|\}$ by induction on n. Now suppose the maximum is attained just once, say $|a_1| > |a_j|$ for $j = 2, \ldots, n$. Then, writing $b = a_2 + \cdots + a_n$, we have $|a_1 + b| \leqslant |a_1|$ and $|\pm b| \leqslant \max\{|a_2|, \ldots, |a_n|\} < |a_1|$. Therefore, in

$$|a_1| = |a_1 + b - b| \leqslant \max\{|a_1 + b|, |-b|\},$$

the larger term on the right must be $|a_1 + b|$, so we have the inequality $|a_1| \leqslant |a_1 + b| = |a_1 + a_2 + \cdots + a_n|$ opposite to the earlier one, and this proves the equality. ■

If $|\ |$ is ultrametric then for $n \in \mathbb{N}$

$$|n| = |1 + \cdots + 1| \leqslant \max\{|1|, \ldots, |1|\} = 1,$$

which is a behavior quite opposite to that of the ordinary $|\ |$ on $\mathbb{Q}$. For the latter we can restate the archimedean property as follows. Given $a, b \in \mathbb{Q}$ with $a \neq 0$, $\exists n \in \mathbb{N} \ni |na| > |b|$, which is why the ordinary $|\ |$ is called archimedean. This use of the word archimedean is naturally extended to absolute values in general, as defined in (5.4).

It is helpful to think of $|a-b|$ as representing the "distance" between a and b. This agrees with the intuitive notion of distance in the case of the ordinary absolute value and suggests the following definition. The **unit disc**, denoted D, is the set of all elements that lie a distance at most 1 from 0:

$$D = \{a \in k : |a| \leqslant 1\}.$$

Thus $0 \in D$ by (AV0), D is multiplicatively closed by (AV2), $1 \in D$ by the lemma above, and $a \in D \Rightarrow -a \in D$. However, in general, D need not be additively closed.

(5.7) PROPOSITION. *Let $|\ |$ be an absolute value on the field k with unit disc D. The following are equivalent*:

(i) *$|\ |$ is ultrametric*;
(ii) *D is a subring of k*;
(iii) $\forall n \in \mathbb{N}$, $|n| \leqslant 1$.

When this is the case, D is a local ring with unique maximal ideal $P = \{a \in k : |a| < 1\}$, and with group of units

$$D^* = \{a \in k : |a| = 1\}. \tag{5.8}$$

Proof. We give the cyclic proof (i) $\Rightarrow$ (ii) $\Rightarrow$ (iii) $\Rightarrow$ (i).

(i) $\Rightarrow$ (ii): From the earlier discussion we need only show that D is additively closed. If $a, b \in D$ then $|a+b| \leqslant \max\{|a|, |b|\} \leqslant 1$, whence $a+b \in D$.

(ii) $\Rightarrow$ (iii): $|1| = 1$ and inductively if $|n| \leqslant 1$ then 1 and n are in D; hence $1 + n \in D$, i.e., $|1+n| \leqslant 1$.

(iii) $\Rightarrow$ (i): Given $a, b \in k$, say $|a| \leqslant |b|$, we wish to show that $|a+b| \leqslant |b|$. Now $\forall m \in \mathbb{N}$,

$$\begin{aligned} |a+b|^m &= \left|a^m + \binom{m}{1} a^{m-1} b + \cdots + b^m\right| \leqslant |a|^m + |a|^{m-1}|b| + \cdots + |b|^m \\ &\leqslant (m+1)|b|^m \end{aligned}$$

since each of the binomial coefficients is a natural number. If we had $|a+b| > |b|$, then $|a+b| > |b|(1+1/h)$ for some $h \in \mathbb{N}$ and we would arrive at the contradiction

$$\begin{aligned} |a+b|^m > |b|^m (1+1/h)^m &= |b|^m \left(1 + \binom{m}{1}\Big/h + \binom{m}{2}\Big/h^2 + \cdots\right) \\ &\geqslant |b|^m \left(1 + m/h + m(m-1)/2h^2\right) > |b|^m (1+m) \end{aligned}$$

by taking $m > 1 + 2(h^2 - h)$.

Now let $|\ |$ be ultrametric and let a be a nonzero element of D, so $|a| \leqslant 1$. Then $a^{-1} \in D$ iff $|a^{-1}| = |a|^{-1} \leqslant 1$, and (5.8) follows. A proper ideal J contains no units; hence $J \subset P$. Finally the set P is a proper ideal since $1 \notin P$; $0 \in P$ by (AV0); if $a \in P, b \in D$, then $ab \in P$ by (AV2); if $a, b \in P$, then $a + b \in P$ by (AV3$^{\#}$). ■

In the ultrametric case D is also called the **valuation ring** and D/P, which is a field by A5.6, is called the **residue field** of the absolute value. If the absolute value is p-adic, then

$$D = \{a \in k : v_p(a) \geqslant 0\}, \qquad D^* = \{a \in k : v_p(a) = 0\},$$

$$P = \{a \in k : v_p(a) > 0\},$$

and we see that the terminology is consistent with that of A6.6.

(5.9) COROLLARY. (α) *If* $\operatorname{char}(k) = p > 0$ *then every absolute value* $|\ |$ *on* k *is ultrametric and restricts to the trivial absolute value on the prime subfield* $\mathbb{F}_p$.

(β) *If* $|\ |$ *is archimedean, so* $\operatorname{char}(k) = 0$ *and* $k \supset \mathbb{Q}$, *then* $|\ |$ *restricts to the ordinary absolute value on* $\mathbb{Q}$.

(γ) *Let* $|\ |$ *be ultrametric,* $\operatorname{char}(k) = 0$, *and* $\operatorname{char}(D/P) = p$. *If* $p = 0$, *then* $|\ |$ *restricts to the trivial absolute value on* $\mathbb{Q}$; *if* $p > 0$, *then the restriction of* $|\ |$ *to* $\mathbb{Q}$ *is p-adic*:

$$|q| = c^{v_p(q)} \qquad \text{for} \quad q \in \mathbb{Q},$$

where $c = |p|$ *satisfies* $0 < c < 1$.

Proof. (α) By (3.53), for $n \in \mathbb{Z}$ and any absolute value on k

$$|n| = \begin{cases} 0 & \text{if} \quad n \equiv 0 \mod p, \\ 1 & \text{if} \quad n \not\equiv 0 \mod p, \end{cases}$$

so (iii) of the proposition is satisfied.

(β) By (iii) $\exists n \in \mathbb{N} \ni |n| > 1$. In view of (AV1), (AV2), and (5.6) it is sufficient to show that

$$m \in \mathbb{N}, \quad m > 1 \qquad \Rightarrow \qquad |m| > 1.$$

However, suppose we had an $m \geqslant 2$ with $|m| \leqslant 1$. For large enough $e \in \mathbb{N}$ we have $m < n^e$ (cf. A3.5) and, since $|n^e| = |n|^e > 1$, $\exists l \in \mathbb{N} \ni m \leqslant l < n^e$, where $|l| \leqslant 1$ and $|l+1| > 1$. Yet then by (AV1), $|l+1| = l+1 \geqslant 3$ and (AV3) gives the contradiction $|l+1| \leqslant |l| + 1 \leqslant 2$.

(γ) For $p = 0$ or a prime,

$$\operatorname{char}(D/P) = p \qquad \Leftrightarrow \qquad p \in P \qquad \Leftrightarrow \qquad |p| < 1.$$

Thus there is at most one prime $p \ni |p| < 1$. If there is no such prime and

$$q = \pm 2^{v_2(q)} 3^{v_3(q)} \cdots \in \mathbb{Q}^*,$$

then

$$|q| = |2|^{v_2(q)} \cdots = 1;$$

hence $|\ |$ is trivial on $\mathbb{Q}$, while if $|p| < 1$, then

$$|q| = |p|^{v_p(q)}. \quad \blacksquare$$

The X-adic absolute value on $\mathbb{Q}(X)$ is an example where the restriction to $\mathbb{Q}$ is trivial. Note the possible combinations.

The **equal characteristic** cases:

$$\text{char}(k) = 0, \quad \text{char}(D/P) = 0; \quad \text{char}(k) = p > 0, \quad \text{char}(D/P) = p.$$

The **unequal characteristic** case:

$$\text{char}(k) = 0, \quad \text{char}(D/P) = p > 0.$$

(*Exercise*: The combination p,0 cannot occur.)

3. COMPLETION

Throughout this section k will denote a valued field, that is, a field equipped with an absolute value $|\ |$. Let $S = k^{\mathbb{N}}$ denote the ring of all sequences $(a_1, a_2, a_3, \ldots)$ of elements $a_i \in k$. As explained in Chapter 2, this is a commutative ring with componentwise operations. The **diagonal map** $\Delta: k \to S$ given by $a \mapsto (a, a, \ldots)$ is an injective ring homomorphism because $\Delta(a+b) = \Delta(a) + \Delta(b)$, $\Delta(ab) = \Delta(a)\Delta(b)$ and $\Delta(1) = 1$.[1]

(5.10) DEFINITION. $(a_1, a_2, \ldots)$ is a **cauchy sequence** if $\forall h \in \mathbb{N}\ \exists N \in \mathbb{N}$ (possibly different N for different h) such that

$$|a_i - a_j| < 1/h, \qquad \forall i, j \geqslant N.$$

The idea behind this definition is to require the members of the sequence to become closer and closer together (thinking of $|a_i - a_j|$ as the "distance" between a_i and a_j) the farther one goes out in the sequence. For a given cauchy sequence a larger h usually requires a larger N.

For instance, the sequence

$$\left(\tfrac{3}{2}, \tfrac{5}{4}, \ldots, 1 + 2^{-n}, \ldots\right) \in \mathbb{Q}^{\mathbb{N}}$$

is cauchy with respect to the ordinary absolute values because if $i < j$, then

$$|a_i - a_j| = |2^{-i} - 2^{-j}| < 2^{-i}$$

and this is less than a given $1/h$ for all $i, j \geqslant N$ if we take for instance $N = h$ (since $2^h > h$, by an easy induction). The definition puts us under no

[1] In the terminology of Section 20 of Chapter 4, Δ makes S a k-algebra.

obligation to find the best possible N: The sequence is cauchy if for each $h \in \mathbb{N}$ we can exhibit *some* N that does the job.

The particular sequence above is not 2-adically cauchy since if $i<j$, then

$$|a_i - a_j|_2 = |2^{-j}(2^{j-i}-1)|_2 = 2^j$$

and this does not become small for large i and j. (*Exercise*: This sequence is not p-adically cauchy for any prime p.) However $(3,5,9,\ldots,1+2^n,\ldots)$ is 2-adically cauchy since now for $i<j$

$$|a_i - a_j|_2 = |2^i - 2^j|_2 = |2^i(1-2^{j-i})|_2 = 2^{-i},$$

which can be made as small as we like by taking i and j sufficiently large.

(5.11) LEMMA. *Cauchy sequences are bounded in absolute value: If $(a_1, a_2, \ldots)$ is cauchy, then $\exists m \in \mathbb{N} \ni |a_i| < m \ \forall i$.*

Proof. Taking $h=1$ in (5.10) we obtain an $N \ni |a_i - a_j| < 1 \ \forall i, j \geqslant N$. In particular,

$$|a_i| = |a_i - a_N + a_N| \leqslant |a_i - a_N| + |a_N| < 1 + |a_N|, \qquad \forall i \geqslant N.$$

Hence $\forall i \geqslant 1$,

$$|a_i| \leqslant \max\{|a_1|,\ldots,|a_{N-1}|, 1+|a_N|\} = m',$$

say, and it remains to take (by the archimedean principle) an $m \in \mathbb{N}$ satisfying $m > m'$. ■

(5.12) PROPOSITION. *Let R denote the set of cauchy sequences in S. Then R is a subring of S.*

Proof. Since $|a-a| = |0| = 0 < 1/h \ \forall h \in \mathbb{N}$, R contains the constant sequences $(a, a, \ldots)$, and in particular R contains $0 = (0,0,\ldots)$ and $1 = (1,1,\ldots)$. Now let $(a_1, a_2, \ldots)$ and $(b_1, b_2, \ldots)$ be elements of R and let h be a natural number.

Then $\exists N \ni |a_i - a_j| < 1/h \ \forall i, j \geqslant N$. Therefore $|(-a_j)-(-a_i)| < 1/h$, which proves that $-(a_1, a_2, \ldots) = (-a_1, -a_2, \ldots) \in R$.

Next, $\exists N_1 \ni |a_i - a_j| < 1/2h \ \forall i, j \geqslant N_1$ and $\exists N_2 \ni |b_i - b_j| < 1/2h \ \forall i, j \geqslant N_2$. Therefore, with $N = \max\{N_1, N_2\}$ we have

$$|(a_i + b_i) - (a_j + b_j)| = |(a_i - a_j) + (b_i - b_j)| \leqslant |a_i - a_j| + |b_i - b_j|$$

$$< 1/h, \qquad \forall i, j \geqslant N,$$

which proves that

$$(a_1, a_2, \ldots) + (b_1, b_2, \ldots) = (a_1 + b_1, a_2 + b_2, \ldots) \in R.$$

Finally we show that R is multiplicatively closed. By the lemma, $\exists h_1, h_2 \ni |a_i| < h_1$ and $|b_i| < h_2 \ \forall i$. Now $\exists N_1, N_2 \ni |a_i - a_j| < 1/2h_1h_2 \ \forall i, j \geqslant N_1$

and $|b_i - b_j| < 1/2h_1h_2\ \forall i, j \geqslant N_2$. Hence

$$|a_ib_i - a_jb_j| = |(a_i - a_j)b_i + a_j(b_i - b_j)| \leqslant |a_i - a_j||b_i| + |a_j||b_i - b_j|$$

$$< \frac{1}{2hh_2}h_2 + h_1\frac{1}{2hh_1} = \frac{1}{h}$$

for all $i, j \geqslant N = \max\{N_1, N_2\}$. ∎

As mentioned in the proof, R contains all the constant sequences and therefore R is actually a k-subalgebra of S.

As outlined in Section 1, the next step is to decide when two cauchy sequences should be regarded as equivalent, or, taking their difference, when a cauchy sequence should be regarded as representing 0.

(5.13) DEFINITION. The sequence $(a_1, a_2, \ldots)$ is **null** if $\forall h \in \mathbb{N}\ \exists N \in \mathbb{N} \ni |a_i| < 1/h\ \forall i \geqslant N$.

(5.14) LEMMA. (i) *Every null sequence is cauchy.*

(ii) *If $(a_1, a_2, \ldots)$ is cauchy but not null, then it is eventually bounded away from* 0: $\exists h, N \in \mathbb{N} \ni |a_i| > 1/h\ \forall i \geqslant N$.

Proof. (i) Let $(a_1, \ldots)$ be null. Given $h \in \mathbb{N}$, $\exists N' \ni |a_i| < 1/2h\ \forall i \geqslant N'$ and therefore $|a_i - a_j| \leqslant |a_i| + |-a_j| < 1/h\ \forall i, j \geqslant N'$.

(ii) Since the sequence is not null there exists an $h_1 \in \mathbb{N}$ for which (5.13) cannot be fulfilled. This means that every $N \in \mathbb{N}$ fails:

$$\forall N \in \mathbb{N}\ \exists i \geqslant N \ni |a_i| > 1/h_1. \tag{5.15}$$

Since the sequence is cauchy $\exists N_1 \ni |a_i - a_j| < 1/2h_1\ \forall i, j \geqslant N_1$. Now, by taking $N = N_1$ in (5.15), we obtain an $i_1 \geqslant N_1 \ni |a_i| \geqslant 1/h_1$. By (5.6) (iv) for $j \geqslant N_1$,

$$|a_j| = |a_{i_1} - (a_{i_1} - a_j)| \geqslant |a_{i_1}| - |a_{i_1} - a_j| > 1/h_1 - 1/2h_1 = 1/2h_1,$$

which proves (ii) with $h = 2h_1$, $N = N_1$. ∎

(5.16) PROPOSITION. *The set M of null sequences is a maximal ideal in R.*

Proof. We first observe that $0 = (0, 0, \ldots) \in M$. Next let $(a_1, a_2, \ldots)$ and $(b_1, b_2, \ldots)$ be null, let $(c_1, c_2, \ldots)$ be any cauchy sequence, and let $h \in \mathbb{N}$.

If $|a_i| < 1/2h$ for $i \geqslant N_1$ and $|b_i| < 1/2h$ for $i \geqslant N_2$, then $|a_i + b_i| < 1/h$ for $i \geqslant \max\{N_1, N_2\}$, which proves that M is additively closed.

If $|c_i| < m\ \forall i$ and $|a_i| < 1/(mh)\ \forall i \geqslant N$, then $|a_ic_i| < 1/h\ \forall i \geqslant N$, which shows that $(a_2, \ldots)(c_1, \ldots) \in M$, and this completes the proof that M is an ideal.

Since $|1| = 1 \not< \frac{1}{2}$, the cauchy sequence $(1, 1, \ldots) \notin M$; therefore M is a proper ideal. To show that M is maximal we must show that for a given

$(d_1, d_2, \ldots) \in R \setminus M$, $\exists (e_1, e_2, \ldots) \in R$ and $(f_1, f_2, \ldots) \in M$ such that

(5.17) $$(d_1, \ldots)(e_1, \ldots) + (f_1, \ldots) = (1, 1, \ldots);$$

in other words, every nonzero element in the factor ring R/M has an inverse: R/M is a field (cf. A5.6). By (5.14) (ii), let $|d_i| \geqslant 1/h_3\ \forall i \geqslant N_3$ and define

$$e_i = \begin{cases} 0 & \text{if} \quad i < N_3, \\ 1/d_i & \text{if} \quad i \geqslant N_3, \end{cases}$$

$$f_i = \begin{cases} 1 & \text{if} \quad i < N_3, \\ 0 & \text{if} \quad i \geqslant N_3. \end{cases}$$

Then (5.17) is satisfied and $(f_1, \ldots)$ is null. It remains to check that $(e_1, \ldots)$ is cauchy. Let $|d_i - d_j| < 1/hh_3^2\ \forall i, j \geqslant N_4$. Then, using (5.6) (ii),

$$|e_i - e_j| = |d_i - d_j| / |d_i||d_j| < 1/h$$

for $i, j \geqslant \max\{N_3, N_4\}$. ■

We denote the field R/M by $\tilde{k}$ and call it the **completion** of k with respect to the absolute value $|\ |$. Since k is a field, the kernel of the combined homomorphism $k \to R \to \tilde{k}$ must be 0, i.e., $k \to \tilde{k}$ is injective. It is easy to explain this directly: If the constant sequences $(a, a, \ldots)$ and $(b, b, \ldots)$ are congruent mod M, then their difference $(a-b, a-b, \ldots)$ is null; hence $|a-b| < 1/h\ \forall h \in \mathbb{N}$, which implies that $a = b$.

This gives us a canonical way of regarding k as a subfield of $\tilde{k}$. Hence

$$\operatorname{char}(\tilde{k}) = \operatorname{char}(k).$$

If k coincides with $\tilde{k}$ we say that k is **complete** (with respect to $|\ |$).

We shall tend to use Greek letters $\alpha, \beta, \ldots$ to denote elements of $\tilde{k}$. Thus

$$\alpha = (a_1, a_2, \ldots) + M$$

in typical notation. We shall also write this as

(5.18) $$\lim_{i \to \infty} a_i = \alpha, \qquad \text{or simply} \quad \lim a_i = \alpha,$$

and call α the **limit** of the sequence. This notation means, by definition, precisely that $(a_1, a_2, \ldots)$ is cauchy and $(a_1, a_2, \ldots) \in \alpha$. If also $\beta = (b_1, \ldots) + M$, then in view of the way we add and multiply componentwise we have the formulas

(5.19) $$\lim(a_i + b_i) = \lim a_i + \lim b_i,$$

(5.20) $$\lim(a_i b_i) = (\lim a_i)(\lim b_i).$$

With the identification of $a \in k$ with the constant sequence $(a, a, \ldots)$ we have $\lim a = a$ and the following special case of (5.20):

(5.21) $$\lim(a a_i) = a \cdot \lim a_i.$$

When $k = \mathbb{Q}$ we have the following special notation. The completion of $\mathbb{Q}$ with respect to the ordinary absolute value is denoted $\mathbb{R}$ and is called the **real field**; the elements of $\mathbb{R}$ are **real numbers**. The completion of $\mathbb{Q}$ with respect to the p-adic absolute value is denoted $\mathbb{Q}_p$ and is called the ***p*-adic field**; its elements are called ***p*-adic numbers**.

If $\tilde{\mathbb{Q}}$ denotes either $\mathbb{R}$ or one of $\mathbb{Q}_2, \mathbb{Q}_3, \ldots$ then we have $\mathbb{Q} \subset \tilde{\mathbb{Q}}$ and $\mathbb{Q}$ is the prime subfield of $\tilde{\mathbb{Q}}$. The elements in $\tilde{\mathbb{Q}} \setminus \mathbb{Q}$ are **irrational** (real or p-adic) **numbers**.

EXERCISES

1. For a valued field k, the bounded sequences comprise a subring B of $k^{\mathbb{N}}$ containing the ring R of cauchy sequences. The set M of null sequences is an ideal in B (as well as in R). The ring B/M is never an integral domain.

2. Every field k is complete with respect to the trivial absolute value defined in (5.5).

4. THE REAL FIELD

Let $(a_1, a_2, \ldots)$ be a cauchy sequence representing the real number α. We say that $(a_1, \ldots)$ is **positive** if $\exists h, N \in \mathbb{N} \ni a_n > 1/h \ \forall n \geqslant N$. If $(a_1, \ldots)$ is positive and $(b_1, \ldots)$ is null then, for some h and N, $a_n > 1/h \ \forall n \geqslant N$ and, for some N_1, $|b_n| < 1/2h \ \forall n \geqslant N_1$. Since $a_n + b_n > 1/2h \ \forall n \geqslant \max\{N, N_1\}$, we see that $(a_1 + b_1, \ldots)$ is positive.

This allows us to define $\alpha = (a_1, \ldots) + M$ to be **positive** if $(a_1, \ldots)$ is positive, as it does not matter which representative $(a_1, \ldots)$ is chosen. We write this $\alpha > 0$. We define α to be **negative** and write $\alpha < 0$ if $-\alpha$ is positive.

If $\alpha \neq 0$, then we must have either $\alpha > 0$ or $\alpha < 0$. For a cauchy sequence $(a_1, \ldots)$, representing α is not null and so $\exists h, N \in \mathbb{N} \ni |a_i| > 1/h \ \forall i \geqslant N$. By taking N large enough we can also ensure that $|a_i - a_j| < 1/2h$ for $i, j \geqslant N$. Thus, if $a_N > 0$, then $\forall i \geqslant N$

$$a_i = a_N + a_i - a_N > 1/h - 1/2h = 1/2h;$$

hence $\alpha > 0$. Similarly, if $a_N < 0$, then $\alpha < 0$.

On the other hand, it is clear from the definition that we cannot have two of $\alpha > 0$, $\alpha = 0$, $\alpha < 0$ simultaneously.

$\alpha < \beta$ and $\beta > \alpha$ are defined to mean $\beta - \alpha > 0$, and $\leqslant$ and $\geqslant$ are defined as usual.[2] We have proved the first statement of the next proposition.

[2] "For $x \gg 0$" is a handy notation for "for x sufficiently large."

(5.22) PROPOSITION. (i) *The relation* $<$ *on* $\mathbb{R}$ *satisfies the law of trichotomy*: *Given* $\alpha, \beta \in \mathbb{R}$, *exactly one of* $\alpha < \beta, \alpha = \beta, \alpha > \beta$ *is true.*

(ii) *This relation restricts to the usual* $<$ *on* $\mathbb{Q}$.

(iii) $\forall \alpha, \beta, \gamma, \delta \in \mathbb{R}$,

$$\alpha < \beta \quad \textit{and} \quad \gamma \leqslant \delta \quad \Rightarrow \quad \alpha + \gamma < \beta + \delta;$$

$$\alpha < \beta \quad \textit{and} \quad \gamma > 0 \quad \Rightarrow \quad \alpha\gamma < \beta\gamma;$$

$$\alpha < \beta \quad \textit{and} \quad \gamma < 0 \quad \Rightarrow \quad \alpha\gamma > \beta\gamma.$$

(iv) *The archimedean property of* $\mathbb{R}$: *Given* $\alpha, \beta \in \mathbb{R}$ *with* $\alpha > 0$, $\exists n \in \mathbb{N} \ni n\alpha > \beta$; *in particular*, $\exists n > \beta$. *Alternatively, given* $\alpha > 0$, $\exists n \in \mathbb{N} \ni 1/n < \alpha$.

The proofs of these statements when expressed in terms of cauchy sequences of rational numbers are quite obvious and need not be written out here.

It follows from (iv) that if $\alpha \in \mathbb{R}$ then the set $\{a \in \mathbb{Z} : a \leqslant \alpha\}$ is bounded above in $\mathbb{Z}$ and is nonempty (the set contains $-n$ if $n \in \mathbb{N}$ and $n \geqslant -\alpha$). The l.u.b. of this set in $\mathbb{Z}$ is the **integral part** of α and is denoted $\lfloor \alpha \rfloor$.

Intuitively we picture the real numbers as points on a line, as Figure 5.2 illustrates. α is to the right of β iff $\alpha > \beta$; $\lfloor \alpha \rfloor$ is the rightmost integer lying at or to the left of α. The real numbers e and π will be defined in (5.228) and (5.232), respectively, and real numbers such as $\sqrt{2}$, $\sqrt{3}$, $2^{-1/3}$ in (5.77).

The following notation will be useful: $\mathbb{R}^{>} = \{\alpha \in \mathbb{R} : \alpha > 0\}$ and $\mathbb{R}^{\geqslant} = \{\alpha \in \mathbb{R} : \alpha \geqslant 0\}$. We shall use the same notation when these sets have additional structure. For example, in some situations we want to regard $\mathbb{R}^{>}$ as multiplicative group.

We can now extend the ordinary absolute value on $\mathbb{Q}$ to the map $| \; | : \mathbb{R} \to \mathbb{R}$ defined by $|\alpha| = \pm\alpha$, whichever is $\geqslant 0$. It follows from the previous proposition that this map satisfies (AV0)–(AV2); (AV3) is proved by an argument identical to that used at the beginning of Section 2 for the ordinary absolute value on $\mathbb{Q}$. This function is therefore an archimedean absolute value on $\mathbb{R}$ according to the following extended

(5.23) DEFINITION. A (real valued) **absolute value** on the field k is a map $| \; | : k \to \mathbb{R}$ satisfying (AV0)–(AV3). An absolute value is **ultrametric** if it satisfies (AV3$^{\#}$); otherwise it is **archimedean**.

Figure 5.2 The real line.

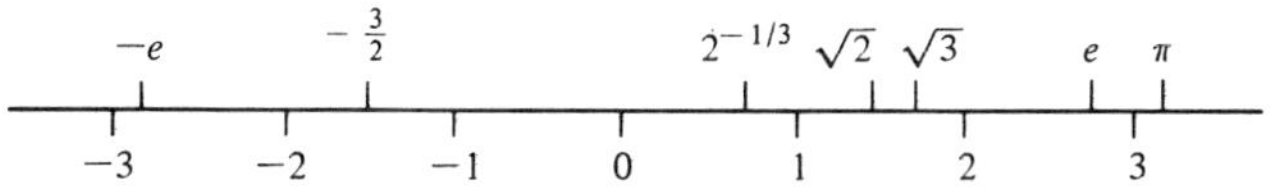

All the absolute values $|\ |: k \to \mathbb{Q}$ discussed so far are, of course, absolute values in this new sense. A **valued field** will now be taken as a field equipped with an absolute value in the sense of (5.23). In (5.202) we shall define α^β for $\alpha \in \mathbb{R}^>$, $\beta \in \mathbb{R}$; it can then be shown that if $|\ |: k \to \mathbb{R}$ is an absolute value and if β is a real number satisfying $0 < \beta < 1$, the function $a \mapsto |a|^\beta$ satisfies (AV0), (AV2), and (AV3) always, and satisfies (AV1) iff $|\ |$ is ultrametric. The purpose of axiom (AV1), which is not adopted in most other books, is to exclude in the archimedean case these unwanted variants, which only tend to complicate proofs; however, in the ultrametric case, the fact that $|\ |^\beta$ is again an absolute value is most useful, allowing us for instance to sharpen certain ancillary statements in the binomial theorem (5.171).

The results of (5.6) along with their proofs all remain valid without change for absolute value in the sense of (5.23). The construction of the completion $\tilde{k} = R/M$ and the various definitions and proofs involved also remain valid. For instance, a sequence $(a_1, a_2, \ldots) \in k^{\mathbb{N}}$ is cauchy iff, $\forall h \in \mathbb{N}, \exists N \in \mathbb{N} \ni |a_i - a_j| < 1/h \ \forall i, j \geqslant N$. (By the archimedean property of $\mathbb{R}$ this is the same as requiring, $\forall \varepsilon \in \mathbb{R}^>, \exists N \in \mathbb{N} \ni |a_i - a_j| < \varepsilon \ \forall i, j \geqslant N$.) Verifying that the generalization (5.23) can be made without perturbing the theory amounts simply to rereading the relevant parts of Sections 2 and 3 and observing that all that is needed of the values $|a|$ $(a \in k)$ follows from (5.22), a task left to the reader.

Let k be a valued field. A sequence $(a_1, a_2, \ldots) \in k^{\mathbb{N}}$ written $a_1 + a_2 + \cdots$ is called an **infinite series**, or simply **series**. This series is said to **converge** if the sequence of (finite) **partial sums** $A_i = a_1 + a_2 + \cdots + a_i$ is cauchy. If $\lim A_i = \alpha \in \tilde{k}$, we say that the series **converges to α** and we write

$$a_1 + a_2 + \cdots = \alpha.$$

α is called the **sum** of the series.

If also $b_1 + b_2 + \cdots = \beta$, such a statement carrying with it the implication that the sequence of partial sums $B_i = b_1 + \cdots + b_i$ is cauchy with limit β, then, since the series $(a_1 + b_1) + (a_2 + b_2) + \cdots$ has partial sums $A_i + B_i$, by (5.19) we have

(5.24)
$$(a_1 + b_1) + (a_2 + b_2) + \cdots = \lim(A_i + B_i) = \lim A_i + \lim B_i = \alpha + \beta.$$

Similarly, (5.21) gives

(5.25)
$$aa_1 + aa_2 + \cdots = a\alpha.$$

Note: When we say that $a_1 + a_2 + \cdots$ is convergent, say $a_1 + \cdots = \alpha \in \tilde{k}$, we do not require, as do some writers, that $\alpha \in k$.

A basic example is the **geometric series** $1 + x + x^2 + x^3 + \cdots$.

(5.26) PROPOSITION. *If* $|x| < 1$, *then*

$$1 + x + x^2 + x^3 + \cdots = 1/(1 - x).$$

Note that, when convergent, the sum is in k. For the proof we shall need the following result, known as **Bernouilli's inequality**.

(5.27) LEMMA. *Let* $\alpha \in \mathbb{R}$, $\alpha \geqslant -2$, *and* $n \in \mathbb{N}$. *Then*

$$(1+\alpha)^n \geqslant 1 + n\alpha.$$

Proof. The inequality is true when $n=1$. Inductively, if $(1+\alpha)^n \geqslant 1+n\alpha$, then, provided $1+\alpha \geqslant 0$ (i.e., $\alpha \geqslant -1$),

$$(1+\alpha)^{n+1} \geqslant (1+n\alpha)(1+\alpha) = 1+(n+1)\alpha + n\alpha^2$$

$$\geqslant 1+(n+1)\alpha,$$

since $\alpha^2 = (-\alpha)^2 \geqslant 0 \ \forall \alpha \in \mathbb{R}$. It remains to consider the case $-2 \leqslant \alpha < -1$, which is left as an exercise.

Proof of (5.26). The statement is obviously true when $x=0$, so we can suppose $x \neq 0$. The ith partial sum is

$$A_i = 1 + x + \cdots + x^{i-1} = \frac{1-x^i}{1-x}$$

($x \neq 1$ since $|x|<1$), and for $i<j$

$$|A_j - A_i| = \left|\frac{x^i - x^j}{1-x}\right| = |x|^i \left|\frac{1-x^{j-i}}{1-x}\right| < \frac{2|x|^i}{|1-x|},$$

where we have used $|1-x^{j-i}| \leqslant |1| + |x^{j-i}| < 1+1=2$. If we put $\alpha = -1 + 1/|x|$, then $|x|^i = 1/(1+\alpha)^i \leqslant 1/(1+i\alpha)$ by the lemma. By the archimedean property of $\mathbb{R}$, let h_1, h_2 be natural numbers such that $|1-x| > 1/h_1$, $|\alpha| > 1/h_2$. Then, for a given $h \in \mathbb{N}$, we have $|A_j - A_i| < 1/h$, provided $i, j \geqslant N = 2h_1h_2h$. ∎

For instance, in $\mathbb{R}$

(5.28)
$$\tfrac{9}{10} + \tfrac{9}{100} + \tfrac{9}{1000} + \cdots = \tfrac{9}{10}\left(1 + \tfrac{1}{10} + \left(\tfrac{1}{10}\right)^2 + \cdots\right)$$

$$= \tfrac{9}{10} \cdot \frac{1}{1-\frac{1}{10}} = 1.$$

The convergence is with reference to the absolute value defined on $\mathbb{R}$ by $|\alpha| = \pm\alpha \geqslant 0$. This is the only absolute value we shall consider on $\mathbb{R}$ and it is the one that is always assumed in any discussion of real numbers.

The series $1+2+4+8+\cdots$ is **divergent** (i.e., not convergent) with regard to the ordinary absolute value on $\mathbb{Q}$. However, it does converge with respect to the 2-adic absolute value since then $|2|<1$ and therefore, by (5.26),

(5.29) $1+2+\cdots+2^n+\cdots = 1/(1-2) = -1$ (2-adically).

The following result, known as the **Cauchy convergence criterion**, is stated here for the case of a sequence of rationals converging to a real number. This criterion will be generalized to arbitrary valued fields in the next section (cf. (5.38)).

(5.30) PROPOSITION. *Let* $(a_1, a_2, \ldots) \in \mathbb{Q}^{\mathbb{N}}$ *and* $\alpha \in \mathbb{R}$. *Then with respect to the ordinary absolute value on* $\mathbb{Q}$, $(a_1, a_2, \ldots)$ *is cauchy with limit* α *iff*, $\forall h \in \mathbb{N}, \exists N \in \mathbb{N} \ni |a_i - \alpha| < 1/h \; \forall i \geqslant N$.

Proof. First suppose $(a_1, a_2, \ldots)$ is cauchy and $\lim a_i = \alpha$. Since $|x| = \pm x$ for $x \in \mathbb{R}$, for a given $h \in \mathbb{N}$ we wish to find an $N \in \mathbb{N} \ni$

$$-1/h < a_i - \alpha < 1/h, \qquad \forall i \geqslant N.$$

Now α is represented by the cauchy sequence $(a_1, a_2, \ldots)$, and the rational number a_i regarded as a real number is represented by the constant sequence $(a_i, a_i, \ldots)$. Thus $a_i - \alpha$ is represented by $(a_i - a_1, a_i - a_2, \ldots, 0, a_i - a_{i+1}, \ldots)$. Similarly, h is represented by $(1/h, 1/h, \ldots)$ and by definition of $<$ on $\mathbb{R}$ (cf. (5.22)), the statement $a_i - \alpha < 1/h \; \forall i \geqslant N$ means that $\exists n, N' \in \mathbb{N} \ni a_i - a_j + 1/n < 1/h, \; \forall i \geqslant N, \; \forall j \geqslant N'$. We obtain this from the fact that $(a_1, a_2, \ldots)$ is cauchy: $\exists N \ni |a_i - a_j| < 1/2h \; \forall i, j \geqslant N$. Therefore, if we take $n = 1/2h$, we have $a_i - a_j + 1/n < 1/h \; \forall i, j \geqslant N$.

Similarly from $|a_i - a_j| < 1/2h$ we deduce that $-1/h + 1/2h < a_i - a_j$; hence $-1/h < a_i - \alpha$. Thus $|a_i - \alpha| \leqslant 1/h \; \forall i \geqslant N$.

Conversely, suppose that the criterion of the proposition is satisfied. Then, for a given $h \in \mathbb{N}$, $\exists N_1 \in \mathbb{N} \ni |a_i - \alpha| < 1/2h \; \forall i \geqslant N_1$; hence $|a_i - a_j| = |a_i - \alpha + \alpha - a_j| \leqslant |a_i - \alpha| + |\alpha - a_j| < 1/h$ for $i, j \geqslant N_1$, which implies that $(a_1, a_2, \ldots)$ is cauchy. Now α, like every real number, is represented by a cauchy sequence of rational numbers $(b_1, b_2, \ldots)$, say, and by what has already been proved, given $h \in \mathbb{N}$ $\exists N_2 \in \mathbb{N} \ni |b_i - \alpha| < 1/2h$. Therefore $|a_i - b_i| \leqslant |a_i - \alpha| + |\alpha - b_i| < 1/h$ for $i \geqslant \max\{N_1, N_2\}$; hence $(a_1 - b_1, a_2 - b_2, \ldots)$ is null, and consequently $\lim a_i = \lim b_i = \alpha$. ■

EXERCISES

1. For $r \in \mathbb{R}$ and $n \in \mathbb{N}$, $\lfloor \lfloor r \rfloor / n \rfloor = \lfloor r/n \rfloor$.

2. If $x, y \in \mathbb{R}^{>}$ and $x + y = 1$, then $(1 + 1/x)(1 + 1/y) \geqslant 9$.

3. For any real $\alpha > 1$ and $k \in \mathbb{Z}$, the sequence of real numbers $n^k \alpha^{-n}$, $n = 1, 2, \ldots$, is null.

4. Let k be a valued field and I a set. Then the set of bounded functions $\{f \in k^I : \exists r \in \mathbb{R}^{>} \ni |f(i)| < r \; \forall i \in I\}$ is a vector subspace of k^I containing the subspace $\oplus_I k$.

5. Let X be a set and $R=\mathbb{R}^X$ the ring of all functions $f: X \to \mathbb{R}$. For $Y \subset X$, $J=\{f \in R: f(y)=0\ \forall y \in Y\}$ is an ideal. When $|Y|=1$, J is maximal and is the kernel of a homomorphism $R \to \mathbb{R}$.

5. DECIMAL EXPANSIONS AND g.l.b.s

Given $\alpha \in \mathbb{R}^{\geqslant}$, we construct the sequence of integers $n_0, n_1, n_2, \ldots$ by means of the following algorithm:

$$\begin{aligned} n_0 &= \lfloor \alpha \rfloor, & \alpha_1 &= 10(\alpha - n_0), \\ n_1 &= \lfloor \alpha_1 \rfloor, & \alpha_2 &= 10(\alpha_1 - n_1), \\ &\ \vdots \\ n_i &= \lfloor \alpha_i \rfloor, & \alpha_{i+1} &= 10(\alpha_i - n_i), \\ &\ \vdots \end{aligned}$$

To make the purpose of the algorithm plain, let us anticipate the result in the particular case $\alpha = 13.5024\ldots$, a real number in familiar decimal notation. Then

$$\begin{aligned} n_0 &= 13, & \alpha_1 &= 5.024\ldots, \\ n_1 &= 5, & \alpha_2 &= 0.24\ldots, \\ n_2 &= 0, & \alpha_3 &= 2.4\ldots, \\ &\ \vdots \end{aligned}$$

Since

$$\begin{aligned} \alpha &= n_0 + \alpha_1 10^{-1} \\ &= n_0 + n_1 10^{-1} + \alpha_2 10^{-2} \\ &= a_i + \alpha_{i+1} 10^{-i-1}, \end{aligned}$$

where

$$a_i = n_0 + n_1 10^{-1} + \cdots + n_i 10^{-i},$$

and since $0 \leqslant \alpha_i < 10$ for $i \geqslant 1$ (by definition of the integral part function), we have

$$0 \leqslant \alpha - a_i = \alpha_{i+1} 10^{-i-1} < 10^{-i}. \tag{5.31}$$

Therefore, by the Cauchy convergence criterion (5.30), $\lim a_i = \alpha$. That is,

$$n_0 + n_1/10 + n_2/10^2 + \cdots = \alpha.$$

We abbreviate this by using the positional notation $\alpha = n_0.n_1 n_2\ldots$ and call this the **decimal representation** of α. This notation is truncated to $\alpha =$

$n_0.n_1\ldots n_r$ if $n_i=0\ \forall i>r$. If $\alpha<0$ and $-\alpha=n_0.n_1n_2\ldots$, then the decimal representation of α is defined to be $-n_0.n_1n_2\ldots$. (The algorithm does not give this directly. For example, if $\alpha=-\frac{3}{2}$, then $\lfloor\alpha\rfloor=-2$ while the decimal representation is $-1.5000\ldots=-1.5$.)

Conversely if $n_0+n_1 10^{-1}+\cdots$ is any such series, where the n_i are integers satisfying $0\leqslant n_i\leqslant 9\ \forall i$, and we denote the partial sums by a_i, then, for $i<j$,

$$0\leqslant a_j-a_i=n_{i+1}10^{-(i+1)}+\cdots+n_j 10^{-j}<9\cdot 10^{-(i+1)}(1+10^{-1}+\cdots)$$

$$=9\cdot 10^{-(i+1)}\cdot\frac{1}{1-10^{-1}}=10^{-i}.$$

It follows that the sequence $(a_1,a_2,\ldots)$ is cauchy and therefore $n_0+n_1 10^{-1}+\cdots$ converges to some real number α. With one proviso, which we now explain, the n_i give the decimal representation: $\alpha=n_0.n_1n_2\ldots$.

Let us call the series $n_0+n_1 10^{-1}+\cdots$ and the associated decimal representations $\pm n_0.n_1n_2\ldots$ **proper** if the n_i are not all eventually 9, i.e., if, $\forall i,\ \exists j>i\ni n_j\leqslant 8$. By (5.28), every improper series can be replaced by a proper one. For example,

$$50.8039999\ldots=50+\frac{8}{10}+\frac{3}{10^3}+\frac{9}{10^4}\left(1+\frac{1}{10}+\cdots\right)$$

$$=50+\frac{8}{10}+\frac{3}{10^3}+\frac{1}{10^3}=50.804.$$

Thus every real number has a proper decimal representation. Now if $\alpha=n_0+n_1 10^{-1}+\cdots$ is proper, then $\forall i\ \exists j>i\ni n_i\leqslant 8$, and therefore

$$0\leqslant n_{i+1}10^{-1}+n_{i+2}10^{-2}+\cdots\leqslant 9(10^{-1}+10^{-2}+\cdots)-10^{-(j-i)}$$

$$=1-10^{-(j-i)}<1.$$

These inequalities for $i=0,1,\ldots$ give in succession

$$\lfloor\alpha\rfloor=\lfloor n_0+n_1 10^{-1}+\cdots\rfloor=n_0,\qquad \alpha_1=10(\alpha-n_0),$$

$$\lfloor\alpha_1\rfloor=\lfloor n_1+n_2 10^{-1}+\cdots\rfloor=n_1,\ldots.$$

Hence $n_0.n_1n_2\ldots$ is indeed the proper decimal representation of the real number $n_0+n_1 10^{-1}+\cdots$.

The preceding discussion can be summed up by saying that the real numbers are in bijection with the proper decimal expansions. Henceforth a decimal expansion is always assumed to be proper. Thus $\pm m_0.m_1m_2\ldots=\pm n_0.n_1n_2\ldots$ iff the signs are the same and $m_i=n_i$ for each $i\geqslant 0$.

Also, if $\alpha=m_0.m_1m_2\ldots$ and $\beta=n_0.n_1n_2\ldots$, then $\alpha<\beta$ iff $\exists i\ni m_i\neq n_i$ and if j is the smallest such i then $m_j<n_j$. For if this condition is true then

$$\beta-\alpha>\frac{1}{10^j}-\left(\frac{9}{10^{j+1}}+\frac{9}{10^{j+2}}+\cdots\right)=0.$$

Conversely, if $\alpha<\beta$ then, since $\alpha\neq\beta$, $\exists i \ni m_i\neq n_i$; say j is the smallest such i. If $m_j>n_j$, we would have $\alpha>\beta$ by the remark above. Therefore $m_j<n_j$.

(5.32) PROPOSITION. *If X is a nonempty set of real numbers that is bounded below, say $\beta\leqslant\alpha$ $\forall\alpha\in X$, then X has a unique greatest lower bound, abbreviated* g.l.b.(X). *Similarly, if X is nonempty and bounded above, then it has a unique least upper bound, denoted* l.u.b.(X).

Remark. Unlike the simple situation in $\mathbb{Z}$, the g.l.b. (or l.u.b.) may or may not belong to X. For instance $\mathbb{R}^{\geqslant}$, but not $\mathbb{R}^{>}$, contains g.l.b.$\mathbb{R}^{\geqslant}=$ g.l.b.$\mathbb{R}^{>}=0$. Standard alternative terms are

$$\text{g.l.b.}(X)=\inf(X)=\text{the } \textbf{infimum} \text{ of } X,$$

$$\text{l.u.b.}(X)=\sup(X)=\text{the } \textbf{supremum} \text{ of } X.$$

Proof. As in (2.7), the uniqueness of the g.l.b. or l.u.b. follows from the principle of trichotomy; and the second statement is reduced to the first by replacing X by $\{-\alpha:\alpha\in X\}$.

Let $X\neq\varnothing$ be bounded below by β. For any λ, $\beta+\lambda$ is a lower bound for $X'=\{\alpha+\lambda:\alpha\in X\}$ and if γ is a g.l.b. for X', then $\gamma-\lambda$ is a g.l.b. for X. By shifting back and forth in this manner we can assume that $\beta\geqslant 0$. The point of this is that now we can easily describe the effective construction of g.l.b.$(X)=n_0.n_1n_2\ldots$ one digit at a time.

For $m=0,1,2,\ldots$ the set of integers $\{\lfloor 10^m\alpha\rfloor:\alpha\in X\}$ is bounded below by 0 and therefore has a g.l.b. in $\mathbb{Z}$, say b_m. Let $a_m=10^{-m}b_m$. Since $0\leqslant b_{m+1}-10b_m\leqslant 9$, the decimal expansions of a_m and a_{m+1} agree up to the term in 10^{-m} and we can write $a_m=n_0.n_1\ldots n_m$. In other words, having reached $a_m=n_0.n_1\ldots n_m$, we choose n_{m+1} from $0,\ldots,9$ as large as possible consistent with $n_0.n_1\ldots n_{m+1}\leqslant\alpha$, $\forall\alpha\in X$.

Thus $\gamma=\lim(a_1,a_2,\ldots)\leqslant\alpha$, $\forall\alpha\in X$ (cf. A10.1). If δ is a lower bound for X and $\delta>\gamma$, say $\delta-\gamma>1/h$, where $h\in\mathbb{N}$, then since $h<10^h$ we find that, $\forall\alpha\in X$, $10^h\alpha-b_h\geqslant 10^h\delta-10^h\gamma>1$, in contradiction with the definition of b_h. Therefore $\gamma=$ g.l.b.(X). ∎

Irrational real numbers are easily distinguished from rational numbers by their decimal expansions:

(5.33) PROPOSITION. *The real number α is rational iff its decimal expansion $\pm n_0.n_1n_2\ldots$ is eventually periodic, that is, iff $\exists h,N\in\mathbb{N}\ni n_{i+h}=n_i$ $\forall i\geqslant N$.*

Proof. Suppose first that the expansion is eventually periodic. Putting

$$a=n_0+n_1 10^{-1}+\cdots+n_{N-1}10^{-(N-1)},$$

and

$$b = n_N 10^{-N} + n_{N+1} 10^{-(N+1)} + \cdots + n_{N+h-1} 10^{-(N+h-1)}$$

yields

$$\alpha = \pm\big(a + b(1 + 10^{-h} + 10^{-2h} + \cdots)\big) = \pm\big(a + b/(1 - 10^{-h})\big) \in \mathbb{Q}.$$

Conversely, let $\alpha = \pm a/b$, where a and b are integers and $a \geqslant 0$, $b > 0$. In the algorithm for the decimal representation of $|\alpha|$,

$$\lfloor |\alpha| \rfloor = n_0, \qquad \alpha_1 = 10(a/b - n_0),$$

$$\lfloor \alpha_1 \rfloor = n_1, \qquad \alpha_2 = 10(\alpha_1 - n_1) = 10(10(a/b - n_0) - n_1),$$

and so on, the α_i can all be written as rational numbers in the form $10a_i/b$, where $0 \leqslant a_i < b$ (since $0 \leqslant \alpha_i < 10$ for $i \geqslant 1$). There are only b possible values for a_i and therefore after at most b steps some a_i must equal a previous one, say $a_{N+h} = a_N$. Then $n_{N+h} = n_N$. Hence $\alpha_{N+h+1} = \alpha_{N+1}$ and $n_{N+h+1} = n_{N+1}$, and so on, ad infinitum. ■

Here is a numerical example. Let $\alpha = 5.03190190\ldots$; the repeated part or **period** is sometimes indicated by $\alpha = 5.03\overline{190}$ or $5.03\dot{1}9\dot{0}$. Then

$$\alpha = \frac{503}{100} + \frac{190}{10^5}\left(1 + \frac{1}{10^3} + \frac{1}{10^6} + \cdots\right) = \frac{503}{100} + \frac{19}{10^4}\frac{1}{1 - 10^{-3}} = \frac{502687}{99900}.$$

Using decimal notation we can now prove that "almost all real numbers are irrational" by the famous **diagonal method** of Cantor. (The following discussion is self-contained and straightforward. It is independent of the infinite set theory of Chapter 4, Section 8.)

Recall from Chapter 1 that a set X is defined to be infinite when there exists an injection $\mathbb{N} \to X$. We now divide infinite sets into two types. X is **countable** if there exists a bijection $\mathbb{N} \to X$, **uncountable** if there is no such bijection. In other words, X is countable if its members can be listed in a sequence $x_1, x_2, \ldots$ ($n \mapsto x_n$ being the bijection $\mathbb{N} \to X$). For instance, $\mathbb{Q}$ is countable since we can systematically list all the rational numbers a/b in order of increasing $|a| + |b|$, alternating the positive and negative numbers: Writing $T = |a| + |b|$, the list begins

$$\underbrace{0 = \tfrac{0}{1},}_{T=1} \qquad \underbrace{1 = \tfrac{1}{1}, -1,}_{T=2} \qquad \underbrace{\tfrac{1}{2}, -\tfrac{1}{2}, 2 = \tfrac{2}{1}, -2,}_{T=3}$$

$$\underbrace{\tfrac{1}{3}, -\tfrac{1}{3}, 3, -3,}_{T=4} \qquad \underbrace{\tfrac{1}{4}, -\tfrac{1}{4}, \tfrac{2}{3}, -\tfrac{2}{3}, \tfrac{3}{2}, -\tfrac{3}{2}, 4, -4,}_{T=5} \qquad \ldots.$$

Of course there are injections $\mathbb{N} \to \mathbb{R}$ (even a canonical one $n \mapsto n$); the diagonal method proves that none is surjective: $\mathbb{R}$ is uncountable. The intuitive interpretation is that $\mathbb{R}$ is "too big" to be accommodated in a merely countable sequence (despite the fact that there are infinitely many rationals between any two irrationals, cf. A10.1). The argument goes as follows.

Suppose we had managed to list all the real numbers $x_1, x_2, \ldots$ and let their decimal representations be

$$x_1 = \pm n_1.d_{11}d_{12}d_{13}\ldots,$$
$$x_2 = \pm n_2.d_{21}d_{22}d_{23}\ldots,$$
$$\vdots$$

We obtain a contradiction by displaying a real number $x = 0.e_1e_2e_3\ldots$ that is not in the list. We take

$$e_i = \begin{cases} 1 & \text{if } d_{ii} = 0, \\ d_{ii} - 1 & \text{if } d_{ii} > 0. \end{cases}$$

No $e_i = 9$ (so there is no danger of repeated 9s), and $x \neq x_i$ since their decimal representations differ in the ith place. (Of course the construction can be varied to exhibit "many" missing numbers.)

A consequence is that the set $\mathbb{R} \setminus \mathbb{Q}$ of irrational numbers is uncountable (hence "almost all real numbers are irrational"), for if these were listed as $x_1, x_2, \ldots$ then we could couple this with a listing $q_1, q_2, \ldots$ of $\mathbb{Q}$, hence obtaining a listing

$$x_1, q_1, x_2, q_2, x_3, \ldots$$

of $\mathbb{R} = (\mathbb{R} \setminus \mathbb{Q}) \amalg \mathbb{Q}$. We know, however, that this is impossible.

EXERCISES

1. Write $0.\dot{0}2\dot{7}$ as a rational fraction in lowest terms.

2. Show that $\mathbb{Q}(X)$ is countable.

6. COMPLETENESS

Since $\mathbb{R}$ is equipped with an absolute value we can form its completion $\tilde{\mathbb{R}}$. However, we obtain nothing new.

(5.34) PROPOSITION. $\mathbb{R}$ *is complete*: *As a subfield of* $\tilde{\mathbb{R}}$, $\mathbb{R}$ *coincides with* $\tilde{\mathbb{R}}$.

Proof. Let $(\alpha_1, \alpha_2, \ldots)$ be a cauchy sequence of real numbers and let α_i have the decimal expansion $\pm n_{i0}.n_{i1}n_{i2}\ldots$. Define the sequence $(a_1, a_2, \ldots)$ of rational numbers by $a_i = \pm(n_{i0} + n_{i1}10^{-1} + \cdots + n_{ii}10^{-i})$, the sign being that of α_i. Now $|a_i - a_j| = |a_i - \alpha_i + \alpha_i - \alpha_j + \alpha_j - a_j| \leqslant |a_i - \alpha_i| + |\alpha_i - \alpha_j| + |\alpha_j - a_j| < 10^{-i} + |\alpha_i - \alpha_j| + 10^{-j}$ by (5.31), and since $(\alpha_1, \alpha_2, \ldots)$ is cauchy we can make the three terms 10^{-i}, $|\alpha_i - \alpha_j|$, and 10^{-j} small by taking i and j large. Thus $(a_1, a_2, \ldots)$ is a cauchy sequence of rational numbers (with respect to the ordinary absolute value), and therefore $\lim a_i$ is a real number; let us denote it α.

Regarded as an element of $\tilde{\mathbb{R}}$, α is represented by the constant sequence $(\alpha, \alpha, \ldots)$. We claim that $(\alpha_1, \alpha_2, \ldots)$ and $(\alpha, \alpha, \ldots)$ represent the same element of $\tilde{\mathbb{R}}$; in other words, $(\alpha_1, \alpha_2, \ldots)$ is congruent modulo null sequences to the real number α, which will complete the proof. We wish to show that $|\alpha_i - \alpha|$ is small for large i. Since

$$|\alpha_i - \alpha| = |\alpha_i - a_i + a_i - \alpha| \leqslant |\alpha_i - a_i| + |a_i - \alpha| \leqslant 10^{-i} + |a_i - \alpha|,$$

the desired result follows from (5.30). ■

The reason we used decimal representations in this proof was simply to avoid an appeal to the axiom of choice. A proof can be based on taking any cauchy sequence $(a_{i1}, a_{i2}, \ldots)$ to represent α_i, and then taking $a_i = a_{ij}$ for j appropriately large, but unless some prescription is stated as to which cauchy sequence is to be chosen, the axiom of choice is needed to make these infinitely many selections. In fact, the reader can verify that everything we prove about the real, p-adic, and complex numbers is done so constructively, without depending on the axiom of choice. This is true in particular of *the fundamental theorem of algebra* (5.135).

Let $|\ |: k \to \mathbb{R}$ be an absolute value and $\alpha = (a_1, a_2, \ldots) + M \in \tilde{k}$ in the usual notation. Then

$$|a_i - a_j| \geqslant |a_i| - |a_j|$$

and

$$|a_i - a_j| = |-(a_j - a_i)| \geqslant |a_j| - |a_i|;$$

hence

$$||a_i| - |a_j|| \leqslant |a_i - a_j|. \tag{5.35}$$

On the left, the outer absolute value refers to $\mathbb{R}$ and the inner ones to k. Since $(a_1, a_2, \ldots)$ is cauchy, $|a_i - a_j|$ is small for large i and j and therefore (5.35) shows that the sequence of real numbers $(|a_1|, |a_2|, \ldots)$ is also cauchy. By the previous proposition, $\lim|a_i|$ is a real number, and we define

$$|\alpha| = \lim|a_i|. \tag{5.36}$$

(5.37) PROPOSITION. *If* $\alpha = (a_1, a_2, \ldots) + M \in \tilde{k}$, *then* (5.36) *gives a well-defined map* $|\ |: \tilde{k} \to \mathbb{R}$ *and this map is an absolute value extending the original one on* k. *The extended* $|\ |$ *is ultrametric iff the original* $|\ |$ *is ultrametric.*

Remark. It is an easy exercise to check that the resulting $|\ |$ on $\tilde{k} = \mathbb{R}$ is the usual absolute value.

Proof. If $\alpha=(b_1,b_2,\dots)+M$, then $(a_1-b_1,a_2-b_2,\dots)$ is null; hence $|a_i-b_i|$ is small for large i and therefore, by (5.35), so is $||a_i|-|b_i||$. This proves that $(|a_1|-|b_1|,\dots)$ is a null sequence of real numbers; hence $\lim|a_i|=\lim|b_i|$, and therefore $|\alpha|$ is well defined. Whether an absolute value is ultrametric or not is determined by its behavior on $\mathbb{N}$ (cf. (5.7)). This makes the final statement clear, and the remaining details of the proof are left as an exercise. ■

We can now state the general **Cauchy convergence criterion.**

(5.38) PROPOSITION. *Let k be a field with an absolute value $|\ |: k\to\mathbb{R}$, $\tilde{k}$ its completion, $(a_1,a_2,\dots)\in k^{\mathbb{N}}$ a cauchy sequence, and $\alpha\in\tilde{k}$. Then* $\lim a_i=\alpha$ *iff*, $\forall h\in\mathbb{N}$, $\exists N\in\mathbb{N}\ni|a_i-\alpha|<1/h\ \forall i\geq N$.

Remark. This allows $k=\tilde{k}$ and therefore extends (5.30) in the case $k=\mathbb{R}$ because now the a_i can be real numbers.

Proof. Suppose first that $\lim a_i=\alpha$ and let h be a given natural number. Then the element $a_i-\alpha$ of k is represented by the cauchy sequence $(a_i-a_1,a_i-a_2,\dots)$ and $\exists N\ni|a_s-a_t|<1/h\ \forall s,t\geq N$. Hence, by (5.36) and A10.1(ii),

$$|a_i-\alpha|=\lim_{t\to\infty}|a_i-a_t|\leq 1/h,\qquad \forall i\geq N.$$

The proof of the converse is identical to that of (5.30), with $\mathbb{Q}$ and $\mathbb{R}$ replaced by k and $\tilde{k}$. ■

(5.39) COROLLARY. *Let k be a valued field, $\alpha\in\tilde{k}$, and $h\in\mathbb{N}$. Then* $\exists a\in k\ni|\alpha-a|<1/h$.

Proof. If $(a_1,\dots)$ is any cauchy sequence in k with limit α, we can take $a=a_i$ for i sufficiently large. ■

This corollary says that k is dense in its completion. (The precise definition of *dense* will be given in Section 17.) The case of the real line "peppered" with rational points is typical.

Another obvious application of the criterion gives

(5.40) COROLLARY. *If* $\lim(a_1,a_2,\dots)=\alpha$ *and if $\{i_1,i_2,\dots\}$ is an infinite subset of $\mathbb{N}$, where $i_1<i_2<\cdots$, then the* **subsequence** *$(a_{i_1},a_{i_2},\dots)$ is again cauchy with limit α.*

We can now prove the general case of (5.34); we had to treat the case $\mathbb{R}$ first in order to be able to make the definition (5.36).

(5.41) PROPOSITION. *The completion $\tilde{k}$ is complete.*

Proof. Let $(\alpha_1, \alpha_2, \ldots)$ be a cauchy sequence of elements $\alpha_i \in \tilde{k}$, and for each i choose a cauchy sequence $(a_{i1}, a_{i2}, \ldots) \in \alpha_i$. (In this generality the axiom of choice is unavoidable.) For each i, $\exists N_i \ni |a_{is} - a_{it}| < 1/i$, $\forall s, t \geqslant N_i$. We define $a_i = a_{iN_i}$ and we complete the proof as in (5.34) by showing that $(a_1, a_2, \ldots)$ is cauchy, say $\lim a_i = \alpha \in \tilde{\tilde{k}}$, and that $(\alpha_1, \alpha_2, \ldots)$ and $(\alpha, \alpha, \ldots)$ represent the same element of $\tilde{\tilde{k}}$. Now

$$|a_i - a_j| = |a_i - \alpha_i + \alpha_i - \alpha_j + \alpha_j - a_j| \leqslant |a_i - \alpha_i| + |\alpha_i - \alpha_j| + |\alpha_j - a_j|,$$

which is small for large i and j because each of the three terms on the right is small for the following reasons.

$a_i - \alpha_i$ is an element of $\tilde{k}$ and is represented by the cauchy sequence $(a_i - a_{i1}, a_i - a_{i2}, \ldots)$. By definition,

$$|a_i - \alpha_i| = \lim_{j \to \infty} |a_i - a_{ij}|.$$

However, since $|a_i - a_{ij}| = |a_{iN_i} - a_{ij}| < 1/i$ for $j \geqslant N_i$, it follows by A10.1(ii) that $|a_i - \alpha_i| \leqslant 1/i$; similarly, $|\alpha_j - a_j| \leqslant 1/j$. Moreover, $|\alpha_i - \alpha_j|$ is small for large i and j since $(\alpha_i, \alpha_2, \ldots)$ was assumed to be cauchy. This proves that $(a_1, a_2, \ldots)$ is cauchy.

Let $\lim a_i = \alpha \in \tilde{k}$, so $|a_i - \alpha|$ is small for large i by (5.38). Hence $|\alpha_i - \alpha| \leqslant |\alpha_i - a_i| + |a_i - \alpha| \leqslant 1/i + |a_i - \alpha|$ is small for large i, and therefore, by the other half of (5.38), $\lim \alpha_i = \alpha$. ■

Assignment 10

A10.1. (i) If $\alpha < \beta$ are given real numbers prove that there exist infinitely many rational q and infinitely many irrational γ satisfying $\alpha < q < \beta$ and $\alpha < \gamma < \beta$.

(ii) Let $(\alpha_1, \alpha_2, \ldots)$ and $(\beta_1, \beta_2, \ldots)$ be cauchy sequences of real numbers and suppose $\alpha_i < \beta_i$, $\forall i$. Show that $\lim \alpha_i \leqslant \lim \beta_i$ and give an example where equality occurs.

(iii) If $\alpha \in \mathbb{R}$ show that there exist cauchy sequences $(a_2, \ldots)$ and $(b_1, \ldots)$ of rational numbers both with limit α and satisfying $a_i < \alpha < b_i$, $\forall i$.

A10.2. (i) If $\alpha, \beta \in \mathbb{R}^{\geqslant}$ and $n \in \mathbb{N}$, show that

$$\alpha < \beta \quad \Leftrightarrow \quad \alpha^n < \beta^n.$$

Show that if n is odd this is true for all real α and β.

(ii) Use Bernouilli's inequality to derive the following multiplicative version of the archimedean principle: If $\alpha, \beta \in \mathbb{R}$ and $\alpha > 1$, then $\exists n \in \mathbb{N} \ni \alpha^n > \beta$.

(iii) If $\alpha, \beta \in \mathbb{R}^{>}$ prove $\exists! n \in \mathbb{Z} \ni$

$$\alpha^{n+1} < \beta \leqslant \alpha^n, \text{ if } \alpha < 1, \qquad \alpha^n < \beta \leqslant \alpha^{n+1}, \text{ if } \alpha > 1.$$

A10.3. A set of absolute values $\{| \ |_1,\ldots,| \ |_n\}$ on the field k is **independent** if for each subscript i $\exists z_i \in k \ni$

$$|z_i|_i > 1 \quad \text{and} \quad |z_i|_j < 1 \quad \text{for all} \quad j \neq i.$$

(i) If $k = Q(A)$, where A is a U.F.D. and $| \ |_i$ is the p_i-adic absolute value, where $p_1,\ldots,p_n$ are nonassociated irreducible elements of A, show that $\{| \ |_1,\ldots,| \ |_n\}$ is independent; show that in the case $A = \mathbb{Z}$ the set remains independent when the ordinary absolute value is added.

(ii) Prove **the approximation theorem**: If $\{| \ |_1,\ldots,| \ |_n\}$ is an independent set of absolute values on the field k, if $a_1,\ldots,a_n \in k$, and if $h \in \mathbb{N}$, then $\exists x \in k \ni$

$$|x - a_i|_i < 1/h \quad \text{for} \quad i = 1,2,\ldots,n.$$

(*Hint*: $x = \Sigma a_i z_i^N/(1 + z_i^N)$ for large N.) Find $x \in \mathbb{Q} \ni |x + \frac{3}{2}|_\infty < 1/2$, $v_3(x) > 1$, and $v_7(x - \frac{2}{3}) > 1$.

A10.4. If a is an element of the valued field k and $r \in \mathbb{R}^>$, then

$$D_r(a) = \{b \in k : |b - a| < r\}$$

is the **disc of radius *r*** and **center *a*** (or **open disc** to distinguish it from the **closed disc** $V_r(a) = \{b : |b - a| \leqslant r\}$. It is helpful to visualize $D_r(a)$ as the set of interior points of the disc in $\mathbb{R}^2$ of radius r centered at a point labeled a, and $V_r(a)$ as the whole disc including the boundary.) If $| \ |$ is archimedean, show that the disc uniquely determines its radius and center:

$$D_r(a) = D_s(b) \quad \Rightarrow \quad r = s \quad \text{and} \quad a = b.$$

However, if $| \ |$ is ultrametric, then every point in the disc serves as a center! —show that

$$b \in D_r(a) \quad \Rightarrow \quad D_r(a) = D_r(b).$$

A10.5. Let k be a field with an ultrametric absolute value $| \ |$ and valuation ring D.

(i) If $(a_1, a_2,\ldots)$ is a cauchy sequence in k, show that either $\lim|a_i| = 0$, when $(a_1,\ldots)$ is null, or the sequence $|a_i|$ is eventually constant, i.e., $\exists N \ni |a_i| = |a_N| \ \forall i \geqslant N$. (Hence (5.36) reduce to

$$|\alpha| = \begin{cases} 0 & \text{if} \quad \alpha = 0, \\ |a_i| & \text{otherwise} \quad \text{for all sufficiently large } i, \end{cases}$$

and the set of values $\{|a| : a \in k\} = \{|a| : a \in \tilde{k}\}$ in $\mathbb{R}$ is not enlarged when an ultrametric field is completed.)

(ii) For each real number λ satisfying $0 < \lambda \leqslant 1$ show that

$$I_\lambda = \{a \in k : |a| < \lambda\} \quad \text{and} \quad J_\lambda = \{a \in k : |a| \leqslant \lambda\}$$

are ideals in D (not necessarily distinct) and that conversely every nonzero ideal is among these. Deduce that the ideals form a chain with respect to inclusion. (In thc notation of (5.7), $P = I_1$. This exercise generalizes part of A6.6(ii).)

A10.6. (i) Let A be an integral domain, $k = Q(A)$, and $|\ |: A \to \mathbb{R}$ a map satisfying (AV0)–(AV3). Show that there is a unique absolute value on k extending the given map $|\ |$ on A; and that this absolute value is ultrametric if $|\ |$ satisfies (AV3#) on A.

(ii) If $|\ |$ is an ultrametric absolute value on the field k, using (i) show that

$$|a_0 + a_1 X + \cdots + a_n X^n| = \max\{|a_i|\}$$

defines an absolute value on $k(X)$.

Remarks. Only the verification of (AV2), which can be regarded as a generalization of the Gauss content lemma (3.72), requires any effort. In general, an archimedean absolute value on k cannot be extended to $k(X)$—the Gelfand–Mazur theorem (5.312).

A10.7. (i) Let $a_1, a_2, \ldots$ be a null sequence of real numbers satisfying $a_1 > a_2 > \cdots$ (so all $a_i > 0$ and $\lim a_i = 0$). Show that the series $a_1 - a_2 + a_3 - \cdots$ is convergent, say with sum α, and that the partial sums $A_n = a_1 - \cdots + (-1)^{n-1} a_n$ satisfy

$$A_{2m} < \alpha < A_{2m+1} \quad \text{and} \quad |\alpha - A_n| < a_n.$$

(A series of this form, or its negative $-a_1 + a_2 - \cdots$, is called an **alternating series**. Thus every alternating series is convergent.) Hence calculate $1 - \frac{1}{2} + \frac{1}{3} - \frac{1}{4} + \cdots$ to one decimal place. (By A4.5(ii) the **harmonic series** $1 + \frac{1}{2} + \frac{1}{3} + \cdots$ is divergent.)

(ii) Use (5.40) to show that if $b_1 + b_2 + \cdots$ converges to β, then so does the series $c_1 + c_2 + \cdots$ obtained by grouping terms $c_1 = b_1 + \cdots + b_{i_1}$, $c_2 = b_{i_1+1} + \cdots + b_{i_2}$, and so on. Deduce that

$$1 + \frac{1}{4} + \cdots + \frac{1}{n^2} + \cdots = (2-1) + \left(\frac{3}{4} - \frac{1}{2}\right) + \cdots + \left(\frac{n+1}{n^2} - \frac{1}{n}\right) + \cdots$$

is convergent in $\mathbb{R}$.

7. p-ADIC NUMBERS AND FORMAL POWER SERIES

Every nonzero p-adic number $\alpha \in Q_p{}^*$ has a unique representation, called its ***p*-adic expansion**, as a series in the form

$$\alpha = a_n p^n + a_{n+1} p^{n+1} + a_{n+2} p^{n+2} + \cdots, \tag{5.42}$$

where each a_i is an integer satisfying $0 \leqslant a_i \leqslant p-1$, $n \in \mathbb{Z}$, and $a_n \neq 0$. This will be proved in the next section. In this section we perform a few sample calculations to familiarize ourselves with the arithmetic of various $\mathbb{Q}_p$ (and formal power series fields that we describe later), leaving justifications for the most part until Sections 8 and 9.

However, there is one basic result that will aid greatly in following the calculations, and that shows at least that every series (5.42) is convergent (with respect to the p-adic absolute value, of course).

(5.43) PROPOSITION. *Let k be a valued field and let $a_1, a_2, \ldots$ be elements of k. In order that the infinite series $a_1 + a_2 + \cdots$ be convergent it is necessary that* $\lim|a_i| = 0$. *If* $|\ |$ *is ultrametric, this condition is also sufficient.*

Proof. Let $A_i = a_1 + \cdots + a_i$. If the series is convergent, then, given $h \in \mathbb{N}$, $\exists N \ni |A_i - A_{i-1}| = |a_i| < 1/h\ \forall i \geqslant N$. Thus $\lim|a_i| = 0$. Now suppose that $|\ |$ is ultrametric and $\lim|a_i| = 0$. Then, given $h \in \mathbb{N}$, $\exists N \ni |a_i| < 1/h$ $\forall i \geqslant N$. Hence $\forall j > i \geqslant N$

$$|A_j - A_i| = |a_{i+1} + \cdots + a_j| \leqslant \max\{|a_{i+1}|, \ldots, |a_j|\} < 1/h. \quad \blacksquare$$

The series

$$1! + 2! + 3! + 4! + \cdots$$

does not converge with respect to the ordinary absolute value on $\mathbb{Q}$, but for each p it does converge to some element $\alpha_p \in \mathbb{Q}_p$ since $v_p(n!)$ becomes large with n (cf. 5.156), so the sequence of p-adic absolute values

$$|n!| = p^{-v_p(n!)}$$

converges to 0.

If $\alpha \in \mathbb{N}$, then its p-adic expansion (5.42) terminates, i.e., $a_i = 0$ for all $i >$ some N, and (5.42) is the analog of the decimal expansion (2.10). With 10 replaced by p, the algorithm described there now gives the p-adic digits a_i. For example, if $\alpha = 13$ and $p = 2$, the sequence of divisions

$$\begin{aligned} 13 &= 2 \cdot 6 + 1, \\ 6 &= 2 \cdot 3 + 0, \\ 3 &= 2 \cdot 1 + 1, \\ 1 &= 2 \cdot 0 + 1, \end{aligned}$$

shows that the 2-adic (or **binary**) expansion of 13 is

$$13 = 1 + 0 \cdot 2 + 1 \cdot 2^2 + 1 \cdot 2^3 + 0 \cdot 2^4 + 0 \cdot 2^5 + \cdots.$$

Similarly we find the p-adic expansions of 13 for the next few p:

$$\begin{aligned} 13 &= 1 + 1 \cdot 3 + 1 \cdot 3^2, \\ 13 &= 3 + 2 \cdot 5, \\ 13 &= 6 + 1 \cdot 7, \\ 13 &= 2 + 1 \cdot 11, \\ 13 &= 1 \cdot 13. \end{aligned}$$

For $p > 13$ the expansion reduces to $13 = 13 + 0 \cdot p + 0 \cdot p^2 + \cdots$.

The 2-adic expansion of -1 is given in (5.29), and by the same reasoning in $\mathbb{Q}_p$,

$$-1=(p-1)+(p-1)p+(p-1)p^2+\cdots.$$

The way to obtain the p-adic expansion of an integer $m<-1$ is to subtract the expansion of $-(m+1)$ from that of -1, as the following example illustrates. In $\mathbb{Q}_7$, since $13=6+1\cdot 7$,

$$\begin{aligned}-14&=-1-13=(6+6\cdot 7+6\cdot 7^2+\cdots)-(6+1\cdot 7)\\&=5\cdot 7+6\cdot 7^2+6\cdot 7^3+\cdots.\end{aligned}$$

We illustrate the addition of p-adic expansions by interpreting the equation $-1+1=0$ in $\mathbb{Q}_3$ in this notation:

$$\begin{aligned}-1&=2+2\cdot 3+2\cdot 3^2+\cdots,\\1&=1+0\cdot 3+0\cdot 3^2+\cdots.\end{aligned}$$

The procedure is somewhat like adding two real numbers in decimal notation except that we work our way from left to right. In the p^0 column we add the two digits 2 and 1 to get 3, which we take as $0+1\cdot 3$, that is, 0 with a "carry" of 1. This carry plus the two digits in the p^1 column give $1+2+0=0+1\cdot 3$, again 0 with a carry of 1. This pattern persists and the result is $0+0\cdot 3+0\cdot 3^2+\cdots=0$.

When calculating with elements in $\mathbb{Q}_p$ it is often convenient to allow series of the form $b_n p^n+b_{n+1}p^{n+1}+\cdots$, where the b_i are any integers, converting only the final answer into its p-adic expansion. All such series are convergent by (5.43). For instance, when we multiply we usually make the preliminary calculation

$$\begin{aligned}&(a_m p^m+a_{m+1}p^{m+1}+\cdots)(b_n p^n+b_{n+1}p^{n+1}+\cdots)\\&\quad=a_m b_n p^{m+n}+(a_m b_{n+1}+a_{m+1}b_n)p^{m+n+1}+\cdots.\end{aligned}$$

For example, in $\mathbb{Q}_5$,

$$\begin{aligned}&(3\cdot 5^{-2}+4+3\cdot 5^2+4\cdot 5^4+\cdots)(1\cdot 5+2\cdot 5^2+3\cdot 5^3+1\cdot 5^4+2\cdot 5^5+\cdots)\\&\quad=3\cdot 5^{-1}+6+13\cdot 5+11\cdot 5^2+\cdots\\&\quad=3\cdot 5^{-1}+(1+1\cdot 5)+(3+2\cdot 5)5+(1+2\cdot 5)5^2+\cdots\\&\quad=3\cdot 5^{-1}+1+4\cdot 5+3\cdot 5^2+\cdots.\end{aligned}$$

The result is accurate to the four digits displayed in the last line since any further terms can contribute only to 5^i with $i>2$. If we multiply the terms by appropriate powers of 5, the product becomes

$$\begin{aligned}&(3+4\cdot 5^2+3\cdot 5^4+4\cdot 5^6+\cdots)(1+2\cdot 5+3\cdot 5^2+1\cdot 5^3+2\cdot 5^4+\cdots)\\&\quad=3+1\cdot 5+4\cdot 5^2+3\cdot 5^3+\cdots,\end{aligned}$$

and now, by truncating each of the series at the 5^3 term, we obtain the congruence

$$(3+4\cdot 5^2)(1+2\cdot 5+3\cdot 5^2+1\cdot 5^3)\equiv 3+1\cdot 5+4\cdot 5^2+3\cdot 5^3 \mod 5^4,$$

i.e.,

$$103\cdot 211\equiv 483 \mod 625.$$

The multiplication if carried out to n 5-adic digits can be interpreted as an ordinary congruence mod 5^n.

Indeed any equation between p-adic numbers (if necessary multiplied by a power of p to shift out negative exponents) can be interpreted as a sequence of congruences modulo successively higher powers of p. For instance to find the 7-adic expansion of $-43/7\cdot 24$ correct to the term in 7^2, we first find $-43/24\equiv 1899 \mod 7^4$ (e.g., by the method mentioned in A6.2(β)). Since $1899=2+5\cdot 7+3\cdot 7^2+5\cdot 7^3$,

$$-43/7\cdot 24=2\cdot 7^{-1}+5+3\cdot 7+5\cdot 7^2+\cdots.$$

The situation is similar to that when calculating with real numbers; we carry a certain number of "significant digits" in order to obtain a result to a certain degree of accuracy—to a desired number of decimal places. However, there is one important difference. When we add real numbers the **round-off errors** (the differences between the actual numbers and the approximations to them that we are using in the calculations) can accumulate. For instance if 10.1 and 9.8 are approximations to the real numbers α and β, correct to one decimal place, so that

$$10.1-0.05\leqslant\alpha\leqslant 10.1+0.05$$

and similarly for β, then $10.1-9.8=0.3$ as an approximation to $\alpha-\beta$ could be out by as much as 0.1. Because of the strong triangle inequality such deterioration of accuracy does not occur in the ultrametric case.

Sometimes it is more convenient to work with series than with congruences. One way to find the expansion $a_n p^n+a_{n+1}p^{n+1}+\cdots$ of $a=c/b$ for given $b=b_m p^m+\cdots$ and $c=c_{m+n}p^{m+n}+\cdots$ is to write

$$(b_m p^m+\cdots)(a_n p^n+\cdots)=c_{m+n}p^{m+n}+\cdots$$

and solve in succession for $a_n, a_{n+1},\ldots$—the so called **method of undetermined coefficients**. For instance, to find the 7-adic expansion of $-43/7\cdot 24$ by this method we write $24=3+3\cdot 7$ and

$$7(3+3\cdot 7)(a_{-1}7^{-1}+a_0+a_17+\cdots)=-43$$

or

$$3a_{-1}+(3a_{-1}+3a_0)7+(3a_0+3a_1)7^2+\cdots=6+0\cdot 7+6\cdot 7^2+6\cdot 7^3+\cdots.$$

Comparing the coefficients of 7^0, we require

$$3a_{-1}\equiv 6 \mod 7,$$

that is, $3a_{-1}=6+7x$ allowing a carry of x, whence $a_{-1}=2$. Next,

$$3a_{-1}+3a_0\equiv 6+3a_0\equiv 0 \mod 7,$$

so $a_0=5$ and $3a_{-1}+3a_0=0+7\cdot 3$. Taking account of the carry of 3, the next one is

$$3+3a_0+3a_1\equiv 18+3a_1\equiv 6 \mod 7;$$

hence $a_1=3$ and $3+3a_0+3a_1=6+7\cdot 3$. Next,

$$3+3a_1+3a_2\equiv 12+3a_2\equiv 6,$$

so $a_2=5$ with a carry 3 and

$$3+3a_2+3a_3\equiv 6.$$

The situation is identical to that when we were determining a_1 and therefore the pair of digits 3,5 is repeated ad infinitum:

$$-43/7\cdot 24=2\cdot 7^{-1}+5+3\cdot 7+5\cdot 7^2+3\cdot 7^3+5\cdot 7^4+3\cdot 7^5+\cdots.$$

Check: By (5.26) the right side is

$$2\cdot 7^{-1}+(5+3\cdot 7)(1+7^2+7^4+\cdots)=2/7+26/(1-7^2)=-43/7\cdot 24.$$

We shall see in (5.57) that, as in the case of decimal expansions of real numbers, a p-adic number $a_n p^n+a_{n+1}p^{n+1}+\cdots$ is rational iff the sequence $a_n, a_{n+1},\ldots$ is eventually periodic.

If we define $v:\mathbb{Q}_p\to\mathbb{Z}\amalg\{\infty\}$ by $v(0)=\infty$ and $v(a_n p^n+a_{n+1}p^{n+1}+\cdots)=n$ if $0<a_n<p$, then v extends the p-adic valuation on $\mathbb{Q}$, and $|\alpha|=p^{-v_p(\alpha)}$ is the extension to $\mathbb{Q}_p$ of the p-adic absolute value as defined in (5.36). Notice that the extended $|\ |$ does not require any new values in $\mathbb{R}$. It is an ultrametric absolute value on the field $\mathbb{Q}_p$ and the valuation ring is denoted

$$\mathbb{Z}_p=\{\alpha\in\mathbb{Q}_p:|\alpha|\leqslant 1\},$$

and is called the **ring of *p*-adic integers**. The **group of *p*-adic units** is

$$\mathbb{Z}_p^*=\{\alpha\in\mathbb{Q}_p:|\alpha|=1\}.$$

$\mathbb{Z}_p$ is a P.I.D. and, within a unit factor $u\in\mathbb{Z}_p^*$, p is the only irreducible element: Every $\alpha=a_n p^n+a_{n+1}p^{n+1}+\cdots\in\mathbb{Q}_p^*$ ($a_n\neq 0$) has the unique factorization $\alpha=p^{v(\alpha)}u$, where $v(\alpha)=n\in\mathbb{Z}$ and $u=a_n+a_{n+1}p+\cdots\in\mathbb{Z}_p^*$. Thus the absolute value on $\mathbb{Q}_p$ is just another example of (5.2). For all of this see the next section.

We now look at a few simple cases of factoring a polynomial over $\mathbb{Q}_p$. The polynomial X^2-2 is irreducible in $\mathbb{Q}_2$ since if β were a root we would have $2v(\beta)=v(\beta^2)=v(2)=1$, which contradicts $v(\beta)\in\mathbb{Z}$. The same type of reasoning shows that if $X^n-\alpha$ has a root in $\mathbb{Q}_p^*$, then $n|v(\alpha)$.

Next consider $f(X)=X^2+1\in\mathbb{Q}_2[X]$. If β is a root, then $v(\beta)=v(-1)/2=0$, so $\beta=1+a_1 2+a_2 2^2+\cdots$, where each a_i is 0 or 1. Squaring gives

$$\beta^2 = 1 + (2a_1)2 + (2a_2 + a_1^2)2^2 + \cdots = 1 + 0\cdot 2 + (a_1 + a_1^2)2^2 + \cdots,$$

which cannot coincide with $-1 = 1 + 2 + 2^2 + \cdots$. Thus X^2+1 is irreducible over $\mathbb{Q}_2$. It is also irreducible over $\mathbb{Q}_3$ because

$$(a_0 + a_1 3 + \cdots)^2 = a_0^2 + 2a_0a_1 3 + \cdots = 2 + 2\cdot 3 + \cdots$$

$$\Rightarrow \quad a_0^2 \equiv 2 \mod 3,$$

which has no solution.

However, X^2+1 does factor over $\mathbb{Q}_5$. From

$$\begin{aligned}(a_0 + a_1 5 + a_2 5^2 + \cdots)^2 &= a_0^2 + 2a_0a_1 5 + (2a_0a_2 + a_1^2)5^2 \\ &\quad + (2a_0a_3 + 2a_1a_2)5^3 + \cdots \\ &= 4 + 4\cdot 5 + \cdots,\end{aligned}$$

we obtain first $a_0^2 \equiv 4 \mod 5$, and thus $a_0 \equiv \pm 2$, i.e., $a_0 = 2$ or 3. Let us choose $a_0 = 2$. Then $a_1, a_2, \ldots$ are uniquely determined in succession:

$$\begin{aligned} 4a_1 &\equiv 4 &&\Rightarrow && a_1 = 1, \\ 4a_2 + 1 &\equiv 4 &&\Rightarrow && a_2 = 2, \quad \text{carry } 1, \\ 1 + 4a_3 + 4 &\equiv 4 &&\Rightarrow && a_3 = 1, \quad \text{carry } 1, \end{aligned}$$

and so on. Over any field of characteristic $\neq 2$, it is customary to denote the roots of X^2+1 by i and $-i$ (in some order). Thus

$$i = a_0 + a_1 5 + \cdots = 2 + 5 + 2\cdot 5^2 + 5^3 + \cdots$$

is one of the square roots of -1 in $\mathbb{Q}_5$. Since i is irrational its 5-adic expansion never becomes periodic. The other square root of -1 is $-i = 3 + 3\cdot 5 + 2\cdot 5^2 + 3\cdot 5^3 + \cdots$, which we would have obtained above if we had chosen $a_0 = 3$. In $\mathbb{Q}_5[X]$ we have

$$X^2 + 1 = (X - i)(X + i).$$

We turn now to another type of complete field. Let F be any field, $F[X]$ the polynomial ring over F, v_X the X-adic valuation on $k = F(X)$ and, with some c satisfying $0 < c < 1$, let

$$|\alpha| = c^{v_X(\alpha)}$$

be the corresponding X-adic absolute value. Thus

$$|X^2 + X^4| = |X^2||1 + X^2| = c^2c^0 = c^2,$$

$$\left|1 + \frac{1}{X}\right| = \left|\frac{X+1}{X}\right| = c^{-1}, \qquad |0| = 0.$$

The X-adic completion of k, as we shall prove in the next section, can be identified with the field of formal power series $F((X))$. The nonzero elements of this field have unique X-adic expansions

(5.44) $$\alpha = a_n X^n + a_{n+1} X^{n+1} + a_{n+2} X^{n+2} + \cdots,$$

where $a_i \in F$, $n \in \mathbb{Z}$, and $a_n \neq 0$. We define $v(\alpha) = n$ and $|\alpha| = c^{v(\alpha)}$. The ring operations are simpler than in $\mathbb{Q}_p$ since there is no carrying or borrowing:

$$\sum_{i \geqslant n} a_i X^i + \sum_{i \geqslant n} b_i X^i = \sum_{i \geqslant n} (a_i + b_i) X^i,$$

(where we have inserted terms $0X^i$ as needed to give the series a common starting index n). For example, in $\mathbb{Q}((X))$

$$(-\tfrac{1}{2}X^{-3} + 5 + \tfrac{7}{3}X^4 + \cdots)$$
$$+(\tfrac{1}{2}X^{-3} - 5 + X + \tfrac{2}{3}X^4 + \cdots) = X + 3X^4 + \cdots.$$

Next,

$$\Big(\sum_{i \geqslant m} a_i X^i\Big)\Big(\sum_{j \geqslant n} b_j X^j\Big) = \sum_{r \geqslant m+n} c_r X^r,$$

where

$$c_r = \sum_{i=m}^{r-n} a_i b_{r-i}.$$

For example, in $\mathbb{F}_3((X))$,

$$(1-X)^2(1 - X + X^2 - X^3 + \cdots) = 1 - 3X + 4X^2 - 4X^3 + 4X^4 - \cdots$$
$$= 1 + X^2 - X^3 + X^4 - \cdots.$$

Since $|aX^m| = 0$ or c^{-m}, by (5.43) all series of the form (5.44) are convergent with respect to the X-adic absolute value. This convergence should not be confused with that of power series, which refers to the following situation. Suppose F is equipped with an absolute value $|\ |'$ and we choose some $a_n X^n + a_{n+1} X^{n+1} + \cdots \in F((X))$ and some $x \in F^*$. We then can ask whether $a_n x^n + a_{n+1} x^{n+1} + \cdots$ is convergent with respect to $|\ |'$; cf (5.68). When we refer to (5.44) as a formal power series, the word *formal* emphasizes that we are not imposing any such requirement on the series. Thus in some contexts $1 + X + X^2 + \cdots$ is a formal series, while in (5.26) it was considered as a power series.

The series α in (5.44) is **regular** if $n \geqslant 0$, or if $\alpha = 0$. The regular series form a subring of $F((X))$, denoted $F[\![X]\!]$, and

$$F((X)) = Q(F[\![X]\!]).$$

We now describe the embedding $k \subset \tilde{k}$, i.e., the identification of rational functions $\alpha \in k = F(X)$ with formal power series. For polynomials there is no problem. For example,

$$1 - X + X^3 = 1 - X + 0X^2 + X^3 + 0X^4 + \cdots,$$

and we have $F[X] \subset F[\![X]\!]$. In general, for $\alpha \neq 0$, let $v_X(\alpha) = n$ so that $\alpha = X^n\beta$, where β is a rational function of the form

$$\frac{b_0 + b_1X + \cdots + b_rX^r}{c_0 + c_1X + \cdots + c_sX^s}, \qquad b_0c_0 \neq 0.$$

By dividing top and bottom by c_0, we can assume that $c_0 = 1$. Now apply (5.26):

$$\begin{aligned}\beta &= (b_0 + \cdots + b_rX^r)\big[1 - (c_1X + \cdots + c_sX^s) \\ &\quad + (c_1X + \cdots + c_sX^s)^2 - \cdots\big] \\ &= d_0 + d_1X + \cdots,\end{aligned}$$

say, and then $\alpha = d_0X^n + d_1X^{n+1} + \cdots$. For instance, in $\mathbb{R}((X))$ (indeed in any $F((X))$),

$$\begin{aligned}1/(1 + X + X^2) &= 1 - (X + X^2) + (X + X^2)^2 - \cdots \\ &= 1 - X + X^3 - X^4 + X^6 - X^7 + \cdots + X^{3n} - X^{3n+1} + \cdots.\end{aligned}$$

Check: $(1 - X)(1 + X^3 + X^6 + \cdots) = (1 - X)/(1 - X^3) = 1/(1 + X + X^2)$. Any formal power series whose coefficients are eventually periodic is easily "summed" and seen to be a rational function. However, unlike $\mathbb{R}$ and $\mathbb{Q}_p$, this eventual periodicity is not necessary for rationality. For instance the coefficients in

$$1/(1 - X)^2 = 1 + 2X + 3X^2 + 4X^3 + \cdots$$

are not periodic if $\operatorname{char}(F) = 0$. The test for rationality of a given formal power series will be discussed in (5.57).

In the polynomial ring $F((X))[Y]$ let us determine a root $\alpha = 1 + a_1X + a_2X^2 + \cdots$ of $Y^2 - (1 + X)$. The following is valid when $\operatorname{char}(F) \neq 2$. We write

$$1 + X = (1 + a_1X + a_2X^2 + \cdots)^2 = 1 + 2a_1X + (2a_2 + a_1^2)X^2 + \cdots$$

and compare coefficients to obtain

$$\begin{aligned} 2a_1 &= 1 &&\Rightarrow && a_1 = \tfrac{1}{2}, \\ 2a_2 + a_1^2 &= 0 &&\Rightarrow && a_2 = -\tfrac{1}{8}, \\ 2a_3 + 2a_1a_2 &= 0 &&\Rightarrow && a_3 = \tfrac{1}{16}, \\ 2a_4 + 2a_3a_1 + a_2^2 &= 0 &&\Rightarrow && a_4 = -\tfrac{5}{128}, \end{aligned}$$

and so on. It will be shown in (5.171) that

$$a_n = (-1)^{n-1}b_n/2^{2n},$$

where $b_n = (2n)!/((2n-1)(n!)^2) \in \mathbb{Z}$.

For any $a \in F$, the $(X - a)$-adic completion of $k = F(X)$ can be identified with $F((T))$, where we have chosen a different letter for the variable since now the embedding $F(X) \to F((T))$ is given by $X \mapsto T + a$. The canonical identification of $k=F(X)$ as a subfield of $k=F((T))$ is obtained by setting $X=T+a$ and rewriting each rational function as a formal power series in T. For example, if $a=-1$, then

$$\frac{X+1}{X}=\frac{-(X+1)}{1-(X+1)}=\frac{-T}{1-T}=-T-T^2-T^3-\cdots.$$

The p-adic completion of $F(X)$ when p is an irreducible polynomial of degree >1 can be identified with $F'((T))$, where F' is the field $F[X]/pF[X]$, but we refrain from giving more details at this time.

EXERCISES

1. Verify the following "long division" in $\mathbf{Q}_5$:

$$\begin{array}{r|l}
 & 3+0\cdot5+4\cdot5^2+3\cdot5^3+\cdots \\ \hline
2+5+3\cdot5^2+5^3+\cdots & 1+4\cdot5+2\cdot5^2+5^3+\cdots \\
 & 1+4\cdot5+4\cdot5^2+4\cdot5^3+\cdots \\ \cline{2-2}
 & \qquad\qquad 3\cdot5^2+5^3+\cdots \\
 & \qquad\qquad 3\cdot5^2+0\cdot5^3+\cdots \\ \cline{2-2}
 & \qquad\qquad\qquad\quad 5^3+\cdots \\
 & \qquad\qquad\qquad\quad 5^3+\cdots \\ \cline{2-2}
 & \qquad\qquad\qquad\qquad \ddots
\end{array}$$

2. For $p=2,3$, and 5, find the p-adic expansions of $\frac{1}{2}$, $\frac{2}{3}$, and $-\frac{1}{6}$ and verify in each case that their sum is 1.

3. If $\alpha\in\mathbf{Q}_p$ has the standard p-adic expansion $a_m p^m+a_{m+1}p^{m+1}+\cdots$ (so $a_i\in\{0,1,\ldots,p-1\}$ and $a_m>0$), find the standard p-adic expansion of $-\alpha$.

4. (i) Verify to the indicated accuracy that in $\mathbf{Q}_2$, $\sqrt{-7}$ has the two values $\alpha=1+2+2^3+2^6+\cdots$ and $-\alpha=1+2^2+2^4+2^5+\cdots$.
   (ii) Calculate the unique root of X^6+X+1 in $\mathbf{Q}_3$ up to the term in 3^3.

5. Calculate the six roots of X^6-1 in $\mathbf{Q}_7$ up to the term in 7^3.

6. Let $\mathbf{A},\mathbf{B}\in\mathrm{Mat}_n(\mathbf{Z}_p)$ and suppose $|\mathbf{A}|\in\mathbf{Z}_p{}^*$, so by A9.7, $\mathbf{A}^{-1}\in\mathrm{Mat}_n(\mathbf{Z}_p)$. (In other words, $\mathbf{A}\in\mathrm{GL}_n(\mathbf{Z}_p)$.) Show that $\mathbf{X}^2-\mathbf{AX}+p\mathbf{B}$ has a unique root $\mathbf{X}\in\mathrm{Mat}_n(\mathbf{Z}_p)\ni\mathbf{X}\equiv\mathbf{A}\bmod p$.

8. DISCRETELY VALUED FIELDS

By a **discrete absolute value** on the field k we understand an absolute value $|a|$ of the form $c^{v_p(a)}$, where v_p is the p-adic valuation for an irreducible element p of some U.F.D. A, where $Q(A)=k$. We abbreviate v_p to v. Let

$$D=\{a\in k:|a|\leqslant1\}=\{a:v(a)\geqslant0\}$$

denote the valuation ring and

$$P=\{a\in k:|a|<1\}=\{a:v(a)>0\}$$

its unique maximal ideal (cf. (5.7)). The elements of D are called **p-adic integers** and the elements of

$$D^*=D\setminus P=\{a:|a|=1\}=\{a:v(a)=0\}$$

are called **p-adic units**. Let $\kappa=D/P$ denote the residue field.

The notation $A, k, D, P, p, \kappa, v, c$ will remain fixed in this section.

We recall from A6.6 that D is the local ring A_{pA}, P is the principal ideal pD, and D is a U.F.D. with the single class of irreducible elements up, $u\in D^*$. Thus every $a\in k^*$ has the unique factorization

$$a=up^{v(a)},\qquad u\in D^*,$$

and D can play the role of A in the definition of discrete absolute value just given. As explained in Chapter 3, p can be replaced by any associate up without affecting v, and hence without affecting D, P, or κ. Any such element up with $v(up)=1$ is called a **uniformizer** for the discrete absolute value. Since $v(a)\geqslant n\Leftrightarrow a=p^nb$ for some $b\in D$, we have, for $c,d\in D$,

$$c\equiv d \mod p^n \qquad\Leftrightarrow\qquad v(c-d)\geqslant n.$$

A discrete absolute value is ultrametric (cf. (5.7)). For an example of an ultrametric absolute value that is not discrete see A12.4.

(5.45) PROPOSITION. *An absolute value $|\ |$ on a field K is discrete iff it is ultrametric, the maximal ideal P of the valuation ring D is principal, say $P=pD$, and $p\neq 0$. Then D is a U.F.D., p is (within a unit factor) the only irreducible element, and the absolute value is given by $|a|=c^{v(a)}$, where $c=|p|$ and $v=v_p$.*

Remark. The condition $p\neq 0$ ensures that $|\ |$ is not the trivial absolute value for which $D=K$, $P=0$.

Proof. It remains to prove the converse: suppose $|\ |$ is ultrametric, $P=pD$, and $p\neq 0$. Since maximal ideals are prime, p is an irreducible element of D (cf. (3.44)). Define $c=|p|$, so $0<c<1$. For a nonzero element a of the field, by A10.2(iii), $\exists n\ni c^{n+1}<|a|\leqslant c^n$. Put $u=a/p^n$, so $c<|u|\leqslant 1$. If $|u|<1$, then we would have $u\in P$; hence $u=px$ for some $x\in D$ and $|u|=|p||x|\leqslant c$, a contradiction. It follows that $a=p^nu$, where $|u|=1$, so $u\in D^*$, and $|a|=c^n$. The factorization $a=p^nu$ shows that D satisfies (U1) and that p is the only irreducible element. Since pD is maximal it is prime, and (U2′) is also satisfied. ■

(5.46) COROLLARY. *The extended* $|\ |$ *on* $\tilde{k}$ *is also discrete and* p *is a uniformizer.*

Proof. The extended $|\ |$ is ultrametric by (5.37). We let $\tilde{D}$ denote the valuation ring in $\tilde{k}$ and $\tilde{P}$ its maximal ideal. We conclude the proof by showing that $\tilde{P}=p\tilde{D}$. Because $|p|<1$, we have $p\tilde{D}\subset\tilde{P}$. Conversely, if $\alpha(\neq 0)\in\tilde{P}$ is represented by the cauchy sequence $(a_1,a_2,\ldots)$, then, by A10.5, $v(\alpha)=v(a_i)$ for all sufficiently large i. Therefore if $\beta=\alpha/p$, then $v(\beta)=\lim v(a_i/p)\geqslant 0$; hence $\alpha=p\beta\in p\tilde{D}$. ■

Thus the elements of $\tilde{D}$ are also called p-adic integers.

No element of k has value strictly between $|p|$ and 1. Similarly there are gaps between 1 and $|p|^{-1}$, $|p|^2$, and $|p|$, and so on. The existence of these gaps is characteristic of discrete absolute values:

(5.47) PROPOSITION. *Let* $|\ |$ *be a nontrivial absolute value on the field* K *that is not discrete. Then the values of elements of* K *come arbitrarily close to every positive real number. That is, if* $\alpha\in\mathbb{R}^>$ *and* $h\in\mathbb{N}$, *then* $\exists a\in K\ni ||a|-\alpha|<1/h$.

Proof. Let us prove this in the following form: If

$$\mu=\text{l.u.b.}\{|a|: a\in K \text{ and } |a|<1\}$$

satisfies $0<\mu<1$, then $|\ |$ is discrete. (The statement in the proposition follows easily; we leave this as an exercise.)

$|\ |$ is ultrametric since otherwise the set of values would include all positive rational numbers. Next we observe that $\exists p\in K\ni|p|=\mu$. If not, we could pick $a\in K$ with $\mu^2<|a|<\mu$ and then pick $b\ni|a|<|b|<\mu$ which leads to the contradiction $\mu<|a/b|<1$. If $q\in P$, then $|q|\leqslant\mu$. Hence $q=pr$, where $|r|\leqslant 1$. Thus $P=pD$, and the result follows from the previous proposition. ■

The ring of p-adic integers in $\mathbb{Q}_p$ has the special notation $\mathbb{Z}_p$. (This notation is quite standard nowadays, but unfortunately some authors use $\mathbb{Z}_p$ to denote $\mathbb{F}_p$.) We shall see a little later that, in the completion $F((X))$ of $F(X)$, $\tilde{D}$ consists of the regular formal power series $\tilde{D}=F[[X]]$.

(5.48) PROPOSITION. *The choice of the constant* c *does not affect the construction of* $\tilde{k}$: *If also* $0<c_1<1$ *and we define* $|a|_1=c_1^{v(a)}$, *then the sequence* $(a_1,a_2,\ldots)\in k^{\mathbb{N}}$ *is cauchy* (*resp. null*) *with respect to* $|\ |$ *iff it is cauchy* (*resp. null*) *with respect to* $|\ |_1$.

Proof. Suppose $(a_1,a_2,\ldots)$ is $|\ |$-null and $h\in\mathbb{N}$. By A10.1, $\exists n\in\mathbb{N}\ni c_1{}^n<c$ and $\exists N\in\mathbb{N}\ni|a_i|<1/h^n\ \forall i\geqslant N$. Thus $c_1{}^{nv(a_i)}<1/h^n$, and hence $c_1{}^{v(a_i)}<$

$1/h$, which proves that the sequence is $|\ |_1$-null. Similarly, $|\ |$-cauchy $\Rightarrow$ $|\ |_1$-cauchy and, of course, vice versa. ■

In the following when we discuss, for instance, "the" p-adic $|\ |$ on $\mathbb{Q}$ or $\mathbb{Q}_p$, there is implied a choice of c that we shall not usually bother to make explicit. The statements of results will be seen to be correct for any choice and it may be convenient not to be tied down to one value such as $c = 1/p$.

It follows from the definitions that $D \subset \tilde{D}$ and $P = D \cap \tilde{P}$. Therefore $a + P \mapsto a + \tilde{P}$ defines an injective ring homomorphism $\kappa \to \tilde{\kappa} = \tilde{D}/\tilde{P}$.

(5.49) PROPOSITION. *The canonical map $\kappa \to \tilde{\kappa}$ is an isomorphism.*

Proof. Given a nonzero element $\alpha + \tilde{P}$ of $\tilde{\kappa}$ we want to find $a \in k$ such that $a + P \mapsto \alpha + \tilde{P}$, i.e., $\alpha - a \in \tilde{P}$. If $(a_1, a_2, \ldots)$ is a cauchy sequence representing α, it is simply a matter of taking $a = a_N$ for N sufficiently large, as we now explain. Since $(a_1, \ldots)$ is not null, $\exists N \ni \forall i, j \geqslant N, |a_i| = |\alpha|$ (by A10.5) and $|a_i - a_j| < \max\{1, |\alpha|\}$. Thus the cauchy sequence $(a_1 - a_N, a_2 - a_N, \ldots)$ converges to $\alpha - a_N$ and $|\alpha - a_N| = \lim|a_i - a_N| < 1$, as required. ■

Thus we can make the identification $\kappa = \tilde{\kappa}$. There is a simple direct description of this field when A is a P.I.D.

(5.50) PROPOSITION. *When A is a P.I.D., κ can be identified with A/pA.*

Proof. A nonzero element a of A contains p in its unique factorization iff $v(a) > 0$. Thus $pA = P \cap A$ and $a + pA \mapsto a + P$ defines an injective homomorphism f: $A/pA \to \kappa$. Now, if $b + P$ is any element of κ, so $v(b) \geqslant 0$, we can write $b = q/r$, where q and r are elements of A and $p \nmid r$. By (3.62), $\exists s \in A \ni rs \equiv 1 \bmod pA$; hence $b + P = qs + P$. This shows that f is surjective. ■

As particular cases we have

(5.51) COROLLARY. (i) *The p-adic residue field of $\mathbb{Q}$ (hence of $\mathbb{Q}_p$) is $\mathbb{Z}/p\mathbb{Z} = \mathbb{F}_p$;*

(ii) *if p is an irreducible polynomial in $F[X]$, the p-adic residue field of $F(X)$ is $F[X]/pF[X]$.*

These two examples illustrate

(i) the unequal characteristic case: char$(k) = 0$, char$(\kappa) = p > 0$; and
(ii) the equal characteristic case: char$(k) =$ char(κ) $(\geqslant 0)$.

If $v(\alpha) = n > 0$ (resp. < 0) then α is said to have a **zero of order n** (resp. a **pole of order n**). This terminology is more common in the equal characteristic case.

Let S be a set of representatives in D of the elements of κ. Thus S contains exactly one element from each congruence class $a+P$. (In more abstract terms, one can define S as the image of an injective map $\sigma\colon \kappa \to D$ such that $\sigma\pi = 1_D$, where $\pi\colon D \to \kappa$ is the canonical projection. Such a σ is called a **section** of π.) We further stipulate that

$$\boxed{0 \in S \qquad \text{and} \qquad 1 \in S}$$

so 0 is the representative of P and 1 that of $1+P$. This is not strictly necessary, but will simplify certain statements, e.g., (5.54). Thus

$$s \in S,\ \ s \neq 0 \qquad \Rightarrow \qquad s+P \neq P \qquad \Rightarrow \qquad s \in D \backslash P = D^*.$$

S will have this fixed meaning for the rest of the section.

If $n \in \mathbb{Z}$ and $a_i \in S$, by (5.43) every series of the form

$$a_n p^n + a_{n+1} p^{n+1} + \cdots \tag{5.52}$$

converges to an element $\alpha \in k$. We call the series a ***p*-adic expansion** of α; a_i is understood to be 0 for $i<n$.

(5.53) PROPOSITION. *Once the uniformizer p and the set of representatives S are chosen, each $\alpha \in \tilde{k}$ has a unique p-adic expansion. When $\alpha \neq 0$,*

$$v(\alpha) = \min\{n : a_n \neq 0\}. \tag{5.54}$$

Remarks. In the case of $\mathbb{Q}_p$, we have $\kappa = \mathbb{Z}/p\mathbb{Z}$ and we can take $S = \{0,1,2,\dots,p-1\}$. Remember that these are elements of $\mathbb{Z}$, not $\mathbb{Z}/p\mathbb{Z}$. Of course, another S may be more convenient in some cases. For instance, when $k=\mathbb{Q}_3$ we can take $S=\{0,1,-1\}$, or $\{0,1,4/5\}$, or even $\{0,1,s\}$ for an appropriate irrational $s \in \mathbb{Z}_3$. A roughly analogous observation for $\mathbb{R}$ is that every real number can be written in the form $a_n 3^{-n} + a_{n+1} 3^{-(n+1)} + \cdots$, where $a_i \in \{0,1,-1\}$. However, the analogy breaks down when we consider uniqueness, since for $\mathbb{R}$ we must disallow, say, series in which the a_i are all eventually 1 (as we disallow repeated 9s in the usual decimal representation).

In the case of the $(X-a)$-adic completion of $F(X)$, the residue field is $\kappa = F[X]/(X-a)F[X] = F$ and we have the canonical choice $S=F$.

Proof. Let us first prove (5.54) in the slightly generalized form

$$\alpha = c_r p^r + c_{r+1} p^{r+1} + \cdots, \quad c_r \in \tilde{D}^*, \quad c_i \in \tilde{D}, \quad \forall i > r \tag{5.55}$$

$$\Rightarrow \qquad v(\alpha) = r.$$

Since $v(c_r p^r) = v(c_r) + v(p^r) = 0 + r = r$ and $v(c_i p^i) \geqslant i$ for $i>r$,

$$v(\alpha) = \lim_{N\to\infty} v\big(c_r p^r + \cdots + c_N p^N\big) = \lim_{N\to\infty} r = r.$$

Suppose (5.52) and $b_m p^m + b_{m+1} p^{m+1} + \cdots$ both converge to α, where $b_i \in S$ and some $b_r \neq a_r$. If r is the minimal such index, by (5.19) we have

$$0 = (a_r - b_r)p^r + (a_{r+1} - b_{r+1})p^{r+1} + \cdots.$$

Since a_r and b_r are distinct elements of S, $a_r + P \neq b_r + P$. Hence $a_r - b_r \in D \setminus P$ and by (5.55) we derive the contradiction $v(0) = r$. This proves the uniqueness of the p-adic expansion.

We establish the existence by describing an algorithm that can be likened to the one used to obtain the decimal expansion of a real number. Let $\alpha \in \tilde{k}^*$ and $v(\alpha) = n$. Then $p^{-n}\alpha = \alpha_n$ is an element of $\tilde{D}^*$ and is congruent mod $\tilde{P}$ to a unique nonzero element a_n of S. (In the notation for the *section* mentioned earlier, $a_n = \sigma\pi(\alpha_n)$.) The general step for $i \geqslant n$ is

$$\alpha_{i+1} = (\alpha_i - a_i)/p, \qquad \alpha_{i+1} \equiv a_{i+1} \mod \tilde{P}, \qquad a_{i+1} \in S.$$

Since

$$\alpha - (a_n p^n + a_{n+1} p^{n+1} + \cdots + a_N p^N) = p^{N+1} \alpha_{N+1}$$

has value $\geqslant N + 1$, by the cauchy criterion

$$\alpha = a_n p^n + a_{n+1} p^{n+1} + \cdots. \quad \blacksquare$$

(5.56) COROLLARY. *The elements of* $\tilde{D} = \{\alpha \in \tilde{k} : |\alpha| \leqslant 1\}$ *are those with p-adic expansions of the form* $\alpha = a_0 + a_1 p + a_2 p^2 + \cdots$; $\alpha \in \tilde{D}^*$ (*resp.* $\alpha \in \tilde{P}$) *iff* $a_0 \neq 0$ (*resp.* $a_0 = 0$).

For instance, the valuation ring in the X-adic completion $F((X))$ of $F(X)$ is the ring $\tilde{D} = F[\![X]\!]$ of regular formal power series, as defined in the last section.

(5.57) PROPOSITION. *Let* $\alpha \in \tilde{k}^*$ *have the p-adic expansion* $a_n p^n + a_{n+1} p^{n+1} + \cdots$.

(i) *If* $\tilde{k} = \mathbb{Q}_p$ *and* $S \subset \mathbb{Q}$, *then* $\alpha \in \mathbb{Q}$ *iff the sequence* a_i *is eventually periodic.*

(ii) *If* $k = F((X))$, $p = X$, *and* $S = F$, *then* $\alpha \in F(X)$ *iff the sequence* a_i *eventually satisfies a linear recurrence with coefficients in* F, *that is, iff for some* $h \in \mathbb{N}$, $N \geqslant n$, *and* $c_1, \ldots, c_h \in F$,

$$a_{i+h} = c_1 a_{i+h-1} + \cdots + c_h a_i, \qquad \forall i \geqslant N. \tag{5.58}$$

Proof. (i) If $a_{i+h} = a_i$ $\forall i \geqslant N$ and we define

$$\beta = a_N p^N + a_{N+1} p^{N+1} + \cdots,$$

then

$$\beta = a_N p^N + \cdots + a_{N+h-1} p^{N+h-1} + p^h \beta.$$

Solving this equation for β shows that β is rational and therefore also $\alpha = a_n p^n + \cdots + a_{N-1}p^{N-1} + \beta \in \mathbb{Q}$.

Conversely, let $\alpha \in Q^*$. Since the p-adic expansion of $p^{-n}\alpha$ is that of α shifted over n places, we can assume that $\alpha = a/b$, where a and b are integers, neither of which are divisible by p. We choose a common denominator $d \in \mathbb{N}$ for the finitely many elements in S, so $da \in \mathbb{Z}$, $\forall a \in S$, and for $i \geqslant 0$ we define $\alpha_i \in \mathbb{Z}$ by

$$d\left(a - b\sum_{j=0}^{i-1} a_j p^j\right) = \alpha_i p^i.$$

If $|\ |_\infty$ denotes the ordinary real absolute value and $m = \max\{|a|_\infty : a \in S\}$, then

$$|\alpha_i|_\infty \leqslant d\left(|a|_\infty + |b|_\infty \sum_{j=0}^{i-1} mp^j\right)/p^i$$

$$= d\big(|a|_\infty + |b|_\infty m(p^i - 1)/(p-1)\big)/p^i.$$

Hence the integers α_i are bounded and we must have $\alpha_N = \alpha_{N+h}$ for some N and $h > 0$. This implies that $a_i = a_{i+h}$ $\forall i \geqslant N$.

(ii) If (5.58) is satisfied then

$$(5.59)\qquad a_n X^n + \cdots + a_{N-1}X^{N-1} + \frac{b_N X^N + \cdots + b_{N+h-1}X^{N+h-1}}{1 - c_1 X - c_2 X^2 - \cdots - c_h X^h}$$

$$= a_n X^n + \cdots + a_N X^N + \cdots,$$

where

$$b_N = a_N,$$
$$b_{N+1} = a_{N+1} - c_1 a_N,$$
$$\vdots$$
$$b_{N+h-1} = a_{N+h-1} - c_1 a_{N+h-2} - \cdots - c_{h-1} a_N.$$

This follows from

$$b_N X^N + \cdots + b_{N+h-1}X^{N+h-1} = \left(1 - c_1 X - \cdots - c_h X^h\right) \times \left(a_N X^N + a_{N+1}X^{N+1} + \cdots\right),$$

which is substantially the same statement as (5.58).

To complete the proof, all that needs to be added is the remark that any $f \in F(X)^*$ can be written in the form of the left side of (5.59) by the following procedure. Regard f as a rational function in the variable $Y = 1/X$ and write $f = Y^m g/e$, where g and e are polynomials in Y, neither divisible by Y, with e monic. Let $g = eq + r$, where $r = 0$ or $\deg(r) < \deg(e)$, then rewrite $Y^m(q + r/h)$ in terms of X. This puts f in the required form. ∎

An example of this procedure is

$$f=\frac{-1+4X^3}{2X-2X^2+X^3}=\frac{Y^2(-Y^3/2+2)}{Y^2-Y+1/2}$$

$$=Y^2\left(-Y/2-1/2+\frac{-Y/4+9/4}{Y^2-Y+1/2}\right)$$

$$=-X^{-1}/2-1/2+\frac{-X/4+9X^2/4}{1-X+X^2/2}$$

$$=-X^{-1}/2-1/2-X/4+2X^2+a_3X^3+\cdots,$$

where $a_3=a_2-a_1/2=\frac{17}{8}$, and so on.

An example will be given in Section 11 of the 5-adic expansion of 2, using an S containing irrational numbers, that never becomes periodic.

9. ABSOLUTE CONVERGENCE

The justifications of the manipulations of series in Section 7 all come down to the following notion.

(5.60) DEFINITION. Let k be a valued field (ultrametric or archimedean) and let $a_i\in k$. The series $a_1+a_2+\cdots$ is **absolutely convergent** if the series of real numbers $|a_1|+|a_2|+\cdots$ is convergent.

For instance, if $a\in k$ and $|a|<1$, then the geometric series $1+a+a^2+\cdots$ is absolutely convergent since the real series $1+|a|+|a^2|+\cdots=1+|a|+|a|^2+\cdots$ is convergent by (5.26).

(5.61) PROPOSITION. *An absolutely convergent series $a_1+a_2+\cdots$ is convergent and $|a_1+a_2+\cdots|\leqslant|a_1|+|a_2|+\cdots$.*

Proof. Given $h\in\mathbb{N},\exists N\ni\forall j>i\geqslant N$,

$$|a_{i+1}+\cdots+a_j|\leqslant|a_{i+1}|+\cdots+|a_j|<1/h.$$

This proves convergence; say $a_1+a_2+\cdots=\alpha$.

If $|a_1|+|a_2|+\cdots=\lambda$, then $\forall r$

$$|a_1+\cdots+a_r|\leqslant|a_1|+\cdots+|a_r|\leqslant\lambda;$$

hence $|\alpha|=\lim|a_1+\cdots+a_r|\leqslant\lambda$ by A10.1. ■

Caution. The converse is not true. A4.5(ii) and A10.7(i) show that the alternating series $1-\frac{1}{2}+\frac{1}{3}-\cdots$ is convergent in $\mathbb{R}$ but not absolutely convergent. In the case of a discrete absolute value, whether a series converges absolutely or not can depend on the choice of the constant c. For example, in $\mathbb{Q}_2$, $1+2+2+4+4+4+4+8+\cdots$ (where 2^n occurs 2^n times) is convergent (with sum $-\frac{1}{3}$) since $\lim|a_i|=0$. Yet if $|2|=\frac{1}{2}$, then

$|1|+|2|+|2|+\cdots=1+(\frac{1}{2}+\frac{1}{2})+\cdots=1+1+\cdots$ is divergent. However if $|2|=c$, where $c<\frac{1}{2}$, then it is easy to see that $1+c+c+c^2+\cdots$ converges (cf. (5.63)).

A convergent series that is not absolutely convergent is said to be **conditionally convergent**.

Note that in the ultrametric case if $a_1+a_2+\cdots$ converges to α (absolutely or conditionally) then

$$|\alpha|=\lim|a_1+\cdots+a_n|\leqslant\lim\max\{|a_1|,\ldots,|a_n|\} \qquad \text{by A10.1}$$
$$\leqslant\max\{|a_1|,\ldots,|a_n|\} \qquad \forall \text{ sufficiently large } n.$$

If $a_1+a_2+\cdots=\alpha\in\tilde{k}$, then alterations of finitely many terms of the series, as typified by the following examples, affect the sum in the expected way:

$$b+a_1+a_2+\cdots=b+\alpha,$$
$$a_2+a_3+\cdots=\alpha-a_1,$$
$$a_2+a_1+a_3+\cdots=\alpha,$$
$$a_1+(a_2+a_3)+a_4+\cdots=\alpha,$$

where the last series is meant to be $b_1+b_2+\cdots$, where $b_1=a_1$, $b_2=a_2+a_3$, and $b_i=a_{i+1}$ for $i>2$. The verifications are quite trivial.

However, infinitely many alterations on nonabsolutely convergent series in general have "unpredictable" results. For example, $1-1+1-1+\cdots$ is divergent since $\lim(\pm 1)\neq 0$. Yet, grouping the terms as $(1-1)+(1-1)+\cdots$ yields the convergent series $0+0+\cdots=0$. On the other hand, we might reasonably argue that if $\alpha=1-1+1-\cdots$, then $\alpha=1-(1-1+\cdots)=1-\alpha$, so $\alpha=\frac{1}{2}$.

We shall see in (5.64) that the terms in an absolutely convergent series can be permuted and regrouped without restriction.

(5.62) LEMMA. *If $\mu_1<\mu_2<\cdots$ is an increasing sequence of real numbers for which $\mu_r\leqslant\lambda$ $\forall r$, then $\lim\mu_r=\mu$ exists and $\mu\leqslant\lambda$.*

Proof. Let $\mu=\sup\{\mu_1,\mu_2,\ldots\}$, so that $\mu\leqslant\lambda$. Given $h\in\mathbb{N}$, $\exists N\ni\mu-\mu_N<1/h$, whence $|\mu-\mu_r|<1/h$, $\forall r\geqslant N$. Therefore $\lim\mu_r=\mu$. ■

(5.63) COROLLARY. *In order that a series $a_1+a_2+\cdots$ of elements of a valued field be absolutely convergent it is necessary and sufficient that the set of real numbers $A_S=\Sigma_{i\in S}|a_i|$, where S runs through the finite subsets of $\mathbb{N}$, be bounded above. Hence if $a_1+a_2+\cdots$ is absolutely convergent and $\{n_1,n_2,\ldots\}\subset\mathbb{N}$ (we do not require $n_1<n_2<\cdots$), then $a_{n_1}+a_{n_2}+\cdots$ is absolutely convergent.*

Proof. If $a_1+\cdots$ is absolutely convergent, then the sequence $\mu_r=|a_1|+\cdots+|a_r|$ is cauchy, and hence bounded in absolute value: For some

λ, $\mu_r = |\mu_r| \leqslant \lambda \ \forall r$. If S is a finite subset of $\mathbb{N}$, then $\exists r \ni S \subset \{1,\ldots,r\}$ and $A_S \leqslant \mu_r < \lambda$.

Conversely, if all $A_S \leqslant \lambda$, then in particular all $\mu_r \leqslant \lambda$ and absolute convergence is assured by the lemma. ■

(5.64) PROPOSITION. *Let $a_1 + a_2 + \cdots = \alpha \in \tilde{k}$ be absolutely convergent, let $\mathbb{N} = I_1 \amalg I_2 \amalg \cdots$ be a partition into disjoint subsets $I_i = \{n_{i1}, n_{i2}, \ldots\}$, and put $b_i = a_{n_{i1}} + a_{n_{i2}} + \cdots$. Then $b_1 + b_2 + \cdots = \alpha$.*

Proof. If $A_i = a_1 + \cdots + a_i$, then, for a given $h \in \mathbb{N}$, by taking N sufficiently large we have, for all $j > i \geqslant N$, both $|A_i - \alpha| < 1/2h$ and $|a_{i+1}| + |a_{i+2}| + \cdots + |a_j| < 1/2h$; consequently $|a_{i+1}| + |a_{i+2}| + \cdots \leqslant 1/2h \ \ \forall i \geqslant N$. There exists an M such that

$$\{1,2,\ldots,N\} \subset \bigcup_{r=1}^{M} I_r$$

and, if we write $B_i = b_1 + \cdots + b_i$, then for each $i \geqslant M$ we have

$$\begin{aligned} |B_i - \alpha| &\leqslant |A_N - \alpha| + |B_i - A_N| \\ &< 1/2h + (|a_{N+1}| + |a_{N+2}| + \cdots) \leqslant 1/h. \quad ■ \end{aligned}$$

It follows that if I is any countable set and $a_i \in k$ for $i \in I$, it is meaningful to ask whether Σa_i is absolutely convergent, and if so to say that $\Sigma a_i = \alpha \in \tilde{k}$, without having chosen any particular order for the elements of I.

(5.65) COROLLARY. *If $\Sigma a_i = \alpha$ and $\Sigma b_j = \beta$ are absolutely convergent series, then so is $\Sigma a_i b_j$ and*

$$\Sigma a_i b_j = \alpha\beta,$$

the sum being over all pairs $(i, j) \in \mathbb{N} \times \mathbb{N}$.

Hence $c_1 + c_2 + \cdots = \alpha\beta$, where $c_n = a_1 b_n + a_2 b_{n-1} + \cdots + a_n b_1$.

Proof. From $|a_1| + \cdots + |a_m| \leqslant \lambda, |b_1| + \cdots + |b_n| \leqslant \lambda'$ we deduce that

$$\sum_{(i,j) \in S} |a_i b_j| \leqslant \lambda\lambda'$$

for all finite subsets S of $\mathbb{N} \times \mathbb{N}$. This guarantees the absolute convergence of the product series. By the proposition,

$$\sum_{i,j} a_i b_j = \sum_i \Big(\sum_j a_i b_j \Big) = \sum_i (a_i \beta) = \Big(\sum_i a_i \Big) \beta = \alpha\beta. \quad ■$$

The particular regrouping of terms $a_i b_j$ to form the series $c_1 + c_2 + \cdots$ is known as the **cauchy product** of the two series.

(5.66) PROPOSITION (**The comparison test**). *If $a_1+a_2+\cdots$ is absolutely convergent and $|b_i|\leqslant\gamma|a_i|$ for a fixed real number γ and all i, then $b_1+b_2+\cdots$ is absolutely convergent.*

Remark. As another way of wording this is, if $M_1, M_2, \ldots$ are real numbers, $|b_n|\leqslant M_n$, and $M_1+M_2+\cdots$ is convergent, then $b_1+\cdots$ is absolutely convergent.

Proof. If $|a_1|+|a_2|+\cdots=\lambda$, then $\forall r$ $|b_1|+|b_2|+\cdots+|b_r|\leqslant\gamma\lambda$. The result then follows from (5.63). ∎

(5.67) COROLLARY. *If k is discretely valued, then every series of the form*

$$a_n p^n + a_{n+1}p^{n+1}+\cdots, \qquad a_i\in D,$$

in particular every p-adic expansion, is absolutely convergent.

This results from comparing the series with the absolutely convergent geometric series $1+p+p^2+\cdots$. We can rearrange the iterated series

$$\sum_{i\geqslant m} a_i\Big(\sum_{j\geqslant n} b_{ij}p^j\Big)p^i = \sum_{r\geqslant m+n}\ \sum_{i=1}^{m} a_i b_{i,r-i}p^r,$$

and this is sufficient to justify the calculational procedures used in Section 7.

(5.68) COROLLARY. *If the power series $a_0+a_1X+a_2X^2+\cdots$ is convergent for $X=a$, then it is absolutely convergent for all $X=b$ satisfying $|b|<|a|$.*

Proof. $\lim a_n a^n=0$ by (5.43). Hence $\exists M\in\mathbb{R}^{>}\ni|a_n a^n|<M$, $\forall n$, and $|a_n b^n|<Mr^n$, where $r=|b|/|a|<1$. Thus comparison with the convergent geometric series proves the absolute convergence of $a_0+a_1b+\cdots$. ∎

EXERCISE

Find an example of a series $a_1+a_2+\cdots$ of rational numbers that converges in $\mathbb{R}$ and in every $\mathbb{Q}_p$.

10. ZEROS OF POLYNOMIALS; RATIONAL EXPONENTS

This section begins with a result of Bolzano, of which a particular case is the Weierstrass zeros theorem: If f is a real polynomial whose value is negative at one point and positive at another then f has the value 0 at some intermediate point. (This result, which is generalized to all continuous functions in A12.6(δ), depends crucially on the completeness of $\mathbb{R}$—the conclusion is not true over $\mathbb{Q}$. For instance, if $f=X^2-2$, then $f(1)<0<f(2)$, but f has no root in $\mathbb{Q}$.) Exploiting this simple idea to the full leads to

Sturm's theorem, which allows the exact determination of the number of real roots in a given interval. The next topic we discuss is rational exponents, particularly with regard to real numbers. The section closes with the formulas for the roots of quadratic, cubic, and quartic polynomials.

We need some preliminary results on the derivative of a polynomial. If $f = a_n X^n + \cdots + a_0 \in k[X]$ (k any commutative ring), the **Taylor expansion** of f is the following expression in $k[X, Y]$ obtained by substituting $X + Y$ for X:

$$f(X+Y) = f(X) + f_1(X)Y + f_2(X)Y^2 + \cdots + f_n(X)Y^n.$$

For instance, if $f = X^3 - 3X + 2$, then

$$\begin{aligned} f(X+Y) &= (X+Y)^3 - 3(X+Y) + 2 \\ &= X^3 - 3X + 2 + (3X^2 - 3)Y + 3XY^2 + Y^3, \end{aligned}$$

so $f_1 = 3X^2 - 3$, $f_2 = 3X$, $f_3 = 1$. The binomial theorem $(X+Y)^i = X^i + iX^{i-1}Y + \cdots$ immediately shows that

$$f_1 = na_n X^{n-1} + (n-1)a_{n-1}X^{n-2} + \cdots + a_1.$$

This polynomial is called the **derivative** of f and is customarily denoted f'. For two polynomials f, g, we have

$$\begin{aligned} (fg)(X+Y) &= f(X+Y)g(X+Y) \\ &= (f(X) + f_1(X)Y + \cdots)(g(X) + g_1(X)Y + \cdots) \\ &= (fg)(X) + (f(X)g_1(X) + f_1(X)g(X))Y + \cdots \\ &\quad + (f(X)g_i(X) + f_1(X)g_{i-1}(X) + \cdots)Y^i + \cdots. \end{aligned}$$

The rule for the derivative of a product is therefore

$$(fg)' = f'g + fg'.$$

(5.69) PROPOSITION. *Let $f \in \mathbb{R}[X]$ and let α, β, μ be real numbers such that $f(\alpha) < \mu < f(\beta)$. Then there exists a real number ξ between α and β such that $f(\xi) = \mu$.*

Proof. For definiteness let us assume that $\alpha < \beta$. The other case is reduced to this by interchanging α and β and replacing f and μ by $-f$ and $-\mu$. We show that

$$\xi = \text{g.l.b.}\{\beta' : \beta' > \alpha \text{ and } f(\beta') \geqslant \mu\}$$

has the required property by deriving a contradiction first from the assumption $f(\xi) > \mu$, and secondly from $f(\xi) < \mu$. Observe that $\forall \gamma > 0$, $\exists \beta'$ in the set defining $\xi \ni \xi > \beta' - \gamma$, since otherwise $\xi + \gamma$ would serve as a lower bound of that set.

Let $f = a_n X^n + \cdots + a_0$ and write

$$f(X+Y) = f(X) + f_1(X)Y + f_2(X)Y^2 + \cdots + f_n(X)Y^n$$

as above. Put

$$M=\max\left\{\binom{r}{s}|a_r|:1\leqslant s\leqslant r\leqslant n\right\}\qquad\text{and}\qquad \eta=\max\{1,|\xi|\}.$$

For $1\leqslant i\leqslant n$, $f_i(\xi)$ consists of at most n terms $\binom{r}{i}a_r\xi^j$, each of absolute value at most $M\eta^n$. Hence $|f_i(\xi)|\leqslant nM\eta^n$ and for any $\theta\ni|\theta|\leqslant 1$,

$$(5.70)\qquad |f(\xi+\theta)-f(\xi)|=|f_1(\xi)\theta+f_2(\xi)\theta^2+\cdots+f_n(\xi)\theta^n|$$
$$\leqslant n^2M\eta^n|\theta|=C|\theta|,$$

say. Suppose $f(\xi)>\mu$. Then by (5.70), $f(\xi-\theta)>\mu$ for θ satisfying $0<\theta\leqslant 1$ and

$$\theta<(f(\xi)-\mu)/C,$$

which contradicts the definition of ξ.

Suppose $f(\xi)<\mu$. Now $\exists\beta'=\xi+\theta$ such that $f(\beta')\geqslant\mu, 0<\theta\leqslant 1$, and

$$\theta<(\mu-f(\xi))/C.$$

Again (5.70) supplies the necessary contradiction. ∎

The particular case $f(\alpha)<0<f(\beta)\Rightarrow f$ has a root between α and β is known as the **Weierstrass Nullstellensatz** (or zeros theorem, **zero** being another term for root). In Figure 5.3, which displays

$$(5.71)\qquad f=X^3-3X+1,$$

f has three distinct real zeros since $f(-2)<0<f(-1)$ and $f(1)<0<f(2)$.

(5.72) COROLLARY. *Every $f\in\mathbb{R}[X]$ of odd degree has a root $\xi\in\mathbb{R}$.*

Proof. We can assume that $f=X^n+a_1X^{n-1}+\cdots+a_n$ is monic. Put $b=\max\{1,|a_1|+\cdots+|a_n|\}$. Then the result follows from $f(-b)\leqslant 0\leqslant f(b)$,

Figure 5.3

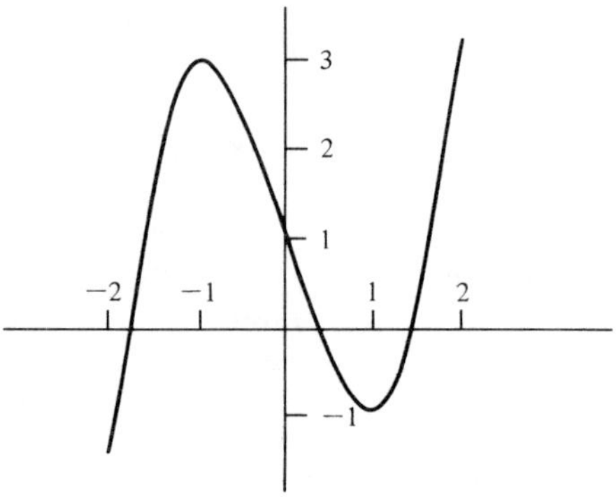

which we now verify.

$$f(b)=b^n+a_1b^{n-1}+\cdots+a_n \geqslant b^n-|a_1|b^{n-1}-|a_2|b^{n-2}-\cdots-|a_n|$$
$$\geqslant b^n-(|a_1|+\cdots+|a_n|)b^{n-1} \geqslant 0,$$

and similarly,

$$f(-b)=-b^n+a_1b^{n-1}-a_2b^{n-2}+\cdots \leqslant -b^n+(|a_1|+\cdots+|a_n|)b^{n-1}$$
$$\leqslant 0. \quad \blacksquare$$

The Nullstellensatz asserts that, under appropriate conditions, at least one root exists between certain limits. The following result of Sturm shows how to calculate precisely the number of real roots between two given limits.

Some general terminology: If f is a polynomial over the commutative ring K and has the factorization $f=(X-\theta)^e g$ in $K[X]$, where $(X-\theta)\nmid g$, then θ is referred to as a root of **multiplicity** e. When $e=1,2,\ldots$, θ is called a **simple root**, **double root**,.... When we say that θ is a **multiple** or **repeated root** we mean that $e>1$.

(5.73) PROPOSITION. *Let f_0 be a real polynomial of positive degree, let f_1 denote its derivative, and let*

$$f_0=q_1f_1-f_2, \qquad f_1=q_2f_2-f_3, \qquad \ldots, \qquad f_{r-1}=q_rf_r$$

be the result of Euclid's algorithm, modified slightly by multiplying the remainders by -1. For $\alpha\in\mathbb{R}$, let $w(\alpha)$ denote the number of variations of sign in the sequence

$$f_0(\alpha),\ f_1(\alpha),\ \ldots,\ f_r(\alpha)$$

with 0s disregarded (i.e., if the nonzero values in the sequence in order are $x_1,\ldots,x_s$ $(s\leqslant r)$, then each instance of $x_i<0<x_{i+1}$ or $x_i>0>x_{i+1}$ contributes 1 to $w(\alpha)$). If $\alpha<\beta$ and neither α nor β is a root of f_0, then the number of real roots of f_0 (multiple roots counted only once) between α and β is precisely $w(\alpha)-w(\beta)$.

Proof. Since $f_r=\text{g.c.d.}(f_0,f_1)$ within a constant factor, $f_r|$each f_i. If we write $f_i=f_rg_i$, then

(i) g_0 has precisely the same roots (in $\mathbb{R}$) as f_0 except that they are now all simple: In $f_0=f_rg_0$, f_r contains all the repeated factors. This is because if $v_{X-\gamma}(f_0)=e$, say $f_0=(X-\gamma)^e h$, then

$$f_0(X+Y)=(X+Y-\gamma)^e h(X+Y)$$
$$=\big((X-\gamma)^e+e(X-\gamma)^{e-1}Y+\cdots\big)\big(h(X)+h_1(X)Y+\cdots\big)$$
$$=f_0(X)+\big(e(X-\gamma)^{e-1}h(X)+(X-\gamma)^e h_1(X)\big)Y+\cdots.$$

Hence $f_1=(X-\gamma)^{e-1}(eh(X)+(X-\gamma)h_1(X))$, which shows that $v_{X-\gamma}(f_1)=e-1$ and therefore that g_0 contains $X-\gamma$ only to the first power.

(ii) g.c.d.$(g_0, g_1)=1$ and the (modified) euclidean algorithm for this pair is obtained from the one for f_0, f_1 by dividing each line by f_r. Although $g_1 \neq g_0'$ when $\deg(f_r)>0$, for every α that is not a root of f_r, the number of variations of sign in the sequence $f_i(\alpha)=f_r(\alpha)g_i(\alpha)$ is the same as that in the sequence $g_i(\alpha)$.

If we think of α as being fixed and β as increasing, in view of (i) and (ii) it remains to show that the number of sign variations $w(\beta)$ in the sequence $g_i(\beta)$ decreases by 1 as β passes over a root of g_0 and otherwise remains constant.

As β passes over an interval containing no root of any of the g_i, $w(\beta)$ remains constant since by the Nullstellensatz none of the $g_i(\beta)$ changes sign. Let us now examine the effect on $w(\beta)$ as β passes over a root γ of some g_i with $i>0$. Since g.c.d.$(g_i, g_j)=g_r=1$, γ is not a root of any other g_j; also $i<r$. Therefore the sequence of signs in

$$\ldots,\quad g_{i-1}(\beta),\quad g_i(\beta),\quad g_{i+1}(\beta),\quad \ldots$$

remains fixed except for the sign of $g_i(\beta)$, which is reversed. From $g_{i-1}= q_i g_i - g_{i+1}$ we see that $g_{i-1}(\gamma)$ and $g_{i+1}(\gamma)$ have opposite signs and that therefore $g_{i-1}(\beta)$ and $g_{i+1}(\beta)$ have opposite signs throughout the interval $\gamma-\varepsilon<\beta<\gamma+\varepsilon$, for sufficiently small positive ε. Hence $w(\gamma-\varepsilon)=w(\gamma)= w(\gamma+\varepsilon)$.

Finally, let us see what happens in the case of a root γ of g_0. In the notation of (i) above, $f_0=(X-\gamma)^e h$ and $g_0=(X-\gamma)k$, where k is a polynomial dividing h and $k(\gamma)\neq 0$. An easy calculation, which we leave to the reader, gives $g_1=ek+(X-\gamma)s$ for some polynomial s. The signs of $g_i(\beta)$ for $i>0$ and of $k(\beta)$ again remain fixed throughout a small interval $\gamma-\varepsilon<\beta<\gamma+\varepsilon$. However, as β passes from $\gamma-\varepsilon$ to $\gamma+\varepsilon$ the sign of g_0 changes from that of $-k(\gamma)$ to that of $+k(\gamma)$, while g_1 keeps the sign of $ek(\gamma)$ i.e., the sign of $k(\gamma)$. This means a change from a variation of sign to a nonvariation, hence a drop of 1 in the value of w. ■

It follows from the last part of the proof, writing f for f_0, that if γ is a root of f then, for sufficiently small positive ε, $f(\gamma-\varepsilon)$ and $f'(\gamma-\varepsilon)$ have opposite signs, while $f(\gamma+\varepsilon)$ and $f'(\gamma+\varepsilon)$ have the same sign. Hence if $\delta>\gamma$ is another root of f, and f has no roots between γ and δ so that the sign of f does not change in this interval, then the sign of f' is obliged to change. This implies that f' has a root (strictly) between γ and δ. Combining this with the observation that if $f(\gamma)=a$ then γ is a root of $f-a$, we have **Rolle's theorem**:

(5.74) COROLLARY. *Let $f\in\mathbb{R}[X]$ and let $\gamma<\delta$ be real numbers $\ni f(\gamma)= f(\delta)$. Then $\exists\eta\ni$*

$$\gamma<\eta<\delta \qquad \textit{and} \qquad f'(\eta)=0.$$

If $g \in \mathbb{R}[X]$ and we "tilt" the axes (see Figure 5.4) by defining

$$f(X) = g(X) - \frac{g(\delta) - g(\gamma)}{\delta - \gamma} X$$

so that $f(\gamma) = f(\delta)$, we obtain the **mean value theorem**:

(5.75) COROLLARY. *If* $g \in \mathbb{R}[X]$ *and* $\gamma < \delta$ *are real numbers, then* $\exists \eta \ni$

$$\gamma < \eta < \delta \qquad \textit{and} \qquad g'(\eta) = \frac{g(\delta) - g(\gamma)}{\delta - \gamma}.$$

In elementary calculus, Rolle's theorem and the mean value theorem are proved for a much wider class of functions than polynomials, but of course Sturm's theorem is no longer applicable.

To illustrate Sturm's theorem we take $f_0 = X^6 + aX^2 + X + 1$, where $a \neq 0$, so $f_1 = 6X^5 + 2aX + 1$, and division gives

$$f_2 = -\tfrac{2}{3}aX^2 - \tfrac{5}{6}X - 1, \qquad f_3 = bX + c,$$

where

$$b = -2a - \frac{27}{2a^2} + \frac{675}{16a^3} - \frac{1875}{128a^4}, \qquad c = -1 + \frac{135}{4a^3} - \frac{1125}{64a^4},$$

and, provided $b \neq 0$,

$$f_4 = -f_2(-c/b) \qquad \text{(a constant)}.$$

If we give X a large negative value, which we can indicate conveniently by $X = -\infty$, then $f_0(-\infty)$ is dominated by the term $(-\infty)^6 = +\infty$, so its sign is that of $+1$. Similarly, $f_1(-\infty) < 0$ because $(-\infty)^5 = -\infty$ is the dominant term. (We have already seen how to make detailed estimates for inequalities of this type in the proof of (5.72).) The sequence of signs to be

Figure 5.4 Rolle's theorem and the mean-value theorem.

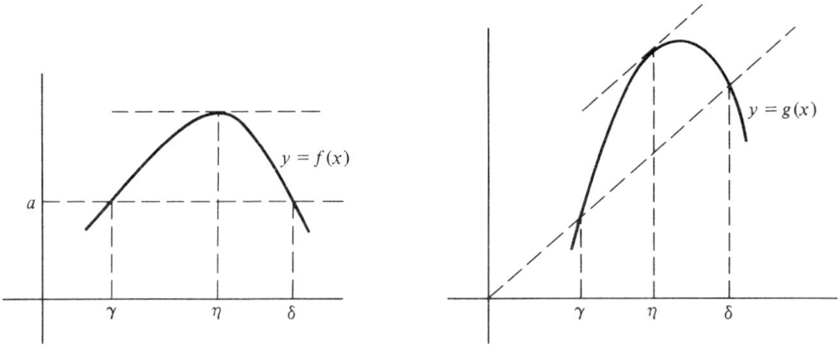

considered is

$$1, \quad -1, \quad -a, \quad -b, \quad f_4.$$

Similarly, when $X=\infty$ (i.e., X is large and positive), the sequence can be written

$$1, \quad 1, \quad -a, \quad b, \quad f_4.$$

For instance, if $a=-10$, so that

$$f_0 = X^6 - 10X^2 + X + 1,$$

then (very approximately) $b \doteq 20$, $c \doteq -1$, $f_4 \doteq 1$, and the sequences are

$$X=-\infty: \quad 1,-1,10,-20,1, \qquad w(-\infty)=4,$$

$$X=+\infty: \quad 1,1,10,20,1, \qquad w(+\infty)=0.$$

Hence the number of real roots is

$$w(-\infty)-w(+\infty)=4-0=4.$$

These four roots are distinct since g.c.d.$(f_0, f_0')=f_4$ is a constant. Evaluating the f_i at $X=0$ gives

$$X=0: \quad 1,1,-1,-1,1, \qquad w(0)=2.$$

This shows that f_0 has $w(-\infty)-w(0)=2$ negative roots and, similarly, 2 positive roots.

We wish to discuss next the roots of the binomial equation $X^n-\alpha=0$. First we make some general remarks.

Each $q \in \mathbb{Q}$ is uniquely representable in the form $q=um/n$, where $u \in \{1,-1\}$, $m \in \mathbb{M}$, $n \in \mathbb{N}$, g.c.d.$(m,n)=1$, and $u=1$ if $q=0$.

(5.76) DEFINITION. With $q=um/n$ as above and a an element of the commutative ring A, $\{a^q\}$ denotes the set of roots in A of the polynomial

$$X^n - a^m = 0 \qquad \text{if} \quad u=1,$$

$$a^m X^n - 1 = 0 \qquad \text{if} \quad u=-1.$$

In general, a^q is an ambiguous symbol denoting any one of the roots; nevertheless the notation is convenient. For instance, $a^q \notin A$ means that $\{a^q\}=\varnothing$ (which is the case when $q<0$ and $a \notin A^*$). On the other hand in certain circumstances $\{a^q\}$ contains a distinguished or "canonical" element, usually called the **principal value**, and then we reserve the symbol a^q to denote the principal value; cf. the remarks after (5.77), (5.103), and (5.248).

When $q=1/n$ we call $a^{1/n}$ an ***n*th root of *a*** (in A). Alternative notation for this is $\sqrt[n]{a}$, or simply $\sqrt{a}$ when $n=2$. (In cases where $a^{1/n}$ is restricted to mean the principal value, $\sqrt[n]{a}$ is also restricted to denote this particular value.) $\sqrt{a}$ and $\sqrt[3]{a}$ are also called a **square root** and a **cube root** of a. In general, $\sqrt[n]{a}$ is referred to as a **radical**. Thus, if $c=\sqrt{a}-3\sqrt[3]{b}/7$, we say that c has been expressed in terms of radicals.

These rational exponents only partly obey the usual rules. If $t \in \mathbb{M}$, it follows from the definition that

$$\{x^t : x \in \{a^q\}\} \subset \{a^{qt}\} \subset \{(a^t)^q\},$$

and if $a \in A^*$ this extends to all $t \in \mathbb{Z}$. This is the analog of the rule $(a^q)^t = a^{qt}$ for $q, t \in \mathbb{M}$. However, in general for $q, t \in \mathbb{Q}$ neither of the sets

$$\bigcup \{\{x^t\} : x \in \{a^q\}\}, \qquad \{a^{qt}\}$$

contains the other. For instance, if $A = \mathbb{Z}$, $a = 2$, $q = \frac{2}{3}$, $t = \frac{3}{2}$, then the set on the right is $\{2^1\} = \{2\}$, while the union on the left is empty. If $q = 0$, $t = \frac{1}{2}$, the union is $\{1, -1\}$ while the set on the right is $\{1\}$.

It is clear that

$$\{xy : x \in \{a^q\}, y \in \{b^q\}\} \subset \{(ab)^q\},$$

and, for $t \in \mathbb{M}$, that

$$\{a^t x : x \in \{a^q\}\} \subset \{a^{q+t}\}.$$

Again, however, simple examples show that in general, for $t \in \mathbb{Q}$, neither of the sets

$$\{xy : x \in \{a^q\}, y \in \{a^t\}\}, \qquad \{a^{q+t}\}$$

contains the other.

(5.77) PROPOSITION. *Let $\alpha \in \mathbb{R}$ and $n \in \mathbb{N}$. If n is odd, then α has a unique nth root in $\mathbb{R}$. If n is even and $\alpha > 0$, then α has exactly two nth roots in $\mathbb{R}$.*

Remark. In the first case we can write $\xi = \alpha^{1/n} = \sqrt[n]{\alpha}$ unambiguously. We have the factorization

$$X^n - \alpha = (X - \xi)(X^{n-1} + \xi X^{n-2} + \xi^2 X^{n-3} + \cdots + \xi^{n-1}).$$

Note also that

$$\sqrt[n]{-\alpha} = -\sqrt[n]{\alpha} \qquad (n \text{ odd}),$$

since $(-1)^n = -1$.

In the second case, since $(-\xi)^n = \xi^n$, the roots are negatives of each other. The symbols $\sqrt[n]{\alpha}$ ($\sqrt{\alpha}$ when $n = 2$) and $\alpha^{1/n}$ in this case always denote the unique positive nth root (the principal value, as will be explained after the proof). With $\xi = \sqrt[n]{\alpha}$,

$$X^n - \alpha = (X - \xi)(X + \xi)(X^{n-2} + \xi^2 X^{n-4} + \xi^4 X^{n-6} + \cdots + \xi^{n-2}).$$

Of course $\sqrt[n]{0} = 0$ for all n.

Proof. In both cases the uniqueness of $\sqrt[n]{\alpha}$ follows from A10.2, and it remains to prove existence.

If n is odd, $X^n - \alpha$ has a root by (5.72), so let n be even and $\alpha > 0$. If ξ is a root of $X^n - \alpha$, then $1/\xi$ is a root of $X^n - 1/\alpha$. Thus we can assume that $\alpha \geqslant 1$. If $f = X^{n+1} - \alpha X$, then $f(1) \leqslant 0$ and $f(\alpha) \geqslant 0$, so again the result follows from (5.72) (with the additional information $1 \leqslant \sqrt[n]{\alpha} \leqslant \alpha$). ■

Let $\alpha \in \mathbb{R}^>$, $m \in \mathbb{Z}$, $n \in \mathbb{N}$, $d = \text{g.c.d.}(m,n)$, $m = \mu d$, $n = \nu d$, and $\beta = \sqrt[\nu]{\alpha^\mu}$. Then $\forall e \in \mathbb{N}$, β is the unique positive root $\sqrt[\nu e]{\alpha^{\mu e}}$ of $X^{\nu e} - \alpha^{\mu e}$ and, in particular, $\beta = \sqrt[n]{\alpha^m}$. Putting $q = m/n = \mu/\nu$, we can restate matters as follows.

For $\alpha > 0$ and $q \in \mathbb{Q}$, $\{\alpha^q\}$ contains a unique positive element β, called the **principal value**, and $\beta = \sqrt[n]{\alpha^m}$ for any pair m, n, with $m \in \mathbb{Z}$, $n \in \mathbb{N} \ni m/n = q$. In this case α^q stands for the principal value. For example, we write the negative real root of $X^4 - 2^3$ as $-2^{3/4}$.

The next proposition will be concerned with a vector space written multiplicatively. In Section 2 of Chapter 4, following (4.8), we rewrote the vector space axioms in multiplicative notation. We label the corresponding equations the same way in the proposition.

(5.78) PROPOSITION. *Let $\mathbb{R}^>$ denote the multiplicative group of positive real numbers, let $\alpha \in \mathbb{R}^>$, and let $q \in \mathbb{Q}$. With $\alpha \mapsto \alpha^q$ as scalar multiplication, $\mathbb{R}^>$ is a vector space over $\mathbb{Q}$. Therefore*

(i) *for fixed $q \neq 0$, $\alpha \mapsto \alpha^q$ is an automorphism of the group $\mathbb{R}^>$; hence*

(V1) $(\alpha\beta)^q = \alpha^q \beta^q$,

and in particular for $m, n \in \mathbb{N}$,

$$\sqrt[n]{\alpha\beta} = \sqrt[n]{\alpha}\,\sqrt[n]{\beta},$$

$$\sqrt[n]{\alpha^m} = \sqrt[n]{\alpha}^{\,m},$$

$$\sqrt[n]{\alpha/\beta} = \sqrt[n]{\alpha}\,/\sqrt[n]{\beta} \qquad (\beta \neq 0);$$

(ii) *for fixed $\alpha \neq 1$, $q \mapsto \alpha^q$ is an injective homomorphism from the additive group of $\mathbb{Q}$ to $\mathbb{R}^>$, and hence*

(V2) $\alpha^{q+r} = \alpha^q \alpha^r$;

(iii) *for $q, r \in \mathbb{Q}$,*

(V3) $(\alpha^q)^r = \alpha^{qr}$,

and in particular,

$$\sqrt[n]{\sqrt[m]{\alpha}} = \sqrt[mn]{\alpha};$$

(iv) *for all* $\alpha \in \mathbb{R}^>$,

(V4) $\alpha^1 = \alpha$.

Proof. To use the more familiar additive notation for a moment, if V is a vector space and a a nonzero scalar, then $\mathbf{v} \mapsto a\mathbf{v}$ defines an automorphism of the additive group of V; this follows immediately from axioms (V1)–(V4) and the existence of a^{-1}. It is also immediate from the axioms that, if $\mathbf{v} \neq \mathbf{0}$, then $a \mapsto a\mathbf{v}$ defines an injective homomorphism from the additive group of the field into that of V.

Thus we only need to verify (V1)–(V4) and these follow easily from the rules for integer exponents. If $q = m/n$, where $m \in \mathbb{Z}$ and $n \in \mathbb{N}$, then α^q is characterized by $\alpha^q > 0$ and $(\alpha^q)^n = \alpha^m$. Therefore (V1) follows from $\alpha^q\beta^q > 0$ and

$$(\alpha^q\beta^q)^n = (\alpha^q)^n(\beta^q)^n = \alpha^m\beta^m = (\alpha\beta)^m.$$

If $r = s/t$, where $s \in \mathbb{Z}$, $t \in \mathbb{N}$, then $q + r = (mt + sn)/nt$ and (V2) follows from $\alpha^q\alpha^r > 0$ and

$$(\alpha^q\alpha^r)^{nt} = (\alpha^q)^{nt}(\alpha^r)^{tn} = \alpha^{mt}\alpha^{sn} = \alpha^{mt+sn}.$$

(V3) is a consequence of $qr = ms/nt$ and

$$\begin{aligned}((\alpha^q)^r)^{nt} &= ((\beta^r)^t)^n \qquad (\text{where } \beta = \alpha^q)\\ &= (\beta^s)^n = ((\alpha^q)^n)^s\\ &= (\alpha^m)^s = \alpha^{ms}.\end{aligned}$$

(V4) is true by definition. ■

(5.79) COROLLARY. *Let q be a positive rational and $|\ |$ an ultrametric absolute value on the field k. Then the map $|\ |^q \colon k \to \mathbb{R}$ given by $a \mapsto |a|^q$ is also an absolute value on k and, as in* (5.48), *a sequence is cauchy or null with respect to $|\ |$ iff it is so with respect to $|\ |^q$.*

Proof. Axiom (AV0) for $|\ |^q$ is obvious. By (5.7), (AV1) is vacuous. (AV2) follows from (V1) of the proposition. (AV3) is a consequence of

(5.80) $$\alpha^q < \beta^q \iff \alpha < \beta \qquad (\alpha, \beta \in \mathbb{R}^>,\ \ q \in \mathbb{Q}^>),$$

which follows from the proposition and A10.2. The easy proofs of the facts concerning sequences are left to the reader. ■

We conclude this section by describing explicit formulas for the roots of quadratic, cubic, and quartic polynomials.

(5.81) PROPOSITION. *Let k be a field of characteristic $\neq 2$, $f = aX^2 + bX + c \in k[X]$ with $a \neq 0$, and let $d = b^2 - 4ac$. Then f has a root in k iff d*

has a square root in k. If $e^2=d$, *then* $f=a(X-r)(X-r')$, *where* $r=(-b+e)/2a$ *and* $r'=(-b-e)/2a$.

Proof. If $f=a(X-r)(X-r')=aX^2-a(r+r')X+arr'$, then $a^2(r-r')^2=a^2(r+r')^2-4a^2rr'=(-b)^2-4ac=d$. The formulas given for r and r' prove the converse. ■

These formulas are often written

(5.82) $$r,r'=\left(-b\pm\sqrt{b^2-4ac}\right)/2a.$$

For instance,

(5.83) $$X^3-1=(X-1)(X^2+X+1)$$

has the roots

$$1,\quad \left(-1\pm\sqrt{-3}\right)/2,$$

presuming that X^2+3 has roots in k. If we choose one value for $\sqrt{-3}$ (so the other root of $X^2+3=0$ is $-\sqrt{-3}$) and define

(5.84) $$\omega=\left(-1+\sqrt{-3}\right)/2,$$

then the roots of (5.83) are

$$\omega,\quad \omega^2=\left(-1-\sqrt{-3}\right)/2=-1-\omega,\quad \omega^3=1.$$

This is not applicable when $\mathrm{char}(k)=2$, and indeed then it is not possible to express the roots of the general quadratic in terms of square roots of elements written as polynomials in the coefficients of the quadratic. For instance, the roots of $X^2+X+1\in\mathbb{F}_2[X]$ are

(5.85) $$\omega,\omega^2\in\mathbb{F}_4=\{0,1,\omega,\omega+1:\omega^2=\omega+1\}$$

and obviously these cannot be written as rational functions over $\mathbb{F}_2$ in the quantities $\sqrt{0}=0,\sqrt{1}=1$.

As an application, let us determine when $f=aX^2+bX+c$ is a square in $k[X]$. First, if $\mathrm{char}(k)=2$ then, since $(sX+t)^2=s^2X^2+t^2$, the necessary and sufficient conditions are that a and c be squares in k and that $b=0$. For $\mathrm{char}(k)\neq 2$,

(5.86) COROLLARY. *Let* $f=aX^2+bX+c\in k[X]$, *where k is a field of characteristic* $\neq 2$ *and* $a\neq 0$. *Then* $f=(sX+t)^2$ *for some* $s,t\in k$ *iff a is a square in k and* $b^2=4ac$.

Proof. If $a=s^2$ and $b^2=4ac$, then $f=(sX+b/(2s))^2$. Conversely, if $f=(sX+t)^2$, then in the notation of the proposition, $r=r'=-t/s$. Hence $d=0$. ■

As a further application we determine when a quadratic polynomial in two variables is a product of two linear factors.

(5.87) COROLLARY. *Let*

$$F = aX^2 + 2hXY + bY^2 + 2gX + 2fY + c \in k[X, Y],$$

where k *is a field of characteristic* $\neq 2$ *and where* a, h, b *are not all* 0. *Then* F *is a product of two factors of the form* $uX + vY + w$ *in* $k[X, Y]$ *iff either*

(i) $h^2 - ab$ *is a nonzero square in* k *and*

$$af^2 + bg^2 + ch^2 = abc + 2fgh; \tag{5.88}$$

(ii) $a \neq 0$, $h^2 = ab$, $hg = af$, *and* $g^2 - ac$ *is a square in* k; *or*
(iii) $a = g = h = 0$ (*so* $b \neq 0$) *and* $f^2 - bc$ *is a square in* k.

Remark. We have used the notation for the coefficients that is standard in all the old books on geometry. F is the equation of a conic section except when F is a product of two linear factors; then the curve is a *degenerate conic* consisting of one or two lines.

Proof. First suppose $h^2 - ab = s^2$, where $s \in k^*$, and that (5.88) is satisfied. If $a \neq 0$, then

$$F = (aX + (h+s)Y + g + (hg - af)/s)$$

$$\times (aX + (h-s)Y + g - (hg - af)/s)/a,$$

while if $a = 0$ (so $h = \pm s \neq 0$), then

$$F = (2hX + bY + 2f - bg/h)(Y + g/h).$$

Second, if the conditions of (ii) are met, say $g^2 - ac = t^2$, $t \in k$, then

$$F = (aX + hY + g + t)(aX + hY + g - t)/a.$$

Third, under the conditions of (iii) with $f^2 - bc = w^2$,

$$F = (bY + f + w)(bY + f - w)/b.$$

Conversely, let F be a product of two linear polynomials and suppose first that $a \neq 0$. Then F, regarded as a quadratic in the variable X over the field $k(Y)$, has two roots in $k(Y)$. Hence by the proposition,

$$(hY + g)^2 - a(bY^2 + 2fY + c) = (h^2 - ab)Y^2 + 2(hg - af)Y + g^2 - ac$$

is a square in $k(Y)$ and therefore in $k[Y]$ (by 3.73). If $h^2 - ab \neq 0$, the first corollary gives the condition (5.88). We leave it to the reader to sort out the remaining cases. ■

In the case of the cubic

$$f = X^3 + a_2X^2 + a_1X + a_0$$

we have to exclude characteristic 3. The substitution $X = X' - a_2/3$ results in a polynomial of the form $X'^3 + a'_1 X' + a'_0$. Thus we can make the quadratic term vanish, and since this considerably simplifies the formula, we assume that this simple translation has been carried out. For further simplification we write the coefficient of X in the form $3a$.

As in the case of the quadratic, the purpose of the formula for the roots of a cubic is to express them in terms of radicals. In this sense, for a cubic of the form $X^3 + b$ there is nothing to do: Its set of roots is $\{(-b)^{1/3}\}$. It is convenient to exclude this type from the statement of the formula.

(5.89) PROPOSITION. *Let k be a field of characteristic $\neq 3$, let*

$$f = X^3 + 3aX + b \in k[X], \qquad a \neq 0,$$

and suppose $Y^2 + bY - a^3$ has a root r in k. Then for each

$$q \in \{r^{1/3}\},$$

we have $q \neq 0$ and $q - a/q$ is a root of f.

Proof. Since $a \neq 0$, $r \neq 0$ and $q \neq 0$. (If we use the other root r' of the quadratic then, since $rr' = -a^3$, in effect q is replaced by $-a/q$ and $q - a/q$ stays the same.) An easy calculation completes the proof. ■

If q is one cube root of r then the others are $q\omega$ and $q\omega^2$, where ω is given by (5.84), or (5.85) in characteristic 2.

When char$(k) \neq 2$ (and $\neq 3$), we can write the cubic in the form

$$f = X^3 + 3aX - 2c. \tag{5.90}$$

Then $r = c + \sqrt{d}$, where $d = a^3 + c^2$ and the formula for the roots of f takes the form

$$\sqrt[3]{c + \sqrt{d}} - a \Big/ \sqrt[3]{c + \sqrt{d}}\,.$$

This is known as **Cardan's formula**. When k is "large enough" it contains three cube roots of $c + \sqrt{d}$ and Cardan's formula gives the three roots of f.

The ***casus irreducibilis*** is the situation where k contains a root of f not calculable in k according to the formula either because $r \notin k$ or $r \in k$ but $r^{1/3} \notin k$. For instance, none of the real roots of (5.71) is given in terms of real radicals by the formula since $d = -\frac{3}{4}$ has no square root in $\mathbb{R}$. An analysis of the different possibilities is given in A11.5.

Another new feature is the occurrence of "nontrivial relations" among radicals. For instance, Cardan's formula applied to

$$f = X^3 + 3X - 4 = (X - 1)(X^2 + X + 4)$$

gives

$$1 = \sqrt[3]{2 + \sqrt{5}} - 1 \Big/ \sqrt[3]{2 + \sqrt{5}}\,.$$

Finally we consider the quartic in characteristic $\neq 2$. Replacing X by $X - a_3/4$ converts the polynomial $X^4 + a_3X^3 + a_2X^2 + a_1X + a_0$ into one with $a_3 = 0$, and for simplicity we assume that this has already been done. A quartic of the form $X^4 + aX^2 + c$ can be regarded as a quadratic in X^2, and so has the roots

$$\pm\sqrt{\frac{-a \pm \sqrt{a^2 - 4c}}{2}}$$

(with four variations of signs). For convenience we exclude this type from the formula.

As in the cubic case, the formula depends upon first finding a root of an auxiliary polynomial, called the **resolvent**. (In the former case it was a quadratic; here it is a cubic.) Again a *casus irreducibilis* can occur when k fails to contain a root of the resolvent.

Before stating the formula we should give some indication of how it might have been discovered. The cubic resolvent (of Lagrange) for the quartic $f = x^4 + ax^2 + bx + c$ is arrived at in the following way. We define $y = x^2$, so the equation $f = 0$ is equivalent to the system

$$\begin{aligned} y^2 + ay + bx + c &= 0, \\ x^2 - y &= 0. \end{aligned} \tag{5.91}$$

(Geometrically, we are representing the four roots $x_1, \ldots, x_4$ of f by means of the four points $P_i = (x_i, y_i)$ of intersection of the two curves (called parabolas; see Figure 5.5) given by (5.91).) Subtracting r times the second equation from the first gives the equivalent system

$$y^2 + (a + r)y - rx^2 + bx + c = 0,$$

$$x^2 - y = 0,$$

Figure 5.5

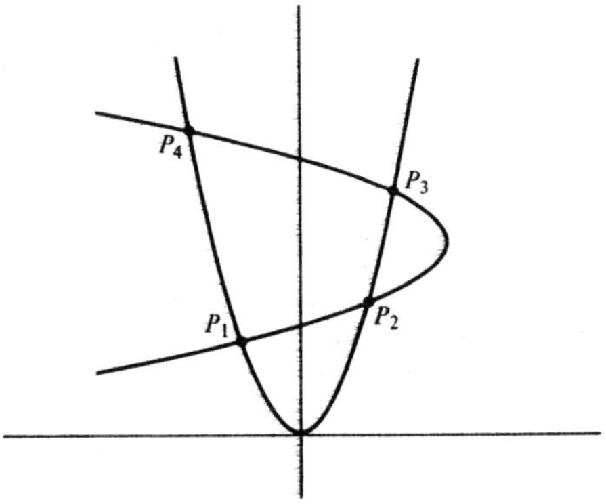

and the idea now is to choose r so that the first polynomial, call it F, is a product of two linear factors, say $F = LM$. (Geometrically, the parabola F has degenerated into two lines; see Figure 5.6.) L has the form $ux + vy + w = 0$ and the system $L = 0$, $y = x^2$ is easily solved (if it is solvable at all in k), giving two of the roots. The other two roots are the solutions of the system $M = 0$, $y = x^2$. The criterion in (5.87) applied to F requires r to be a root of a cubic:

(5.92) PROPOSITION. *Let k be a field of characteristic $\neq 2$ and let*

$$f = X^4 + aX^2 + bX + c \in k[X], \qquad b \neq 0;$$

let r be a root of

$$G = Z^3 + 2aZ^2 + (a^2 - 4c)Z - b^2$$

and let $s \in \{r^{1/2}\}$. Then $s \neq 0$ and

$$f = \left(X^2 + sX + \frac{a+r}{2} - \frac{b}{2s} \right)\left(X^2 - sX + \frac{a+r}{2} + \frac{b}{2s} \right) = LM,$$

say. Hence the roots of the two quadratics L and M together comprise the roots of f, and with the correct multiplicities.

We leave the verification as a straightforward calculation.

As a numerical example, consider

$$f = X(X-6)(X-8)^2 = X^4 + 6X^2 + X \in \mathbb{F}_{11}[X].$$

In this case

$$G = Z^3 + 5Z^2 - 1 = (Z-3)(Z-9)^2.$$

Figure 5.6

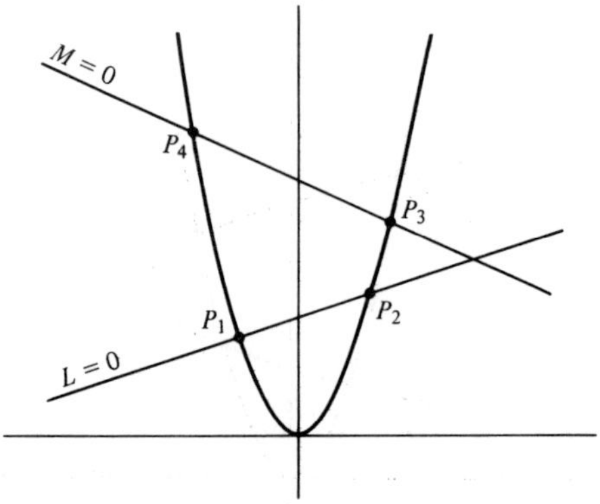

If we take $r=3, s=5$, then

$$L=X^2+5X=X(X-6), \qquad M=X^2-5X+9=(X-8)^2,$$

while if we take $r=9$, $s=3$ then

$$L=X^2+3X=X(X-8), \qquad M=X^2-3X+4=(X-6)(X-8).$$

Of necessity we stop at the quartic: It can be shown that it is not possible to express the roots of certain quintics—for instance, $X^5+X+1\in\mathbb{Q}[X]$—in terms of radicals of roots of polynomials (over $\mathbb{Q}$ for this example) of degree <5. In fact, for every $n>4$ there are polynomials over $\mathbb{Q}$ of degree n whose roots cannot be given by formulas of the type we have for degrees $\leqslant 4$. Of course the roots of *some* polynomials of higher degree (e.g., $X^5+1=(X+1)(X^4+\cdots)$) can be expressed in terms of radicals.

EXERCISES

1. If $f\in k[X]$, then the derivative of f^e is $ef^{e-1}f'$. Hence if f has a repeated factor (e.g., a repeated root), then g.c.d.$(f,f')\neq 1$.

2. For $b\in\mathbb{R}$, X^3-3X+b has at most one real root α satisfying $-1<\alpha<1$.

3. Let $a_1<a_2<\cdots<a_n$ be real numbers. Then

$$\frac{1}{X-a_1}+\frac{1}{X-a_2}+\cdots+\frac{1}{X-a_n}=0$$

has real zeros $\lambda_1<\cdots<\lambda_{n-1}$ satisfying $a_i<\lambda_i<a_{i+1}$. (Laguerre proved the more difficult estimate $a_i+b_i\leqslant\lambda_i\leqslant a_{i+1}-b_i$, where $b_i=(a_{i+1}-a_i)/n$.)

4. By Sturm's theorem, X^4-X-a has two real roots when $a>-3\sqrt[3]{2}/8$.

5. A sharpened form of Rolle's theorem for polynomials: If $\gamma<\delta$ are successive roots of $f\in\mathbb{R}[X]$, then f' has an odd number of roots strictly between γ and δ, where a root of multiplicity e is counted e times.

6. (i) $x\in\mathbb{R}$ and $x\geqslant -1\Rightarrow(1+x)^{1/2}\leqslant 1+x/2$ with equality iff $x=0$.
(ii) Let $c\in\mathbb{R}$ with $c\geqslant -1/4$ and $\alpha=(1+\sqrt{1+4c})/2$. Let $a_1\in\mathbb{R}$ with $a_1\geqslant\alpha$ and define recursively $a_{n+1}=\sqrt{c+a_n}$. Then $\lim a_n=\alpha$. For example, $\sqrt{}(6+\sqrt{}(6+\sqrt{}(6+\cdots)=3$.

7. Let $a_1+a_2+\cdots$ be a series of elements of a valued field.
(i) The **ratio test**: If $\exists h,N\in\mathbb{N}\ni\forall n>N, a_n\neq 0$ and $|a_{n+1}/a_n|<1-1/h$, then $a_1+a_2+\cdots$ converges absolutely.
(ii) The **root test**: If $\exists h,N\in\mathbb{N}\ni\forall n>N, \sqrt[n]{|a_n|}<1-1/h$, then $a_1+a_2+\cdots$ converges absolutely.
(iii) If the ratio test predicts convergence then so does the root test.

8. Let G be a group, H and K subgroups $\ni H \cap K = 1$, $hk = kh$ $\forall h \in H$ and $k \in k$, and $G = HK$; i.e., every $g \in G$ can be written in the form hk. Prove that $(h,k) \mapsto hk$ defines an isomorphism $H \times K \to G$. In these circumstances G is said to be the **internal direct product** of H and K. Show that when n is odd, $\mathrm{GL}_n(\mathbb{R})$ is internally the direct product of $\mathrm{SL}_n(\mathbb{R})$ and the subgroup of scalar matrices $cI, c \in \mathbb{R}^*$.

9. With ω a cube root of 1 as in (5.84) or (5.85), verify that $(X+\omega Y+\omega^2 Z)^3 + (X+\omega^2 Y+\omega Z)^3 = (2X-Y-Z)(2Y-Z-X)(2Z-X-Y)$.

10. With f as in A3.6(iii), $(1-X)\Sigma_{n=1}^{\infty} f(n) X^n = X \Sigma_{n=1}^{\infty} X^{f^*(n)}$. When $r \in \mathbb{N}$ and $f(x) = \lfloor \sqrt[r]{x} \rfloor$,

$$\sum_{k=1}^{n} f(k) + \sum_{k=1}^{f(n)} k^r = (n+1) f(n).$$

11. Let $\alpha = 1+\sqrt{2} \in \mathbb{R}$ and define $a_n, b_n \in \mathbb{N}$ by $\alpha^n = a_n + b_n\sqrt{2}$. Then $(1-\sqrt{2})^n = a_n - b_n\sqrt{2}$ and $|a_n/b_n - \sqrt{2}| < 1/b_n^2$ (hence the fractions a_n/b_n are uncommonly good approximations to $\sqrt{2}$). The sequences a_n and b_n both satisfy the linear recurrence

$$x_{n+2} = 2x_{n+1} + x_n.$$

12. (i) Let the pair of sequences $(u_1, u_2, \ldots) = (1,3,4,6,8,9,\ldots), (v_1, v_2, \ldots) = (2,5,7,10,\ldots)$ be defined by the three properties

a. $u_1 = 1$;
b. $v_n = u_n + n$;
c. u_{n+1} is the least positive integer distinct from $u_1, \ldots, u_n, v_1, \ldots, v_n$.

(Hence the sequences are *complementary*: $\mathbb{N} = \{u_n\} \amalg \{v_n\}$.) Then

$$(*) \qquad u_n = \left\lfloor n\left(1+\sqrt{5}\right)/2 \right\rfloor, \qquad v_n = \left\lfloor n\left(3+\sqrt{5}\right)/2 \right\rfloor.$$

(*Hint*: If the first N natural numbers contain r us and s vs, as defined in $(*)$, then $N \leqslant r+s < N+1$, and so $N = r+s$. The rule $u_{v_n} = u_n + v_n$, first noticed by W. Jonsson, is not so easily proved.)

(ii) By the same argument, for any irrational $\alpha \in \mathbb{R}^{>}$ the sequences $u_n = \lfloor n(1+1/\alpha) \rfloor$, $v_n = \lfloor n(1+\alpha) \rfloor$ are complementary.

13. Let k be a field and let V denote the vector space $k[X]$. Show that $f \mapsto f'$ defines an element of End V. (This linear transformation is denoted d/dX and is called **differentiation**. Thus df/dX is an alternative notation for f'.)

11. NEWTON'S METHOD AND HENSEL'S LEMMA

(5.93) PROPOSITION. *Let k be a complete valued field, $f \in k[X]$, and $(\xi_1, \xi_2, \ldots)$ a cauchy sequence in k with limit ξ. Then $(f(\xi_1), f(\xi_2), \ldots)$ is cauchy with limit $f(\xi)$. In particular, if $(f(\xi_1), \ldots)$ is null then ξ is a root of f.*

Remark. As will be explained in Section 16, $\lim f(\xi_i)=f(\lim \xi_i)$ expresses the continuity of the function $x \mapsto f(x)$.

Proof. Let $f=a_0+\cdots+a_nX^n$, let $\max\{|a_0|,\ldots,|a_n|\}=A$, and by (5.11) let $B\in\mathbb{R}^>$ satisfy $B\geqslant|\xi_r|$, $\forall r$, and $B\geqslant|\xi|$. Then

$$\begin{aligned}|f(\xi)-f(\xi_i)| &= |a_1(\xi-\xi_i)+a_2(\xi^2-\xi_i^2)+\cdots| \\ &= |\xi-\xi_i||a_1+a_2(\xi+\xi_i)+\cdots \\ &\qquad +a_n(\xi^{n-1}+\xi^{n-2}\xi_i+\cdots+\xi_i^{n-1})| \\ &\leqslant |\xi-\xi_i|C,\end{aligned}$$

where $C=n^2AB^n$ is independent of i. The result follows by the Cauchy convergence criterion. ■

If ξ_1 is an approximation or guess at a root ξ of the polynomial f then the following algorithm, known as **Newton's method**, produces a sequence $\xi_2, \xi_3, \ldots$ that in favorable circumstances converges to ξ:

$$\xi_{i+1}=\xi_i-f(\xi_i)/f'(\xi_i). \tag{5.94}$$

Of course, if $f(\xi_i)=0$ the algorithm is terminated. The formula is suggested by elementary calculus, where the derivative $f'(\xi_i)$ is the slope of the line tangent to the curve $y=f(x)$ at $x=\xi_i$ (Figure 5.7). However, Newton's method can be used for polynomials over any valued field k. In the case $k=\mathbb{R}$ it is not easy to give simple yet comprehensive criteria that ensure that the algorithm will succeed. Roughly speaking, one must choose ξ_1 "sufficiently close" to ξ and "sufficiently far" from all other roots (including complex roots; cf. Section 14). The method works well for the root $\sqrt[n]{\alpha}$ of $X^n-\alpha$; the case $n=2$ occurs in A11.7.

Newton's method is well adapted to ultrametric valued fields (discrete or not) as we see in the following result, known as **Hensel's lemma** (for linear factors).

Figure 5.7 Newton's method.

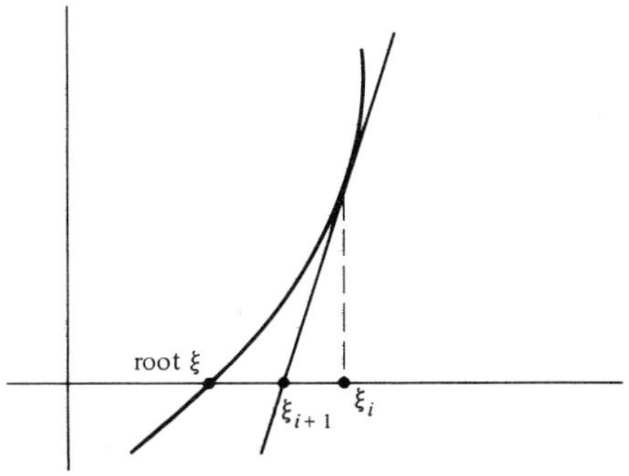

(5.95) PROPOSITION. *Let k be a complete ultrametric valued field with valuation ring D, let $f \in D[X]$, and let $\xi_1 \in D$ satisfy*

$$|f(\xi_1)| < |f'(\xi_1)|^2. \tag{5.96}$$

Then $\exists! \xi \in k \ni$

$$f(\xi) = 0 \quad \text{and} \quad |\xi - \xi_1| \leqslant |f(\xi_1)/f'(\xi_1)|. \tag{5.97}$$

This root is in D and can be obtained by Newton's method (5.94):

$$\xi = \lim \xi_i.$$

The progress of the convergence is measured by

$$|\xi - \xi_i| = |f(\xi_i)/f'(\xi_1)|. \tag{5.98}$$

Remarks. For a given $f = a_n X^n + \cdots + a_0 \in k[X]$ first replace f by af, for appropriate $a \in k$, to ensure that $f \in D[X]$, and with $v(a)$ as small as possible so that (5.96) demands as little as possible of ξ_1. For example, when $|\ |$ is discrete with uniformizer p, take $a = p^{-m}$, where $m = \min\{v(a_n), \ldots, v(a_0)\}$. (5.98) shows that there is equality in the second member of (5.97); it is written as an inequality so that the uniqueness statement points out that no other root of f is as close to ξ_1 as ξ.

Proof of the existence of ξ. (5.96) guarantees that $f'(\xi_1) \neq 0$ and (5.94) gives $\xi_2 = \xi_1 + \delta_1$, where $f(\xi_1) + \delta_1 f'(\xi_1) = 0$. Let

$$f(X+Y) = f(X) + f_1(X)Y + \cdots + f_n(X)Y^n \tag{$*$}$$

be the Taylor expansion of f, so $f_1 = f'$. As explained in Section 10, this works in any characteristic. Each $f_j \in D[X]$; hence $f_j(\xi_1) \in D$. In particular, by (5.96), $|\delta_1| < |f'(\xi_1)| \leqslant 1$. Thus $\delta_1 \in D$ and $\xi_2 \in D$. Substituting $X = \xi_1$, $Y = \delta_1$ in ($*$), and writing $K = |f(\xi_1)/f'(\xi_1)^2|$ yields

$$\begin{aligned} |f(\xi_2)| &\leqslant \max\{|f_2(\xi_1)\delta_1^2|, \ldots, |f_n(\xi_1)\delta_1^n|\} \\ &\leqslant |\delta_1|^2 = K|f(\xi_1)|, \quad \text{where} \quad K < 1. \end{aligned}$$

The analog of ($*$) for $g(X) = f'(X)$ gives

$$|f'(\xi_2)| = |f'(\xi_1) + \delta_1 g_1(\xi_1) + \delta_1^2 g_2(\xi_1) + \cdots| = |f'(\xi_1)|$$

since $|\delta_1^j g_j(\xi_1)| \leqslant |\delta_1| < |f'(\xi_1)|$ for $j > 0$.

Thus $|f(\xi_2)| < |f'(\xi_2)|^2$ and the process can be repeated. By induction,

$$|f'(\xi_i)| = |f'(\xi_1)|,$$

$$|f(\xi_i)/f'(\xi_i)^2| \leqslant K,$$

and

$$|f(\xi_{i+1})| \leqslant K|f(\xi_i)|,$$

where $\xi_{i+1} = \xi_i + \delta_i$ and δ_i is defined by $f(\xi_i) + \delta_i f'(\xi_i) = 0$. (Of course the process stops if $f(\xi_i) = 0$.) Then

$$|\delta_i| = |f(\xi_i)|/|f'(\xi_i)| = |f(\xi_i)/f'(\xi_1)| \leqslant K|\delta_{i-1}| \leqslant K^{i-1}|\delta_1|.$$

If $i < j$, then

$$|\xi_j - \xi_i| = |\delta_i + \cdots + \delta_{j-1}| \leqslant K^{i-1}|\delta_1|.$$

Since $K < 1$, this shows that $(\xi_1, \xi_2, \ldots)$ is cauchy, say $\lim \xi_i = \xi$, and since $|f(\xi_i)| < K^{i-1}|f(\xi_1)|$, by (5.93) $f(\xi) = 0$. Since $|\delta_i| > |\delta_{i+1}| > \cdots$,

$$|\xi - \xi_i| = \lim_{j\to\infty} |\delta_i + \cdots + \delta_j| = \lim_{j\to\infty} |\delta_i| = |\delta_i|.$$

Proof of the uniqueness of ξ. If $\xi' = \xi + \eta \in D$ also satisfies (5.97), then, substituting $X = \xi$, $Y = \eta$ in $(*)$ gives

(5.99) $$0 = f'(\xi)\eta + f_2(\xi)\eta^2 + \cdots.$$

By (5.93), $|f'(\xi)| = \lim |f'(\xi_i)| = |f'(\xi_1)|$. The assumption $\eta \neq 0$ gives a contradiction:

$$\begin{aligned} |\eta| &= |\xi' - \xi_1 + \xi_1 - \xi| \leqslant \max\{|\xi' - \xi_1|, |\xi_1 - \xi|\} \\ &\leqslant |f(\xi_1)/f'(\xi_1)| < |f'(\xi_1)|. \end{aligned}$$

Hence for $i > 1, |f_i(\xi)\eta^i| \leqslant |\eta^2| < |f'(\xi)\eta|$, which is incompatible with (5.99). ■

Distinct $\xi_1 \in D$ can lead to the same root ξ. For instance

$$f = X^2 - 1 \equiv 0 \mod 16$$

has the four roots $\pm 1, \pm 7 \in \mathbb{Z}/16\mathbb{Z}$, but each of these must lift to one of the two roots ± 1 of f in $\mathbb{Q}_2$. In fact, $\xi_1 = 7$ lifts to -1 by (5.98) since $|7+1| = |f(7)/f'(7)|$.

Before our next example $X^{p-1} - 1 \in \mathbb{Q}_p[X]$ we make some general remarks.

The roots of the polynomial $X^n - 1$ are called the ***n*th roots of unity** and the expression ***k* contains the *n*th roots of unity** means that $X^n - 1$ factors into linear factors in $k[X]$. Since $X^2 - 1 = (X-1)(X+1)$ every field contains the square roots of 1. An nth root of unity α is also an nNth root of unity $\forall N \in \mathbb{N}$ since $\alpha^n = 1 \Rightarrow \alpha^{nN} = 1$. Notice that in any case $\{1^{1/n}\} = \{\alpha \in k : \alpha^n - 1 = 0\}$ is a finite subgroup of k^*. For $1^n = 1$ and if $\alpha^n = \beta^n = 1$, then $(\alpha^{-1})^n = (\alpha^n)^{-1} = 1$ and $(\alpha\beta)^n = \alpha^n\beta^n = 1$.

Conversely, if G is a finite subgroup of k^*, say $|G| = n$, then G consists entirely of nth roots of unity since, by Lagrange's theorem, $\alpha^n = 1$ $\forall \alpha \in G$.

(5.100) COROLLARY. $\mathbb{Q}_p$ *contains the group of* $(p-1)$*th roots of* 1.

Proof. If $f(X)=X^{p-1}-1$ and ξ_1 is any natural number $\ni 1\leqslant\xi_1\leqslant p-1$, then by Fermat's little theorem

$$v(f(\xi_1))\geqslant 1>2\cdot v(f'(\xi_1))=2\cdot v\big((p-1)\xi_1{}^{p-2}\big)=0.$$

By Hensel's lemma, $\mathbb{Q}_p$ contains a root of unity $\zeta_1\equiv\xi_1 \bmod p$, i.e.,

$$\zeta_1=\xi_1+a_1p+a_2p^2+\cdots.$$

Taking $\xi_1=1,2,\ldots,p-1$ we thus obtain $p-1$ distinct roots $\zeta_1,\ldots,\zeta_{p-1}$ and

(5.101) $$X^{p-1}-1=\prod_{i=1}^{p-1}(X-\zeta_i). \quad\blacksquare$$

Since $1^{p-1}=1$ we have $\zeta_1=1$, and when $p>2$, since $(-1)^{p-1}=1$ and $-1=(p-1)+(p-1)p+\cdots$, we have $\zeta_{p-1}=-1$. See A11.3(i).

Notice that $S=\{0,1,\zeta_2,\ldots,\zeta_{p-1}\}$ can be taken as a set of representatives (known as the **Teichmuller representatives**) of κ (cf. 5.53) and the fact that S is multiplicatively closed, though of course not a subfield, can be an advantage in some situations.

Caution: The rationality criterion (5.57) is not valid for this S. For instance, in $\mathbb{Q}_5$,

$$X^4-1=(X-1)(X+1)(X-i)(X+i),$$

where $i=2+5+2\cdot5^2+5^3+\cdots$, $-i=3+3\cdot5+2\cdot5^2+3\cdot5^3+\cdots$ (as we saw in Section 7), and when $S=\{0,\pm1,\pm i\}$ we have, for example,

$$2=i+(-1)5+(-i)5^2+0.5^3+\cdots.$$

From (5.59) and the irrationality of i, it is easy to see that the coefficients in this expansion never become periodic.

If $\operatorname{char}(k)=p>0$, k contains the pth roots of 1 since $X^p-1=(X-1)^p$ by (3.52). However, if $p>2$, 1 is the only pth root of 1 in $\mathbb{Q}_p$ (a fortiori in $\mathbb{Q}$) because if $Y=X-1$, then

(5.102) $$X^p-1=(Y+1)^p-1$$
$$=Y\left[Y^{p-1}+\binom{p}{1}Y^{p-2}+\cdots+\binom{p}{p-1}\right]=Yg(Y),$$

say, and $g(Y)$ has no root in $\mathbb{Q}_p$; indeed, $g(Y)$ is irreducible by Eisenstein's criterion (the U.F.D. being $\mathbb{Z}_p$).

Hensel's lemma applied to $X^n-\alpha$ starting at $\xi_1=1$ gives the following analog of (5.77) in which "positiveness" is replaced by "nearness to 1."

(5.103) COROLLARY. *Let k be a complete ultrametric valued field, let $n\in\mathbb{N}$, and let $\alpha\in k$ satisfy $|1-\alpha|<|n|^2$. (This precludes $n=0$ in k.) Then α has a unique nth root in k satisfying*

$$\left|1-\sqrt[n]{\alpha}\right|\leqslant|(1-\alpha)/n|.$$

In these circumstances the symbols $\sqrt[n]{\alpha}$ and $\alpha^{1/n}$ are reserved to denote this particular root which is called the **principal value** or the **principal *n*th root of α**. Thus $\sqrt[n]{1}=1$ in any such k. In $\mathbb{Q}_2$, when $\alpha\equiv 1 \bmod 8$, $\sqrt{\alpha}$ denotes that square root of α that $\equiv 1 \bmod 4$. For example, $\sqrt{9}=-3$: The 2-adic principal value of $\sqrt{9}$ is -3.

In (5.171) we shall see that if $\alpha=\beta^m$ for some $m\in\mathbb{Z}$ and if $|1-\beta|<|n|^2$, then $(\beta^m)^{1/n}=(\beta^{1/n})^m$. In these circumstances the notation $\beta^{m/n}$ is unambiguous.

EXERCISES

1. Redo exercises 4 and 5 after Section 7 using Hensel's lemma.

2. Calculate the principal value of $\sqrt[n]{\alpha}$ up to the term in p^4 in $\mathbb{Q}_p$:
   (i) $p=3$, $n=2$, $\alpha=7$;
   (ii) $p=2$, $n=3$, $\alpha=3$;
   (iii) $p=2$, $n=2$, $\alpha=17$;
   (iv) $p=2$, $n=4$, $\alpha=-31$;
   (v) $p=3$, $n=3$, $\alpha=28$.

   Now calculate $\sqrt{\sqrt[3]{28}-1}$ in $\mathbb{Q}_3$ up to the term in 3^3.

3. Let F be a field and $f=\alpha_0+\alpha_1 Y+\cdots+\alpha_n Y^n\in F[\![X]\!][Y]$ where $\alpha_i=a_{i0}+a_{i1}X+\cdots$. If $a_{00}=0$ and $a_{10}\neq 0$, then f has a root in $F[\![X]\!]$. Calculate up to the term in X^4 (i) (when $\operatorname{char}(F)\neq 2$) $\sqrt{1+X}$; and (ii) (when $\operatorname{char}(F)\neq 5$) the root of Y^5+XY^2+1 that begins $-1-X/5+\cdots$.

4. For each prime p, $\mathbb{Q}_p$ contains infinitely many irrationals of the form $\sqrt{n}$, where n is a square free integer.

5. Let n be an odd natural number and k a field containing the nth roots of 1. Then k contains the $2n$th roots of 1.

6. Let f be a monic polynomial over the field k of degree n, let $d\mid n$, and suppose $\operatorname{char}(k)\nmid d$. Then f has a unique **approximate *d*th root**, i.e., a monic polynomial g of degree $n/d \ni \deg(f-g^d)<n-n/d$. (*Hint*: Write T for $1/X$ and truncate the dth root of $f=T^{-n}(1+a_1T+\cdots)$ given by Hensel's lemma.)

12. SYMMETRIC POLYNOMIALS

In this section we prove a basic fact about the coefficients of polynomials that will be needed in Section 14.

Let $A=\mathbb{Z}[Z_1,\ldots,Z_n]$ be the polynomial ring in n variables and consider the polynomial $g(X)\in A[X]$ in the variable X defined by

$$g=(X-Z_1)(X-Z_2)\cdots(X-Z_n). \tag{5.104}$$

If we write g as

$$g = X^n - s_1X^{n-1} + s_2X^{n-2} - \cdots + (-1)^n s_n, \tag{5.105}$$

then

$$\begin{aligned} s_1 &= Z_1 + Z_2 + \cdots + Z_n, \\ s_2 &= Z_1Z_2 + Z_1Z_3 + \cdots + Z_1Z_n \\ &\quad + Z_2Z_3 + \cdots + Z_2Z_n \\ &\qquad + \cdots + Z_{n-1}Z_n, \\ s_3 &= \sum_{1 \leq i<j<k \leq n} Z_iZ_jZ_k, \\ &\vdots \\ s_r &= \sum_{1 \leq i_1 < i_2 < \cdots < i_r \leq n} Z_{i_1} \cdots Z_{i_r}, \\ &\vdots \\ s_n &= Z_1Z_2 \cdots Z_n. \end{aligned} \tag{5.106}$$

In the last case the sum over all n-tuples reduces to a single term. s_i is an example of a polynomial in several variables $\Sigma aZ_1^{e_1} \cdots Z_n^{e_n}$ (for various coefficients a) that is **homogeneous of degree i**; that is, each monomial term $aZ_1^{e_1} \cdots$ with $a \neq 0$ has total degree $e_1 + \cdots e_n = i$. Such a polynomial is also called a **form**; for example, s_2 is a quadratic form. The zero polynomial is homogeneous of degree i $\forall i$.

Each permutation $\sigma \in \mathrm{Sym}(n)$ of the n element set $\{1,2,\ldots,n\}$ gives rise to a ring automorphism σ' of $A[X]$ as follows: σ' replaces Z_i everywhere by $Z_{\sigma(i)}$, and $\sigma'(X) = X$. For instance, if $n = 3$ and $\sigma(1) = 3$, $\sigma(2) = 1$, $\sigma(3) = 2$ ($\sigma = (123)$ in the cyclic notation of Section 19 of the previous chapter), then

$$\sigma'(5 - 6Z_1{}^2 + 8Z_1Z_2X^2) = 5 - 6Z_3{}^2 + 8Z_3Z_1X^2.$$

σ' is an automorphism since it merely interchanges the notation used for the n variables $Z_1, \ldots, Z_n$. (The situation can be described formally in terms of the universal property of polynomial rings, but this is hardly necessary.) By (5.104), $\sigma'(g) = g$, and therefore by (5.105)

$$\sigma'(s_r) = s_r, \qquad \forall \sigma \in \mathrm{Sym}(n). \tag{5.107}$$

An element of A, such as s_r, which is invariant under the action of $\mathrm{Sym}(n)$ in the sense of (5.107) is called a **symmetric polynomial**. Of course, the s_r are not the only symmetric polynomials. For example, when $n = 2, 1 + Z_1{}^4 + Z_2{}^4$ is symmetric: it is not changed by any permutation of the Zs.

The σ' restrict to automorphisms of A that we again denote $\sigma'(Z_i) = Z_{\sigma(i)}$. Since

$$(\sigma\tau)'(Z_i) = Z_{\sigma\tau(i)} = \sigma'(Z_{\tau(i)}) = \sigma'(\tau'(Z_i)) = (\sigma'\tau')(Z_i),$$

therefore

$$(\sigma\tau)' = \sigma'\tau'. \tag{5.108}$$

In particular, $\sigma'(\sigma^{-1})' = (\sigma^{-1})'\sigma' = 1$, and hence σ' is a member of the group $\mathrm{Aut}_{\mathrm{ring}}(A)$ of ring automorphisms of A. If $\sigma \neq \tau$, then $\sigma' \neq \tau'$ and (5.108) shows that $\sigma \mapsto \sigma'$ defines an injective group homomorphism

$$\mathrm{Sym}(n) \to \mathrm{Aut}_{\mathrm{ring}}(A). \tag{5.109}$$

($\mathrm{Aut}_{\mathrm{ring}}(A)$ contains "many" elements not of the form σ'; for example, when $n = 2$, $Z_1 \mapsto 2 - Z_1 + 3Z_2^2$, $Z_2 \mapsto Z_2$.)

(5.110) LEMMA. *If R is ring and G is a subgroup of* $\mathrm{Aut}_{\mathrm{ring}}(R)$ *then*

$$S = \{r \in R : \sigma(r) = r\ \forall \sigma \in G\}$$

is a subring of R. It is called the **ring of G-invariants** *of R.*

Proof. $\sigma(1) = 1$ for every automorphism, so $1 \in S$. If $a, b \in S$, then $\sigma(a+b) = \sigma(a) + \sigma(b) = a + b$, $\sigma(ab) = \sigma(a)\sigma(b) = ab$, and $\sigma(-a) = -\sigma(a) = -a$ $\forall \sigma \in G$. Hence $a+b$, ab, and $-a$ are in S. ■

Thus the symmetric polynomials form a subring S of A, namely, the ring of $\mathrm{Sym}(n)$-invariants. The next result, known as the **fundamental theorem on symmetric functions,** states that S coincides with $\mathbb{Z}[s_1,\ldots,s_n]$, the subring generated by the s_i (Section 20 of Chapter 4). We have already observed that the s_i are symmetric and, since S is a ring, $S \supset \mathbb{Z}[s_1,\ldots,s_n]$. Therefore the thrust of the proposition is that every symmetric polynomial can be written as a polynomial with integer coefficients in $s_1,\ldots,s_n$. For instance,

$$\begin{aligned} 3 + Z_1^2 + \cdots + Z_n^2 &= 3 + (Z_1 + \cdots + Z_n)^2 \\ &\quad - 2(Z_1Z_2 + Z_1Z_3 + \cdots + Z_{n-1}Z_n) \\ &= 3 + s_1^2 - 2s_2. \end{aligned}$$

For this reason $s_1,\ldots,s_n$ are called the **elementary symmetric polynomials.**

(5.111) PROPOSITION. *The set of symmetric polynomials in $\mathbb{Z}[Z_1,\ldots,Z_n]$ coincides with the subring $\mathbb{Z}[s_1,\ldots,s_n]$.*

Proof. The proof will proceed by induction on n. The case $n = 1$ is obvious since then $s_1 = Z_1$. Let $s_1,\ldots,s_n$ be the elementary symmetric polynomials in the variables $Z_1,\ldots,Z_n$, as in (5.106), and let $s_1',\ldots,s_{n-1}'$ denote the elementary symmetric polynomials in $Z_1,\ldots,Z_{n-1}$. By (5.104) and (5.105),

$$g = (X^n - s_1X^{n-1} + \cdots) = (X^{n-1} - s_1'X^{n-2} + \cdots)(X - Z_n)$$

and hence

$$s_r = s_r' + Z_n s_{r-1}', \tag{5.112}$$

where $s_0'=1$ and $s_n'=0$. Repeated application of this gives

$$\begin{aligned}(5.113)\qquad s_r' &= s_r - Z_n s_{r-1}'\\ &= s_r - Z_n(s_{r-1} - Z_n s_{r-2}')\\ &\vdots\\ &= s_r - Z_n s_{r-1} + Z_n^2 s_{r-2} - \cdots + (-1)^r Z_n^r.\end{aligned}$$

We use the notation $A=\mathbb{Z}[Z_1,\ldots,Z_n]$, $A'=\mathbb{Z}[Z_1,\ldots,Z_{n-1}]$, $B=\mathbb{Z}[s_1,\ldots,s_n]$, $B'=\mathbb{Z}[s_1',\ldots,s_{n-1}']$ and let S (resp. S') denote the ring of symmetric polynomials in A (resp. in A'). Thus $S\supset B$ and $S'=B'$ by induction.

If $f\in S$, then since $A=A'[Z_n]$ we can write $f=f_0+f_1Z_n+\cdots+f_mZ_n^m$ with $f_i\in S'$. By induction, $f_i\in B'$ and then, by (5.113), $f\in B[Z_n]$. When we rewrite the coefficients of f in this way and collect terms we obtain

$$f=F_0+F_1Z_n+\cdots+F_tZ_n^t,\qquad F_i\in B.$$

Since $f, F_i\in S$ this equation remains valid when Z_n and Z_i are interchanged, i.e., $f=F(Z_i)\ \forall i$, where $F=F_0+F_1X+\cdots+F_tX^t\in B[X]$. Divide F by g (defined in (5.104)) in the ring $B[X]$:

$$F=g\gamma+\rho,\qquad \rho=r_{n-1}X^{n-1}+\cdots+r_0.$$

Then $\rho-f=r_{n-1}X^{n-1}+\cdots+(r_0-f)=F-f+g\gamma$ has the n roots $X=Z_1,\ldots,Z_n$ and therefore by (3.38) must be 0. Thus $f=r_0\in B$. ■

We give an example (due to Newton) of this proposition. If $s_r^{(i)}$ denotes the rth symmetric polynomial of $n-1$ variables $Z_1,\ldots,\hat{Z}_i,\ldots,Z_n$, then from (5.113) we derive

$$(*)\qquad s_r^{(i)}=s_r-Z_is_{r-1}+Z_i^2s_{r-2}+\cdots+(-1)^rZ_i^r.$$

Since

$$X^{n-1}-s_1^{(i)}X^{n-2}+\cdots+(-1)^{n-1}s_{n-1}^{(i)}=g/(X-Z_i),$$

if we add these equations for $i=1,\ldots,n$, using

$$\sum_i g/(X-Z_i)=g',$$

which comes from the product rule for derivatives $(g_1g_2\cdots g_n)'=g_1'g_2\cdots g_n+g_1g_2'g_3\cdots g_n+\cdots$ applied to (5.104), we obtain

$$\sum_i s_r^{(i)}=(n-r)s_r.$$

Combining this with $(*)$ and writing

$$p_r=\sum_i Z_i^r,$$

we obtain

$$(n-r)s_r = ns_r - p_1 s_{r-1} + p_2 s_{r-2} - \cdots + (-1)^r p_r,$$

or

$$p_r = p_{r-1}s_1 - p_{r-2}s_2 + \cdots + (-1)^r p_1 s_{r-1} + (-1)^{r+1} r s_r. \tag{5.114}$$

Taking $r = 1,2,3,\ldots$ in succession yields **Newton's formulas**:

$$\begin{aligned} p_1 &= s_1, \\ p_2 &= p_1 s_1 - 2s_2 = s_1^2 - 2s_2, \\ p_3 &= p_2 s_1 - p_1 s_2 + 3s_3 = s_1^3 - 3s_1 s_2 + 3s_3, \\ p_4 &= s_1^4 - 4s_1^2 s_2 + 4s_1 s_3 + 2s_2^2 - 4s_4, \\ &\ \vdots \end{aligned} \tag{5.115}$$

It is a trivial matter to generalize the foregoing to $A = K[Z_1,\ldots,Z_n]$, where K is a commutative ring: None of (5.104)–(5.115) is affected by this change (the σ' are defined as K-algebra homomorphisms). We took $K = \mathbb{Z}$ for simplicity, and in any case the ring homomorphism $\mathbb{Z}[Z_1,\ldots] \to K[Z_1,\ldots]$ given by $Z_i \mapsto Z_i$ carries over all polynomial identities.

Consider now the effect of substituting values $z_1,\ldots,z_n$ in a commutative ring for $Z_1,\ldots,Z_n$. This ring homomorphism[3] preserves polynomial identities. For instance, when $n = 3$ and we specialize Z_1, Z_2, Z_3 to $1,2,3$, we get

$$g = (X-1)(X-2)(X-3) = X^3 - 6X^2 + 11X - 6$$

and (5.106) becomes

$$s_1 = 6, \qquad s_2 = 11, \qquad s_3 = 6.$$

Newton's formulas read

$$1^2 + 2^2 + 3^2 = 6^2 - 2\cdot 11,$$

and so forth. In this case there are no ring homomorphisms effecting the various permutations of the roots $1,2,3$. Nevertheless, for convenience we still use the work "symmetric." For instance, we still say that $s_2 - s_3$ (which actually has the value 5) is a symmetric polynomial of the roots of g, although strictly speaking this terminology is ambiguous.

Here is an example that will be needed in Section 14. If

$$X^n - s_1 X^{n-1} + \cdots \pm s_n = (X-\alpha_1)\cdots(X-\alpha_n) \in k[X], \qquad h \in \mathbb{Z},$$

$$g = \prod_{1 \leqslant i < j \leqslant n} (X - (\alpha_i + \alpha_j) - h\alpha_i\alpha_j),$$

---

[3] This is the composition of n substitution homomorphisms as in Section 10, of Chapter 3:

$$K[Z_1,\ldots,Z_n] \to K[Z_1,\ldots,Z_{n-1}] \to \cdots \to K.$$

The first arrow comes from $Z_n \mapsto z_n$, the second from $Z_{n-1} \mapsto z_{n-1}$, and so on.

then one says that the coefficients of g are symmetric in the αs and therefore can be written as polynomials with integer coefficients in the s_i. This statement is an obvious abbreviation of the formal explanation that if we take the general polynomial

$$X^n - S_1X^{n-1} + \cdots \pm S_n = (X - Z_1)\cdots(X - Z_n) \in \mathbb{Z}[Z_1,\ldots,Z_n,X]$$

and form

$$G = \prod(X - (Z_i + Z_j) - hZ_iZ_j),$$

then G is symmetric in the Z_i (according to the original definition) and therefore the coefficients of G are in $\mathbb{Z}[S_1,\ldots,S_n]$. The previous statement follows by applying the ring homomorphism determined by $Z_i \mapsto \alpha_i$.

EXERCISES

1. If α, β are the roots of $X^2 - (a+d)X + ad - bc$, then α^3, β^3 are the roots of $X^2 - (a^3 + b^3 + 3abc + 3bcd)X + (ad - bc)^3$.

2. Write $(X^2Y + Y^2Z + Z^2X)(XY^2 + YZ^2 + ZX^2)$ as a polynomial in the elementary symmetric functions of X, Y, Z.

3. If $\alpha, \beta, \gamma, \delta$ are the roots of $X^4 - s_1X^3 + s_2X^2 - s_3X + s_4$, write the coefficients of the cubic whose roots are $\alpha\beta + \gamma\delta$, $\alpha\gamma + \beta\delta$, and $\alpha\delta + \beta\gamma$ as polynomials (with integer coefficients) in the s_i.

4. Determine which $\sigma \in \mathrm{Sym}(4)$ satisfy $\sigma f = f$ (where σf is defined by (5.109)) when $f = X_1X_2 + X_3X_4$ and when $f = X_1X_2 + X_2X_3 + X_3X_4$.

5. Let f be a real polynomial of degree n with n distinct real roots. Then the derivative f' has $n-1$ distinct real roots. Hence (by induction on n) if $f = X^n + a_{n-1}X^{n-1} + \cdots + a_0$, then $a_m{}^2 > (m + 1/m)a_{m-1}a_{m+1}$ for $1 \leqslant m < n$, where $a_n = 1$. (*Hint*: Write $f = \Sigma c_m X^m/m!$ and prove $c_m{}^2 > c_{m-1}c_{m+1}$.)

6. If f and g are homogeneous polynomials of degree d and e, respectively, then fg is homogeneous of degree $d + e$.

13. ROOT FIELDS; THE DISCRIMINANT

(5.116) PROPOSITION. *Let f be a polynomial of positive degree over the field k. Then there exists a field k' containing k as a subfield such that f factors into linear factors over k'.*

Proof. This is an application of the ideas developed in Section 10 of Chapter 3. Let p be an irreducible factor of f in $k[X]$, and let I denote the ideal $pk[X]$, k_1 the factor ring $k[X]/I$, which is a field by (3.62), and θ the element $X + I$ in k_1. As explained in that section, we can regard k as a subfield of k_1 (there we had A as a subring of B) and p is the minimum polynomial of θ over k: For any $h \in k[X]$,

$$h(\theta)=0 \quad \Leftrightarrow \quad p \mid h.$$

In particular, θ is a root of p. Hence $k_1[X]$, $p(X)=(X-\theta)q(X)$, say, and therefore f acquires the linear factor $X-\theta$ in enlarging the field k to k_1. (This process is referred to as **adjoining the root θ** to k. The field k_1 can be denoted $k(\theta)$ or $k[\theta]$.) It is now simply a matter of repeating the process until k is extended to a field k' containing all the roots of f. ■

A field containing all the roots of f (and containing k as a subfield) is called a **root field** or **splitting field of f**. Thus every polynomial has a root field.

(5.117) EXAMPLES

1. $f=(X^2-5)(X^2-X+1)=p_1p_2 \in \mathbb{Q}[X]$. Using a self-explanatory notation, over the field $k_1=\mathbb{Q}[\theta:\theta^2=5]$ we have $p_1=(X-\theta)(X+\theta)$. As it happens, p_2 also factors over k_1: by (5.81), $p_2=(X-(1+\theta)/2)(X-(1-\theta)/2)$. Hence k_1 is a root field of f. $\mathbb{R}$ is also a root field of f since in $\mathbb{R}[X]$,

$$f=\left(X-\sqrt{5}\right)\left(X+\sqrt{5}\right)\left(X-\left(1+\sqrt{5}\right)/2\right)\left(X-\left(1-\sqrt{5}\right)/2\right).$$

Of course, $\mathbb{R}$ is "bigger than necessary." For the relationship of k_1 to $\mathbb{R}$, see (5.120) (1).

2. $f=X^p-t \in k[X]$, where $k=\mathbb{F}_p(t)$, t an indeterminate. If $k_1=k[\theta:\theta^p=t]$ then by (3.52), $f=(X-\theta)^p$ so θ is a root of multiplicity p and k_1 is a root field of f.

3. $f=(X^2-2)(X^2-3)=p_1p_2 \in \mathbb{Q}[X]$. Over $k_1=\mathbb{Q}[\theta:\theta^2=2]$, p_2 remains irreducible, for $(a+b\sqrt{2})^2=a^2+2b^2+2ab\sqrt{2}=3$ implies, since $\{1,\sqrt{2}\}$ is linearly independent over $\mathbb{Q}$, that $2ab=0$, which in turn leads to $2b^2=3$ or $a^2=3$, neither of which is possible. A root field for f is $k_1[\varphi:\varphi^2=3]$. Alternatively, we can first form $k_2=\mathbb{Q}[\varphi:\varphi^2=3]$ and then $k_2[\theta:\theta^2=2]$ is a root field for f. Now a natural question is whether $k_1[\varphi]$ and $k_2[\theta]$ are essentially the same. This is true and is tied up with the general fact that given two fields k_1 and k_2 containing k there exists a common overfield k_3.

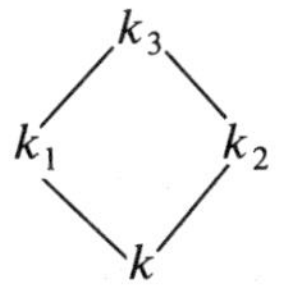

However, this is not really needed at the moment and we do not enter into the details.

(5.118) PROPOSITION. *Let p be an irreducible polynomial of degree $n>0$ over the field k, let $k_1=k[X]/pk[X]$, let k' be a root field of p, and let $\lambda_1,\ldots,\lambda_m$ be the distinct roots of p in k' (so $m \leqslant n$). (See Figure 5.8.) Then*

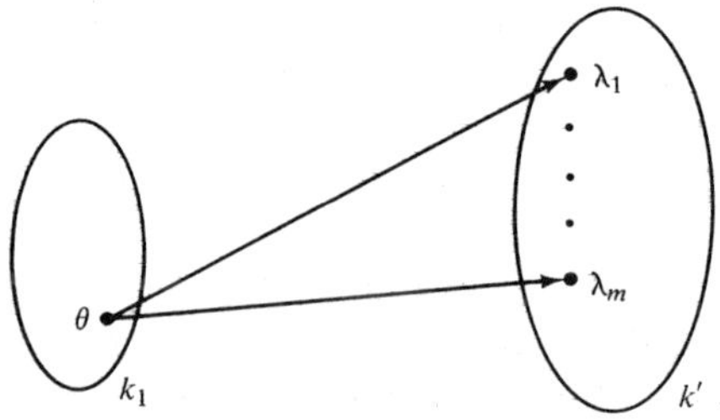

Figure 5.8 Embeddings of k_1 in k'.

there exist precisely m k-algebra homomorphisms g_i: $k_1 \to k', i = 1,\dots, m$. *If* θ *denotes the element* $X + pk[X]$ *of* k_1, *they are given by*

$$g_i\left(a_0 + a_1\theta + \cdots + a_{n-1}\theta^{n-1}\right) = a_0 + a_1\lambda_i + \cdots + a_{n-1}\lambda_i^{n-1},$$

where $a_j \in k$, *and these give isomorphisms between the field* k_1 *and the subfields* $k[\lambda_i]$ *of* k'.

Proof. p is the minimum polynomial over k of λ_i and of θ. The g_i are the only k-algebra homomorphisms g: $k_1 \to k'$ since $p(\theta) = 0$ and therefore $g(p(\theta)) = p(g(\theta)) = 0$, so $g(\theta) = \lambda_i$ for some i, hence $g = g_i$. The remaining details are left to the reader. ■

If h_i denotes the isomorphism $k_1 \to k[\lambda_i]$ (this is just g_i with the codomain restricted) then $h_j h_i^{-1}$ is a k-algebra isomorphism $k[\lambda_i] \to k[\lambda_j]$. Now if $\lambda_j \in k[\lambda_i]$ then $k[\lambda_j] \subset k[\lambda_i]$ and $k[\lambda_j]$ is a k-vector subspace of $k[\lambda_i]$. Since both have dimension n, $k[\lambda_j] = k[\lambda_i]$. Thus

(5.119) COROLLARY. *If* $\lambda_j \in k[\lambda_i]$, *then*

$$a_0 + a_1\lambda_i + \cdots \mapsto a_0 + a_1\lambda_j + \cdots$$

defines an automorphism of the field $k[\lambda_i]$ *in which each element of the subfield k is left fixed.*

(5.120) EXAMPLES

1. $p = X^2 - 5 \in \mathbb{Q}[X], k' = \mathbb{R}$. The two embeddings $k_1 = \mathbb{Q}[\theta : \theta^2 = 5] \to \mathbb{R}$ are

$$g_1(a + b\theta) = a + b\sqrt{5}, \quad \text{and} \quad g_2(a + b\theta) = a - b\sqrt{5}.$$

One can think of θ as an "abstract square root of 5", while $\sqrt{5}$ and $-\sqrt{5}$ are its two representations in $\mathbb{R}$. We have $\mathrm{Im}(g_1) = \mathrm{Im}(g_2) = \mathbb{Q}(\sqrt{5})$ so h_1, h_2 are distinct isomorphisms from the field k_1 to $\mathbb{Q}(\sqrt{5})$. The automorphism $h_1 h_2^{-1}$ of $\mathbb{Q}(\sqrt{5})$ is given by $a + b\sqrt{5} \mapsto a - b\sqrt{5}$ and coincides with its inverse $h_2 h_1^{-1}$.

2. $p = X^2 + X + 1 \in \mathbb{F}_2[X]$, $k' = k_1 = \mathbb{F}_2[\theta : \theta^2 + \theta + 1 = 0]$. As soon as a field $k'(\supset k)$ contains one root of a quadratic it contains the other since their sum is s_1, the first symmetric polynomial. In this case $s_1 = 1$ and the two roots of p in k' are θ

and $1-\theta=1+\theta$. This four-element field $\{0,1,\theta,1+\theta\}$ was first encountered in Section 10 of Chapter 3 and is denoted GF(4) or $\mathbb{F}_4$. Since $(a+b\theta)^2=a+b(1+\theta)$, the automorphism $a+b\theta \mapsto a+b(1+\theta)$ is the Frobenius automorphism F (cf. (3.52)) and, as in the previous example, $F^2=1$.

3. It is essential in the proposition that p be irreducible otherwise there may be no homomorphism taking λ_i to λ_j. For instance, $f=X(X^2-2)\in\mathbb{Q}[X]$ has roots $0,\sqrt{2},-\sqrt{2}$ in $\mathbb{R}$, but among

$$\mathbb{Q}[X]/f\mathbb{Q}[X],\quad \mathbb{Q}[0]=\mathbb{Q},\quad \mathbb{Q}\left[\sqrt{2}\right],\quad \mathbb{Q}\left[-\sqrt{2}\right]$$

only the last two are isomorphic (via $\sqrt{2}\mapsto-\sqrt{2}$; they both coincide with the $\mathbb{Q}$-subalgebra $\{a+b\sqrt{2} : a,b\in\mathbb{Q}\}$ of $\mathbb{R}$).

4. Here is an example of $\lambda_j\notin k[\lambda_i]$. Let $p=X^3-4X+2\in\mathbb{Q}[X]$. It is clear from the plot of p in Figure 5.9 that p has three real roots. For a strict verification by the Weierstrass Nullstellensatz, we observe that $p(-3)=-13$ and $p(1)=-1$ are negative, while $p(0)=2$ and $p(2)=2$ are positive. Now,

$$D=(\lambda_1-\lambda_2)^2(\lambda_2-\lambda_3)^2(\lambda_3-\lambda_1)^2$$

is clearly a symmetric polynomial in the roots and therefore $D\in\mathbb{Z}$. In fact $D=148=4\cdot 37$. (It would be quite a chore to calculate this directly, even with the aid of Newton's formulas. In (5.129) we shall see that D is the discriminant of p, and (5.124) shows how to calculate D "the right way.")

If we had $\lambda_2\in\mathbb{Q}(\lambda_1)$, then $\lambda_3=-\lambda_1-\lambda_2\in\mathbb{Q}(\lambda_1)$; hence $(\lambda_1-\lambda_2)(\lambda_2-\lambda_3)(\lambda_3-\lambda_1)=\pm\sqrt{D}=\pm 2\sqrt{37}\in\mathbb{Q}(\lambda_1)$. A7.5 shows that this is impossible since $[\mathbb{Q}(\sqrt{37}):\mathbb{Q}]=2$ is not a divisor of $[\mathbb{Q}(\lambda_1):\mathbb{Q}]=3$. It follows that the three $\mathbb{Q}(\lambda_i)$ are isomorphic but distinct subfields of $\mathbb{R}$:

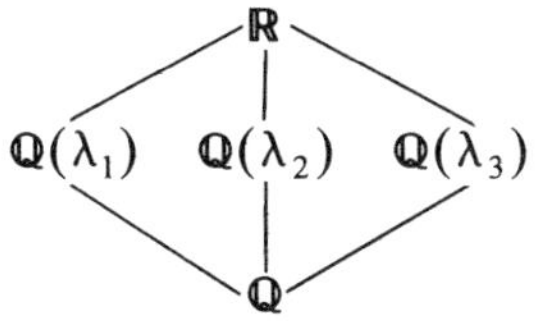

Figure 5.9

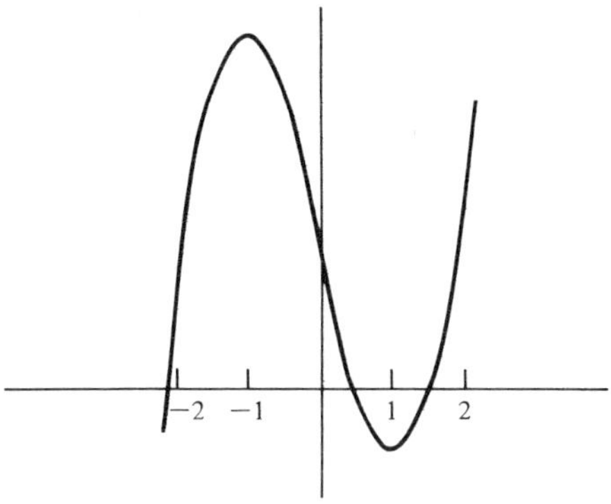

Let k be a field and $f \in k[X]$ a polynomial of degree $n \geqslant 2$. The **discriminant** of f is the element of k defined in terms of the resultant of f and its derivative by

$$\mathrm{Dis}(f) = (-1)^{n(n-1)/2} R(f, f'). \tag{5.121}$$

Thus if $f = X^n - s_1 X^{n-1} + \cdots$, then

$$\mathrm{Dis}(f) = (-1)^{n(n-1)/2} \begin{vmatrix} 1 & -s_1 & s_2 \cdots \\ 0 & 1 & -s_1 \cdots \\ & \vdots & \\ n & -(n-1)s_1 & \cdots \\ 0 & n & \cdots \\ & \vdots & \end{vmatrix}$$

Plainly the discriminant is a symmetric polynomial (i.e., a polynomial in the s_i).

When $f = X^2 + aX + b$, $f' = 2X + a$ and

$$\mathrm{Dis}(f) = -\begin{vmatrix} 1 & a & b \\ 2 & a & 0 \\ 0 & 2 & a \end{vmatrix} = a^2 - 4b. \tag{5.122}$$

Similarly one calculates

$$\mathrm{Dis}(X^3 + aX^2 + bX + c) = -4a^3c + a^2b^2 + 18abc - 4b^3 - 27c^2; \tag{5.123}$$

in particular,

$$\mathrm{Dis}(X^3 + bX + c) = -4b^3 - 27c^2, \tag{5.124}$$

and

(5.125)

$$\begin{aligned} \mathrm{Dis}(X^4 + aX^3 + bX^2 + cX + d) = {} & -27a^4d^2 + 18a^3bcd - 4a^3c^3 - 4a^2b^3d \\ & + a^2b^2c^2 + 144a^2bd^2 - 6a^2c^2d \\ & - 80ab^2cd + 18abc^3 - 192acd^2 \\ & + 16b^4d - 4b^3c^2 - 128b^2d^2 \\ & + 144bc^2d - 27c^4 + 256d^3. \end{aligned}$$

The above definition of the discriminant must be amended in one respect. If $\deg(f) = n$ then in (5.121), f' is always to be treated as a polynomial of degree $n-1$ (with leading coefficient taken as zero when $\mathrm{char}(k) | n$). Thus in characteristic 2, $\mathrm{Dis}(X^2 + aX + b) = a^2$. (Of course, what is really involved is first a definition in characteristic 0 with general coefficients, then a specialization of the coefficients to values in K.)

(5.126) PROPOSITION. *Let f, g be polynomials over the field k of positive degrees m, n, respectively, and suppose that f has the factorization $a(X-z_1)\cdots(X-z_m)$ in $k[X]$. Then*

$$R(f,g)=a^n\prod g(z_i). \tag{5.127}$$

Hence, if $g=b(X-y_1)\cdots(X-y_n)$ in $k[X]$, then

$$R(f,g)=a^nb^m\prod(z_i-y_j). \tag{5.128}$$

Proof. By (4.124) we can assume $a=b=1$. It is sufficient to prove (5.127) for the general polynomials $f=(X-Z_1)\cdots(X-Z_m)$ and $g=T_nX^n+\cdots+T_0$ in $A=\mathbb{Z}[Z_1,\ldots,Z_m,T_n,\ldots,T_0]$ since a particular case of (5.127) can be obtained by substitutions $Z_i\mapsto z_i$ and $T_j\mapsto t_j$. We can extend $Q(A)$ to a root field k of g and regard $f,g\in k[X]$ because $R=R(f,g)$ is defined in terms of the coefficients of f and g and its value is not affected by an enlargement of the ground ring. Thus we can take g in the form $(X-Y_1)\cdots(X-Y_n)$ and we may as well start afresh with $f,g\in B[X]$, where $B=\mathbb{Z}[Z_1,\ldots,Z_m,Y_1,\ldots,Y_n]$.

By (4.125), $R=\lambda f+\mu g$ with $\lambda,\mu\in B[X]$. Substituting $X\mapsto Z_i$ gives

$$R=\mu(Z_i)g(Z_i)=\mu(Z_i)(Z_i-Y_1)\cdots(Z_i-Y_n).$$

By (3.71), B is a U.F.D. and Z_i-Y_j are irreducible elements. No two of these mn elements are associates since $B^*=\{\pm 1\}$. Therefore

$$R=h\prod_{i=1}^{m}g(Z_i)$$

for some $h\in B$. Finally, we see that $h=1$ by comparing the terms in $(Y_1Y_2\cdots Y_n)^m$ as follows.

Write $g=s_0X^n-s_1X^{n-1}+\cdots\pm s_n$ so that $s_0=1$, $s_n=Y_1\cdots Y_n$, and so on. In the determinant (4.126) for R the diagonal entries consist of n 1s followed by $(-1)^ns_n$ repeated m times; the entries below the diagonal are $\pm s_i$ or 0; and those above are symmetric polynomials in the Z_i. In the expansion (4.120) of this determinant, let us regard the terms as polynomials in the variables Y_j (with the Z_i in the ground ring), and let *degree* refer to the total degree in the Ys (so the degree of $cZ_1^{d_1}\cdots Z_m^{d_m}Y_1^{e_1}\cdots Y_n^{e_n}$ is $e_1+\cdots+e_n$.) Then $\deg(s_i)=i$ and the term of highest degree is the product of the diagonal elements

$$1^n((-1)^ns_n)^m=(-1)^{mn}(Y_1\cdots Y_n)^m$$

because all other terms in the expansion involve an m-fold product of various s_i with at least one $i<n$. This coincides with the term of highest degree (in the Y_j) in

$$\prod_i g(Z_i)=\prod_{i,j}(Z_i-Y_j).$$

Comparing coefficients gives $h=1$. ∎

(5.129) COROLLARY

$$\mathrm{Dis}(a(X-z_1)\cdots(X-z_m)) = a^{2m-1}\prod_{1\leqslant i<j\leqslant m}(z_i-z_j)^2.$$

Proof. By (5.121) and the proposition,

$$\mathrm{Dis} = a^{2m-1}(-1)^{m(m-1)/2}\prod_i f'(z_i).$$

The product rule for derivatives applied to $f(X)=(X-Z_1)\cdots(X-Z_m)$ gives

$$f'(z_i) = \prod_{j=1, j\neq i}^{m}(z_i-z_j).$$

For a given j, the number of i satisfying $1\leqslant i<j$ is $j-1$. Therefore the number of pairs (i,j) with $1\leqslant i<j\leqslant m$ is $1+2+\cdots+(m-1)=m(m-1)/2$. ■

In the discussion of Cardan's formula for the general cubic $f=X^3+tX^2+\cdots$ we first made the substitution $X\mapsto X-t/3$ in order to obtain a polynomial $g(X)=f(X-t/3)$ whose coefficient of X^2 is 0. This translates the roots: if z is a root of f, then $z+t/3$ is a root of g. A similar translation was made in the case of the quartic. Such translations do not affect the discriminant, as we state in general in the following corollary. We leave the deduction from the previous corollary as an exercise.

(5.130) COROLLARY. *Let $f\in k[X]$, $h\in k$ and define $g\in k[X]$ by $g(X)=f(X+h)$. Then* $\mathrm{Dis}(g)=\mathrm{Dis}(f)$.

When locating the real roots of a real polynomial f, usually the first thing one does is plot a part of the curve $y=f(x)$, or at least make a rough sketch. Here are a few simple "graphical heuristics." Let $f=X^n+a_{n-1}X^{n-1}+\cdots\in\mathbb{R}[X]$. The possibilities when $n=2$ are shown in Figure 5.10; the

Figure 5.10

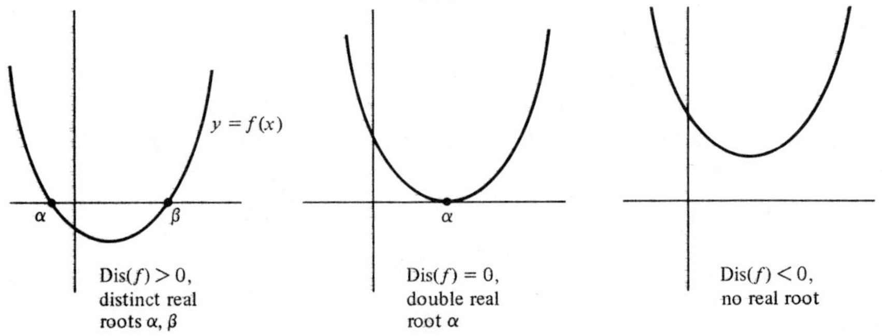

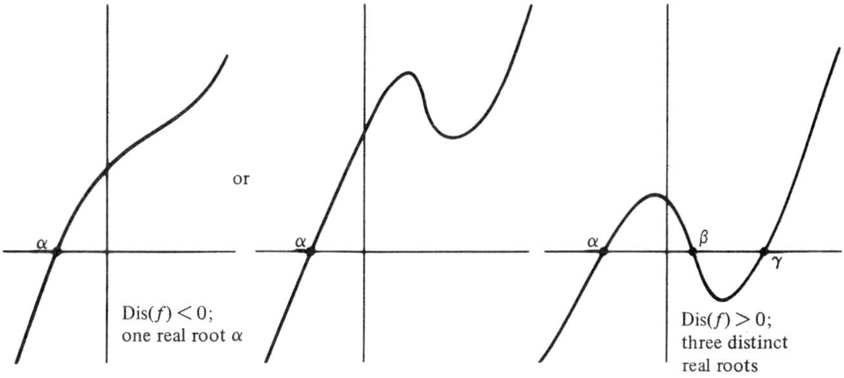

Figure 5.11

possibilities when $n=3$ appear in Figures 5.11 and 5.12, the latter comprising the two cases when $\mathrm{Dis}(f)=0$. In all these figures the y axis is positioned arbitrarily. Figure 5.13 gives an indication of the general case.

A crest or trough (the proper terms being *local maximum* and *local minimum*, respectively) can occur only at a root of f' and there are therefore together at most $n-1$ of them. This is a consequence of Rolle's theorem (5.74).

EXERCISES

1. **(i)** $k=\mathbb{Q}[\theta:\theta^3=7\theta+7]$ is a field.

(ii) $f=X^3-7X-7$ factors completely$/k$. (*Hint*: Another root of f is $-14+b\theta+c\theta^2$ for certain $b,c\in\mathbb{Z}$.)

(iii) Write $\alpha=1/(1-\theta)$ in the form $a_1+a_2\theta+a_3\theta^2$, $a_i\in\mathbb{Q}$, and show that $\mathbb{Q}(\alpha)=k$.

2. For $n\equiv\pm1 \bmod 6, (X+Y)^n-X^n-Y^n$ is divisible by X^2+XY+Y^2.

Figure 5.12

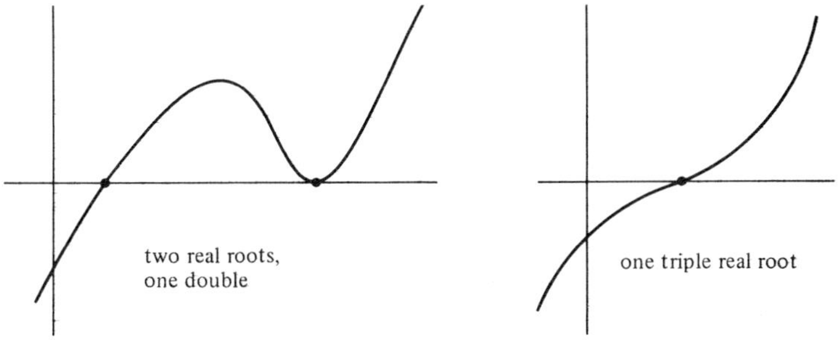

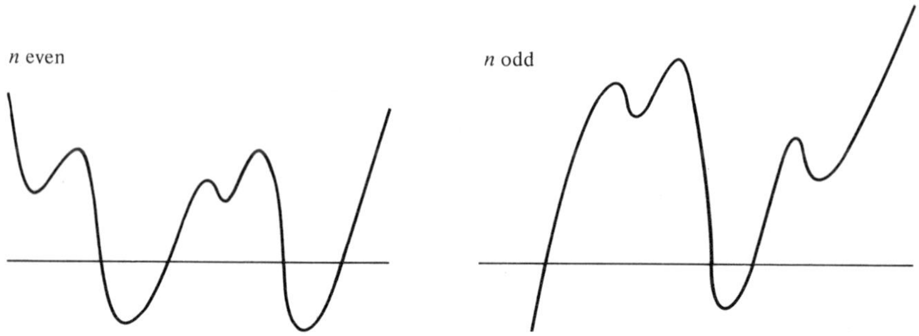

Figure 5.13

3. Let a, b be relatively prime positive integers, let $\theta = \sqrt[n]{a/b} \in \mathbb{R}$, and suppose $[\mathbb{Q}(\theta):\mathbb{Q}] < n$. Then there exist integers $c, d, e, f \ni a = c^e,\ b = d^f$ where g.c.d. $(e, f, n) > 1$.

4. A quartic f and its resolvent cubic G, as in (5.92), have the same discriminant.

5. $\mathrm{Dis}(X^n - a) = (-1)^{(n-1)(n+2)/2} n^n a^{n-1}$.

14. THE COMPLEX FIELD

Over the real field the following polynomials are irreducible:

(i) $X + a$ for all $a \in \mathbb{R}$; and
(ii) $X^2 + aX + b$ for all $a, b \in \mathbb{R}$ such that $d = a^2 - 4b < 0$ (cf. 5.81).

We shall see that this is a complete catalog of all monic irreducible polynomials in $\mathbb{R}[X]$. (It follows by (3.76)(2) that there is no U.F.D. $A \subsetneq \mathbb{R} \ni Q(A) = \mathbb{R}$. This is unlike the case of an ultrametric valued field k since then $k = Q(D)$, where D is the valuation ring.)

(5.131) DEFINITION. The field k is **algebraically closed** if every polynomial over k of positive degree has a root in k.

Hence if $f \in k[X]$ and $n = \deg(f) > 0$, then $f = (X - \alpha_1) f_1$ for some $\alpha_1 \in k$, and by repetition, $f = a(X - \alpha_1) \cdots (X - \alpha_n)$ where a is the leading coefficient of f. Thus an equivalent definition of k being algebraically closed is that $X - \alpha$ for $\alpha \in k$ are the only monic irreducible polynomials.

$\mathbb{R}$ is not algebraically closed since $X^2 + 1$ is irreducible.

(5.132) DEFINITION. The field

$$\mathbb{C} = \mathbb{R}[X]/(X^2 + 1)\mathbb{R}[X]$$

is called the **complex field** and its elements are called **complex numbers**.

Complex numbers were originally called *imaginary numbers*, and it has become traditional to use the initial letter i to denote the complex number $X+(X^2+1)\mathbb{R}[X]$. In the notation of (5.117),

$$\mathbb{C}=\mathbb{R}[i:i^2=-1]$$

and every complex number α is uniquely represented in the form

$$(5.133) \qquad \alpha=a+bi, \qquad a,b\in\mathbb{R}.$$

The **real part** of α is a; the term **imaginary part** is used to mean either b or bi, according to context. For instance, "α has positive imaginary part" leaves no doubt as to its meaning. Such notation as $\alpha=a+bi$ or $z=x+iy$ always carries with it the understanding that a and b, or x and y, are real numbers.

We regard $\mathbb{R}$ as a subfield of $\mathbb{C}$ under the usual identification $a=a+0i$. It is not possible to define a relation $<$ on $\mathbb{C}$ satisfying (5.22) because $i^2=(-i)^2=-1$.

The **conjugate** of $\alpha=a+bi$ is $\bar{\alpha}=a-bi$. For instance, $\overline{2+3i}=2-3i$, $\overline{-i}=i$, $\overline{-\sqrt{2}}=-\sqrt{2}$. Clearly $\bar{\bar{\alpha}}=\alpha$ and $\alpha=\bar{\alpha}\Leftrightarrow\alpha\in\mathbb{R}$.

As a vector space over $\mathbb{R}$, $\mathbb{C}$ has dimension 2; a basis is $\{1,i\}$. We can picture complex numbers as points in the real plane $\mathbb{R}\times\mathbb{R}$ by plotting $\alpha=a+bi$ as the point with coordinates (a,b). This representation (Figure 5.14) is referred to as the **Argand diagram** or the **complex plane** (although the correct term is "complex line" since $\mathbb{C}$ has dimension 1 as a vector space over $\mathbb{C}$). Notice that conjugation is effected by reflection through the real axis, while passing from α to $-\alpha$ is by reflection through the origin. The two axes break the plane up into four **quadrants** numbered from 1 to 4, as shown in Figure 5.14.

Figure 5.14 The Argand diagram.

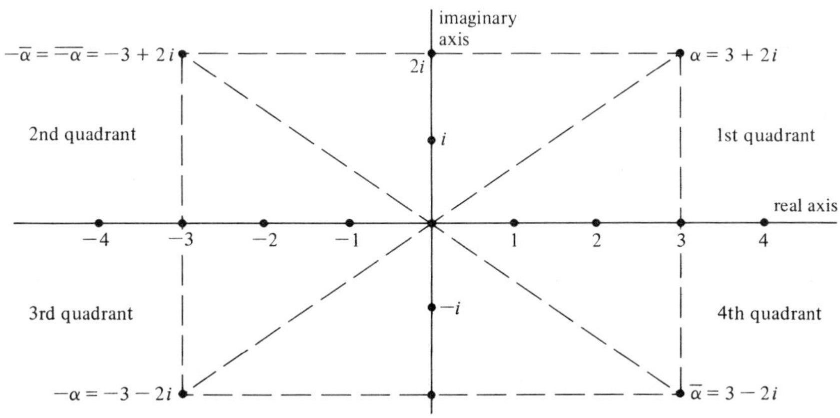

By (5.119), $\alpha \mapsto \bar{\alpha}$ is an automorphism of $\mathbb{C}$, and hence

(5.134) $$\overline{\alpha+\beta}=\bar{\alpha}+\bar{\beta}, \qquad \overline{\alpha\beta}=\bar{\alpha}\bar{\beta}.$$

Of course, it is easy to prove these rules by direct calculation, but it is good to know the theoretical reason why $\mathbb{C}$ has this automorphism.

Recall from Chapter 3 the method of *rationalizing* the denominator (perhaps "realizing" is the better word here): For example,

$$\frac{1+2i}{-3+4i}=\frac{(1+2i)(-3-4i)}{(-3+4i)(-3-4i)}=\frac{5-10i}{3^2+4^2}=\frac{1}{5}-\frac{2}{5}i$$

and, similarly,

$$\left(\tfrac{1}{2}-i\right)^{-1}=\left(\tfrac{1}{2}+i\right)\big/\left(\left(\tfrac{1}{2}\right)^2+(-1)^2\right)=\tfrac{2}{5}+\tfrac{4}{5}i.$$

The following theorem, first proved by Gauss, was long ago named **the fundamental theorem of algebra**.

(5.135) THEOREM. $\mathbb{C}$ *is algebraically closed.*

Proof. Let $f\in\mathbb{C}[X]$ have degree $n>0$. We prove the existence of a root in four steps:

1. $n=2$.
2. $f\in\mathbb{R}[X]$, n odd.
3. $f\in\mathbb{R}[X]$, general n.
4. general $f\in\mathbb{C}[X]$.

We can assume that f is monic.

Step 1. Every complex number $\alpha=a+bi$ has a square root $\in\mathbb{C}$. Indeed if $\sqrt{c}$ denotes the unique nonnegative square root when $c\in\mathbb{R}^{\geqslant}$, and if $u=1$ or -1 according to whether $b\geqslant 0$ or $b<0$, then

(5.136) $$\pm\left(\sqrt{\frac{\sqrt{a^2+b^2}+a}{2}}+u\sqrt{\frac{\sqrt{a^2+b^2}-a}{2}}\,i\right)$$

are the square roots of α. We now appeal to (5.81).

Step 2. By the Weierstrass Nullstellensatz, f has a root in $\mathbb{R}$; hence it has one in $\mathbb{C}$.

Step 3. Let $f=X^n+a_{n-1}X^{n-1}+\cdots+a_0$, $a_j\in\mathbb{R}$, and $n=2^q m$, where $2\nmid m$. We prove by induction on q that f has a root $\in\mathbb{C}$. The case $q=0$ is step 2; thus suppose $q>0$, so n is even.

If we think of $f\in\mathbb{C}[X]$, then f has a root field $k\supset\mathbb{C}$, say $f=(X-\alpha_1)\cdots(X-\alpha_n)$, $\alpha_i\in k$. (The choice of $k\supset\mathbb{C}$ rather than simply $k\supset\mathbb{R}$ will be important.) Define

$$g=\prod_{1\leqslant i<j\leqslant n}\left(X-(\alpha_i+\alpha_j)-h\alpha_i\alpha_j\right)\in k[X],$$

where h is an integer to be specified in a moment. As explained in Section 12, the coefficients of g are symmetric polynomials in the α_i, hence are polynomials with integer coefficients in the elementary symmetric polynomials $\pm a_i$, and are therefore real numbers: $g \in \mathbb{R}[X]$. Now $\deg(g) = n(n-1)/2 = 2^{q-1}m(n-1) = N$, say, and $m(n-1)$ is odd. By induction on q, at least one of the roots $\alpha_i + \alpha_j + h\alpha_i\alpha_j$ is in $\mathbb{C}$. (It is here that we want $k \supset \mathbb{C}$.) This is true for each of the $N+1$ polynomials corresponding to $h = 0, 1, \ldots, N$, and since there are only N pairs, some pair must occur twice: There must be two values of h, say $h_1 \neq h_2$, such that, for some $i<j$, $\alpha_i + \alpha_j + h_1\alpha_i\alpha_j$ and $\alpha_i + \alpha_j + h_2\alpha_i\alpha_j$ are both in $\mathbb{C}$. Subtracting and dividing by $h_1 - h_2$, we see that $\alpha_i\alpha_j \in \mathbb{C}$ and therefore also $\alpha_i + \alpha_j \in \mathbb{C}$. Hence

$$(X-\alpha_i)(X-\alpha_j) = X^2 - (\alpha_i + \alpha_j)X + \alpha_i\alpha_j \in \mathbb{C}[X].$$

By step 1, the roots α_i and α_j of this quadratic are in $\mathbb{C}$. Hence f has roots in $\mathbb{C}$.

Step 4. By A5.5(α), conjugation extends to a ring endomorphism of $\mathbb{C}[X]$ given by

$$f = \alpha_0 + \alpha_1 X + \alpha_2 X^2 + \cdots \mapsto \bar{f} = \bar{\alpha}_0 + \bar{\alpha}_1 X + \bar{\alpha}_2 X^2 + \cdots.$$

Since $\bar{\bar{f}} = f$, this is an automorphism. Now if f is any polynomial over $\mathbb{C}$ of positive degree and we put $g = f\bar{f}$, then

$$\bar{g} = \overline{f\bar{f}} = \bar{f}\bar{\bar{f}} = \bar{f}f = g;$$

hence $g \in \mathbb{R}[X]$. By step 3, g has a root $\alpha \in \mathbb{C}$: $g(\alpha) = f(\alpha)\bar{f}(\alpha) = 0$. If $f(\alpha) = 0$, we have the required root α of f. Otherwise $\bar{f}(\alpha) = 0$, but then

$$\overline{\bar{f}(\alpha)} = \bar{0} = 0; \qquad \text{i.e.,} \quad f(\bar{\alpha}) = 0,$$

and again f has a root in $\mathbb{C}$. ∎

We can now prove the statement made at the beginning of this section.

(5.137) COROLLARY. *An $f \in \mathbb{R}[X]$ of positive degree has a factorization in the form*

$$f = \alpha_0(X-\alpha_1)\cdots(X-\alpha_m)q_1\cdots q_r,$$

where $m \geqslant 0$, $r \geqslant 0$, $q_j = X^2 + \beta_j X + \gamma_j$, $\alpha_j, \beta_j, \gamma_j \in \mathbb{R}$, and $\delta_j = \beta_j^2 - 4\gamma_j < 0$. The roots of q_j are

$$\left(-\beta_j \pm \sqrt{-\delta_j}\, i\right)/2$$

and therefore the complex roots of a real polynomial occur in conjugate pairs.

Proof. Each real root α of course gives rise to a linear factor $X-\alpha$. Now suppose $\lambda = \beta + \gamma i$ is a complex root with $\gamma \neq 0$. Using the fact that the coefficients of f are real, we have $f(\bar{\lambda})=\overline{f(\lambda)}=0$ and therefore $\bar{\lambda}$ is also a root. Thus f is divisible by

$$q=(X-\lambda)(X-\bar{\lambda})=X^2-2\beta X+(\beta^2+\gamma^2)$$

in $\mathbb{C}[X]$, and thus in $\mathbb{R}[X]$ since $q\in\mathbb{R}[X]$. ■

Consider the example $f=X^2+X+i$. Since $(1-4i)^{1/2}$ has the values

$$\pm\left(\sqrt{\frac{\sqrt{17}+1}{2}}-\sqrt{\frac{\sqrt{17}-1}{2}}\,i\right),$$

by (5.136), the two roots of f are

$$-\frac{1}{2}\pm\sqrt{\frac{\sqrt{17}+1}{8}}\mp\sqrt{\frac{\sqrt{17}-1}{8}}\,i,$$

where $\mp$ stands for the sign opposite to that chosen for $\pm$. These complex numbers are not conjugates of one another, which underlines the fact that the statement concerning conjugate pairs of roots in the corollary refers to real polynomials only.

Similarly one finds that the two square roots of i are $\pm\zeta$ where

(5.138) $$\zeta=(1+i)/\sqrt{2}\,.$$

EXERCISE

Verify the following table of values of ζ^n:

(5.139)

n	1	2	3	4	5	6	7	8
ζ^n	ζ	i	$-\bar{\zeta}$	-1	$-\zeta$	$-i$	$\bar{\zeta}$	1

These are displayed in Figure 5.15 on the **unit circle** $=\{\xi\in\mathbb{C}:\xi\bar{\xi}=1\}$.

(5.140) COROLLARY. *Let k be a field containing $\mathbb{R}$ as a proper subfield such that every $x\in k\setminus\mathbb{R}$ is algebraic over $\mathbb{R}$ (cf. Section* 10 *of Chapter* 3). *Then $k=\mathbb{C}$; more precisely, $\exists\mathbb{R}$-algebra isomorphism $\mathbb{C}\to k$.*

Proof. Choose any $x\in k\setminus\mathbb{R}$ and let f be the minimum polynomial of x over $\mathbb{R}$. By the previous corollary, f is quadratic, and by the fundamental theorem, in $\mathbb{C}[X]$, $f=(X-\lambda)(X-\bar{\lambda})$, say. Since $\lambda\notin\mathbb{R}$ and $\dim_{\mathbb{R}}(\mathbb{C})=2$, $\mathbb{R}(\lambda)=\mathbb{C}$. As explained in (5.118), $\lambda\mapsto x$ defines an $\mathbb{R}$-algebra isomorphism ψ: $\mathbb{C}\to\mathbb{R}(x)\subset k$. Hence by the fundamental theorem, the minimum polynomial of any $y\in k$ over the subfield $\mathbb{R}(x)$ must be linear. Therefore $\psi(\mathbb{C})=\mathbb{R}(x)=k$. ■

Every complex number $\alpha=a+bi$ is a root of a real quadratic polynomial, namely,

$$(X-\alpha)(X-\bar{\alpha})=X^2-(\alpha+\bar{\alpha})X+\alpha\bar{\alpha}=X^2-T(\alpha)X+N(\alpha),$$

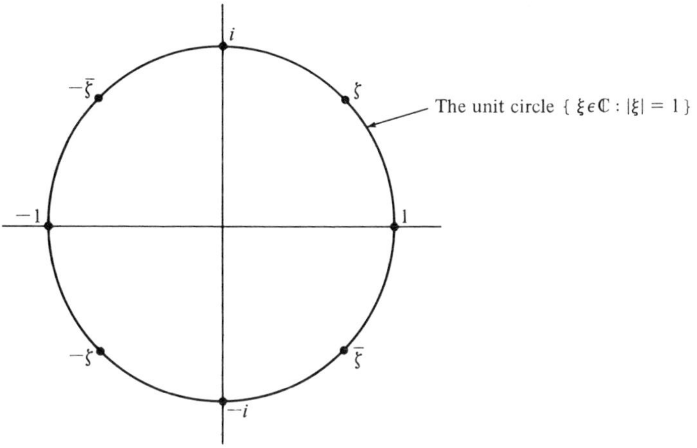

Figure 5.15

where

$$T(\alpha) = \alpha + \bar{\alpha} = 2a = T(\bar{\alpha})$$

is called the **trace** of α (and $\bar{\alpha}$) and

$$N(\alpha) = \alpha\bar{\alpha} = a^2 + b^2 = N(\bar{\alpha})$$

is called the **norm**. Since a and b are real, $a^2 + b^2 \geqslant 0$ and we define the **absolute value** by

$$(5.141) \qquad |\alpha| = \sqrt{\alpha\bar{\alpha}} \in \mathbb{R}^{\geqslant}.$$

Thus $|a + bi| = \sqrt{a^2 + b^2}$ and $|\bar{\alpha}| = |\alpha|$.

(5.142) PROPOSITION. *The map* $|\ |$: $\mathbb{C} \to \mathbb{R}^{\geqslant}$ *defined by* (5.141) *is an archimedean absolute value extending the usual absolute value on the subfield* $\mathbb{R}$. *Moreover, equality occurs in* $|\alpha + \beta| \leqslant |\alpha| + |\beta|$ *iff either* $\beta = 0$ *or* $\alpha = a\beta$ *for some* $a \in R^{\geqslant}$, *and consequently equality occurs in* $|\alpha - \beta| \geqslant |\alpha| - |\beta|$ *iff either* $\beta = 0$ *or* $\alpha = a\beta$ *where* $a \in \mathbb{R}$ *and* $a \geqslant 1$.

Proof. (AV0) follows from the fact that $a^2 + b^2 = 0 \Leftrightarrow$ both a and b are 0. Since

$$|a + 0i| = \sqrt{a^2 + 0^2} = \pm a, \qquad \text{whichever is } \geqslant 0,$$

$|\ |$ extends the absolute value on $\mathbb{R}$ and (AV1) is satisfied. (AV3) is proved by the calculation

$$|\alpha\beta| = \sqrt{\alpha\beta\,\overline{\alpha\beta}} = \sqrt{\alpha\beta\bar{\alpha}\bar{\beta}} = \sqrt{\alpha\bar{\alpha}}\,\sqrt{\beta\bar{\beta}} = |\alpha||\beta|.$$

To prove the triangle inequality $|\alpha + \beta| \leqslant |\alpha| + |\beta|$, and to determine when equality occurs, we can assume that $\beta \neq 0$ and define $\gamma = \alpha/\beta = a + bi$.

Then

$$|\alpha+\beta|=|1+\gamma||\beta|,$$

$$|\alpha|+|\beta|=(1+|\gamma|)|\beta|,$$

$$|1+\gamma|^2=(1+a)^2+b^2=1+a^2+b^2+2a,$$

$$(1+|\gamma|)^2=1+a^2+b^2+2\sqrt{a^2+b^2}\,.$$

Thus $|\alpha+\beta|\leqslant|\alpha|+|\beta|$ is a consequence of the obvious inequality $2a\leqslant 2\sqrt{a^2+b^2}$, and equality occurs iff $b=0$ and $a\geqslant 0$. Finally, equality occurs in $|\alpha+\beta|-|\beta|\leqslant|\alpha|$ under the same conditions, which can be rewritten in the form given in the proposition by replacing α by $\alpha-\beta$. ■

(5.143) PROPOSITION. *The sequence of complex numbers* $\alpha_n=a_n+ib_n$ *is cauchy (resp. null) iff both the sequences* a_n *and* b_n *are cauchy (resp. null) in* $\mathbb{R}$. *When this is the case, say* $\lim\alpha_n=\alpha$, $\lim a_n=a$, $\lim b_n=b$, *we have* $\alpha=a+ib$. *Also* $\lim\bar{\alpha}_n=\bar{\alpha}$ *and* $\lim|\alpha_n|=|\alpha|$.

Proof. The first statement follows from the fact that

$$|\alpha_p-\alpha_q|=\sqrt{(a_p-a_q)^2+(b_p-b_q)^2} \qquad \left(\text{resp. } |\alpha_p|=\sqrt{a_p{}^2+b_p{}^2}\right)$$

is small iff both $|a_p-a_q|$ and $|b_p-b_q|$ (resp. $|a_p|$ and $|b_p|$) are small. The remaining statements follow by the Cauchy convergence criterion and $\big||\alpha|-|\alpha_n|\big|\leqslant|\alpha-\alpha_n|$. ■

It follows that every cauchy sequence of complex numbers has a limit in $\mathbb{C}$:

(5.144) COROLLARY. *As a valued field,* $\mathbb{C}$ *is complete.*

(5.145) COROLLARY. *The infinite series* $\Sigma\alpha_n$ *of complex numbers* $\alpha_n=a_n+ib_n$ *is convergent (resp. absolutely convergent) iff both the real series* Σa_n *and* Σb_n *are convergent (resp. absolutely convergent). When the series are convergent, say* $\Sigma\alpha_n=\alpha$, $\Sigma a_n=a$, $\Sigma b_n=b$, *we have* $\alpha=a+ib$ *and* $\Sigma\bar{\alpha}_n=\bar{\alpha}$.

Only the statements concerning absolute convergence require further explanation. If $\Sigma|\alpha_n|$ is convergent, then since $|\alpha_n|=\sqrt{a_n{}^2+b_n{}^2}\geqslant|a_n|$, $\Sigma|a_n|$ is convergent; similarly, $\Sigma|b_n|$ is convergent. Conversely, if $\Sigma|a_n|$ and $\Sigma|b_n|$ are convergent, then since

$$|\alpha_n|=|a_n+ib_n|\leqslant|a_n|+|ib_n|=|a_n|+|b_n|,$$

$\Sigma|\alpha_n|$ is convergent, and with sum $\leqslant\Sigma|a_n|+\Sigma|b_n|$. ■

The fundamental theorem guarantees that, for instance,

$$f = X^{10} + \left(\tfrac{2}{3} - \sqrt[3]{7+\sqrt{2}\,i}\right)X^9 + 50X^6 + iX - i/6$$

has a factorization $f = (X-\alpha_1)\cdots(X-\alpha_{10}) \in \mathbb{C}[X]$. However, as already mentioned at the end of Section 10, there is no general formula expressing these roots in terms of radicals as there is for the roots of a quadratic, cubic, and quartic. Even the effective approximation to the α_i, that is, calculating the real and imaginary parts to a specified number of decimal places, as a practical matter presents considerable difficulties and is a central problem in numerical analysis.

However, we can present an approach that theoretically gives an algorithm to calculate the roots of a given $f \in \mathbb{C}[X]$. (This method gives a list of candidates that must be tested to see which are the roots of f. Numerically this may require going back to calculate these candidates more accurately.)

(1) Sturm's theorem (but more likely in practice, Newton's method) allows us to calculate the real roots of a real polynomial within any desired positive margin of error.

(2) By replacing f by $f\bar{f}$, we see that it is enough to be able to calculate the roots of a real polynomial.

(3) We reduce the problem of calculating the (complex) roots of a given $f \in \mathbb{R}[X]$ to calculating the real roots of an auxiliary real polynomial in the following way. Write

$$f(U+iV) = g(U,V) + ih(U,V),$$

where $g, h \in \mathbb{R}[U,V]$, so that the roots of f are obtained as the solutions of the system of algebraic (polynomial) equations

$$(*) \qquad \begin{aligned} g(U,V) &= 0, \\ h(U,V) &= 0. \end{aligned}$$

(The individual equations can be viewed as describing curves in the plane $\mathbb{R}^2$; and the solutions we seek are the points of intersection of these two curves.) One way of handling this problem is afforded by (4.124): If we regard g and h as polynomials, say in the variable V over the field $\mathbb{R}(U)$, then they have a common root V only if the resultant vanishes:

$$R(g,h) = 0.$$

This gives a real polynomial equation in the *single* real variable U.

This method of finding the points of $\cap$ is generally known as **elimination theory** and can be applied to any pair of plane curves described by polynomial equations as in $(*)$ (provided g and h do not have as a common factor a polynomial in V, so that by (4.124) R is not identically 0). Elimination theory is the starting point of classical algebraic geometry.

We illustrate the method for $f = X^3 + 3aX - 2c$, assuming that $\mathrm{Dis}(f) = -108d < 0$, where $d = a^3 + c^2$, so that f has one real root λ and a pair $\alpha, \bar{\alpha}$ of complex roots. (Compare A11.5. Of course in practice we would not use elimination theory for a cubic since we have a formula: The roots are $\lambda = \mu - a/\mu$, where

$$\mu = \sqrt[3]{a + \sqrt{d}}\,, \qquad \alpha = \mu\omega - a/\mu\omega, \quad \omega = \left(-1 + \sqrt{3}\,i\right)/2.\Big)$$

$$g = -3UV^2 + (U^3 + 3aU - 2c),$$
$$h = V\left(-V^2 + (3U^2 + 3a)\right) = Vh_1,$$

say. Since we are interested in solutions with $V \neq 0$, to simplify R we take

$$R = R(g, h_1) = \begin{vmatrix} -3U & 0 & U^3 + 3aU - 2c & 0 \\ 0 & -3U & 0 & U^3 + 3aU - 2c \\ -1 & 0 & 3U^2 + 3a & 0 \\ 0 & -1 & 0 & 3U^2 + 3a \end{vmatrix}.$$

Applying the row operations $E_{31}(-3U)$ and $E_{42}(-3U)$, we find that $R = (8U^3 + 6aU + 2c)^2$. Hence we are led to

$$4U^3 + 3aU + c = 0. \tag{5.146}$$

The unique real root $-\lambda/2$ is the value of U we seek. The two values of V are obtained by setting $h_1 = 0$:

$$V = \pm\sqrt{3U^2 + 3a}\,.$$

EXERCISES

1. Find complex numbers $z, w \ni$

$$(1 + 2i)z + (3 + 4i)w = 5 + 6i,$$
$$(6 - 5i)z + (-4 + 3i)w = 2 - i.$$

2. Knowing that one root in $\mathbb{C}$ of $X^4 - 3X^2 + 6X - 2$ is $1 + i$, find the others.

3. For $a, b, c, d \in \mathbb{R}$ and $z \in \mathbb{C}$,

$$\mathrm{Imag}\left(\frac{az + b}{cz + d}\right) = \frac{\mathrm{Imag}(z)}{|cz + d|^2}.$$

4. Adapt Euclid's proof of (1.27) to show that no finite field $\mathbb{F}_q$ is algebraically closed (i.e., consider $1 + \prod\{X - a : a \in \mathbb{F}_q\}$).

Assignment 11

A11.1. If $a_1,\ldots,a_n \in \mathbb{R}^{>}$ we define their **arithmetic mean**

$$A=\frac{a_1+a_2+\cdots+a_n}{n},$$

geometric mean

$$G=\sqrt[n]{a_1a_2\cdots a_n},$$

harmonic mean

$$H=n\left(\frac{1}{a_1}+\frac{1}{a_2}+\cdots+\frac{1}{a_n}\right)^{-1},$$

root mean square

$$R=\sqrt{\frac{a_1^{\,2}+a_2^{\,2}+\cdots+a_n^{\,2}}{n}},$$

and **standard deviation**

$$\sigma=\sqrt{\frac{1}{n}\Sigma(a_i-A)^2}.$$

Thus σ is the root mean square of the quantities $a_1-A,\ldots,a_n-A$. In mathematical statistics, σ^2 is known as the **variance** of $a_1,\ldots,a_n$. Prove that

$$R^2=A^2+\sigma^2, \qquad \text{and} \qquad R\geqslant A\geqslant G\geqslant H;$$

and that all these inequalities are strict unless $a_1=a_2=\cdots=a_n$. (*Hints*: $G\geqslant H$ (and $>$ unless ...) is an easy deduction from

$$(*) \qquad A\geqslant G (\text{and } A>G \text{ unless } \ldots).$$

By replacing a_n by $(a_1+\cdots+a_{n-1})/(n-1)$, show that $(*)$ for n quantities implies $(*)$ for $n-1$ quantities. Then prove $(*)$ by induction on k for the special values $n=2^k$.)

A11.2. **(i)** Let $p=2n+1$ be an odd prime. Show that in $\mathbb{Q}_p$,

$$\tfrac{1}{2}=n+1+np+np^2+\cdots, \qquad -\tfrac{1}{2}=n+np+np^2+\cdots.$$

Find similar formulas for $\pm\frac{1}{3}$ and $\pm\frac{2}{3}$ when p has the form $3n+1$ and $3n+2$. (The latter case is a little harder.)

(ii) Let $\alpha=a_0+a_1p+\cdots\in\mathbb{Z}_p$ with $a_i\in\{0,1,\ldots,p-1\}$ as usual. Prove that the expansion is purely periodic, i.e., for some $h\in\mathbb{N}$, $a_{i+h}=a_i$ $\forall i\geqslant 0$, iff α is rational and $-1\leqslant\alpha\leqslant 0$. Find a characterization of the real numbers with purely periodic decimal expansion $0.d_1d_2\ldots$.

(iii) Show that the real number $\Sigma_{n\in\mathbb{N}}10^{-n^2}$ and the p-adic numbers $\Sigma_{n\in\mathbb{N}}p^{n^2}$ (p any prime) are irrational. Similarly show that $\Sigma_{n\in\mathbb{N}}X^{n^2}\in F((X))\setminus F(X)$ (F any field).

A11.3. (i) If $a,b \in \mathbb{Z}$, $m,n \in \mathbb{N}$, and $a \equiv b \bmod m^n$, show that $a^m \equiv b^m \bmod m^{n+1}$. Deduce that the sequence $a, a^p, a^{p^2}, \ldots$ is cauchy in $\mathbb{Q}_p$ and that its limit is 0 if $p|a$ and otherwise is a $(p-1)$th root of 1 in $\mathbb{Q}_p$ (the one $\equiv a \bmod p$, cf. (5.101)).

(ii) Let F be a field of characteristic $p > 0$. Show that the roots of $X^p - X + T$ in $F((T))$ are $a + T + T^p + T^{p^2} + \cdots$, where $a = 0, 1, \ldots, p-1$.

(iii) Let k be a discretely valued field with uniformizer p and residue field κ of characteristic $\neq 2$; let a be a p-adic unit with no square root in k. Show that the quadratic form[4]

$$N = X^2 - pY^2 - aZ^2 + apU^2$$

has no nontrivial zero $(X,\ldots,U) = (x,\ldots,u) \in k^4$. (*Hint*: If not, by multiplying by an appropriate power of p, it can be assumed that $\min\{v(x),\ldots,v(u)\} = 0$, whence a contradiction results. N is a **quaternion norm form**; this result will be used in A12.10.)

A11.4. Let $\tilde{\mathbb{Q}}$ denote a completion of $\mathbb{Q}$ with respect to an absolute value $|\ |$ (so by (5.9), $\tilde{\mathbb{Q}} = \mathbb{Q}$ if $|\ |$ is trivial, $\tilde{\mathbb{Q}} = \mathbb{R}$ if $|\ |$ is archimedean, and otherwise $\tilde{\mathbb{Q}} = \mathbb{Q}_p$ for some prime p).

(i) Show that the only automorphism of the field $\tilde{\mathbb{Q}}$ is 1. (*Hint*: If σ is a nontrivial automorphism of $\tilde{\mathbb{Q}} = \mathbb{R}$ (resp. $\mathbb{Q}_p$) then $\exists \alpha \in \tilde{\mathbb{Q}} \ni \alpha > 0$ and $\sigma\alpha < 0$ (resp. $|\alpha - 1| < 1$, $|\sigma\alpha - 1| = 1$). However, then α has a square root (resp. $(p-1)$th root) while $\sigma\alpha$ does not—a contradiction.)

(ii) Prove that no two of the fields $\tilde{\mathbb{Q}}$ are isomorphic.

(*Remark*. If F is a field and $b \in F^*$ then $\Sigma a_n T^n \mapsto \Sigma a_n b^n T^n$ defines an automorphism of $F((T))$ (leaving the elements of F fixed), and for every $c \in F$ the $(X+c)$-adic completion of $F(X)$ is isomorphic to $F((T))$. Hence the statements in (i) and (ii) are not true for all valued fields.)

A11.5. In this question we elaborate on Cardan's formula (5.89), with the following notation:

k is a field of characteristic $\neq 3$;

$f = X^3 + 3aX + b \in k[X]$ with $a \neq 0$;

$d = 4a^3 + b^2$ (by (5.124), $\mathrm{Dis}(f) = -27d$);

$g = Y^2 + bY - a^3$;

r and $r' = -b - r$ the two roots of g (when they exist in k);

$q \in \{r^{1/3}\}$ (so Cardan's formula reads: root of f is $q - a/q$);

$h = Z^2 - bZ + 3a^3 + b^2$;

---

[4]A **quadratic form** is a polynomial in several variables all of whose terms are of total degree 2.

N is the number of roots of f in k, counted with their multiplicities: $N=0$, 1, or 3 according as f is a product of 1, 2, or 3 irreducible factors in $k[X]$;

n is the number of roots given by Cardan's formula, again with repetitions counted: $n=0$ if g has no root in k, and otherwise $n=|\{r^{1/3}\}|$ (which coincides with $|\{r'^{1/3}\}|$ since $rr'=-a^3$).

(i) Suppose $N=3$; say,

$$f=(X-\lambda_1)(X-\lambda_2)(X-\lambda_3)\in k[X].$$

Show that

$$s=\left(\lambda_1\lambda_2^{\,2}+\lambda_2\lambda_3^{\,2}+\lambda_3\lambda_1^{\,2}\right)/3,$$

$$s'=\left(\lambda_1^{\,2}\lambda_2+\lambda_2^{\,2}\lambda_3+\lambda_3^{\,2}\lambda_1\right)/3$$

are the roots of h and deduce that

$$(s-s')^2=-3d.$$

(ii) Suppose again that $N=3$ and also that k contains the cube roots of unity ω,ω^2 (as in (5.84) or (5.85)). Show that

$$r=\frac{\omega^2-1}{3}(\omega^2 s+b)$$

is a root of g.

(iii) Show that if char$(k)\neq 2$ (and $\neq 3$) and if f has a repeated root λ in some root field, then in fact $\lambda\in k$; hence $f=(X-\lambda)^2(X+2\lambda)$ in $k[X]$. Show that this is the case iff $r=r'$ iff $s=s'$ iff $d=0$. (*Hint*: Calculate discriminants.)

(iv) If $d\neq 0$ and k contains a root λ_1 of f and the roots s,s' of h, show that

$$(*)\qquad \lambda_2=\frac{(s'-s)}{3d}\left[6a^2-(b+s)\lambda_1+3a\lambda_1^{\,2}\right]$$

is another root of f (the third being given by a similar expression with s and s' interchanged). Consequently $N=3$. (*Hint*: Prove that $f=(X-\lambda_1)(X^2+\lambda_1X+\lambda_1^{\,2}+3a)$ and that λ_2,λ_3 as given in $(*)$ satisfy $\lambda_2+\lambda_3=-\lambda_1$, $\lambda_2\lambda_3=\lambda_1^{\,2}+3a$.)

(v) In the accompanying table, the symbol $\in$ in the r (resp. s,ω) column means that k contains the roots of g (resp. h, X^2+X+1) while $\notin$ means the contrary. Verify that the table is complete: no other combination of the five entries can occur.

r	s	ω	n	N	Example k	Example f
				$d=0$		
$\in$	$\in$	$\in$	3	3	$\mathbb{F}_7$	X^3+X+2
$\in$	$\in$	$\notin$	1	3^a	$\mathbb{F}_2$	X^3+X
$\notin$	$\notin$	$\notin$	0	1^b	$\mathbb{F}_2(T)$	X^3+TX
$\notin$	$\notin$	$\in$	0	1^b	$\mathbb{F}_4(T)$	X^3+TX
				$d\neq 0$		
$\in$	$\in$	$\in$	3	3	$\mathbb{F}_7$	X^3+3X
$\in$	$\in$	$\in$	0	0	$\mathbb{F}_7$	X^3+X+1
$\in$	$\notin$	$\notin$	1	1	$\mathbb{F}_5$	X^3+2X
$\notin$	$\notin$	$\in$	0	1	$\mathbb{F}_7$	X^3+X
$\notin$	$\in$	$\notin$	0	0	$\mathbb{F}_2$	X^3+X+1
$\notin$	$\in$	$\notin$	0	3^c	$\mathbb{F}_5$	X^3+X
$\in$	$\notin$	$\notin$	0	0	$\mathbb{Q}$	X^3+6X+2
$\notin$	$\notin$	$\in$	0	0	$\mathbb{F}_7(T)$	X^3+TX+T
$\notin$	$\notin$	$\notin$	0	0	$\mathbb{Q}$	X^3+X+1
$\notin$	$\notin$	$\notin$	0	1	$\mathbb{F}_5(T)$	X^3+TX

[a]Cardan's formula gives the simple (nonrepeated) root.
[b]These cases occur only in characteristic 2.
[c]This is the case usually called the *casus irreducibilis*.

(vi) Deduce that when $k=\mathbb{R}$ the possibilities are as follows:

Dis(f)	r	s	n	N	f has
>0	$\notin$	$\in$	0	3^c	three distinct real roots
0	$\in$	$\in$	1	3^a	three real roots, two coincident
<0	$\in$	$\notin$	1	1	just one real root

[a,c]See the previous table. (For the trigonometric solution of real cubics see Exercise 3 following Section 20.)

A11.6. Let k be a field and let W denote the vector space $k^{\mathbb{M}}$ of all sequences $(u_0, u_1, \ldots)$. The **forward shift operator** is the linear transformation $s \in \mathrm{End}(W)$ defined by

$$s(u_0, u_1, \ldots) = (u_1, u_2, \ldots),$$

and the **forward difference operator** is $\Delta = s - 1$.

(i) Show that $\Delta n^{(k)} = kn^{(k-1)}$ for $k \geqslant 1$. (Recall that $n^{(k)} = n(n-1)\cdots(n-k+1)$, which as a function of $\mathbb{M} \to k$, can be identified with $(0^{(k)}, 1^{(k)}, \cdots)$.)

(ii) Let $c_1, \ldots, c_r \in k$. Show that the set V of $u = (u_0, u_1, \ldots)$ that satisfy the linear recurrence relation

$$u_{n+r}=c_1u_{n+r-1}+c_2u_{n+r-2}+\cdots+c_ru_n, \qquad \text{for } n\geqslant 0$$

is a subspace of W of dimension r.

(iii) Show that if $u\in V$, then $su\in V$; hence s restricts to an endomorphism of V, which we denote by f. Thus $f\in \operatorname{End} V$. Show that f is a root of

$$\Lambda(X)=X^r-c_1X^{r-1}-\cdots-c_r.$$

(iv) Let λ be a root of Λ in k of multiplicity $e\geqslant 1$. Show that for $0\leqslant j<e$, $u_n=n^j\lambda^n$ defines a member of V.

(v) Hence prove that the sequence of **Fibonacci numbers** $(1,1,2,3,5,8,13,\ldots)$ defined by $u_{n+2}=u_{n+1}+u_n$ is given by

$$u_n=\frac{1}{\sqrt{5}}\left[\left(\frac{1+\sqrt{5}}{2}\right)^{n+1}-\left(\frac{1-\sqrt{5}}{2}\right)^{n+1}\right]$$

(provided $\operatorname{char}(k)\neq 2$ or 5 and $\sqrt{5}\in k$). Find the formula for u_n when $k=\mathbb{F}_5$.

(vi) For $\Lambda=c_0X^r+c_1X^{r-1}+\cdots+c_r\in k[X]$, let V_Λ denote the subspace of $u=(u_0,u_1,\ldots)\in k^{\mathbb{M}}$ satisfying $c_0u_{n+r}+\cdots+c_ru_n=0$ for $n\geqslant 0$. Show that for a given u, $\{\Lambda: u\in V_\Lambda\}$ is an ideal. Also show that $\cup V_\Lambda$, where Λ runs over the nonzero polynomials, is a proper subspace of $k^{\mathbb{M}}$.

A11.7. **Newton's method for square roots in $\mathbb{R}^{>}$.** Let $\alpha\in\mathbb{R}^{>}$ and define the sequence $(a_1,a_2,\ldots)\in\mathbb{Q}^{\mathbb{N}}$ by $a_1=1$ and

$$a_{n+1}=\tfrac{1}{2}(a_n+\alpha/a_n)=a_n-f(a_n)/f'(a_n),$$

where $f(X)=X^2-\alpha$. Prove that the sequence converges to $\sqrt{\alpha}$ in $\mathbb{R}$. Hence calculate $\sqrt{30/7}$ correct to four decimal places. (*Hint*: Write $a_n=\sqrt{\alpha}+\delta_n$ so that $\delta_{n+1}=\delta_n^2/2a_n$, and find a convenient bound for the error term $|\delta_n|$.)

A11.8. Find the minimum polynomial/$\mathbb{Q}$ of $\theta=\sqrt{2}+i$. (*Hint*: By taking more and more terms of $1,\theta,\theta^2,\ldots$ eventually one gets linear dependence over $\mathbb{Q}$.)

15. THE EXTENDED BINOMIAL THEOREM IN VALUED FIELDS

The binomial theorem expressed in A3.5 gives the expansion of $(x+y)^n$ for element x, y of a commutative ring and $n\in\mathbb{M}$. When the ring is a complete valued field k and $\operatorname{char}(k)=0$ (resp. $\operatorname{char}(k)=p>0$) this has a generalization to $n\in k$ (resp. $n\in\mathbb{Z}_p$) for suitably restricted x, y, as we shall see in the main theorem of this section, (5.171) below. This will allow us to make sense of expressions such as $2^{\sqrt{2}+\sqrt{3}}$ in $\mathbb{R}$, $(1+i)^i$ in $\mathbb{C}$, and for any $n\in\mathbb{Z}_2, 3^n$ in

$\mathbb{Q}_2$ and $(1+X)^n$ in $\mathbb{F}_2((X))$. However, we must first generalize the binomial coefficients.

If x is an element of a commutative ring, the symbolic powers of x were defined in A7.4:

$$x^{(0)}=1, \qquad x^{(n)}=x(x-1)(x-2)\cdots(x-n+1) \quad \text{for} \quad n\in\mathbb{N}. \tag{5.147}$$

Thus we can rewrite (3.8)

$$\binom{q}{n}=\frac{q^{(n)}}{n!}. \tag{5.148}$$

We now take this as the definition of the binomial coefficient for $n\in\mathbb{M}$ and q any element of a field of characteristic 0. (In a moment we shall define $\binom{q}{n}$ in fields of positive characteristic p for $n\in\mathbb{M}$ and $q\in\mathbb{Z}_p$, extending the usual meaning when $q\in\mathbb{M}$.) Notice that $\binom{q}{n}=0$ iff $q\in\mathbb{M}$ and $n>q$.

From this definition we immediately deduce the following identities.

$$\binom{q}{n+1}=\binom{q}{n}\frac{q-n}{n+1}, \tag{5.149}$$

$$\binom{q+1}{n+1}=\binom{q}{n+1}+\binom{q}{n}, \tag{5.150}$$

$$\binom{-q}{n}=(-1)^n\binom{q+n-1}{n}. \tag{5.151}$$

For example,

$$\binom{-1}{n}=(-1)^n, \qquad \binom{-2}{n}=(-1)^n(n+1),$$

and in general, $\forall q\in\mathbb{Z}$ we have $\binom{q}{n}\in\mathbb{Z}$.

Here is a more complicated identity that will be needed later.

(5.152) PROPOSITION

$$\binom{q}{m}\binom{q}{n}=\sum_{s=0}^{m}\binom{q}{s+n}\binom{s+n}{n}\binom{n}{m-s}.$$

Proof. If we replace q by the variable X, we can regard the difference of the two sides of the proposed equation as a polynomial $f(X)\in\mathbb{Q}[X]$. By A3.6(ii), f has infinitely many roots $N\in\mathbb{N}$; hence $f(X)=0$. This gives $f(q)=0$ under any $\mathbb{Q}$-algebra homomorphism determined by $X\mapsto q$. ■

Let us apply similar reasoning to the identity

$$((1+T)^M)^N=(1+T)^{MN}, \tag{5.153}$$

where $M, N\in\mathbb{N}$. Let $(1+T)^M=1+U$, so the left side is

$$1+\binom{N}{1}U+\binom{N}{2}U^2+\cdots.$$

For $m, n \in \mathbb{N}$, the coefficient of T^n in

$$U^m = \left[\binom{M}{1}T + \binom{M}{2}T^2 + \cdots + T^M\right]^m$$

is

$$\Sigma \binom{M}{j_1} \cdots \binom{M}{j_m},$$

where the sum is over all $(j_1, \ldots, j_m) \in \mathbb{N}^m \ni j_1 + \cdots + j_m = n$. Summing over m we obtain the coefficient of T^n in $(1+T)^{MN}$:

$$\binom{MN}{n} = \sum_{m=0}^{n} \binom{N}{m} \sum_{j_1 + \cdots + j_m = n} \binom{M}{j_1} \cdots \binom{M}{j_m}.$$

The argument that this is true for "general" M and N follows familiar lines: We replace M by X and N by Y and call the difference of the two sides $f(X,Y) \in \mathbb{Q}[X,Y]$. For each N the polynomial $f(X,N) \in \mathbb{Q}[X]$ has infinitely many roots $X = 1,2,\ldots$; hence $f(X,N) = 0$. Since the polynomial $f(X,Y) \in \mathbb{Q}(X)[Y]$ has infinitely many roots $Y = 1,2,\ldots$, we must have $f(X,Y) = 0$. As before, we can assign values $X \mapsto q, Y \mapsto r$, where q and r are elements of any field of characteristic 0, or for that matter, elements of any $\mathbb{Q}$-algebra:

(5.154) PROPOSITION

$$\binom{qr}{n} = \sum_{m=0}^{n} \binom{r}{m} \Sigma \binom{q}{j_1} \cdots \binom{q}{j_m},$$

where the last sum is over all $(j_1, \ldots, j_m) \in \mathbb{N}^m \ni j_1 + \cdots + j_m = n$.

As a corollary, the right side must have the same value when q and r are interchanged.

The identity between binomial coefficients similarly obtainable from

$$(1+T)^M (1+T)^N = (1+T)^{M+N}$$

is proved in a different way in (5.168) below.

Let $x_1, \ldots, x_n$ be integers, p a prime, and let ν_i denote the number of x_j with $v_p(x_j) \geqslant i$. If $v_p(x_j) = m$, then x_j contributes 1 to each of $\nu_1, \nu_2, \ldots, \nu_m$ and 0 to $\nu_{m+1}, \ldots$. Since $v_p(\Pi x_j) = \Sigma v_p(x_j)$, it follows that

$$v_p\left(\prod x_j\right) = \sum_{i \in \mathbb{N}} \nu_i. \tag{5.155}$$

As a particular case take $x_j = j$, so $\Pi x_j = n!$. Since for $q \in \mathbb{N}$, $p^i q \leqslant n$ iff $q \leqslant \lfloor n/p^i \rfloor$, we have $\nu_i = \lfloor n/p^i \rfloor$, and thus the formula

$$v_p(n!) = \sum_{i \in \mathbb{N}} \lfloor n/p^i \rfloor. \tag{5.156}$$

For instance $v_2(10!) = \lfloor 10/2 \rfloor + \lfloor 10/4 \rfloor + \lfloor 10/8 \rfloor (+0 \text{ terms}) = 5+2+1 = 8$, which agrees with the direct calculation

$$10! = 2\cdot 3\cdot 2^2\cdot 5\cdot(2\cdot 3)\cdot 7\cdot 2^3\cdot 3^2\cdot(2\cdot 5) = 2^8\cdot 3^4\cdot 5^2\cdot 7.$$

It follows from (5.156) and (5.26) that

$$v_p(n!) < n\left(\frac{1}{p}+\frac{1}{p^2}+\cdots\right) = \frac{n}{p-1}. \tag{5.157}$$

A refinement of this will appear in (5.166).

(5.158) PROPOSITION. *Let k be an ultrametric field of characteristic* 0, *$q \in k$, and $n \in \mathbb{N}$. If $|q| \leqslant 1$, then*

$$\left|\binom{q}{n}\right| \leqslant \frac{1}{|n!|}. \tag{5.159}$$

If $|q| > 1$, then

$$\left|\binom{q}{n}\right| = \frac{|q|^n}{|n!|}. \tag{5.160}$$

Proof. Since $|\ |$ is ultrametric, $|j| \leqslant 1\ \forall j \in \mathbb{N}$. Hence if $|q| \leqslant 1$, then $|q-j| \leqslant 1$ and

$$\left|\binom{q}{n}\right| = \frac{|q||q-1|\cdots|q-(n-1)|}{|n!|} \leqslant \frac{1}{|n!|}.$$

If $|q|>1$, then $|q-j| = |q|$ and (5.160) follows. ∎

When $|\ |$ is discrete, (5.160) can be rewritten

$$v\left(\binom{q}{n}\right) = nv(q) - v(n!) \qquad (\text{when } v(q)<0). \tag{5.161}$$

For instance,

$$\binom{-\frac{11}{10}}{5} = \frac{r}{2^a 5^b},$$

where

$$a = -5v_2(-\tfrac{11}{10}) + v_2(5!) = 5 + \lfloor 5/2 \rfloor + \lfloor 5/4 \rfloor = 8,$$

and similarly $b=6$. Direct evaluation confirms these values and gives $r = -3\cdot 7\cdot 11\cdot 17\cdot 31\cdot 41$. The above proposition does not predict that $r \in \mathbb{Z}$, only that $3r \in \mathbb{Z}$. This will be remedied in the next proposition by an improvement of (5.159) for $q \in \mathbb{Q}$.

Let

$$q = c/d, \qquad c, d \in \mathbb{Z}, \qquad d>0, \qquad \text{g.c.d.}(c,d) = 1. \tag{5.162}$$

Then

$$(5.163)\qquad \mathbb{Z}[q]=\mathbb{Z}[1/d]=S^{-1}\mathbb{Z},$$

where $S=\{1,d,d^2,\ldots\}$, because $\mathbb{Z}[1/d]$ contains $c(1/d)=q$ and, conversely, if $1=cs+dt$, then $1/d=qs+t\in\mathbb{Z}[q]$. It follows that a rational number x is in $\mathbb{Z}[q]$ iff $d^m x\in\mathbb{Z}$ for some $m\in\mathbb{N}$, alternatively iff for every prime p,

$$v_p(x)<0 \quad\Rightarrow\quad p\,|\,d.$$

Clearly $\mathbb{Z}[q]=\mathbb{Z}$ iff $q\in\mathbb{Z}$.

(5.164) PROPOSITION. *If $q\in\mathbb{Q}$, $n\in\mathbb{N}$, and p is a prime, then*

$$v_p\left(\binom{q}{n}\right)<0 \quad\Leftrightarrow\quad v_p(q)<0.$$

Hence $\binom{q}{n}\in\mathbb{Z}[q]$.

Proof. With q as in (5.162), $\binom{q}{n}=N/d^n n!$, where

$$N=c(c-d)(c-2d)\cdots(c-(n-1)d).$$

If $v_p(q)<0$, i.e., if $p|d$, then $v_p(\binom{q}{n})<0$ by (5.161). Thus suppose $p\nmid d$. We wish to show that $v_p(\binom{q}{n})\geqslant 0$.

For each $m\in\mathbb{N}$ we have $n=a_m p^m+b_m$, where $a_m=\lfloor n/p^m\rfloor$ and $0\leqslant b_m<p^m$. Since $p\nmid d$, we have $d\in(\mathbb{Z}/p^m\mathbb{Z})^*$ and $xd\equiv y \bmod p^m$ has a solution x, uniquely determined mod p^m, for each given y. Hence $c, c-d, c-2d,\ldots,c-(a_m p^m-1)d$ are congruent mod p^m in some order to $c,c-1,c-2,\ldots,c-(p^m-1)$ each repeated a_m times. In particular, exactly a_m of $c,c-d,\ldots,c-(a_m p^m-1)d$ are $\equiv 0 \bmod p^m$. Since these a_m numbers together with the b_m numbers $c-a_m p^m d,\ldots,c-(n-1)d$ are factors of N, by (5.155) and (5.156)

$$v_p\left(\binom{q}{n}\right)=v_p(N)-v_p(n!)\geqslant \sum_{m\in\mathbb{N}} a_m-\sum_{m\in\mathbb{N}}\left\lfloor\frac{n}{p^m}\right\rfloor=0. \quad ■$$

It follows from this proposition and (5.161) that for $n\in\mathbb{N}$ a prime p occurs in the denominator of $\binom{q}{n}$ iff it occurs in the denominator of q. We now generalize this to $q\in\mathbb{Q}_p$ and give a corresponding result for the numerator. We write v for v_p.

(5.165) PROPOSITION. *Let $q\in\mathbb{Q}_p$ and $n\in\mathbb{N}$.*

(i) $v(\binom{q}{n})<0\Leftrightarrow v(q)<0$ *(and then (5.161) applies).*

(ii) *Let $v(q)\geqslant 0$ and let q and n have the p-adic expansions $q=a_0+a_1p+\cdots$, $n=b_0+b_1p+\cdots b_\nu p^\nu$, where $a_i,b_i\in\{0,1,\ldots,p-1\}$. Then $v(\binom{q}{n})>0$ iff $a_i<b_i$ for some i.*

Proof. We define $q' \in \mathbb{Q}$ as follows. If $q \in \mathbb{M}$, we take $q' = q$. Otherwise the p-adic expansion $q = a_r p^r + a_{r+1} p^{r+1} + \cdots$ contains a nonzero term $a_N p^N$ with $N > \nu$ and we take $q' = a_r p^r + \cdots + a_N p^N$. In the latter case none of the assumptions or conclusions is affected by replacing q by q', as we now verify.

For $j \in \mathbb{M}$ and $j < n$, either $v(q') < 0$, and then $v(q' - j) = v(q')$, or $q' - j$ is a natural number $\leqslant q'$ and has a p-adic expansion $d_0 + \cdots + d_\mu p^\mu$ for some $\mu \leqslant N$. In either case $v(q' - j) \leqslant N$. Since $v(q - q') > N$ we have

$$v(q-j) = v(q - q' + q' - j) = v(q' - j),$$

and in particular, $v(q) = v(q')$. Consequently

$$v\left(\binom{q}{n}\right) = v(q) + v(q-1) + \cdots + v(q-(n-1)) - v(n!) = v\left(\binom{q'}{n}\right).$$

Thus we can assume that $q = q' \in \mathbb{Q}$.

(i) is now a direct consequence of the previous proposition.

In (ii), $q \in \mathbb{M}$. If $q < n$, then clearly some $a_i < b_i$, in agreement with $v(\binom{q}{n}) = v(0) = \infty > 0$. Therefore we can assume that $q - n \in \mathbb{M}$, so the p-adic expansion $q - n = c_0 + c_1 p + \cdots$ is finite. By (5.156),

$$(5.166) \qquad v(q!) = \sum_{i \geqslant 1} \lfloor q/p^i \rfloor = \sum_{i \geqslant 1} [a_i + a_{i+1} p + \cdots]$$

$$= \sum_{i \geqslant 1} a_i [1 + p + \cdots + p^{i-1}] = \sum_{i \geqslant 0} a_i \frac{p^i - 1}{p - 1}$$

$$\text{(introducing} \quad a_0 0 = 0)$$

$$= (q - a)/(p-1),$$

where $a = \Sigma a_i$. Similarly

$$v(n!) = (n-b)/(p-1), \qquad v((q-n)!) = (q-n-c)/(p-1),$$

where $b = \Sigma b_i$ and $c = \Sigma c_i$. Thus

$$v\left(\binom{q}{n}\right) = v\left(\frac{q!}{n!(q-n)!}\right) = \frac{b+c-a}{p-1}.$$

We leave as an exercise the deduction of the criterion in (ii) as well as the following more general result of Kummer:

$v\left(\binom{q}{n}\right) =$ the number of carries in the p-adic addition $n + (q-n) = q$. ■

If k is a field of characteristic $p>0$, we can identify $\mathbb{F}_p$ both as the prime subfield of k and as the residue field of $\mathbb{Q}_p$. The canonical map

$$\rho: \mathbb{Z}_p \to \mathbb{F}_p \subset k$$

gives k the structure of a $\mathbb{Z}_p$-algebra. This simply amounts to the extension $\rho(a_0+a_1p+\cdots)=a_0$ of the usual convention of regarding integers as elements of k via the homomorphism $\mathbb{Z}\to k$.

As a corollary of the proposition just proved, $\binom{q}{n}$ is defined (using ρ) as an element of k for $q\in\mathbb{Z}_p$ and $n\in\mathbb{N}$. For instance, in $\mathbb{Q}$

$$\binom{\frac{3}{2}}{1}=\frac{\frac{3}{2}}{1!}=\tfrac{3}{2},$$

$$\binom{\frac{3}{2}}{3}=\frac{(\frac{3}{2})(\frac{1}{2})(-\frac{1}{2})}{3!}=\frac{-1}{16},$$

and therefore

$$\binom{\frac{3}{2}}{1}=0, \qquad \binom{\frac{3}{2}}{3}=2 \quad \text{in} \quad \mathbb{F}_3.$$

Caution. The parameters q,n must not be taken mod p—they are elements of $\mathbb{Z}_p$ and $\mathbb{N}$, not k. For example, $0\equiv 3 \bmod 3$ but $\binom{\frac{3}{2}}{0}=1\neq\binom{\frac{3}{2}}{3}$ in $\mathbb{F}_3$.

To sum up, $\binom{q}{n}$ is an element of k, defined $\forall n\in\mathbb{N}$ and for the following values of q:

(i) If $\operatorname{char}(k)=0$, then q can be any element of k, in particular any element of $\mathbb{Q}$.
(ii) If $\operatorname{char}(k)=p>0$, then $q\in\mathbb{Z}_p$, in particular q can be any rational number with $v_p(q)\geqslant 0$.

Of course, when $q\in\mathbb{Z}$, $\binom{q}{n}$ is an integer and is defined in every ring.

Applying the homomorphism $\rho: \mathbb{Z}_p\to k$ in case (ii), we see that relations such as (5.150)–(5.152) and (5.154) remain valid in k. However (5.149) is no longer generally correct since $n+1$ can be 0 in k.

Symbolic powers satisfy the **symbolic binomial theorem**:

(5.167) PROPOSITION. *If x,y are elements of a commutative ring and $n\in\mathbb{N}$, then*

$$(x+y)^{(n)}=\sum_{j=0}^{n}\binom{n}{j}x^{(j)}y^{(n-j)}.$$

Proof. When $n=0$ both sides are 1. Inductively,

$$\begin{aligned}(x+y)^{(n+1)} &= (x+y)^{(n)}(x+y-n)\\ &= \sum_{j=0}^{n}\binom{n}{j}x^{(j)}y^{(n-j)}(x-j+y-(n-j))\\ &= \sum\binom{n}{j}\left[x^{(j+1)}y^{(n-j)}+x^{(j)}y^{(n+1-j)}\right]\\ &= \sum_{r=0}^{n+1}\left[\binom{n}{r-1}+\binom{n}{r}\right]x^{(r)}y^{(n+1-r)}\\ &\quad \left(\text{where }\binom{n}{-1}=\binom{n}{n+1}=0\right),\\ &= \sum_{r=0}^{n+1}\binom{n+1}{r}x^{(r)}y^{(n+1-r)} \qquad \text{(by A2.6(ii)).} \quad \blacksquare\end{aligned}$$

(5.168) COROLLARY. *Let* $n\in\mathbb{N}$, *let* k *be a field with* $\operatorname{char}(k)=0$ (*resp.* $\operatorname{char}(k)=p>0$) *and let* $q,r\in k$ (*resp.* $q,r\in\mathbb{Z}_p$). *Then*

$$\binom{q}{0}\binom{r}{n}+\binom{q}{1}\binom{r}{n-1}+\cdots+\binom{q}{n}\binom{r}{0}=\binom{q+r}{n}.$$

Proof. First let $\operatorname{char}(k)=0$. The left side is

$$\frac{q^{(0)}}{0!}\frac{r^{(n)}}{n!}+\frac{q^{(1)}}{1!}\frac{r^{(n-1)}}{(n-1)!}+\cdots=\frac{q^{(0)}r^{(n)}+\binom{n}{1}q^{(1)}r^{(n-1)}+\cdots}{n!}$$
$$=(q+r)^{(n)}/n!=\binom{q+r}{n}.$$

Now let $\operatorname{char}(k)>0$, so $q,r\in\mathbb{Z}_p$. The above is a valid equation between elements of $\mathbb{Z}_p$. Therefore, it becomes an equation between elements of k when $\rho\colon\mathbb{Z}_p\to k$ is applied. $\blacksquare$

(5.169) COROLLARY. *If* $\operatorname{char}(k)=p>0$, q *and* $t\in\mathbb{Z}_p$ *and* $v(q-t)=m$, *then in* k

$$\binom{q}{n}=\binom{t}{n} \qquad \text{for} \quad n=0,1,\ldots,p^m-1.$$

In particular (*when* $t=0$), *if* $v(q)=m$, *then* $\binom{q}{n}=0$ *in* k *for* $n=1,2,\ldots,$ p^m-1.

Proof. Let $r=t-q=a_mp^m+a_{m+1}p^{m+1}+\cdots$ and $0<n<p^m$ so $n=b_ip^i+\cdots$, where $0<b_i<p$ for some $i<m$. Thus $a_i=0<b_i$ and by (5.165), $\binom{r}{n}\equiv 0 \bmod p$. In the previous corollary only the $\binom{r}{0}=1$ term survives, leaving $\binom{q}{n}\equiv\binom{t}{n} \bmod p$. $\blacksquare$

As we saw at the end of Section 2, ultrametric absolute values on a field k

can be divided into three types (κ denotes the residue field):

(1) $\operatorname{char}(k)=\operatorname{char}(\kappa)=0$;
(2) $\operatorname{char}(k)=0$, $\operatorname{char}(\kappa)=l>0$; and
(3) $\operatorname{char}(k)=\operatorname{char}(\kappa)=p>0$.

We shall use the expression **0-ultrametric** (resp. **l-ultrametric**) as a convenient way of saying that $|\ |$ is ultrametric of type 1 (resp. type 2). In these cases the prime subfield of k is $\mathbb{Q}$ and the restriction of $|\ |$ to $\mathbb{Q}$ is trivial (resp. l-adic). In the latter case every l-adic expansion $a_n l^n + a_{n+1} l^{n+1} + \cdots (a_j \in \{0,1,\ldots,l-1\})$ converges to a limit in $\tilde{k}$ and therefore we can regard $\tilde{k} \supset \mathbb{Q}_l$. (This will be expanded on in (5.191).) It is in this sense that we use $k \cap \mathbb{Z}_l$ in the following lemma.

(5.170) LEMMA. *Let k be a valued field with* $\operatorname{char}(k)=0$ *(resp.* $\operatorname{char}(k)=p>0$*), let $q \in k$ (resp. $q \in \mathbb{Z}_p$), and let $a \in k$ with $|a|<1$. When k is l-ultrametric, write $L=|l|^{1/(l-1)}$. Define*

$$\lambda_q = \begin{cases} \min\{1, 1/|q|\} & \text{if } |\ | \text{ is 0-ultrametric}, \\ L/|q| & \text{if } |\ | \text{ is } l\text{-ultrametric and } |q|>1, \\ L & \text{if } |\ | \text{ is } l\text{-ultrametric}, \ |q|\leqslant 1, \ q \notin \mathbb{Z}_l, \\ 1 & \text{otherwise}, \end{cases}$$

(so $0<\lambda_q \leqslant 1$ and $\lambda_q = 1$ when $q \in \mathbb{Z}$), and let

$$E_a = \{q : \lambda_q > |a|\}.$$

Then (i) *E_a is as follows:*

$$E_a = \begin{cases} k & \text{if } |\ | \text{ is archimedean}, \\ \{q \in k : |qa| < 1\} & \text{if } |\ | \text{ is 0-ultrametric}, \\ \{q \in k : |qa| < L\} & \text{if } |\ | \text{ is } l\text{-ultrametric and } |a|<L, \\ k \cap \mathbb{Z}_l & \text{if } |\ | \text{ is } l\text{-ultrametric and } |a| \geqslant L, \\ \mathbb{Z}_p & \text{if } \operatorname{char}(k)=p>0. \end{cases}$$

Hence E_a is an additive group in each case.

(ii) *If $|\ |$ is ultrametric, then*

$$\left|\binom{q}{n}\right| \leqslant \lambda_q^{-n}, \qquad \forall n \in \mathbb{N},$$

and if $|\ |$ is archimedean, then

$$\left|\binom{q}{n}\right| \leqslant (-1)^n \binom{-|q|}{n}.$$

Proof. The routine verification of (i) is left to the reader. The ultrametric cases of (ii) follow directly from (5.158) and (5.165). For the archimedean case we write

$$\binom{q}{n} = (-1)^n\left(1-\frac{q+1}{1}\right)\left(1-\frac{q+1}{2}\right)\cdots\left(1-\frac{q+1}{n}\right)$$

and, by the triangle inequality,

$$\left|1-\frac{q+1}{j}\right| \leqslant \left|1-\frac{1}{j}\right| + \left|\frac{-q}{j}\right| = 1-\frac{1}{j}+\frac{|q|}{j}.$$

Hence

$$\left|\binom{q}{n}\right| \leqslant \prod_{j=1}^{n}\left(1-\frac{-|q|+1}{j}\right) = (-1)^n\binom{-|q|}{n}. \quad \blacksquare$$

Notice that if an ultrametric $|\ |$ is replaced by $|\ |^x$ for some positive rational x as in (5.79), then λ_q is replaced by $\lambda_q{}^x$ while E_a is unaltered.

(5.171) THEOREM. *Let k be a valued field with* $\mathrm{char}(k)=0$ (*resp.* $\mathrm{char}(k)=p>0$) *and $q\in k$ (resp. $q\in\mathbf{Z}_p$).*

(α) *For $a\in k$ with $|a|<\lambda_q$ the* **binomial series**

$$1+\binom{q}{1}a+\binom{q}{2}a^2+\cdots \tag{5.172}$$

converges absolutely; we denote its sum in $\tilde{k}$ by $(1+a)^q$. When $q\in\mathbf{Q}$, $(1+a)^q$ is in the set $\{(1+a)^q\}$ as defined in (5.76).

(β) *$q\mapsto(1+a)^q$ defines a group homomorphism $E_a\to\tilde{k}^*$, i.e., if $q,r\in E_a$, then $(1+a)^q\neq 0$ and*

$$(1+a)^q(1+a)^r=(1+a)^{q+r}.$$

(γ)

$$(1+a)^q(1+b)^q=((1+a)(1+b))^q=(1+a+b+ab)^q$$

provided

$$\lambda_q > \begin{cases} \max\{|a|,|b|\} & \textit{if } |\ | \textit{ is ultrametric},\\ |a|+|b|+|ab| & \textit{if } |\ | \textit{ is archimedean}.\end{cases}$$

(δ)

$$((1+a)^q)^r=(1+a)^{qr}$$

provided

$$|a| < \begin{cases} \lambda_q\lambda_r & \textit{if } |\ | \textit{ is ultrametric},\\ 1-2^{-1/|q|} & \textit{if } |\ | \textit{ is archimedean},\end{cases}$$

or simply $|a|<\lambda_q$ if $r\in\mathbf{Z}$.

Remarks. 1. When $q \in \mathbb{N}$, the series reduces to the usual finite formula of the binomial theorem and of course then the restriction $|a| < \lambda_q$ is not needed.

2. When $q \in \mathbb{Q}, \{(1+a)^q\}$ may contain more than one element. As will be explained later, this multivaluedness can also occur for irrational exponents. With a and q as specified in the theorem, we refer to the sum of the series as the **principal value**, and unless stated otherwise, $(1+a)^q$ will denote this principal value:

$$(1+a)^q = 1 + qa + \binom{q}{2}a^2 + \cdots.$$

In the corollary below we show that this is consistent with the definitions of principal value following (5.77) and (5.103). In particular, $1^q = 1$.

3. The validity of (γ) and (δ) will be extended later for certain fields, but the following example in $\mathbb{C}$ should serve as a caution. If $1 + a = (1+i)/\sqrt{2}$, then $|a| < 1$ and

$$\left((1+a)^8\right)^{1/8} = 1^{1/8} = 1 \neq (1+a)^1.$$

Proof. (α) and (β). Let $\rho = |a|/\lambda_q$. If $|\ |$ is ultrametric, then by (5.170)(ii),

$$\left|\binom{q}{n}a^n\right| \leqslant \rho^n;$$

hence by (5.66) the series is absolutely convergent by comparison with $1 + \rho + \rho^2 + \cdots$.

If $|\ |$ is archimedean, let $|a| < 1 - 1/h$, where $h \in \mathbb{N}$. Then for all $j \geqslant$ an appropriate N,

$$\left|1 - \frac{q+1}{j}\right| \leqslant 1 + \frac{|q+1|}{j} < 1 + \frac{1}{h},$$

and

$$\left|\binom{q}{n}\right| = \prod_{j=1}^{n}\left|1 - \frac{q+1}{j}\right| < M\left(1 + \frac{1}{h}\right)^n, \qquad \forall n \in \mathbb{N},$$

where

$$M = \max_{0 \leqslant j \leqslant N}\left\{\left|\binom{q}{j}\left(1 + \frac{1}{h}\right)^{-j}\right|\right\}.$$

Thus

$$\left|\binom{q}{n}a^n\right| < M\left(1 + \frac{1}{h}\right)^n\left(1 - \frac{1}{h}\right)^n = M\left(1 - \frac{1}{h^2}\right)^n$$

and again absolute convergence is assured by comparison with a convergent geometric series.

By (5.65) we have the cauchy product

$$(1+a)^q(1+a)^r = 1 + c_1a + c_2a^2 + \cdots$$

where

$$c_n = \binom{q}{0}\binom{r}{n} + \binom{q}{n}\binom{r}{n-1} + \cdots + \binom{q}{n}\binom{r}{0} = \binom{q+r}{n}$$

by (5.168). Hence

$$(1+a)^q(1+a)^r = (1+a)^{q+r}$$

and, in particular,

$$(1+a)^q(1+a)^{-q} = (1+a)^0 = 1 + 0a + \cdots = 1.$$

Therefore $(1+a)^q \neq 0$ and $q \mapsto (1+a)^q$ is a homomorphism $E_a \to \tilde{k}^*$.

It follows that if we write $f(q)$ for $(1+a)^q$ and if $q = um/n$, where $u \in \{1,-1\}$ and $m, n \in \mathbb{N}$, then

$$f(q)^{un} = f(unq) = f(m).$$

Since $f(m) = (1+a)^m$ has its usual meaning by the (finite) binomial theorem, this shows that $f(q) \in \{(1+a)^q\}$.

(γ) Suppose $|a| + |b| + |ab| < \lambda_q$; afterward we shall show how this hypothesis can be weakened to $\max\{|a|,|b|\} < \lambda_q$ in the ultrametric case. The expanded sum

$$\begin{aligned}(1+a+b+ab)^q &= \sum_j \binom{q}{j}(a(b+1)+b)^j \\ &= \sum_{j=0}^{\infty}\binom{q}{j}\sum_{n=0}^{j}\binom{j}{n}a^n(b+1)^n b^{j-n} \\ &= \sum_{j=0}^{\infty}\binom{q}{j}\sum_{n=0}^{j}\binom{j}{n}a^n\sum_{s=0}^{n}\binom{n}{s}b^{j-s}\end{aligned}$$

is absolutely convergent because the sum of the absolute values of the individual terms is at most

$$\sum_j\left|\binom{q}{j}\right|\sum_n\binom{j}{n}|a|^n\sum_s\binom{n}{s}|b|^{j-s} = \sum_j\left|\binom{q}{j}\right|(|a|+|b|+|ab|)^j,$$

which is convergent, as we saw in the proof of (α). By (5.64) we can rearrange terms:

$$\begin{aligned}(1+a+b+ab)^q &= \sum_{(n,m)\in\mathbb{N}\times\mathbb{N}} a^n b^m\left[\sum_s\binom{q}{n+s}\binom{n+s}{n}\binom{n}{s}\right], \\ &= \sum a^n b^m\binom{q}{n}\binom{q}{m} \qquad \text{by (5.152)}, \\ &= (1+a)^q(1+b)^q \qquad \text{by (5.65)}.\end{aligned}$$

In the ultrametric case we can improve the result as stated in the theorem by the following line of reasoning. If $h \in \mathbb{N}$ and we replace $|\ |$ by $|\ |^h$ (which is again an absolute value as we saw in (5.79)), then λ_q is replaced by $\lambda_q{}^h$, while the equation we wish to establish is not affected. If $|a|$ and $|b|$ are both strictly less than λ_q, then for sufficiently large h each of $|a|^h$, $|b|^h$, and $|ab|^h$ is less than $\lambda_q^h/3$; hence $|a|^h+|b|^h+|ab|^h<\lambda_q^h$. The result now follows from what has already been proved.

Similarly, to derive (δ) from (5.154), which arises from (5.153), it is sufficient to prove the absolute convergence of the expanded series

$$((1+a)^q)^r=\sum_{m\in\mathbb{M}}\binom{r}{m}\left[\sum_{j\in\mathbb{N}}\binom{q}{n}a^j\right]^m=\sum_m\binom{r}{m}\sum_{n=m}^{\infty}a^n\sum\binom{q}{j_1}\cdots\binom{q}{j_m},$$

where the last sum is over the set $J(m,n)$ of all $(j_1,\ldots,j_m)\in\mathbb{N}^m$ such that $j_1+\cdots+j_m=n$.

(5.173) LEMMA. *The set just defined has cardinality*

$$|J(m,n)|=\binom{n-1}{m-1}.$$

Proof of the lemma. To each $(j_1,\ldots,j_m)\in J(m,n)$ we associate the subset $\{j_1,j_1+j_2,\ldots,j_1+\cdots+j_{m-1}\}$ of $X=\{1,2,\ldots,n-1\}$. An easy argument, which we leave to the reader, shows that this defines a bijection between $J(m,n)$ and the set of $(m-1)$-element subsets of X, i.e., the set of combinations of X $m-1$ elements at a time. The lemma follows from (4.111). ■

Returning to the proof of (δ), suppose first that $|\ |$ is ultrametric. Then, by (5.170)(ii),

$$\left|\binom{q}{j_1}\cdots\binom{q}{j_m}\right|\leqslant\lambda_q^{-(j_1+\cdots+j_m)}=\lambda_q^{-n},$$

and, by the lemma just proved, the sum of the absolute values of the terms of the expanded series is at most

$$E=\sum_{m\in\mathbb{M}}\left|\binom{r}{m}\right|\sum_{n\geqslant m}|a|^n\lambda_q^{-n}\binom{n-1}{m-1}.$$

Put $\rho=|a|/\lambda_q$. Since $0\leqslant\rho<1$ and

$$\binom{-m}{j}=(-1)^j\binom{m+j-1}{m-1},$$

by (α)

$$(1-\rho)^{-m}=\sum_{j=0}^{\infty}\binom{m+j-1}{m-1}\rho^j=\sum_{n=m}^{\infty}\binom{n-1}{m-1}\rho^{n-m}$$

and therefore

$$E=\sum_{m\in\mathbb{M}}\left|\binom{r}{m}\right|\rho^m(1-\rho)^{-m}.$$

As we saw in the proof of (α), this is convergent when $\rho/(1-\rho)<\lambda_r$, which gives $|a|<\lambda_r\lambda_q/(1+\lambda_r)$.

Actually, it is sufficient to assume that $|a|<\lambda_q\lambda_r$, because then $\exists h\in\mathbb{N}$ $\ni |a|<\lambda_q\lambda_r/(1+1/h)$; hence

$$|a|^h<\frac{\lambda_q^h\lambda_r^h}{(1+1/h)^h}\leqslant\frac{\lambda_q^h\lambda_r^h}{1+\lambda_r^h}$$

since $(1+1/h)^h\geqslant 1+h(1/h)=2\geqslant 1+\lambda_r^h$. The result follows by replacing $|\;|$ by $|\;|^h$ as we did in the ultrametric case of (γ).

Finally, we prove (δ) when $|\;|$ is archimedean. By (5.170)(ii),

$$\sum_m\left|\binom{r}{m}\right|\sum_n|a|^n\sum\left|\binom{q}{j_1}\cdots\binom{q}{j_m}\right|$$

$$\leqslant\sum_m\left|\binom{r}{m}\right|\sum_n|a|^n\sum(-1)^{j_1}\binom{-|q|}{j_1}\cdots(-1)^{j_m}\binom{-|q|}{j_m}$$

$$\leqslant\sum_m(-1)^m\binom{-|r|}{m}\left[\sum_{j=1}^{\infty}(-|a|)^j\binom{-|q|}{j}\right]^m$$

$$=\sum_m(-1)^m\binom{-|r|}{m}\left[((1-|a|)^{-|q|}-1)\right]^m \qquad \text{by } (\alpha).$$

This converges if $(1-|a|)^{-|q|}-1<1$, i.e., if

$$(1-|a|)^{|q|}>\tfrac{1}{2}. \tag{5.174}$$

In (5.203) we shall see that this is equivalent to the inequality stated in the theorem. (Of course we must not use (δ) itself to establish this!) So until then, the condition on a in the archimedean case of (δ) is to be taken in the form (5.174). ■

(5.175) COROLLARY. $(1+a)^q$ *coincides with the principal value when defined in the real and ultrametric cases*:

(i) *If* $a,q\in\mathbb{R}$ *with* $|a|<1$, *then* $(1+a)^q>0$; *hence* $(1+a)^q=\sqrt[n]{(1+a)^m}$ *when* $q=m/n\in\mathbb{Q}$.

(ii) *If* $q=m/n$, *where* $m,n\in\mathbb{N}$, $f(X)=X^n-(1+a)^m$, *and* a *is an element of the ultrametric field* $k\ni|f(1)|<|f'(1)|^2$, *i.e.*, $|1-(1+a)^m|<|n|^2$, *and* $|a|<\lambda_q$, *then* $(1+a)^q$ *coincides with the unique root* ξ *of* f *satisfying* $|\xi-1|\leqslant|f(1)/f'(1)|$ (*cf.* 5.103).

Proof. (i) By part (β) of the theorem, $(1+a)^q=((1+a)^{q/2})^2$ is a nonzero square.

(ii) We first observe that the proof can be reduced to the case $m=1$. For $\lambda_{1/n}=\lambda_{m/n}$, $\lambda_m=1$ and $((1+a)^m)^{1/n}=(1+a)^q$ by (δ). With $q=1/n$, the assumption on a reads $|a|<|n|^2$. This implies the other assumption $|a|<\lambda_q$, since either $|n|=1$ and then $\lambda_q=1$, or $|\;|$ is l-ultrametric for some prime l

dividing n and then $|n|^2 \leqslant |l|^{1(l-1)}|n| = \lambda_q$. We wish to show that

$$|(1+a)^{1/n} - 1| \leqslant |a/n|,$$

i.e.,

$$\max_{j \geqslant 1} \left\{ \left| \binom{1/n}{j} a^j \right| \right\} \leqslant |a/n|.$$

If $|n| = 1$, then $|\binom{1/n}{j}| \leqslant 1$ by (5.164), whence the result. In the l-ultrametric case where $l|n$, by (5.160) and the obvious estimate $v_l(j!) \leqslant j-1$,

$$\left| \binom{1/n}{j} a^j \right| = |n|^{-j} |l|^{-(j-1)} |a|^j \leqslant |a/n|$$

since $|a| \leqslant |n|^2 \leqslant |nl|$. ■

(5.176) EXAMPLES

1. When $q = -1$ the theorem recapitulates the formula for geometric series: in every k we have $\lambda_{-1} = 1$, $\binom{-1}{n} = (-1)^n$, and

$$(1+a)^{-1} = 1 - a + a^2 - \cdots, \qquad |a| < 1,$$

or, writing $-a$ for a,

$$(1-a)^{-1} = 1 + a + a^2 + \ldots, \qquad |a| < 1.$$

Similarly, $\lambda_{-2} = 1$ (cf. 5.170), $\binom{-2}{n} = (-1)^n(n+1)$, and

$$(1-a)^{-2} = 1 + 2a + 3a^2 + \cdots, \qquad |a| < 1.$$

2. A value of $(a+b)^q$ is given by the binomial expansion of $a^q(1+b/a)^q$, provided that $|b/a| < \lambda_q$. For instance, in $\mathbb{R}$, by (5.175)(i),

$$\begin{aligned} \sqrt{11} &= \sqrt{9+2} = 3\sqrt{1+\tfrac{2}{9}} \\ &= 3\left[1 + \binom{\frac{1}{2}}{1}\frac{2}{9} + \binom{\frac{1}{2}}{2}\left(\frac{2}{9}\right)^2 + \cdots\right] \\ &= 3\left[1 + \frac{1}{9} - \frac{1}{2\cdot 9^2} + \frac{1}{2\cdot 9^3} + \cdots + \frac{(-1)^{n-1}(2n)!}{18^n(n!)^2(2n-1)} + \cdots\right]. \end{aligned}$$

Alternatively, since $\frac{1}{11} = 1 - \frac{10}{11}$,

$$\sqrt{11} = \left(1 - \tfrac{10}{11}\right)^{-1/2} = 1 + \tfrac{1}{2}\left(\tfrac{10}{11}\right) + \tfrac{3}{8}\left(\tfrac{10}{11}\right)^2 + \cdots.$$

Similarly the theorem does not apply directly to $(1+i)^{1/3}$ in $\mathbb{C}$. Yet $8^{1/3} = 2$ and therefore one of the values is given by

$$(1+i)^{1/3} = 2\left(1 + \frac{i-7}{8}\right)^{1/3} = 2\left[1 + \frac{1}{3}\frac{i-7}{8} - \frac{1}{9}\left(\frac{i-7}{8}\right)^2 + \cdots\right].$$

The process of root extraction in $\mathbb{C}$ will be clarified in (5.249).

3. In $\mathbb{Q}_2$, the binomial expansion

$$\sqrt{9} = (1+8)^{1/2} = 1 + 2^2 + 2^3 + \cdots$$

converges to the principal value $\sqrt{9} = -3 \in \mathbb{Q}_2$; cf. the remarks after (5.103).

4. If F is a field of characteristic $\neq 2$ then in $F((X))$,

$$(1-X+X^2)^{-1/2}=1-\tfrac{1}{2}(-X+X^2)+\tfrac{3}{8}(-X+X^2)^2+\cdots=1+\tfrac{1}{2}X-\tfrac{1}{8}X^2+\cdots.$$

The collecting of terms is justified since the series is X-adically absolutely convergent. (This follows from the fact that when we expand

$$\binom{\frac{1}{2}}{n}(-X+X^2)^n=\binom{\frac{1}{2}}{n}\left[\pm X^n\mp\binom{n}{1}X^{n+1}\pm\cdots+X^{2n}\right],$$

the sum of the absolute values of these $n+1$ terms is at most $(n+1)|X|^n$, and $1+2|X|+3|X|^2+\cdots$ is convergent by example 1.) Similarly, if $F=\mathbb{Q}(Z)$, Z an indeterminate, then $1/\sqrt{1-2ZX+X^2}=(1+a)^{-1/2}$, where $a=-2ZX+X^2$, has the expansion

$$1-\tfrac{1}{2}(-2ZX+X^2)+\tfrac{3}{8}(-2ZX+X^2)^2-\tfrac{5}{16}(-2ZX+X^2)^3+\tfrac{35}{128}(-2ZX+X^2)^4$$
$$-\cdots=1+P_1(Z)X+P_2(Z)X^2+\cdots,$$

where the coefficients

$$P_1(Z)=Z,\qquad P_2(Z)=-\tfrac{1}{2}+\tfrac{3}{2}Z^2,\qquad P_3(Z)=-\tfrac{3}{2}Z+\tfrac{5}{2}Z^3,$$
$$P_4(Z)=\tfrac{3}{8}-\tfrac{15}{4}Z^2+\tfrac{35}{8}Z^4,\qquad \cdots$$

are known as the **Legendre polynomials.**

5. If $k=\mathbb{Q}_3$ and $q=\frac{1}{3}$, then $\lambda_q=|3|^{3/2}$ and the expansion for $\sqrt[3]{1+a}$ is valid for all $a\in\mathbb{Q}_3$ satisfying $v_3(a)>3/2$, i.e., all $a\in 9\mathbb{Z}_3$. For example,

$$\sqrt[3]{10}=1+\tfrac{1}{3}\cdot 9-\tfrac{1}{9}\cdot 9^2+\cdots.$$

EXERCISES

1. Write out the binomial expansions up to the term in X^5:
 (i) $(1+X)^{3/2}$,
 (ii) $(2-3X)^{2/3}$,
 (iii) $(1-X)^{-3/4}$,
 (iv) $\left(\dfrac{a+X}{a-X}\right)^{1/3}$.

2. Show that the binomial series for $(1+57/64)^{1/2}$ converges to $\frac{11}{8}$ in $\mathbb{R}$ and in $\mathbb{Q}_3$, but to $-\frac{11}{8}$ in $\mathbb{Q}_{19}$.

3. If $a,b,c\in\mathbb{R}^{>}$ and $a^2+b^2=c^2$, then $a^3+b^3<c^3$.

4. If $x\in\mathbb{R}$ and $x\geqslant 1$, then $(1+1/x)^x<3$.

5. For integers m,n satisfying $0\leqslant m<n$,

$$\binom{n}{m+1}+\binom{n}{m+2}+\cdots+\binom{n}{n}$$
$$=2^{n-m-1}\binom{m}{m}+2^{n-m-2}\binom{m+1}{m}+\cdots+\binom{n-1}{m}.$$

6. Let $f(n)$ denote the number of meaningful ways of bracketing a product of n factors. Thus $f(4)=5$ since there are five ways of bracketing $xyzw$: $(xy)(zw)$, $(x(yz))w$, $((xy)z)w$, $x(y(zw))$, and $x((yz)w)$.

(i) For $n>1$, $f(n)=\Sigma_{m=1}^{n} f(m)f(n-m)$.

(ii) $(1-\sqrt{1-4X})/2 = X + X^2 + 3X^3 + 5X^4 + \cdots = \Sigma_{n\geqslant 1} f(n)X^n$. (*Hint*: If the series is denoted T, then $T-T^2=X$ by (i).)

(iii) Hence $f(n)=(1/(2n-1))\binom{2n-1}{n}$.

16. METRIC SPACES

Suppose $(q_1, q_2, \ldots)$ is a cauchy sequence of elements in the valued field k and $\lim q_i = q \in k$. It is natural to ask in what circumstances the following is true: If $\alpha \in k$ is such that all α^{q_i} are defined, then $(\alpha^{q_1}, \alpha^{q_2}, \ldots)$ is cauchy and

(5.177) $$\lim \alpha^{q_i} = \alpha^q.$$

For example, if $\lim(1, \frac{14}{10}, \frac{141}{100}, \ldots) = \sqrt{2}$, then it is true, as we shall see, that

$$\lim\left(\sqrt{3}, \sqrt{3}^{\,14/10}, \ldots\right) = \sqrt{3}^{\sqrt{2}},$$

where the value on the right side is principal and so can be calculated by the binomial expansion of $(1+(\sqrt{3}-1))^{\sqrt{2}}$.

However, the conclusion must not be assumed indiscriminately. For instance, in $\mathbb{Q}_5$, $\frac{1}{2} = 3 + 2\cdot 5 + 2\cdot 5^2 + \cdots$, but the sequence

$$(-1)^{3+2\cdot 5+\cdots+2\cdot 5^n} = -1$$

does not converge to a value of $(-1)^{1/2}$.

The situation becomes clearer and easier to deal with when abstracted. The property of the map $f\colon X \to \tilde{k}$ given by $q \mapsto \alpha^q$ (where $X \subset \mathbb{Q}$ is some domain appropriate to α) that is essential here is *uniform continuity*. To obtain a useful general setting to express this idea we make the following definition. We return to the question posed in (5.177) only in (5.200). It will be worthwhile to spend some time on the concepts we are about to develop since they are basic and are used in many other places.

(5.178) DEFINITION. A **metric space** is a set X with a map $d\colon X \times X \to \mathbb{R}$, called the **metric** or **distance function**, satisfying the axioms $(\forall a, b, c \in X)$

(M1) $d(a,b) \geqslant 0$ with equality iff $a=b$;
(M2) $d(a,b)=d(b,a)$; and
(M3) $d(a,b) \leqslant d(a,c)+d(c,b)$.

A field with absolute value $|\ |$ is a metric space if we put

$$d(a,b)=|a-b|.$$

(M3) is again called the triangle inequality. A subset Y of a metric space X with the metric restricted to $Y \times Y$ is again a metric space; it is called a **metric subspace** of X. In particular, any subset of a valued field is a metric space.

For instance the various absolute values on $\mathbb{Q}$ define different metrics. We carry over the terminology: There is the **ordinary metric**, the various **p-adic metrics**, and also the **trivial metric** given by $d(a,b) = \delta_{ab} = 0$ or 1. The subset $Y = \{a \in \mathbb{Q} : |a| \leqslant 1\}$ is a metric subspace in each case.

(5.179) DEFINITION. If X and Y are metric spaces and $a \in X$, a map f: $X \to Y$ is **continuous at a** if, $\forall h \in \mathbb{N}$, $\exists n \in \mathbb{N} \ni$

$$d(a,x) < 1/n \quad \Rightarrow \quad d(f(a), f(x)) < 1/h, \qquad \forall x \in X.$$

f is **continuous** if it is continuous at a, $\forall a \in X$.

We use the same symbol d to denote the metrics on X and Y, adding subscripts such as d_X only when necessary. An obviously equivalent definition is to require $\forall \varepsilon \in \mathbb{R}^{>}$ $\exists \delta \in \mathbb{R}^{>} \ni$

$$d(a,x) < \delta \quad \Rightarrow \quad d(f(a), f(x)) < \varepsilon.$$

In the definition, n depends on h and a (or δ depends on ε and a). Sometimes it is possible to choose n independently of a:

(5.180) DEFINITION. (i) A map f: $X \to Y$ between metric spaces is **uniformly continuous** if, $\forall h \in \mathbb{N}$, $\exists n \in \mathbb{N} \ni$

$$d(a,b) < 1/n \quad \Rightarrow \quad d(f(a), f(b)) < 1/h, \qquad \forall a, b \in X.$$

(A uniformly continuous map is continuous, but the converse is not generally true.)

(ii) f is **isometric**, or is an **isometry**, if

$$d(a,b) = d(f(a), f(b)), \qquad \forall a, b \in X.$$

An isometry is uniformly continuous and is injective because of (M1). (Some authors require an isometry to be bijective.) When f: $X \to Y$ is an isometry we often identify X with the metric subspace $f(X)$.

Notice that if f: $X \to Y$ is continuous or uniformly continuous or an isometry, then so is f': $X' \to Y'$, where $X' \subset X$, $f' = f|X'$, and $f(X') \subset Y' \subset Y$.

A **homeomorphism** between metric spaces X and Y is a bijection f: $X \to Y$ such that both f and f^{-1} are continuous. An example is a bijective isometry, but a homeomorphism is not necessarily an isometry. If $\mathbb{N}_1$ is the set $\mathbb{N}$ with trivial metric $d_1(a,b) = \delta_{ab}$ and $\mathbb{N}_2$ is $\mathbb{N}$ with the ordinary metric d_2, so $d_2(4,7) = d_2(7,4) = 3$, and so on, then the identity mapping f: $\mathbb{N}_1 \to \mathbb{N}_2$, $a \mapsto a$, is a continuous bijection (since $d_1(a,b) < \frac{1}{2} \Rightarrow a = b \Rightarrow d_2(a,b) < 1/m$, $\forall m$), but the inverse map f^{-1}: $\mathbb{N}_2 \to \mathbb{N}_1$ is not continuous and therefore f is not a homeomorphism. If $\mathbb{N}_3$ is $\mathbb{N}$ with the metric $d_3(a,b)=2\delta_{ab}$, then $a \mapsto a$ defines a homeomorphism $\mathbb{N}_1 \to \mathbb{N}_3$ that is not an isometry.

$\mathbb{R}$ or a subset of $\mathbb{R}$ such as the **unit interval** $\{\alpha \in \mathbb{R} : 0 \leqslant \alpha \leqslant 1\}$ when regarded as a metric space is assumed to have the ordinary metric $d(a,b)=|a-b|$. Similarly, $\mathbb{Q}_p$ and subsets such as $\mathbb{Z}_p$ are understood to have a p-adic metric

$$d(a,b)=c^{v_p(a-b)}.$$

Our results will not depend on the choice of c.

We generalize some earlier terminology to a metric space X. A sequence $(a_1, a_2, \ldots) \in X^{\mathbb{N}}$ is **cauchy** if, $\forall h \in \mathbb{N}$, $\exists N \ni$

$$d(a_i, a_j) < 1/h, \qquad \forall i, j \geqslant N.$$

For instance, the constant sequence $(a, a, \ldots)$ is cauchy. As a replacement for the notion that two sequences differ by a null sequence (in general X has no 0 or subtraction), we define two cauchy sequences $(a_1, \ldots)$ and $(b_1, \ldots)$ to be **equivalent** if, $\forall h \in \mathbb{N}$, $\exists N \ni d(a_i, b_i) < 1/h$, $\forall i \geqslant N$. This is clearly an equivalence relation and we let $\tilde{X}$ denote the set of equivalence classes of cauchy sequences.

If $(a_1, a_2, \ldots)$ is cauchy in X and is equivalent to the constant sequence $(a, a, \ldots)$ so, $\forall h \in \mathbb{N}$, $\exists N \ni d(a_i, a) < 1/h$, $\forall i \geqslant N$, then we write

$$\lim a_i = a$$

and we say that the sequence $(a_1, a_2, \ldots)$ **converges to a**. Notice that the limit is unique: If $\lim a_i = b$, then $(a, a, \ldots)$ is equivalent to $(b, b, \ldots)$; hence $d(a,b) < 1/h$ $\forall h$ and therefore $a = b$. (*Exercise*: If $\lim a_i = a$, then the cauchy sequence $(b_1, b_2, \ldots)$ converges to a iff $(b_1, \ldots)$ is equivalent to $(a_1, \ldots)$.)

(5.181) PROPOSITION. *Let $f\colon X \to Y$ be a map between metric spaces and let $a \in X$. Then f is continuous at a iff for every cauchy sequence $(a_1, a_2, \ldots)$ in X with limit a, $(f(a_1), f(a_2), \ldots)$ is cauchy in Y, and* $\lim f(a_i) = f(a)$.

Proof. First let f be continuous at a, let $\lim a_i = a$, and let $h \in \mathbb{N}$. Then $\exists n \ni d(a, a_i) < 1/n \Rightarrow d(f(a), f(a_i)) < 1/h$, and in turn $\exists N \ni d(a, a_i) < 1/n$ $\forall i \geqslant N$.

Conversely, let f satisfy the latter condition of the lemma and let $h \in \mathbb{N}$. We want to show that $\exists n \ni$

$$d(a,x) < 1/n \quad \Rightarrow \quad d(f(a), f(x)) < 1/h.$$

Suppose this is not possible. Then $\forall n$ choose an $a_n \ni d(a, a_n) < 1/n$ but $d(f(a), f(a_n)) \geqslant 1/h$. (This half of the proposition depends on the axiom of choice.) Then $(a_1, a_2, \ldots)$ is cauchy with limit a, but the sequence $f(a_n)$ does not have limit $f(a)$—the required contradiction. ∎

Caution. If $(a_1,\ldots)$ is cauchy in X but $\lim a_i \notin X$, it can happen that for a continuous $f\colon X \to Y, (f(a_1),\ldots)$ is not cauchy. For example, if X is the metric subspace of $\mathbb{R}$ consisting of the points $\{a_1 = 1, a_2 = 1/2,\ldots, a_n = 1/n,\ldots\}$, then the map $f\colon X \to \mathbb{R}$ given by $f(1/n) = n$ is continuous; the sequence $(a_1, a_2,\ldots)$ is cauchy in X but "its limit 0 is missing from X," and $(f(a_1),\ldots) = (1,2,\ldots)$ is not cauchy in $\mathbb{R}$. However, this phenomenon does not occur when the continuity is uniform:

(5.182) PROPOSITION. *Let $f\colon X \to Y$ be a uniformly continuous map between metric spaces and let $(a_1, a_2,\ldots)$ be cauchy in X. Then*

(i) *$(f(a_1), f(a_2),\ldots)$ is cauchy in Y;*

(ii) *if $(b_1,\ldots)$ is another cauchy sequence in X that is equivalent to $(a_1,\ldots)$, then $(f(b_1),\ldots)$ is equivalent to $(f(a_1),\ldots)$.*

Proof. Given $h \in \mathbb{N}$, $\exists n \ni d(a, a') < 1/n \Rightarrow d(f(a), f(a')) < 1/h$.

(i) $\exists n \ni d(a_i, a_j) < 1/n \;\forall i, j \geqslant N$.

(ii) $\exists M \ni d(a_i, b_i) < 1/n \;\forall i \geqslant M$. ■

EXERCISE

Let (X, d) be a metric space. Then $d'(x, y) = d(x, y)/(1 + d(x, y))$ is another metric on X (a so-called **bounded metric**: $d'(x, y) < 1 \;\forall x, y$). If X' denotes the corresponding metric space, then the identity map $X \to X'$ is a homeomorphism.

17. COMPLETE METRIC SPACES

As defined in the last section, $\tilde{X}$ denotes the set of equivalence classes of cauchy sequences. The map $\mu_X\colon X \to \tilde{X}$ assigning to an element a of X the class of the constant sequence $(a, a,\ldots)$ is injective by (M1). The proofs of the following are very similar to the analogous proofs for valued fields and are left to the reader.

If the element α of $\tilde{X}$ is represented by the cauchy sequence $(a_1,\ldots)$, in which case we write $\alpha = \lim a_i$, and if similarly $\beta = \lim b_i$, then

$$d(\alpha, \beta) = \lim d(a_i, b_i)$$

gives a well-defined metric on $\tilde{X}$ and $\mu = \mu_X$ is an isometry. The cauchy convergence criterion is valid: If $(a_1,\ldots)$ is cauchy in X and $\alpha \in \tilde{X}$, then $\alpha = \lim a_i$ iff, $\forall h \in \mathbb{N}$, $\exists N \ni d(\alpha, \mu(a_n)) < 1/h$, $\forall n \geqslant N$. Normally we identify X as a subspace of $\tilde{X}$ using $a = \mu(a)$.

Moreover, $\tilde{X}$ is complete, i.e., $\mu_{\tilde{X}}$ is bijective. The proof can be copied from that of (5.41) replacing $|a - b|$ with $d(a, b)$. This establishes the existence part of the next proposition.

When X is a field k with absolute value $|\;|$ and the metric $d(a, b) = |a - b|$, then $\tilde{X}$ is our previously constructed $\tilde{k}$. With the extra assumption of the field structure we were able to obtain the additional conclusion that $\tilde{k}$ is a field (and the equivalence relation between cauchy sequences was expressible as the congruence relation *modulo null sequences*).

(5.183) PROPOSITION. *For each metric space X there exists an isometry μ_X: $X \to \tilde{X}$ into a complete metric space with the following universal property. If f: $X \to Y$ is a uniformly continuous map of metric spaces then there is a unique uniformly continuous map $\tilde{f}$: $\tilde{X} \to \tilde{Y}$ making*

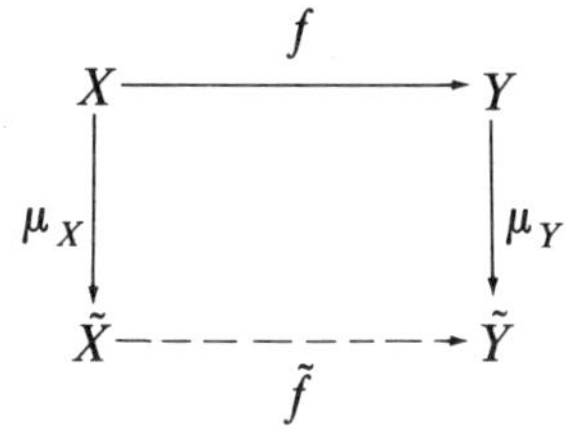

commutative. If f is an isometry so is $\tilde{f}$.
(It is customary to indicate given maps by solid arrows and maps whose existence is not yet proved by dotted arrows.)

Proof. Let $\alpha \in \tilde{X}$ and let $(a_1,\ldots)$ be a cauchy sequence in X representing α. By (5.182)(i), $(f(a_1),\ldots)$ is cauchy in Y and we define $\tilde{f}(\alpha) = \lim f(a_i) \in \tilde{Y}$. By (5.182)(ii), this is well defined.

If $a \in X$, then $\mu_X(a)$ is represented by $(a, a,\ldots)$ and similarly $\mu_Y(f(a))$ is represented by $(f(a), f(a),\ldots)$. Thus $\tilde{f}\mu_X(a) = \mu_Y f(a)$.

We now prove the uniform continuity of $\tilde{f}$. Let $h \in \mathbb{N}$. Then, since f is uniformly continuous, $\exists n \ni \forall a, b \in X$

$$d(a,b) < 1/n \qquad \Rightarrow \qquad d(f(a), f(b)) < 1/h.$$

As before, let $\alpha, \beta \in \tilde{X}$ be represented by $(a_1,\ldots),(b_1,\ldots)$. Now $d(\alpha,\beta) < 1/n$ means that $\lim d(a_i, b_i) < 1/n$ and this implies that $\exists N \ni d(a_i, b_i) < 1/n$, $\forall i \geqslant N$. Then $d(f(a_i), f(b_i)) < 1/h$. Hence $\lim d(f(a_i), f(b_i)) = d(\tilde{f}(\alpha), \tilde{f}(\beta)) \leqslant 1/h$, which gives the result.

$\tilde{f}$ is unique since it is in fact the only continuous map making the diagram commute: Every $\alpha \in \tilde{X}$ is represented by a cauchy sequence $(a_1,\ldots)$ in X, and in order that $\tilde{f}$ be continuous at α, by (5.181) applied to $\tilde{f}$: $\tilde{X} \to \tilde{Y}$ (with X, Y identified as subspaces of $\tilde{X}, \tilde{Y}$, respectively), we must have $\tilde{f}(\alpha) = \tilde{f}(\lim a_i) = \lim f(a_i)$.

Finally, if f is an isometry, then

$$d\big(\tilde{f}(\alpha), \tilde{f}(\beta)\big) = \lim d(f(a_i), f(b_i)) = \lim d(a_i, b_i) = d(\alpha, \beta). \quad ■$$

When Y is complete the universal property reduces to the situation

indicated in the diagram

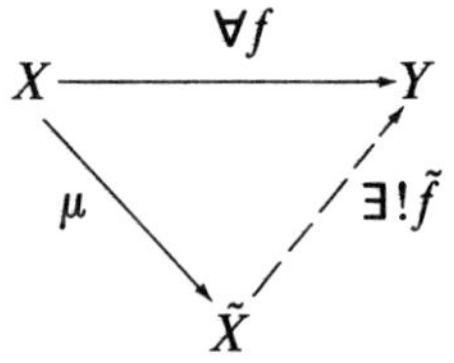

and since we usually regard $X \subset \tilde{X}$, we express this as follows: f has a unique uniformly continuous extension to $\tilde{X}$; it is given by

$$\tilde{f}(\alpha) = \lim f(a_i),$$

where $(a_1, \ldots)$ is cauchy in X and $\lim a_i = \alpha$. The space $\tilde{X}$ (more precisely, μ: $X \to \tilde{X}$) is called the **completion** of X. As usual it is characterized by a universal property:

(5.184) COROLLARY. *Let ν: $X \to Z$ be an isometry into a complete metric space with the universal property that for every isometry f: $X \to Y$ into a complete metric space there is a unique isometry $\bar{f}$: $Z \to Y \ni \bar{f}\nu = f$. Then there is a unique bijective isometry h: $\tilde{X} \to Z$, namely, $h = \tilde{\nu}$, for which the following diagram commutes*:

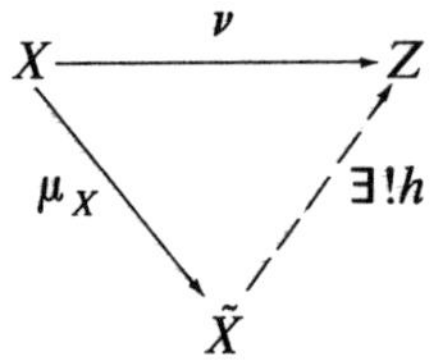

Proof. The universal property of $\tilde{X}$ applied to ν gives an isometry $\tilde{\nu}$: $\tilde{X} \to Z$, while that of Z applied to μ_X gives an isometry $\bar{\mu}_X$: $Z \to \tilde{X}$. Then $\tilde{\nu}\bar{\mu}_X$: $Z \to Z$ is an isometry (cf. A12.1) making the large, outer triangle of the accompanying diagram commute:

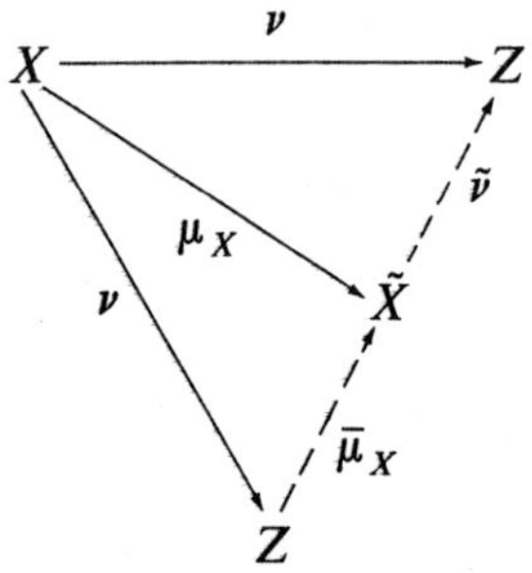

However 1_Z also does this: $1_Z\nu = \nu$, and the uniqueness (of $\bar{f}$ for a given f) implies that $\tilde{\nu}\bar{\mu}_X = 1_Z$. Similarly, $\bar{\mu}_X\tilde{\nu} = 1_X$, and therefore $\tilde{\nu}$ is a bijective isometry. h is unique since it is the only continuous map making the diagram of the corollary commute. ■

We extend the notation of A10.4 to all metric spaces:

> If X is a metric space, $a \in X$ and $r \in \mathbb{R}^{>}$,
>
> $$D_r(a) = \{x \in X: d(a,x) < r\},$$
>
> $$V_r(a) = \{x \in X: d(a,x) \leqslant r\}.$$

(5.185) DEFINITION. Let Y be a subset of a metric space X.

(i) The **closure** of Y (in X), denoted $\bar{Y}$, consists of all $x \in X \ni$, $\forall h \in \mathbb{N}$, $\exists y \in Y \ni d(x,y) < 1/h$ (i.e., there are points of Y arbitrarily close to x).

(ii) Y is **closed** (in X) if $\bar{Y} = Y$.

(iii) Y is **open** (in X) if its complement $X \setminus Y$ is closed.

(iv) Y is **dense** in X if $\bar{Y} = X$.

(5.186) REMARKS AND EXAMPLES

1. $\bar{Y} \supset Y$, for if $y \in Y$ we can then take $y = x$ $\forall h$ in (i). Thus $\bar{X} = X$, while at the other extreme $\bar{\varnothing} = \varnothing$. Hence X and $\varnothing$ are both open and closed. It is also clear that $Y \subset Z \Rightarrow \bar{Y} \subset \bar{Z}$. (*Exercise*: $\bar{\bar{Y}} = \bar{Y}$—the closure is closed.)

2. If $\{Y_i : i \in I\}$ is a collection of closed subsets, then $Y = \bigcap Y_i$ is closed. To see this, note that if $x \notin Y$ then $x \notin Y_i = \bar{Y}_i$ for some i; hence $\exists h \ni$ no $y \in Y_i$, in particular no $y \in Y$, satisfies $d(x,y) < 1/h$. Thus $x \notin \bar{Y}$, hence $\bar{Y} \subset Y$, and therefore $\bar{Y} = Y$. It follows that $\bar{Y}$ is the unique smallest closed set containing Y, just as the subring (or vector subspace,...) generated by a subset Y is the unique smallest subring $\supset Y$.

It follows from DeMorgan's law

$$X \setminus \left(\bigcap Y_i\right) = \bigcup \left(X \setminus Y_i\right)$$

that a union of open sets is open.

3. A subset Y of X is closed, by definition, iff $\forall x \in X \setminus Y$, $D_r(x) \cap Y = \varnothing$ for all sufficiently small r (depending on x). Turning this around, a subset U of X is open iff $\forall x \in U$, $D_r(x) \subset U$ for some r. For instance, every open disc $D_s(a)$ is indeed open since if $x \in D_s(a)$, then $D_r(x) \subset D_s(a)$, where $r = s - d(a,x)$. Combining this with (2) we see that a set U is open iff it is a union of sets of the form $D_r(x)$.

4. If the subset Y of X is regarded as a metric subspace, then the open discs of Y are, in a self-explanatory notation,

$$D_r^Y(a) = D_r^X(a) \cap Y.$$

Taking unions, we see that the open sets of Y are precisely sets of the form $U \cap Y$, where U is open in X. Moreover, by DeMorgan's laws, the closed sets are precisely those sets of the form $V \cap Y$, V closed in X.

5. Every closed disc $V_r(a)$ is in fact closed, because $x \notin V_r(a) \Rightarrow d(a,x) = r+s$ for some $s \in \mathbb{R}^>$ and $D_s(x) \cap V_r(a) = \varnothing$. Thus the complement of $V_r(a)$ is a union of open discs, and so is open. (*Exercise*: In $\mathbb{C}$, show that the closed rectangle $\{\alpha = a+ib : a_1 \leqslant a \leqslant a_2, b_1 \leqslant b \leqslant b_2\}$ is closed.)

6. The closure of the union $Y = Y_1 \cup \cdots \cup Y_n$ of finitely many sets is given by

$$\overline{Y} = \overline{Y}_1 \cup \cdots \cup \overline{Y}_n,$$

because $Y_i \subset Y$, and so $\overline{Y}_i \subset \overline{Y}$. Conversely, if $x \notin \overline{Y}_1 \cup \cdots \cup \overline{Y}_n$ then $\forall i\ \exists r_i \ni D_{r_i}(x) \cap Y_i = \varnothing$, and therefore $D_r(x) \cap Y = \varnothing$, where $r = \min\{r_1,\ldots,r_n\}$. Thus a union of finitely many closed sets is closed; by DeMorgan's laws, then, an intersection of finitely many open sets is open. In particular, since a single point of the metric space X obviously comprises a closed set, every finite subset of X is closed: $Y \neq \overline{Y} \Rightarrow Y$ is infinite. (*Exercise*: The closure of $\{\alpha : 0 < \alpha \leqslant 1\}$ in $\mathbb{R}$ is $\{\alpha : 0 \leqslant \alpha \leqslant 1\}$. Earlier we called the latter set the unit interval; it is sometimes referred to as the *closed* unit interval to emphasize that it contains 0 and 1.)

7. If a is an element of the ultrametric field k, then $D_r(a)$ and $V_r(a)$ are both open and closed (and therefore $V_r(a)$ need not be the closure of $D_r(a)$), for, if c is in the closure of $D_r(a)$, then $\exists b \in D_r(a) \ni |b-c| < r$; hence $|a-c| \leqslant \max\{|a-b|, |b-c|\} < r$, so $c \in D_r(a)$. Similarly, by A10.4,

$$V_r(a) = \bigcup \{D_r(b) : b \in V_r(a)\}$$

is open. (*Exercise*: In $\mathbb{Q}$ with the ordinary metric, $D_r(a)$ is both open and closed iff r is irrational.)

8. If X is a nonempty subset of $\mathbb{R}$ that is bounded above, then $M = \sup(X)$ exists, as we saw in (5.32). If X is closed, then $M \in X$. Similarly, if X is nonempty, bounded below, and closed, then X contains $\inf(X)$.

9. By A10.1 there are rationals arbitrarily close to a given real number; hence $\mathbb{Q}$ is dense in $\mathbb{R}$. Also $\mathbb{Q}$ is dense in each $\mathbb{Q}_p$ because a given $\alpha = a_n p^n + a_{n+1} p^{n+1} + \cdots \in \mathbb{Q}_p$ (where $a_i \in \{0,1,\ldots,p-1\}$, say) can be closely approximated by rationals $a_n p^n + \cdots + a_N p^N$. Similarly, $F(X)$ is dense in $F((X))$.

In fact, by the third corollary of the following proposition, a metric space is dense in its completion. However, it should be noted that this proposition depends on the axiom of choice, whereas none of the statements in 1–9 uses the axiom. We leave it as an exercise to write out direct proofs of the first two corollaries without appeal to the axiom.

(5.187) PROPOSITION. *If Y is a subset of the metric space X, then $\overline{Y}$ consists of all limits in X of cauchy sequences $(y_1, y_2, \ldots)$ in Y.*

Proof. If $x \in \overline{Y}$, then for $h = 1,2,\ldots$ we can choose $y_h \in Y$ with $d(x, y_h) < 1/h$. Then $(y_1, y_2, \ldots)$ is cauchy with limit x. Conversely, if $x = \lim y_i$, where $(y_1, \ldots)$ is cauchy in Y, then $\forall h\ \exists N \ni d(x, y_i) < 1/h$, $\forall i \geqslant N$. Hence $x \in \overline{Y}$. ∎

(5.188) COROLLARY. *Continuous maps that agree on a dense subset agree everywhere: If f, g: $X \to Z$ are continuous maps between metric spaces, and if Y is a dense subset of $X \ni f(y) = g(y)$ $\forall y \in Y$, then $f = g$.*

Proof. If $x \in X$, then $x = \lim y_i$ for some cauchy sequence $(y_1, \ldots)$ in Y. By (5.181),

$$f(x) = \lim f(y_i) = \lim g(y_i) = g(x). \quad \blacksquare$$

Here is a particular case worth pointing out.

(5.189) COROLLARY. *A continuous map f: $X \to Z$ between metric spaces that is constant on a dense subset Y is constant everywhere. That is, if $f(y) = z$ for some fixed $z \in Z$ and all $y \in Y$, then $f(x) = z$ for all $x \in X$.*

This results from the fact that the constant map g: $X \to Z$ given by $g(x) = z$ is continuous.

(5.190) COROLLARY. *Let Y be a subspace of the metric space X and regard $X \subset \tilde{X}$ canonically by means of μ_X. Then $\overline{X} = \tilde{X}$ and $\overline{Y}$ can be identified with $\tilde{Y}$.*

Proof. By construction, every element of $\tilde{X}$ is a limit of a cauchy sequence in X, so $\overline{X} = \tilde{X}$. The inclusion map f: $Y \to \tilde{X}$ is an isometry and therefore $\tilde{f}$: $\tilde{Y} \to \tilde{X}$ is an isometry. Clearly $\operatorname{Im}(\tilde{f}) = \overline{Y}$. $\blacksquare$

(5.191) EXAMPLES

1. If $\alpha < \beta$ are real numbers and Y is any one of the four sets $\{q \in \mathbb{Q} : \alpha <_1 q <_2 \beta\}$, where $<_i$ is either $<$ or $\leqslant$, then $\overline{Y} = \{\gamma \in \mathbb{R} : \alpha \leqslant \gamma \leqslant \beta\}$ can be identified with the completion of Y in the ordinary metric. Similarly the completion of $\{q \in \mathbb{Q} : \alpha <_1 q\}$ with ordinary metric is $\{\gamma \in \mathbb{R} : \alpha \leqslant \gamma\}$.

2. $\mathbb{Z}$ as a subspace of $(\mathbb{R}, |\ |)$ is complete: It is closed in $\mathbb{R}$ because $d(a, b) \geqslant 1$ for integers $a \neq b$, and all cauchy sequences in $\mathbb{Z}$ are eventually constant.

3. The completion of $\mathbb{Z}$ with the p-adic metric is the ring $\mathbb{Z}_p$ of p-adic integers. Also the closure of $\mathbb{N}$ is $\mathbb{Z}_p$, because every p-adic integer $a_0 + a_1 p + \cdots$ is a limit of natural numbers $a_0 + \cdots + a_n p^n + p^{n+1}$; conversely the limit α of a cauchy sequence $(\alpha_1, \alpha_2, \ldots)$ of p-adic integers is again in $\mathbb{Z}_p$ since $v(\alpha) = \lim v(\alpha_i) \geqslant 0$. Similarly, the closure of $Y = \{q \in \mathbb{Q} : v_p(q) \geqslant c\}$ in $\mathbb{Q}_p$ is $\tilde{Y} = \{\alpha \in \mathbb{Q}_p : v_p(\alpha) \geqslant c\}$.

4. Let k be a field that is complete with respect to the absolute value $|\ |$ and of characteristic 0.

(i) If $|\ |$ restricts to the ordinary absolute value on $\mathbb{Q}$, then k contains $\mathbb{R}$ as a subfield and as a metric subspace: The inclusion map f: $\mathbb{Q} \to k$ is an isometry that extends to an isometry $\tilde{f}$: $\mathbb{R} \to k$.

(ii) Similarly if $|\ |$ is l-ultrametric in the sense defined just before (5.170), say $|l| = c < 1$, then k contains $\mathbb{Q}_l$ isometrically as a subfield where the metric on $\mathbb{Q}_l$ is given by $|a| = c^{v(a)}$.

However, if $|\ |$ restricts to the trivial absolute value on $\mathbb{Q}$, then $\mathbb{Q}$ is already complete.

(5.192) PROPOSITION. *Let A be a nonzero additive subgroup of $\mathbb{R}$; define*

$$\mu = \text{g.l.b.}\{\alpha \in A : \alpha > 0\}.$$

If $\mu = 0$, then A is dense in $\mathbb{R}$ ($\bar{A} = \mathbb{R}$), while if $\mu > 0$ then $A = \mathbb{Z}\mu$. (In the second case A is called a **discrete subgroup** *of $\mathbb{R}$.)*

Proof. Suppose first that $\mu = 0$. Given $h \in \mathbb{N}$, $\exists \alpha \in A \ni 0 < \alpha < 1/h$ so that, for any $\beta \in \mathbb{R}, |\beta - n\alpha| < 1/h$, where $n = \lfloor \beta/\alpha \rfloor$. This means that A is dense in $\mathbb{R}$.

Second, suppose that $\mu > 0$. If $\alpha \in A$ and $n = \lfloor \alpha/\mu \rfloor$, then $\alpha - n\mu = \beta \in A$ and $0 \leqslant \beta < \mu$. Hence $\beta = 0$ and $A \subset \mathbb{Z}\mu$. By definition of μ, $\exists \alpha \in A$ satisfying $\mu \leqslant \alpha < 2\mu$; hence $\mu = \alpha$. Thus $\mu \in A$ and $A = \mathbb{Z}\mu$. ■

EXERCISES

1. Let p be a prime, a a natural number not divisible by p, and b any integer. Then

$$\{x \in \mathbb{N} : x \equiv b \bmod a\}$$

is dense in $\mathbb{Z}_p$.

2. The completion of $k = \mathbb{Q}(i)$ (the quotient field of the domain of Gauss integers) with the complex absolute value $|a + bi| = \sqrt{a^2 + b^2}$ can be identified with $\mathbb{C}$.

3. Let $\alpha \in \mathbb{R}^*$ and $S = \{r\alpha + is\alpha : r, s \in \mathbb{Q}\}$. Then S is dense in $\mathbb{C}$. The distances between distinct points in S are all irrational iff α^2 is not of the form $u^2 + v^2$ for some $u, v \in \mathbb{Q}$. Give an example of such an α.

18. UNIFORM CONVERGENCE

We wish to show that in a suitable sense the sum of the binomial series (5.172) for $(1 + a)^q$ is uniformly continuous in q (and in a). This will be used to define α^β for all $\alpha \in \mathbb{R}^>$ and $\beta \in \mathbb{R}$.

(5.193) DEFINITION. Let X be a set and Y a metric space. A sequence of functions $g_n: X \to Y$, $n \in \mathbb{N}$, **converges** to the function $g: X \to Y$ if, $\forall x \in X$, the sequence $(g_1(x), \ldots)$ is cauchy with limit $g(x)$. That is, $\forall h \in \mathbb{N}$, $\exists N \ni$

$$d(g_n(x), g(x)) < 1/h, \qquad \forall n \geqslant N.$$

The convergence is **uniform** if N can be chosen independently of x.

Here is a basic example. Let k be a valued field, $X = \{x \in k : |x| < 1\}$, and $g_n: X \to k$ be the nth partial sum of the geometric series: for $x \in X$,

$$g_n(x) = 1 + x + \cdots + x^{n-1}.$$

The sequence g_n converges to $g\colon X \to k$, where $g(x) = 1/(1-x)$, but not uniformly (unless $|\ |$ is trivial). For

$$d(g_n(x), g(x)) = |g_n(x) - g(x)| = \left|\frac{x^n}{1-x}\right| \leqslant \frac{|x|^N}{|1-x|} \qquad \text{for} \quad n \geqslant N.$$

This cannot be made small uniformly in x if $|1-x|$ can be made arbitrarily small: The closer x is to 1, the larger N must be.

However, if $\rho \in \mathbb{R}$, $0 < \rho < 1$, and X is replaced by $X' = \{x \in k : |x| \leqslant \rho\}$, then the convergence of g_n to g is uniform since now we can pick N so that

$$\frac{|x|^N}{|1-x|} \leqslant \frac{|x|^N}{|1-\rho|} < 1/h, \qquad \forall x \in X'.$$

This argument can be generalized to give the following comparison test known as the **Weierstrass *M*-test**. In general, an infinite series is said to **converge uniformly** if the sequence of partial sums does so in k.

(5.194) PROPOSITION. *Let X be a set, k a valued field, $u_1, u_2, \ldots$ a sequence of functions $X \to k$, and $M_1, M_2, \ldots$ a sequence of real numbers such that*

$$|u_n(x)| \leqslant M_n, \qquad \forall x \in X.$$

If $M_1 + M_2 + \cdots$ converges, then $u_1 + u_2 + \cdots$ converges uniformly on X (to a sum $g\colon X \to \tilde{k}$).

Proof. By (5.66), $u_1(x) + u_2(x) + \cdots$ is absolutely convergent for each $x \in X$, say to $g(x) \in \tilde{k}$. By (5.61),

$$\begin{aligned} |u_1(x) + \cdots + u_n(x) - g(x)| &\leqslant |u_{n+1}(x)| + |u_{n+2}(x)| + \cdots \\ &\leqslant M_{n+1} + M_{n+2} + \cdots. \end{aligned}$$

Given $h \in \mathbb{N}$, $\exists N \ni M_{n+1} + M_{n+2} + \cdots \leqslant 1/h$ $\forall n \geqslant N$, and the same N works uniformly $\forall x$. ■

(5.195) COROLLARY. *Let k be a valued field, $c \in k$, s a real number satisfying $0 \leqslant s < |c|$, $f = a_0 + a_1 T + \cdots$ a power series over k, and suppose f converges (in $\tilde{k}$) when $T = c$. Then the real series $g = \Sigma |a_n| s^n$ converges and consequently f converges absolutely and uniformly on $X = \{a \in k : |a| \leqslant s\}$.*

Proof. Since the sequence $a_n c^n$ is null, it is bounded in absolute value, say $|a_n c^n| < C$ $\forall n$. Then $|a_n| s^n < C t^n$, where $t = s/|c|$ and the convergence of g follows from (5.66) by comparison with $1 + t + t^2 + \cdots$. The rest follows by the Weierstrass M-test, with $M_n = |a_{n-1}| s^{n-1}$. ■

This result permits us to make the following definition. The **radius of convergence** of the power series f is

$$r=\begin{cases}\infty & \text{if } f \text{ converges } \forall a \in k,\\ \text{l.u.b. } \{s \in \mathbb{R}^{\geqslant} : |a| \leqslant s \Rightarrow f(a) \text{ converges}\}.\end{cases}$$

For instance, by (5.26) the radius of convergence of the geometric series $1+T+T^2+\cdots$ is 1 for every k.

With the usual conventions concerning ∞ we have

(5.196) COROLLARY. *For f, r as above and $a \in k$,*

$$|a|<r \quad \Rightarrow \quad f(a) \textit{ converges}, \qquad |a|>r \quad \Rightarrow \quad f(a) \textit{ diverges}.$$

Using (5.47) it is easy to see that if $|\ |$ is not discrete and is not trivial, then these properties characterize r. However, this is not quite the case when $|\ |$ is discrete. For instance when $k=\mathbb{Q}_p$, $f=1+T+T^2+\cdots$ and s is any number satisfying $|p| \leqslant s \leqslant 1$, then

$$|a|<s \quad \Rightarrow \quad f(a) \text{ converges}, \qquad |a|>s \quad \Rightarrow \quad f(a) \text{ diverges}.$$

When $|a|=r$, a is said to be on the **circle of convergence**, and then $f(a)$ may converge or diverge depending on the particular case. When k is ultrametric the series either converges for all a on this "circle" or diverges for all a. (If $|a|=|b|=r$, then $a=bu$, where $|u|=1$ and $f(a)$ converges $\Leftrightarrow$ the sequence $|a_n a^n|=|a_n b^n|$ is null $\Leftrightarrow$ $f(b)$ converges. However, the archimedean case is more complicated.)

For a series of the form

$$f(T)=a_0+a_1(T-d)+a_2(T-d)^2+\cdots$$

there is convergence when $|a-d|<r$ and divergence when $|a-d|>r$. It is helpful to visualize the region of convergence as the interior of a disc possibly together with part of the circle. (See Figure 5.16.) In the case of $\mathbb{R}$ the disc is reduced to a line segment, and the circle to the end points of the segment (possibly "at infinity")—hence the term **interval of convergence** in this case.

The main point about uniform convergence is the following. If X, Y are metric spaces and $g_n\colon X \to Y$ are continuous maps (even uniformly continuous maps) converging to g, it is only when this convergence is uniform that we can conclude that g is continuous. For instance, let $X=Y=\mathbb{R}^{\geqslant}$ and let $g_n(x)=x^{1/n}$. Then the sequence g_n converges to g, where

$$g(x)=1-\delta_{0x}=0 \quad \text{or} \quad 1.$$

(The proof is left as an exercise.) Each of the g_n is continuous, as we shall see in (5.202), but g is certainly not continuous.

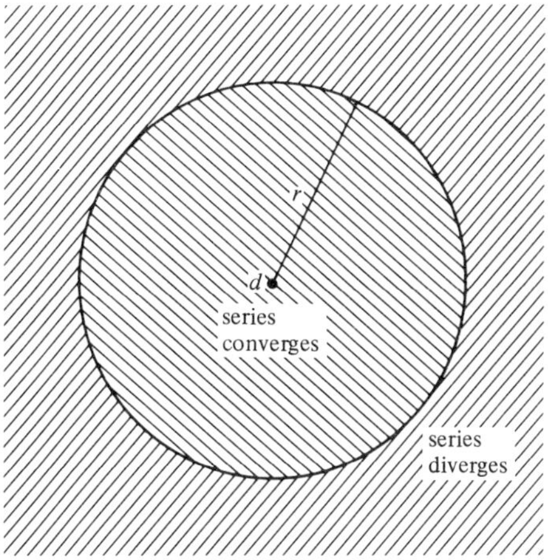

Figure 5.16

(5.197) PROPOSITION. *Let X, Y be metric spaces and let $g_n: X \to Y$ be a sequence of continuous (resp. uniformly continuous) maps converging uniformly to $g: X \to Y$. Then g is continuous (resp. uniformly continuous).*

Proof. Given $h \in \mathbb{N}$, $\exists N$ such that for all $x \in X$ and $n \geqslant N$,

$$d(g_n(x), g(x)) < 1/3h.$$

Secondly, for each $a \in X$ (resp. for all $a \in X$) $\exists m \ni$

$$d(a,b) < 1/m \qquad \Rightarrow \qquad d(g_N(a), g_N(b)) < 1/3h.$$

Then

$$d(g(a), g(b)) \leqslant d(g(a), g_N(a)) + d(g_N(a), g_N(b)) + d(g_N(b), g(b)) < 1/h. \quad \blacksquare$$

Since $a \mapsto a_n a^n$ is uniformly continuous on bounded subsets of a valued field by A12.2(v), by (5.195) and the proposition we have

(5.198) COROLLARY. *If $f = a_0 + a_1 T + \cdots$ is a power series over the valued field k with radius of convergence r and if $s < r$, where $s \in \mathbb{R}^{>}$, then $a \mapsto f(a)$ defines a uniformly continuous function $\{a \in k : |a| \leqslant s\} \to \tilde{k}$.*

For example, if $\lambda < \lambda_q$, then

$$a \mapsto (1+a)^q$$

defines a uniformly continuous function $\{a \in K : |a| \leqslant \lambda\} \to \tilde{k}$. We now investigate the continuity of $(1+a)^q$ with respect to q.

(5.199) PROPOSITION. *Let k be a valued field, $a \in K$ with $|a| < 1$, $\alpha \in \mathbb{R}^{>}$ and, using the notation of* (5.170),

$$X = \{q \in E_a : |q| \leqslant \alpha\}.$$

Then $q \mapsto (1+a)^q$ defines a uniformly continuous map $X \to \tilde{k}$.

Proof. We denote the partial sums of the binomial series by

$$g_N = g_N(a,q) = 1 + \binom{q}{1}a + \cdots + \binom{q}{N}a^N.$$

When $\mathrm{char}(k) = 0$, g_N is a polynomial function of q and therefore is uniformly continuous on X by A12.2(v). When $\mathrm{char}(k) = p > 0$, by choosing m large enough to ensure that $p^m > N$, by (5.169) we have

$$v(q-r) \geqslant m \quad \Rightarrow \quad g_N(a,q) = g_N(a,r),$$

so again $g_N \colon X \to \tilde{k}$ is uniformly continuous. In view of (5.197) it remains to prove the uniform convergence of the series.

We follow the proof of (5.171) except that now we want estimates independent of q. First let $|\ |$ be ultrametric. It is clear from the definition of λ_q in (5.170) that g.l.b. $\{\lambda_q : q \in X\} = \lambda$, say, satisfies $\lambda > |a|$. By (5.170)(ii),

$$\left|\binom{q}{n}a^n\right| \leqslant \lambda^{-n}|a|^n = r^n,$$

say, and the uniform convergence follows by the Weierstrass M-test by comparison with $1 + r + r^2 + \cdots$.

Now suppose $|\ |$ is archimedean so $E_a = k$. Let $r = |a| < 1 - 1/h$, where $h \in \mathbb{N}$. Then

$$\left|\binom{q}{n+1}\right| = \left|1 - \frac{q+1}{n+1}\right|\left|\binom{q}{n}\right| \leqslant \left(1 + \frac{1}{h}\right)\left|\binom{q}{n}\right|, \qquad \forall q \in X,$$

provided $n \geqslant h(\alpha+1)$. Let N denote the smallest integer $\geqslant h(\alpha+1)$. Now $\forall q \in X$ and $0 \leqslant n \leqslant N$,

$$\left|\binom{q}{n}\right| = \left|\frac{q(q-1)\cdots(q-n+1)}{n!}\right| \leqslant (\alpha+N)^N = M,$$

say (by the crude estimates $|n!| \geqslant 1$ and $|q-j| \leqslant \alpha + N$), and for all n

$$\left|\binom{q}{n}\alpha^n\right| \leqslant M'r^n,$$

where $r = 1 - 1/h^2$ and $M' = Mr^{-N}$ are independent of q. The uniform convergence is again a consequence of the M-test. ■

An application of (5.181) gives

(5.200) COROLLARY. *Let k be a valued field, a an element of $k \ni |a| < 1$, and $(q_1, q_2, \ldots)$ a cauchy sequence in E_a with limit $q \in E_a$. Then $((1+a)^{q_1}, (1+a)^{q_2}, \ldots)$ is cauchy in $\tilde{k}$ and has limit $(1+a)^q$.*

(5.201) EXAMPLES. (The notation is as in the corollary.)

1. In $\mathbb{C}$,

$$\lim\big((1+a),(1+a)^{1/2},(1+a)^{1/3},\dots\big)=(1+a)^0=1.$$

2. In $\mathbb{Q}((X))$,

$$\lim\big(1+X,(1+X)^{1+X},(1+X)^{1+X+X^2},\dots\big)=(1+X)^{\frac{1}{1-X}}.$$

3. In $\mathbb{F}_3((X))$, since $\frac{1}{2}=2+3+3^2+\cdots$ in $\mathbb{Z}_3$, so that $\frac{1}{2}=\lim(2,\ 2+3,\ 2+3+3^2,\dots)$, we have

$$\sqrt{1+X}=\lim\big((1+X)^2,(1+X)^5,(1+X)^{14},\dots\big).$$

In the previous proposition and its corollary there is no loss of generality in assuming that k is complete because we can always embed $k\subset\tilde{k}$. Then a perusal of (5.170)(ii) shows that E_a and the X of (5.199) are also complete.

(5.202) PROPOSITION. *Let* $\xi,\rho\in\mathbb{R}^>$ *and* $X=\{q\in\mathbb{Q}:|q|\leqslant\rho\}$. *Then*

(i) $q\mapsto\xi^q$ (*the positive value*) *defines a uniformly continuous map* $X\to\mathbb{R}$ *and consequently has a unique uniformly continuous extension to*

$$\bar{X}=\{\sigma\in\mathbb{R}:|\sigma|\leqslant\rho\}\to\mathbb{R},$$

again denoted $\sigma\mapsto\xi^\sigma$.

(ii) ξ^σ *is positive and coincides with the value given by the binomial series when the latter is defined* (*i.e., when* $\xi<2$).

(iii)

$$\xi<\eta\quad\text{and}\quad\sigma>0\quad\Rightarrow\quad\xi^\sigma<\eta^\sigma,$$

$$\xi>1\quad\text{and}\quad\sigma<\tau\quad\Rightarrow\quad\xi^\sigma<\xi^\tau.$$

(iv) *As in* (5.78), $\mathbb{R}^>$ *is a vector space over* $\mathbb{R}$: *for* $\xi,\eta\in\mathbb{R}^>$ *and* $\sigma,\tau\in\mathbb{R}$,

$$(\xi\eta)^\sigma=\xi^\sigma\eta^\sigma,\qquad \xi^{\sigma+\tau}=\xi^\sigma\xi^\tau,\qquad (\xi^\sigma)^\tau=\xi^{\sigma\tau}.$$

Moreover, $\dim_{\mathbb{R}}(\mathbb{R}^>)=1$.

Proof. (i) The map $X\to X$ given by $q\mapsto -q$ is uniformly continuous, and since $\xi^{-q}=(1/\xi)^q$ by (5.78), we can assume that $\xi<1$. By (5.175), $\xi^q=(1+(\xi-1))^q$ is given by the binomial series and the uniform continuity follows from (5.199) (with $k=\mathbb{Q}$).

(ii) If we take $\alpha=|\xi|$ and $k=\mathbb{R}$ in (5.199), we see that the value given ξ^σ by the binomial series must coincide with the value assigned by the map $\bar{X}\to\mathbb{R}$.

(iii, iv) Let $(q_1,\dots)$ and $(r_1,\dots)$ be cauchy sequences in $\mathbb{Q}$ (ordinary metric) with limits σ and τ, so $\lim\xi^{q_i}=\xi^\sigma$, and so on, by (i) and (5.181) (the half not dependent on the axiom of choice). By (5.78) and (5.19)–(5.21),

$$(\xi\eta)^\sigma=\lim(\xi\eta)^{q_i}=\lim(\xi^{q_i}\eta^{q_i})=\lim\xi^{q_i}\lim\eta^{q_i}=\xi^\sigma\eta^\sigma,$$

and

$$\xi^{\sigma+\tau}=\lim \xi^{q_i+r_i}=\lim \xi^{q_i}\cdot\lim \xi^{r_i}=\xi^{\sigma}\xi^{\tau}.$$

Hence, for any $n\in\mathbb{Z}$,

$$(*)\qquad (\xi^{\sigma})^{n}=\xi^{n\sigma}.$$

Next, for any $q\in\mathbb{Q}$,

$$(**)\qquad (\xi^{q})^{\sigma}=\lim(\xi^{q})^{q_i}=\lim \xi^{qq_i}=\xi^{q\sigma}.$$

Thus, for $n\in\mathbb{N}$,

$$\begin{aligned}(\xi^{\sigma})^{\tau}&=\left((\xi^{\sigma/n})^{n}\right)^{\tau} && \text{by } (*),\\ &=\left(\left((\xi^{1/n})^{\sigma}\right)^{n}\right)^{\tau} && \text{by } (**), \text{ with } q=1/n,\\ &=\left((\xi^{1/n})^{\sigma}\right)^{n\tau} && \text{by } (**), \text{ with } q=n \text{ and } \sigma \text{ replaced by } \tau,\end{aligned}$$

and so on. Since $\lim(\xi,\xi^{1/2},\xi^{1/3},\ldots)=\xi^{0}=1$, by taking n sufficiently large we have $\xi^{1/n}=1+a$, where a satisfies (5.174), which ensures the validity of (5.171)(δ). This gives

$$(\xi^{\sigma})^{\tau}=(\xi^{1/n})^{\sigma n\tau}=\xi^{\sigma\tau}$$

again using $(**)$ (with $q=1/n$ and σ replaced by $\sigma n\tau$).

The two inequalities in (iii) can be written $(\eta/\xi)^{\sigma}>1$ and $\xi^{\tau-\sigma}>1$. Both therefore come down to the statement

$$\xi>1 \quad\text{and}\quad \sigma>0 \qquad\Rightarrow\qquad \xi^{\sigma}>1.$$

This is true if $\sigma=m/n$, where $m,n\in\mathbb{N}$ since $\xi^{\sigma}\leqslant 1\Rightarrow\xi^{\sigma n}=\xi^{m}\leqslant 1\Rightarrow\xi<1$, a contradiction. In general, we can write $\sigma=\lim q_i$, where the q_i are positive rationals, and then $\xi^{\sigma}=\lim\xi^{q_i}\geqslant 1$. Since $\xi^{\sigma}=1\Rightarrow\xi=(\xi^{\sigma})^{1/\sigma}=1^{1/\sigma}=1$, we have in fact $\xi^{\sigma}>1$.

Finally, to prove that $\dim_{\mathbb{R}}(\mathbb{R}^{>})=1$, let $\xi\in\mathbb{R}^{>}$ and $\xi\neq 1$. We wish to show that $\{\xi^{\sigma}:\sigma\in\mathbb{R}\}=\mathbb{R}^{>}$. For a given $\eta\in\mathbb{R}^{>}$, put $X=\{\sigma:\xi^{\sigma}\geqslant\eta\}$ and $\mu=\text{g.l.b.}(X)$. We wish to show that $\xi^{\mu}=\eta$. By definition of μ, if $\nu>\mu$, then $\exists\sigma\in X\ni\nu>\sigma\geqslant\mu$ and then $\xi^{\nu}>\xi^{\sigma}\geqslant\eta$. The assumption $\xi^{\mu}<\eta$ leads to a contradiction: since $\lim(\xi,\xi^{1/2},\ldots)=1$, $\exists n\in\mathbb{N}\ni\xi^{1/n}<\eta/\xi^{\mu}$, and thus $\xi^{\nu}<\eta$, where $\nu=\mu+1/n$. On the other hand, if $\xi^{\mu}>\eta$, then for n sufficiently large we have $\xi^{\mu-1/n}>\eta$, contrary to the definition of μ. Therefore $\xi^{\mu}=\eta$. ■

(5.203) COROLLARY. *The conditions in* (5.171)(δ) *and* (5.174) *are equivalent: if* $\alpha,\sigma\in\mathbb{R}^{>}$ *and* $|\alpha|<1$, *then*

$$\alpha<1-2^{-1/\sigma} \qquad\Leftrightarrow\qquad (1-\alpha)^{\sigma}>\tfrac{1}{2}.$$

The one dimensionality of $\mathbb{R}^{>}$ implies

(5.204) COROLLARY. *If* $\eta,\xi\in\mathbb{R}^{>}$ *and* $\xi\neq 1$, *then* $\exists!\sigma\in\mathbb{R}\ni\xi^{\sigma}=\eta$.

EXERCISES

1. For a sequence of real numbers $c_0, c_1, \ldots$ define $\limsup c_n =$ the smallest number C such that $\forall C' > C$ there are only finitely many (or no) c_n satisfying $c_n > C'$. For instance, if the sequence is convergent then $\limsup c_n = \lim c_n$. If the sequence is unbounded above one writes $\limsup c_n = \infty$. If $a_0 + a_1 X + \cdots$ is a power series over a valued field, use the ratio test (Exercise 7 after Section 10) to prove the following formula for the radius of convergence:
$$r = \frac{1}{\limsup |a_n|^{1/n}},$$
where $1/\infty = 0$.

2. Let $f \in \mathbb{C}[[Z]]$ and suppose f' converges at $Z = a$. Then f also converges at a. (Of course, there is a problem only when a is on the circle of convergence. This question is not easy.)

19. log AND exp IN VALUED FIELDS

If $\alpha = \xi^\sigma$ we write
$$\sigma = \log_\xi \alpha$$
and we say that σ is the **logarithm of α to the base ξ**. As with the symbol ξ^σ when $\sigma \in \mathbb{Q}$, the notation $\log_\xi \alpha$ is ambiguous and really denotes the set $\{\sigma \in k : \xi^\sigma = \alpha\}$. The use of this notation will be confined essentially to cases where a special member or *principal value* can be conveniently chosen. Such is the case when $k = \mathbb{R}$, $\alpha, \xi \in \mathbb{R}^>$, and $\xi \neq 1$, as we just saw in (5.204); then $\log_\xi \alpha$ has a unique value in $\mathbb{R}$. We quote some immediate corollaries of (5.202).

The vector space properties imply that $\log_\xi : \mathbb{R}^> \to \mathbb{R}$ is a group homomorphism. That is, if $\alpha, \beta \in \mathbb{R}^>$ then

(5.205) $$\log_\xi(\alpha\beta) = \log_\xi \alpha + \log_\xi \beta.$$

Some of the other statements of (5.202) translate as follows.

(5.206) $$\xi > 1 \quad \text{and} \quad \alpha < \beta \quad \Rightarrow \quad \log_\xi \alpha < \log_\xi \beta;$$

in particular, since $\log_\xi 1 = 0$, $\alpha < 1 < \beta \Rightarrow \log_\xi \alpha < 0 < \log_\xi \beta$.

(5.207) $$\log_\xi(\alpha^\tau) = \tau \log_\xi \alpha.$$

If also $\eta \neq 1$, then

(5.208) $$\log_\eta \alpha = \log_\eta \xi \log_\xi \alpha.$$

In particular, since $\log_\eta \eta = 1$,

(5.209) $$\log_\eta \xi = 1/\log_\xi \eta.$$

(5.210) PROPOSITION. *If $\xi \in \mathbb{R}$, $\xi > 1$, and $h \in \mathbb{N}$, then* $\exists \eta_0 \ni$
$$\log_\xi \eta < \eta/h, \qquad \forall \eta > \eta_0.$$

Proof. The inequality is equivalent to $\eta<(\xi^{1/h})^{\eta}=(1+b)^{\eta}$, say. If $n=\lfloor\eta\rfloor$ then since $b>0$,

$$(1+b)^{\eta}\geqslant(1+b)^{n}\geqslant 1+nb+n(n-1)b^2/2$$

and the last quantity is $\geqslant\eta$ if $b+(n-1)b^2/2>1$. Hence we can take $\eta_0=2+2|1-b|/b^2$. ■

It is not hard to prove the following elaboration of the proposition: If $f\in\mathbb{R}[X]$, then for all sufficiently large η

(5.211) $$f(\log_{\xi}\eta)<\eta.$$

(5.212) COROLLARY. *Let k be a valued field, let $f=a_0+a_1T+\cdots$ be a power series over k with radius of convergence r, and let the derived series $f'=a_1+2a_2T+\cdots$ have radius of convergence r'. Then, with the usual conventions concerning ∞, $r\leqslant r'$. If* $\operatorname{char}(k)=0$ *and* $|\ |$ *is not discrete, or if* $|\ |$ *is* 0*-ultrametric, then $r=r'$.*

Proof. To show that $r\leqslant r'$ we must show that $f'(a)$ converges when $|a|<r$. When $|\ |$ is ultrametric, $|n|\leqslant 1$; hence $|na_na^{n-1}|\leqslant|a_na^{n-1}|$ and the result follows by comparison with the absolutely convergent series Σa_na^{n-1}. When $|\ |$ is archimedean we choose $h\in\mathbb{N}\ni c=a(1+1/h)$ satisfies $|a|<|c|<r$. For sufficiently large n we have $\log_{1+1/h}n<n-1$; hence $|na_na^{n-1}|\leqslant|a_nc^{n-1}|$ and again the result follows by comparison.

Conversely, we wish to show that in the cases stated $f(b)$ converges when $|b|<r'$. This is accomplished again by a comparison of the form

$(*)$ $$|a_nb^n|\leqslant|na_nc^n|$$

(for n sufficiently large) where $|b|\leqslant|c|<r'$. (Clearly r' is also the radius of convergence of $Tf'(T)$.) When $|\ |$ is 0-ultrametric or archimedean, $|n|\geqslant 1$ $\forall n\in\mathbb{N}$ and we can take $c=b$. There remains the case where $|\ |$ is l-adic and nondiscrete (for an example, see A12.4). Then $|n|\geqslant|l|^{\log_l n}$, where $|l|<1$. The nondiscreteness implies that we can choose $c\in k$ satisfying $|b|<|c|<r'$ and then $(*)$ can be written $\log_l n\log_{|c/b|}|1/l|\leqslant n$, which is true for all sufficiently large n. ■

The following examples show that the hypotheses in the corollary are necessary. In $\mathbb{Q}_p$, $T+T^p+T^{p^2}+\cdots$ has radius of convergence 1 but its derivative $1+pT^{p-1}+\cdots+p^nT^{p^n-1}+\cdots$ has radius of convergence $|1/p|>1$. (*Exercise*: When k is discretely valued with uniformizer p and $\operatorname{char}(k)=0$, then in the notation of the corollary $r'=r$ or $r/|p|$.) In characteristic $p>0$, $f=T^p+T^{2p}+T^{3p}+\cdots$ has radius of convergence 1 but $f'=0$ has radius ∞.

Naturally we would like to have a direct way of obtaining $\log_\xi \alpha$ in the real case and also more information about $\log_\xi$ in other valued fields (notably $\mathbb{C}$).

> For the remainder of this section the discussion refers to a complete valued field k of characteristic 0 (archimedean or ultrametric).

The binomial series can be written in the form

$$(1+a)^q = 1 + aq + a^2 q^{(2)}/2! + a^3 q^{(3)}/3! + \cdots, \tag{5.213}$$

showing a striking symmetry between a and q. Recall the notation of A7.4: For $n \in \mathbb{N}$,

$$q^{(n)} = q(q-1)\cdots(q-n+1) = \sum_{m=1}^{n} s(n,m) q^m. \tag{5.214}$$

(5.215) LEMMA. *With* $s(n,0)=0$, *we have for all* $m, n \in \mathbb{N}$

$$s(n+1,m) = s(n,m-1) - ns(n,m); \tag{5.216}$$

the sign of $s(n,m)$ *is given by*

$$s(n,m) = (-1)^{n-m} |s(n,m)|. \tag{5.217}$$

Proof. (5.216) is a direct consequence of

$$q^{(n+1)} = q^{(n)}(q-n),$$

and now (5.217) follows by a simple induction. ■

It follows from (5.216) that

$$s(n,1) = (-1)^{n-1}(n-1)!. \tag{5.218}$$

It is also easy to show that $s(n,m) \neq 0$ for $1 \leqslant m \leqslant n$. Shown here is a short table of $s(n,m)$.

	m				
n	1	2	3	4	5
1	1				
2	−1	1			
3	2	−3	1		
4	−6	11	−6	1	
5	24	−50	35	−10	1

Substituting (5.214) into (5.213) gives the expanded series

$$1+\sum_{n\in\mathbb{N}}\frac{a^n}{n!}\sum_{m=1}^{n}s(n,m)q^m=S, \tag{5.219}$$

say. In order to rearrange S as a power series in q we need absolute convergence.

(5.220) LEMMA. *The series* (5.219) *is absolutely convergent in the following circumstances*:

(i) $|a|<1$ *and any* $q\in k$ *when* $|\ |$ *is archimedean*,
(ii) $|a|<\min\{1,1/|q|\}$ *when* $|\ |$ *is* 0-*ultrametric, or*
(iii) $|a|<|l|^{1/(l-1)}\min\{1,1/|q|\}$ *when* $|\ |$ *is* l-*ultrametric*.

Proof. Let A denote the series of the absolute values of the terms of the series S. First let $|\ |$ be archimedean. Then by (5.217), A coincides with the expanded series for $(1-|a|)^{-|q|}$, which we know from (5.171) converges for $|a|<1$ and all $|q|$.

Second, let $|\ |$ be ultrametric so that $|s(n,m)|\leqslant 1$. (In the l-ultrametric case this estimate and (iii) can be improved, but we shall not do so here.) By (5.157), $|n!|\geqslant|l|^{n/(l-1)}$. Hence A is at most

$$1+|q|\{x+x^2+\cdots\}+|q|^2\{x^2+x^3+\cdots\}+\cdots,$$

where

$$x=\begin{cases}|a| & \text{in the 0-ultrametric case,}\\ |a||l|^{-1/(l-1)} & \text{in the } l\text{-ultrametric case.}\end{cases}$$

Thus we need $x<1$ in order to get

$$A\leqslant 1+\frac{1}{1-x}\left[|q|x+|q|^2x^2+\cdots\right]$$

and now we also need $|q|x<1$. These conditions give the statements in (ii) and (iii). ■

Under the conditions of the lemma we can rearrange S thus:

$$\begin{aligned}(1+a)^q&=1+\sum_{m\in\mathbb{N}}q^m\sum_{n=m}^{\infty}\frac{s(n,m)}{n!}a^n \\ &=1+\sum_{m\in\mathbb{N}}q^m\Lambda_m,\end{aligned} \tag{5.221}$$

say. Λ_1 is called the **natural logarithm** of $1+a$ and is denoted $\log(1+a)$. When $k=\mathbb{R}$ we shall connect this with $\log_\xi$ in (5.228). By (5.218),

$$\log(1+a)=a-\frac{a^2}{2}+\frac{a^3}{3}-\cdots. \tag{5.222}$$

(5.223) LEMMA. *For* $|a|<1$ *the series* (5.221) *is absolutely convergent and* $\Lambda_m = \Lambda_1{}^m/m!$.

Proof. The derivative of the logarithmic series (5.222) is the geometric series $1-a+a^2-\cdots$, whose radius of convergence is 1. By (5.212), the series for $\log(1+a)$ converges when $|a|<1$ except possibly when $|\ |$ is l-adic and discrete. However, since then $v(a^n/n) \geqslant nv(a) - v(l)\log_l n$, by (5.210) the sequence a^n/n is null when $|a|<1$, and therefore the radius of convergence is 1 also in this case.

By (5.167), for $n \in \mathbb{N}$,

$$(X+Y)^{(n)} = \sum_{m=1}^{n} s(n,m)(X+Y)^m = X^{(n)} + \binom{n}{1} X^{(n-1)}Y^{(1)} + \cdots.$$

If we differentiate with respect to Y and then set $Y=0$ we obtain

$$\sum_{m=1}^{n} ms(n,m)X^{m-1} = \sum_{t=1}^{n} \binom{n}{t} X^{(n-t)}(t-1)!(-1)^{t-1}.$$

Comparing the coefficients of X^{m-1} gives

$$(*) \qquad \frac{ms(n,m)}{n!} = \sum_{t=1}^{n} \frac{(-1)^{t-1}}{t} \frac{s(n-t,m-1)}{(n-t)!}.$$

(The terms of the sum are 0 for $n-m+1<t\leqslant n$). If $m \geqslant 2$ and $(m-1)!\Lambda_{m-1} = \Lambda_1{}^{m-1}$, i.e.,

$$(**) \qquad (m-1)! \sum_{n=m-1}^{\infty} \frac{s(n,m-1)}{n!} a^n = \left[a - a^2/2 + \cdots\right]^{m-1},$$

then multiplying this by (5.221) and rearranging terms using $(*)$ as justified by the absolute convergence, we obtain the next case of $(**)$, with $m-1$ replaced by m. This proves $(**)$ by induction. ■

(5.224) COROLLARY. *Under the conditions of* (5.220),

$$(1+a)^q = 1 + x + \frac{x^2}{2!} + \frac{x^3}{3!} + \cdots,$$

where $x = q\log(1+a)$, *and the series converges absolutely.*

(5.225) COROLLARY. *Let* $|a|<1$, *or* $|a| < |l|^{1/(l-1)}$ *when k is l-ultrametric. Then*

$$\log(1+a) = 0 \quad \Leftrightarrow \quad a = 0,$$

and, when k is ultrametric,

$$|\log(1+a)| = |a|.$$

Proof. Let $x = \log(1+a)$. If $a=0$, then (5.222) $\Rightarrow x=0$. Conversely, when we take $q=1$ in the previous corollary we have $a = x + x^2/2! + \cdots$ under the stated conditions on a, and hence $x=0 \Rightarrow a=0$.

Now let k be ultrametric. Then $|x|=|a|$ will follow from $x = a - a^2/2 + \cdots$ if we show that $|a^n/n| < |a|$ for $n \geqslant 2$. It is convenient to prove the stronger statement that $|a^n/n!| < |a|$ for $n \geqslant 2$. Since $\operatorname{char}(k)=0$, k is either 0-ultrametric or l-ultrametric. In the former case $|a^n/n!| = |a|^n < |a|$ since $|a|<1$. In the latter case $|a| < |l|^{1/(l-1)}$, and using (5.166) we have

$$|a^{n-1}/n!| < |l|^{(n-1)/(l-1)} |l|^{-v(n!)} \leqslant 1. \quad \blacksquare$$

We define the **exponential function** by

$$\exp x = 1 + x + \frac{x^2}{2!} + \cdots = \sum_{n \in \mathbb{N}} \frac{x^n}{n!}. \tag{5.226}$$

(5.227) PROPOSITION. (α) *The exponential series* (5.226) *converges absolutely for $x \in E$ where the additive group E is as follows.*

(i) *$E = k$ when k is archimedean,*
(ii) *$E = \{x \in k : |x| < 1\}$ when k is 0-ultrametric, and*
(iii) *$E = \{x \in k : |x| < |l|^{1/(l-1)}\}$ when k is l-ultrametric.*

(β) *If $x \in E$ then $\exp(x) \neq 0$ and $\exp\colon E \to k^*$ is a group homomorphism: for $x, y \in E$,*

$$\exp(x+y) = \exp(x)\exp(y).$$

(γ) *If $y = 1 + a$, where $|a| < 1$, or $|a| < |l|^{1/(l-1)}$ if k is l-ultrametric, then $\log y \in E$ and*

$$\exp(\log y) = y.$$

Proof. The proposition is obviously true (and devoid of interest) when $|\;|$ is trivial, so assume $|\;|$ is nontrivial. For $x \in E$ choose $a \in k^*$ satisfying $|a|<1$, $|a| < |l|^{1/(l-1)}$ if k is l-ultrametric, so $\log(1+a) \neq 0$, and define $q = x/\log(1+a)$. By the previous corollary, the pair a, q satisfies the conditions of (5.220) and by (5.224) the exponential series converges to

$$\exp x = (1+a)^q.$$

With $r = y/\log(1+a)$, (β) is now a consequence of (5.171)(β) and (γ) is a restatement of parts of the previous two corollaries. $\blacksquare$

If a, b are such that $x = \log(1+a)$, $y = \log(1+b)$, and $z = \log((1+a)(1+b))$ are all defined, then

$$\exp z = (1+a)(1+b) = \exp(x)\exp(y) = \exp(x+y).$$

Writing $A = 1 + a$, $B = 1 + b$, this implies

$$\log(AB) = \log A + \log B + r,$$

where $r \in \operatorname{Ker}(\exp)$. It is therefore of interest to determine this kernel.

(5.228) PROPOSITION. (α) *Let $k = \mathbb{R}$ and define the real number*

$$e = \exp 1 = 1 + 1 + 1/2! + 1/3! + \cdots.$$

Then for all $x \in \mathbb{R}$

$$\exp x = e^x,$$

and for $y = 1 + a \in \mathbb{R}$ with $|a| < 1$,

$$(*) \qquad \log y = \log_e y.$$

Using this to extend the domain of the natural logarithm to all of $\mathbb{R}^>$,

$$\exp: \mathbb{R} \to \mathbb{R}^> \qquad \text{and} \qquad \log: \mathbb{R}^> \to \mathbb{R}$$

are mutually inverse group isomorphisms. In particular,

$$(**) \qquad \log(\exp x) = x, \qquad \forall x \in \mathbb{R},$$

$$(***) \qquad \log(yz) = \log y + \log z, \qquad \forall y, z \in \mathbb{R}^>.$$

(β) *Let k be ultrametric. Then $L = \{1 + a : a \in E\}$ (with E as defined in the previous proposition) is a subgroup of k^* and*

$$\exp: E \to L$$

is a group isomorphism with inverse

$$\log: L \to E.$$

Hence the relations $(**)$ and $(***)$ hold for all $x \in E$ and $y, z \in L$.

Remark. The letter e is standard notation for the real number $\exp 1$. It is easy to calculate e to a few decimal places from the series: The partial sums $s_n = 1 + \cdots + 1/(n-1)!$ are increasing, so

$$s_n < e = s_n + 1/n! + 1/(n+1)! + \cdots$$

$$< s_n + \frac{1}{n!}[1 + \frac{1}{n+1} + \frac{1}{(n+1)^2} + \cdots]$$

$$= s_n + \frac{n+1}{n!n}.$$

The correct value to 15 places is $e = 2.718281828459045\ldots$.

Proof. (α) Taking $1 + a = 1/e$ (so $|a| < 1$) in (5.224) gives

$$\exp(q \log(1/e)) = (1/e)^q.$$

Setting $q=1/\log(1/e)$ gives

$$e=(1/e)^{1/\log(1/e)},$$

and from (5.204) we deduce $\log(1/e)=-1$. Therefore $\exp(-q)=(1/e)^q$; hence $\exp q=(1/e)^{-q}=e^q$.

From (5.227)(γ) and the definition of $\log_e$ we have

$$e^{\log_e y}=y=\exp(\log y)=e^{\log y}$$

and ($*$) follows by (5.204). The remaining statements in (α) are clear.

(β) if $a,\, b\in E$, then by the strong triangle inequality

$$(1+a)(1+b)-1=a+b+ab\in E.$$

Also,

$$\frac{1}{1+a}-1=\frac{-a}{1+a}\in E$$

since $|1+a|=1$. This proves that L is a subgroup of k^*. The map exp: $E\to L$ is surjective by (5.227)(γ). If $a\in E$ then, as we saw in the proof of (5.226), $|a^n/n!|<|a|$ for $n\geqslant 2$; hence

$$|\exp a-1|=|a|.$$

Therefore $\exp a=1\Rightarrow a=0$ and exp: $E\to L$ is a group isomorphism. Now (5.227)(γ) implies that log: $L\to E$ is the inverse isomorphism. ■

(5.229) COROLLARY. *If* $\alpha=a+ib\in\mathbb{C}$, *then*

$$\exp\bar{\alpha}=\overline{\exp\alpha},$$

$$|\exp(ib)|=1,$$

and

$$|\exp\alpha|=|e^a|=e^a.$$

Proof. $e^a\in\mathbb{R}^>$ is a consequence of part (α) of the proposition. By (5.145), $\exp\bar{\alpha}=\overline{\exp\alpha}$; hence

$$|\exp\alpha|^2=\exp(a+ib)\exp(a-ib)=\exp(2a)=e^{2a},$$

whence $|\exp\alpha|=e^a$. Since $|\exp\alpha|=|\exp(a)\exp(ib)|=e^a|\exp(ib)|$, $|\exp(ib)|=1$ follows. ■

EXERCISES

1. (i) The **condensation test**: if a_i are real numbers satisfying $a_1\geqslant a_2\geqslant\cdots\geqslant 0$, then Σa_i converges iff $\Sigma 2^k a_{2^k}=a_1+2a_2+4a_4+\cdots$ converges.
   (ii) By applying the test successively, the following series converge for $s>1$ and diverge for $s\leqslant 1$:

$$\sum_{n=1}^{\infty} n^{-s},\qquad \sum_{n=2}^{\infty} n^{-1}(\log n)^{-s},\qquad \sum_{n=4}^{\infty}(n\log n)^{-1}(\log\log n)^{-s},\ldots.$$

2. e is irrational. (*Hint:* If $e = m/n$, then $n!(e - 1 - 1/1! - \cdots - 1/n!) = 1/(n+1) + 1/(n+1)(n+2) + \cdots \in \mathbb{N}$.)

3. For $x \in \mathbb{R}^>$, $x < 1$, prove that

$$-\log(1-x) > x > \log(1+x) > x - x^2/2,$$

and make the following deductions.

(a) $\lim(1+1/n)^n = e$.

(b) If $u_n = 1 + \frac{1}{2} + \cdots + 1/n - \log n$, then $1 > u_2 > u_3 > \cdots > 0$, and consequently $\lim u_n$ exists. (Its limit is known as **Euler's constant** and is customarily denoted $\gamma = 0.57721566490\ldots$; it has not, as of 1980, been proved to be irrational.)

4. There is a unique continuous $f: \mathbb{Q}_p{}^* \to \mathbb{Q}_p$, called the **Iwasawa log**, such that $f(x) = \log x$ if $|x-1| < 1$, $f(p) = 0$, and $f(xy) = f(x) + f(y)$ $\forall x, y \in \mathbb{Q}_p{}^*$.

5. By subtracting the series for $\log(1+x)$ and $\log(1-x)$ and writing $y = (1+x)/(1-x)$, establish the expansion

$$\log y = 2\left[\left(\frac{y-1}{y+1}\right) + \frac{1}{3}\left(\frac{y-1}{y+1}\right)^3 + \cdots\right].$$

For what y in $\mathbb{R}$ (resp. $\mathbb{Q}_2$) does this series converge to $\log y$?

6. If

$$e^{e^X - 1} = \varpi(0) + \varpi(1)X + \varpi(2)X^2/2! + \cdots$$
$$= 1 + X + X^2 + \tfrac{5}{6}X^3 + \cdots \in \mathbb{Q}((X)),$$

then

$$\varpi(n+1) = \sum_{m=0}^{n} \binom{n}{m} \varpi(m), \qquad \varpi(n) = \sum_{m=0}^{n} S(n,m),$$

(the S are Stirling numbers of the second kind), and $\varpi(n)$ is the number of equivalence relations on a set of n elements. (These positive integers are called **Bell numbers**.)

20. α^β IN $\mathbb{C}$

We have seen that exp: $E \to k$ is injective when k is ultrametric or $k = \mathbb{R}$. In the one remaining case $k = \mathbb{C}$ (for it will be shown in (5.314) that $\mathbb{R}$ and $\mathbb{C}$ are the only complete archimedean fields), Ker(exp) is nontrivial. If $\alpha \in \mathbb{C}$, then $\alpha\mathbb{Z}$ (or $\mathbb{Z}\alpha$) denotes, as before, the additive subgroup $\{n\alpha : n \in \mathbb{Z}\}$ of $\mathbb{C}$.

(5.230) THEOREM. *The homomorphism* $\exp: \mathbb{C} \to \mathbb{C}^*$ *is surjective and*

$$\operatorname{Ker}(\exp) = 2\pi i\mathbb{Z}$$

for a certain positive real number π *whose value to* 15 *decimal places is* $3.141592653589793\ldots$.

Proof. We deal first with the surjectivity of exp. We already know from (5.227)(γ) and (5.228) that the subgroup Im(exp) of $\mathbb{C}^*$ contains $\mathbb{R}^>$ and all complex numbers ξ satisfying $|\xi - 1| < 1$. Let $\alpha \in \mathbb{C}^*$ and put $\beta = \alpha/|\alpha|$ so $|\beta| = 1$. Since $|a| \in \mathbb{R}^>$ it is sufficient to prove that $\beta \in \text{Im}(\exp)$. If $\beta = \gamma^n$ for some $n \in \mathbb{N}$ and $\gamma \in \mathbb{C}^*$, it is enough to prove that $\gamma \in \text{Im}(\exp)$, for if $\gamma = \exp(\eta)$, then $\beta = \exp(\eta)^n = \exp(n\eta)$. We shall show in fact that among the four fourth roots of β, at least one, say γ, satisfies $|\gamma - 1| < 1$.

Since the roots of $X^4 - 1$ are i^n, $n = 1,2,3,4$, if $\gamma_1 = a + bi$ is any root of $X^4 - \beta$ then the four of them are $\{\gamma_1 i^n\} = \{\pm(a+bi), \pm(-b+ai)\}$. We wish to choose $\gamma_1 i^n = x + yi$, say, so that

$$|\gamma_1 i^n - 1| = \sqrt{(x-1)^2 + y^2} < 1.$$

Since $|\gamma_1 i^n| = 1$, we have $x^2 + y^2 = 1$ and this requirement works out to $x > \frac{1}{2}$. Now $a^2 + b^2 = 1$ so at least one of $|a|, |b|$ is $> \frac{1}{2}$ and since all four of $\pm a, \pm b$ are possible values of of x, the result follows. In Figure 5.17 we illustrate a case where γ_1 lies in the third quadrant.

We now determine Ker(exp). If $\zeta = 1 + \alpha \in \mathbb{C}$, where $|\alpha| < 1$, then $\bar{\zeta} = 1 + \bar{\alpha}$, where $|\bar{\alpha}| < 1$. Hence by (5.145) and (5.222)

(5.231) $$\log \bar{\zeta} = \overline{\log \zeta}.$$

If $\log \zeta = x + yi$, then by (5.227) and (5.228),

$$|\zeta|^2 = \zeta\bar{\zeta} = \exp(\log \zeta + \log \bar{\zeta}) = e^{2x}.$$

We now take (as in (5.138)) $\zeta = (1+i)/\sqrt{2}$. Since $|\zeta| = 1$, we have $x = 0$ and $\log \zeta = yi$. We define the real number π by

(5.232) $$\pi = 4y = \frac{4}{i} \log \frac{1+i}{\sqrt{2}}.$$

Figure 5.17

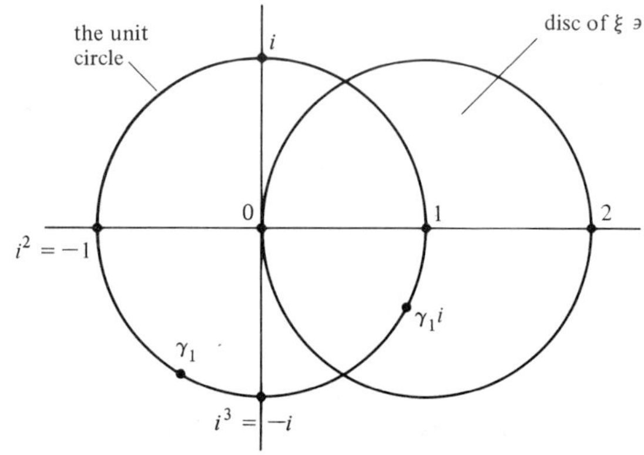

(The factor 4 is present for historical reasons.) By (5.227)(γ), $\exp(\pi i/4)=\zeta$ (hence $\pi\neq 0$) and, by (5.139), (5.227)(β) implies the equations

(5.233) $$\exp(\pi i/2)=i,$$

(5.234) $$\exp(\pi i)=-1 \qquad \text{(Euler's identity)},$$

(5.235) $$\exp(2\pi i)=1.$$

The last one implies that $\operatorname{Ker}(\exp)\supset 2\pi i\mathbb{Z}$.

We now describe a procedure to calculate π and in particular to prove that $\pi>0$. The rearrangements in the following series are justified by absolute convergence (cf. 5.223).

$$\pi/2=\frac{1}{i}\left[\log\zeta-\log\bar{\zeta}\right]=-i\sum_{n\in\mathbb{N}}\frac{(-1)^{n-1}}{n}\left[(\zeta-1)^n-(\bar{\zeta}-1)^n\right]$$

$$=-i\sum_{n\in\mathbb{N}}\frac{1}{n}\left[(1-\bar{\zeta})^n-(1-\zeta)^n\right].$$

Now $(1-\zeta)^4=(6-4\sqrt{2})i$; hence $(1-\zeta)^8=(1-\bar{\zeta})^8=48\sqrt{2}-68=\theta$, say. ($\theta=-0.117749+\varepsilon$, where $|\varepsilon|<10^{-8}$.) Therefore if $n=8a+b$, where $a,b\in\mathbb{M}$ and $b<8$, then

$$(1-\bar{\zeta})^n-(1-\zeta)^n=\theta^a\left[(1-\bar{\zeta})^b-(1-\zeta)^b\right]$$

$$=\theta^a\sum_{r=1}^{b}(-1)^r\binom{b}{r}(\bar{\zeta}^r-\zeta^r)=\theta^a c_b i,$$

say. Since $\bar{\zeta}^r$ is the conjugate of ζ^r, $\bar{\zeta}^r-\zeta^r$ is purely imaginary; that is, its real part is 0. Therefore c_b is real. Thus

(5.236) $$\pi=2\sum_{b=1}^{7}c_b s_b,$$

where

(5.237) $$s_b=\sum_{a=0}^{\infty}\frac{1}{8a+b}\theta^a.$$

In the accompanying table the decimal approximations to c_b and s_b are displayed correct to five places. (Since $\theta<0$, the series for s_b is alternating and it is easy to determine how many terms are needed to give this accuracy, cf. A10.7.) These values in (5.236) give $\pi=3.1416+\varepsilon$, where $|\varepsilon|<10^{-5}$; a more accurate table of c_b and s_b, which we do not take the trouble to write out here, gives the 15-figure approximation to π stated in the theorem.

b	c_b	c_b to five places	s_b to five places
1	$\sqrt{2}$	1.41421	0.98767
2	$2\sqrt{2}-2$	0.82843	0.48894
3	$4\sqrt{2}-6$	-0.34315	0.32330
4	$8\sqrt{2}-12$	-0.68629	0.24083
5	$14\sqrt{2}-20$	-0.20101	0.19155
6	$20\sqrt{2}-28$	0.28427	0.15884
7	$=c_6$	0.28427	0.13556

It remains to show that $\mathrm{Ker(exp)} \subset 2\pi i\mathbb{Z}$. Suppose that $\alpha = a+bi \in \mathrm{Ker(exp)}$. By (5.229), $1 = |\exp\alpha| = e^a$; hence by (5.228) $a=0$. Thus $\mathrm{Ker(exp)} = Bi$, where $B = \{b: bi \in \mathrm{Ker(exp)}\}$ is an additive subgroup of $\mathbb{R}$. As in (5.192) we define

$$\mu = \text{g.l.b.}\{b \in B: b > 0\}.$$

If B were dense in $\mathbb{R}$, then, by (5.189), exp would have the value 1 everywhere, which is not the case. Hence $0 < \mu \leqslant 2\pi$ and

(5.238) $$\mathrm{Ker(exp)} = \mu i\mathbb{Z}.$$

Thus $2\pi = \mu N$ for some $N \in \mathbb{N}$. Finally, to prove that $N=1$ we need to split the exponential series into two subseries. By (5.227)(α),

$$\exp(ix) = 1 + ix - \frac{x^2}{2!} - \frac{ix^3}{3!} + \frac{x^4}{4!} + \frac{ix^5}{5!} - \cdots$$

is absolutely convergent $\forall x \in \mathbb{C}$. We define the **sine** and **cosine** of x by

(5.239) $$\sin x = x - \frac{x^3}{3!} + \frac{x^5}{5!} - \cdots,$$

(5.240) $$\cos x = 1 - \frac{x^2}{2!} + \frac{x^4}{4!} - \cdots;$$

hence

(5.241) $$\exp(ix) = \cos x + i\sin x.$$

This relation is valid for all $x \in \mathbb{C}$. If $x \in \mathbb{R}$ then $\cos x$ and $\sin x \in \mathbb{R}$, and the real (resp. imaginary) part of $\exp(ix)$ is $\cos x$ (resp. $\sin x$).

By (5.227)(β), $\exp(\mu i/2)^2 = \exp(\mu i) = 1$, and, by (5.238), $\exp(\mu i/2) \neq 1$. Hence

$$\exp(\mu i/2) = -1 = \cos(\mu/2) + i\sin(\mu/2)$$

and therefore $\sin(\mu/2)=0$. An easy calculation shows that the series (5.239) is alternating for $0<x<\sqrt{6}$, so, by A10.7, $\sin x>x>0$. Thus $\mu>\sqrt{6}>\pi$ and therefore $N=1$. ■

As a corollary, if $\alpha\in C^*$ and η_1 is any one solution of $\exp(\eta)=\alpha$, then the set of all solutions is

$$\{\eta\in\mathbb{C}:\exp(\eta)=\alpha\}=\{\eta_1+2\pi in:n\in\mathbb{Z}\}.$$

This is the coset containing η_1 of the subgroup $2\pi i\mathbb{Z}$ in the additive group $\mathbb{C}$. If we write $\eta_1=\rho+i\theta_1(\rho,\theta_1\in\mathbb{R})$, then there is precisely one $\eta=\eta_1+2\pi in=\rho+i(\theta_1+2\pi n)=\rho+i\theta$, say, that satisfies

$$-\pi<\theta\leqslant\pi.$$

This value of θ is called the **amplitude** of α and is denoted

$$\theta=\mathrm{am}(\alpha).$$

The **polar form** of α is

(5.242) $$\alpha=r\exp(i\theta),$$

where $r=e^\rho=|\alpha|$ by (5.229), as opposed to the **rectangular** or **cartesian form** $\alpha=a+ib$. We have

(5.243) $$\rho=\log|\alpha|$$

and

$$e^{i\theta}=\cos\theta+i\sin\theta=\alpha/r=(a+ib)/\sqrt{a^2+b^2}\,;$$

hence

(5.244) $$\cos\theta=a/\sqrt{a^2+b^2}\,,\qquad \sin\theta=b/\sqrt{a^2+b^2}\,.$$

The signs of $\cos\theta$ and $\sin\theta$ are determined by the signs of a and b as indicated in Figure 5.18a, which shows an α in the second quadrant. The set of α with fixed absolute value $|\alpha|=r\in\mathbb{R}^>$ form a circle as indicated in Figure 5.18b. If we imagine a point α starting at $\alpha=r$ and moving counterclockwise through ri to $-r$, then $\theta=\mathrm{am}(\alpha)$ starts with the value 0 at $\alpha=r$ and increases steadily through the value $\pi/2$ at $\alpha=ir$ to the value π at $\alpha=-r$; similarly, as α moves clockwise from r through $-ri$ to points in the third quadrant just below $-r$, the value of $\mathrm{am}(\alpha)$ decreases steadily from 0 through $-\pi/2$ at $\alpha=-ri$ to values just above $-\pi$. To express this precisely, without benefit of geometric imagery, let $\alpha_j=a_j+ib_j=r\exp\theta_j$ be complex numbers of absolute value $|\alpha_j|=r$. Then, by (5.244), $a_1>a_2\Rightarrow 1\geqslant\cos\theta_1>\cos\theta_2\geqslant-1$; if in addition b_1 and $b_2\geqslant0$ (resp. <0) then, since $b_j=\sqrt{r^2-a_j^2}$ (resp. $b_j=-\sqrt{r^2-a_j^2}$), we have $0\leqslant b_1<b_2$ (resp. $0>b_1>b_2$). Therefore, by (5.244) and A12.7, when $b_j\geqslant0$

$$0\leqslant\sin\theta_1<\sin\theta_2\leqslant1$$

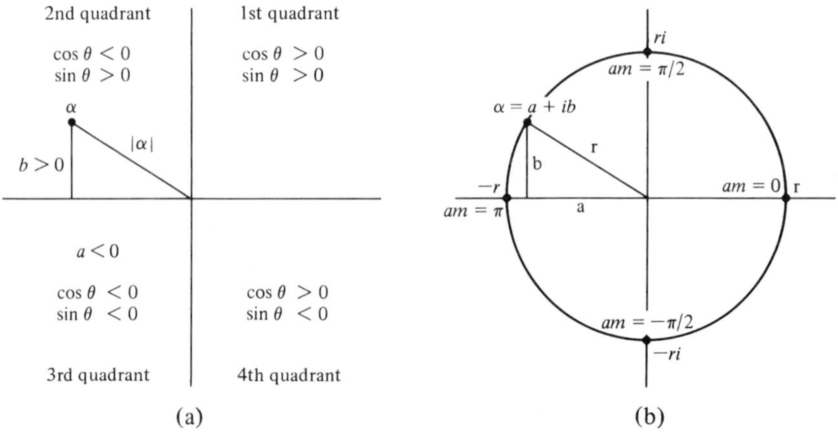

Figure 5.18

so that

$$0 \leqslant \theta_1 < \theta_2 \leqslant \pi;$$

and when $b_j < 0$

$$0 > \sin\theta_1 > \sin\theta_2 \geqslant -1$$

so that

$$0 > \theta_1 > \theta_2 > -\pi.$$

We note the following particular values;

$$\begin{array}{lll} \operatorname{am} r = 0, & \cos 0 = 1, & \sin 0 = 0, \\ \operatorname{am}(ri) = \pi/2, & \cos(\pi/2) = 0, & \sin(\pi/2) = 1, \\ \operatorname{am}(-r) = \pi, & \cos\pi = -1, & \sin\pi = 0, \\ \operatorname{am}(-ri) = -\pi/2, & \cos(-\pi/2) = 0, & \sin(-\pi/2) = -1. \end{array}$$

For $\alpha \in \mathbb{C}^*$ the **principal value** of the logarithm is

$$\log\alpha = \log_e|\alpha| + i\operatorname{am}(\alpha).$$

Henceforth, for $\alpha \in \mathbb{C}^*$, $\log\alpha$ denotes the principal value. It follows from the discussion above that $\log\alpha$ is characterized (i.e., uniquely determined) by the properties

(5.245) $\exp(\log\alpha) = \alpha, \qquad -\pi < \text{imaginary part } (\log\alpha) \leqslant \pi.$

If $\alpha \in \mathbb{R}^>$ this is consistent with our previous use of the term principal value: $\operatorname{am}\alpha = 0$ and $\log\alpha = \log_e|\alpha| = \log_e\alpha$. Note also that $\operatorname{am}(-\alpha) = \pi$, so

(5.246) $\log(-\alpha) = \log\alpha + \pi i, \qquad \alpha \in \mathbb{R}^>,$

and, in particular,

$$\log(-1) = \pi i.$$

There is one further question of consistency of notation:

(5.247) PROPOSITION. *If* $\alpha = 1 + \tau \in \mathbb{C}^*$, *where* $|\tau| < 1$, *then the principal value of the logarithm of* α *as defined in* (5.245) *coincides with the value* $\tau - \tau^2/2 + \cdots$ *given by the logarithmic series.*

Proof. For $z \in C^*$ with $|z-1| < 1$ let $L(z) = (z-1) - (z-1)^2/2 + \cdots$ denote the sum of the logarithmic series, and let $L(\alpha) = r + it$. Then $\exp(r+it) = \alpha$ and it remains to prove that $-\pi < t \leqslant \pi$. We shall show that in fact $|t| < \pi/2$.

Let $\tau = \alpha - 1 = a + bi$. We use the notation $[0, b]$ and the intermediate value theorem as given in A12.6. If $y \in [0, b]$ and $z = 1 + a + iy$ so $|z-1| = a^2 + y^2 \leqslant a^2 + b^2 = |\tau| < 1$, then $L(z)$ is defined, say $L(z) = u + iv$. The function $f: [0, b] \to \mathbb{R}$ defined by $f(y) = v$ is continuous by (5.198) and A12.2. Since $f(0) = 0$ and $f(b) = t$, if we had $|t| \geqslant \pi/2$, then $f(y)$ would assume one of the values $\pm\pi/2$ for some $y \in [0, b]$. However, this is not possible since $\exp(\pm\pi i/2) = \pm i$ and then

$$|z-1| = |\pm e^u i - 1| = \sqrt{1 + e^{2u}} \not< 1. \quad \blacksquare$$

If $\alpha \in \mathbb{C}^*$ and $\beta \in \mathbb{C}$, we now reserve α^β to denote its **principal value**:

$$\alpha^\beta = \exp(\beta \log \alpha). \tag{5.248}$$

For instance

$$i^i = \exp(i\pi i/2) = e^{-\pi/2} = 0.20787957635\ldots.$$

The value assigned to α^β by (5.248) is in agreement with earlier definitions:

(i) when $\beta \in \mathbb{Z}$, as in (3.20)(iii), by (5.227)(β);
(ii) when $|\alpha - 1| < 1$, as in (5.171)(α), by (5.224);
(iii) when $\alpha \in \mathbb{R}^>$ and $\beta \in \mathbb{R}$, as in (5.202), by (5.207) and (5.228).

When $n \in \mathbb{N}$ we also write $\sqrt[n]{\alpha}$ for $\alpha^{1/n}$; as usual this is shortened to $\sqrt{\alpha}$ when $n = 2$. Thus

$$\sqrt{-1} = i$$

and more generally, $\sqrt{-\alpha} = \sqrt{\alpha}\, i$ for $\alpha \in \mathbb{R}^{\geqslant}$.

Since $\log e = 1$, for all $\theta \in \mathbb{R}$ (or, for that matter, all $\theta \in \mathbb{C}$),

$$e^{i\theta} = \exp(i\theta) = \cos\theta + i \sin\theta.$$

For this reason the polar form is often written as

$$\alpha = re^{i\theta}.$$

Unless stated otherwise, such an equation always carries with it the understanding that $r \in \mathbb{R}^{\geqslant}$ and $\theta \in \mathbb{R}$, so $r = |\alpha|$ and $\theta = \mathrm{am}(\alpha) + 2\pi m i$ for some $m \in \mathbb{Z}$.

As an application of the foregoing, we have **DeMoivre's theorem**:

(5.249) PROPOSITION. *If $\alpha = re^{i\theta} \in \mathbb{C}^*$, then the n roots of $X^n - \alpha = (X-\gamma_0)\cdots(X-\gamma_{n-1})$ are given by*

$$\gamma_j = \sqrt[n]{r}\,\exp((\theta + 2\pi j)i/n), \qquad 0 \leqslant j \leqslant n-1,$$

where $\sqrt[n]{r}$ denotes the unique positive nth root of $r \in \mathbb{R}^{>}$.

The verification simply amounts to the observation that the γ_j are distinct and $\gamma_j^n = r\exp(\theta + 2\pi j i) = \alpha$. If $\theta = \mathrm{am}(\alpha) + 2\pi m i$, it is clear that we can allow $m \neq 0$ and that we can take for the values of j any complete residue system mod n. Of course the set of γ_j does not depend on these choices since the factorization of $X^n - \alpha$ in $\mathbb{C}[X]$ is unique.

In Figure 5.19 the γ_j appear as equally spaced points on a circle of radius $\sqrt[n]{r}$ since $\mathrm{am}(\gamma_{j+1}) - \mathrm{am}(\gamma_j) = 2\pi/n$ is independent of j, alternatively since

$$|\gamma_{j+1} - \gamma_j| = |\gamma_j||1 - \gamma_{j+1}\gamma_j^{-1}| = \sqrt[n]{r}\,|1 - e^{2\pi i/n}|$$

is independent of j.

Figure 5.19

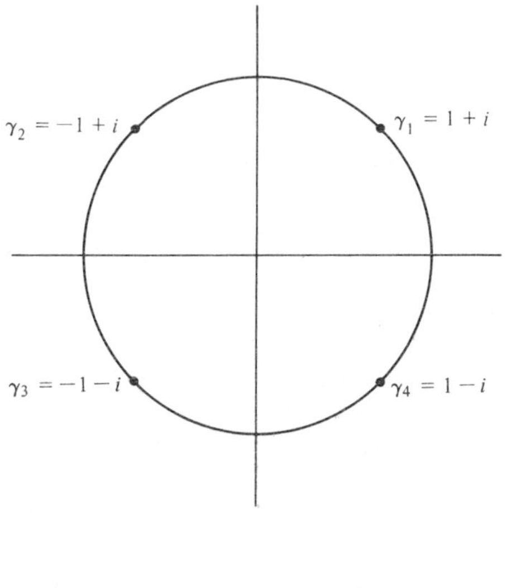

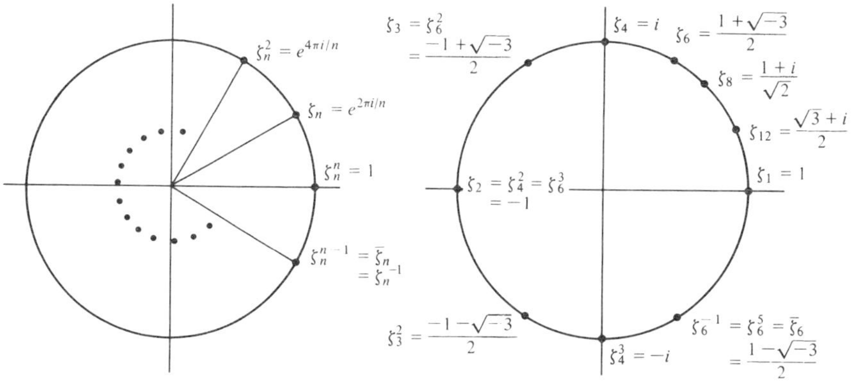

(a) (b)

Figure 5.20

We can define the distance between two points $\alpha, \beta \in \mathbb{R}^2$, with the usual identification of $\mathbb{R}^2$ with $\mathbb{C}$, as $|\alpha - \beta|$.

DeMoivre's theorem applied to $X^n - 1$ shows that the complex nth roots of unity (see Figure 5.20a) are $\zeta_n, \zeta_n{}^2, \ldots, \zeta_n{}^{n-1}$ and $\zeta_n{}^n = 1$, where $\zeta_n = \exp(2\pi i/n)$ and $\zeta_n^j = \exp(2\pi ij/n)$. Thus $\zeta_{mn}{}^m = \zeta_n$.

In Figure 5.20b we indicate a few cases where the rectangular form can be expressed simply in terms of radicals.

EXERCISES

1. Find all $x \in \mathbb{C}$ satisfying

$$\frac{1}{\sqrt{x+\sqrt{x^2-1}}} + \frac{1}{\sqrt{x-\sqrt{x^2-1}}} = 2(x^3+1),$$

where the square root sign denotes the principal value. (*Caution*: Squaring the two sides of an equation can introduce spurious roots. For example, the fact that $\sqrt{x} = -1$ has no (principal value) solution in $\mathbb{C}$ is obliterated by squaring both sides.)

2. If $\alpha = a + bi \in \mathbb{C}$, then one value of $\alpha^{1/4} + \bar{\alpha}^{1/4}$ is $\surd(\surd(2a+2|a|) + 2\sqrt{|\alpha|})$.

3. Let $f = X^3 + 3aX + b$ be real with positive discriminant, so $a < 0$, let $c = \sqrt{-a}$, and let θ be any real number for which $\cos\theta = b/2ac$. Then the roots of f are

$$2c\cos(\theta/3), \qquad 2c\cos(\theta/3 + 2\pi/3), \qquad 2c\cos(\theta/3 + 4\pi/3).$$

4. $2\cos(2\pi/7)$ is a root of $X^3 + X^2 - 2X - 1$.

5. By solving $X^4+X^3+X^2+X+1=0$ (essentially) as a quadratic in $X+1/X$, verify the values ($1°=\pi/180$):

$$\cos 36° = \left(\sqrt{5}+1\right)/4, \qquad \sin 36° = \sqrt{\left(5-\sqrt{5}\right)/8}\,,$$

$$\cos 72° = \left(\sqrt{5}-1\right)/4, \qquad \sin 72° = \sqrt{\left(5+\sqrt{5}\right)/8}\,.$$

6. Let $n\in\mathbb{N}$ and $\zeta=\exp(2\pi i m/n)\in\mathbb{C}$, where $1\leqslant m<n$. Deduce from $\Sigma_{k=1}^{n}\zeta^k=0$ that $\Sigma_{k=1}^{n} f(x+2\pi k/n)=0$ for any f of the form $f(x)=a_1\cos(x)+\cdots+a_m\cos(mx)+b_1\sin(x)+\cdots+b_m\sin(mx)$, $m<n$.

7. Define the two sequences of polynomials $T_n=T_n(X)$, $U_n=U_n(X)$ by $T_0=U_0=1$ and

$$T_{n+1}=XT_n-(1-X^2)U_{n-1}, \qquad U_{n+1}=T_{n+1}+XU_n.$$

(Thus $U_{-1}=0$, $T_1=X$, $U_1=2X$, $T_2=2X^2-1$, and so on.)

(i) Supposing $T_1=\cos\theta$, show that $T_n=\cos n\theta$ and $U_n=\sin(n+1)\theta/\sin\theta$. ($T_n$ and U_n are called **Chebyshev polynomials** of the first and second kinds.)

(ii) Hence obtain $\cos 6\theta=32\cos^6\theta-48\cos^4\theta+18\cos^2\theta-1$ and similarly express $\sin 6\theta$ as a polynomial in $\cos\theta$ and $\sin\theta$. Verify these calculations by expanding $\cos 6\theta+i\sin 6\theta=(\cos\theta+i\sin\theta)^6$.

(iii) A theorem of Markov says that if $f\in\mathbb{R}[X]$, $\deg f=n$, and $|f(x)|\leqslant 1$ for $|x|\leqslant 1$, then $|f'(x)|\leqslant n^2$ for $|x|\leqslant 1$; moreover, the equality $|f'(x)|=n^2$ is attained at most for $x=-1$ and $x=1$, and only if $f=\pm T_n$. Prove these facts in the case $n=2$.

8. Let D_n denote the subgroup $\langle\sigma,\tau\rangle$ of Sym($\mathbb{C}$), where $\sigma(\alpha)=\bar{\alpha}$ and $\tau(\alpha)=\zeta\alpha$, $\zeta=e^{2\pi i/n}$.

(i) D_n is finite of order $2n$ and the elements are uniquely represented as $\sigma^j\tau^k$, $j\in\{0,1\}$, $k\in\{0,1,\ldots,n-1\}$.

(ii) D_4 is isomorphic to the dihedral group of order 8 as defined in Supple-

Figure 5.21

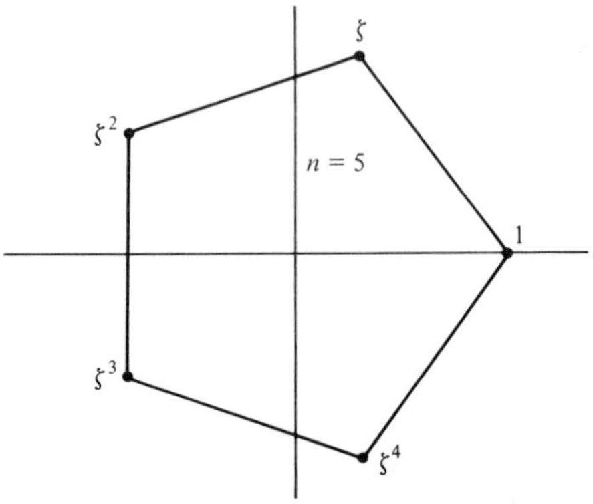

mentary Exercise 15 of Chapter 3. (D_n is called the **dihedral group** of order $2n$.)

(iii) D_n is isomorphic to the subgroup of $GL_2(\mathbb{C})$ generated by

$$\bar{\sigma}=\begin{pmatrix}0&1\\1&0\end{pmatrix} \quad \text{and} \quad \bar{\tau}=\begin{pmatrix}\zeta&0\\0&\bar{\zeta}\end{pmatrix}.$$

(iv) For $n\geqslant 3$, by restricting the action of σ and τ to the n-element set $\{1,\zeta,\dots,\zeta^{n-1}\}$, represent D_n as a subgroup of Sym(n). (See Figure 5.21.) (Geometrically, D_n is the group of rigid motions of the regular n-sided polygon with vertices $1,\zeta,\dots,\zeta^{n-1}$ in the complex plane, where σ is "flip over" and τ is clockwise rotation through $2\pi/n$ radians.)

21. CYCLOTOMY

The n complex nth roots of 1 cut the unit circle $\{\alpha\in\mathbb{C}:|\alpha|=1\}$ into the n parts described by $(j-1)\pi/n\leqslant \text{am}(\alpha)\leqslant j\pi/n$, $j=1,2,\dots,n$. This is the source of the word "cyclotomy," but the term is now used to mean the theory of roots of unity in any field. The discussion of cyclotomy in this section will lead us into a variety of topics: cyclotomic polynomials, Möbius inversion, the inclusion–exclusion principle, cyclic groups, and finally, as an application of (complex) roots of unity to number theory, the law of quadratic reciprocity.

Let k be a field and (in this section) let U_n denote the nth roots of unity in k. As mentioned just before (5.100), U_n is a subgroup of k^*. If $n=dh$ (in $\mathbb{N}$) and $\zeta\in U_d$, then since

$$\zeta^n=(\zeta^d)^h=1,$$

we have $\zeta\in U_n$. In other words, if $d|n$ then, U_d is a subgroup of U_n. More generally, if $m,n\in\mathbb{N}$ and g.c.d. $(m,n)=d$ then

(5.250) $$U_m\cap U_n=U_d,$$

for since $d|m$ and $d|n$, the left side contains the right; conversely, if $\zeta\in U_m\cap U_n$ and $d=mx+ny$, where $x,y\in\mathbb{Z}$, then $\zeta^d=(\zeta^m)^x(\zeta^n)^y=1^x1^y=1$, and so $\zeta\in U_d$.

It follows from this equation that if $\zeta^n=1$ and if d is the smallest positive integer such that $\zeta^d=1$, then $d|n$.

A **primitive *n*th root of 1** is a member ζ of U_n such that $\zeta\notin U_d$ for all $d<n$; equivalently,

(5.251) $$\zeta^m=1 \quad\Leftrightarrow\quad m\equiv 0 \mod n.$$

It follows that $1,\zeta,\dots,\zeta^{n-1}$ are distinct and $U_n=\{1,\zeta,\dots,\zeta^{n-1}\}$. In general, $|U_n|\leqslant n$ since X^n-1 has at most n distinct roots in k, and $|U_n|=n$ is equivalent to the existence in k of a primitive nth root of 1. (If char(k)$=p>0$ and $p|n$, say $n=pm$, then $X^n-1=(X^m-1)^p$ in $k[X]$, so $U_n=U_m$ and there are no primitive nth roots of 1 in k.) If ζ is a primitive nth root of 1 in k, it follows from the characterization in (5.251) and A6.2(β) that ζ^j is a primitive $n/\text{g.c.d.}(j,n)$th root of 1. In particular, ζ^j is a primitive nth root of 1 iff $\text{g.c.d.}(j,n)=1$. Thus

(5.252) PROPOSITION. *The number of primitive nth roots of* 1 *in k is* 0 *or* $\varphi(n)$, *and is* 0 *when* $\text{char}(k)|n$.

In $\mathbb{C}$ the number is $\varphi(n)$ and the polynomial

$$\kappa_n(X)=\prod_{\substack{j=1\\ \text{g.c.d.}(j,n)=1}}^{n}(X-e^{2\pi ij/n}) \tag{5.253}$$

of degree $\varphi(n)$ whose roots are the complex primitive nth roots of 1 is called the ***n*th cyclotomic polynomial**. Since each root ζ of X^n-1 is a root of precisely one κ_d, where $d|n$, namely, the smallest $d\ni\zeta\in U_d$, we have

$$X^n-1=\prod_{d|n}\kappa_d(X). \tag{5.254}$$

If we compare degrees we reestablish (3.64). The first few of these equations are

$$\begin{aligned} X-1&=\kappa_1,\\ X^2-1&=\kappa_1\kappa_2,\\ X^3-1&=\kappa_1\kappa_3,\\ X^4-1&=\kappa_1\kappa_2\kappa_4. \end{aligned}$$

These can be solved in succession for the κ_n:

$$\begin{aligned} \kappa_1&=X-1,\\ \kappa_2&=(X^2-1)/(X-1)=X+1,\\ \kappa_3&=(X^3-1)/(X-1)=X^2+X+1,\\ \kappa_4&=(X^4-1)/(X^2-1)=X^2+1. \end{aligned} \tag{5.255}$$

In order to systematize this process we prove a fundamental combinatorial principle.

(5.256) DEFINITION. The **Möbius function** $\mu:\mathbb{N}\to\mathbb{Z}$ is defined by

$$\mu(n)=\begin{cases}(-1)^m & \text{if } n \text{ is a product of m distinct}\\ & \qquad\text{primes (including } \mu(1)=1),\\ 0 & \text{otherwise.}\end{cases}$$

Thus $\mu(n)\neq 0$ iff n is **square free**, i.e., not divisible by the square of a prime. We recall that the notation $\Sigma_{d|n}$, $\Pi_{d|n}$ implies that the sum or product is extended over all divisors d of n in $\mathbb{N}$.

n	1	2	3	4	5	6	7	8	9	10	11	12
$\mu(n)$	1	-1	-1	0	-1	1	-1	0	0	1	-1	0
$\varphi(n)$	1	1	2	2	4	2	6	4	6	4	10	4

(5.257) PROPOSITION. $\Sigma_{d|n}\mu(d)=\delta_{1n}$ ($=1$ *if* $n=1$ *and* $=0$ *otherwise*).

Proof. The statement is true when $n=1$, so we can suppose $n=p_1^{e_1}\cdots p_r^{e_r}$, where $e_i>0$ and $r>0$. The divisors d for which $\mu(d)\neq 0$ are $d=p_1^{f_1}\cdots p_r^{f_r}$ where each $f_i=0$ or 1. Thus if $m=p_1^{e_1}\cdots p_{r-1}^{e_{r-1}}$ ($m=1$ if $r=1$), then

$$\sum_{d|n}\mu(d)=\sum_{d|m}(\mu(d)+\mu(dp_r))$$
$$=\sum_{d|m}(\mu(d)-\mu(d))=0. \quad \blacksquare$$

The following result is known as the **Möbius inversion formula**:

(5.258) COROLLARY. *If A is an abelian group, written additively, if $a_1, a_2,\ldots$ are elements of A, and if we define*

$$b_n=\sum_{d|n}a_d, \tag{5.259}$$

then

$$a_n=\sum_{d|n}\mu(n/d)b_d. \tag{5.260}$$

Conversely, the relations (5.260) *imply the relations* (5.259).

Proof. With the notation $n=dd'$, assuming (5.259),

$$\sum_{d|n}\mu(n/d)b_b=\sum_{d|n}\mu(d')\sum_{e|d}a_e=\sum_{e|n}\left[\sum_{d'|(n/e)}\mu(d')\right]a_e=a_n,$$

since the inner sum is 0 except when $n/e=1$. Similarly, if we assume (5.260) and write $d=ee'$, then

$$\sum_{d|n}a_d=\sum_{d|n}\sum_{e|d}\mu(e')b_e=\sum_{e|n}\left[\sum_{e'|(n/e)}\mu(e')\right]b_e=b_n. \quad \blacksquare$$

Notice that as d runs through the divisors of n so does n/d, and hence (5.260) can be written

$$a_n=\sum_{d|n}\mu(d)b_{n/d}.$$

Möbius inversion applied to (3.64) gives

$$\varphi(n)=\sum_{d|n}\mu(n/d)d=n\sum_{d|n}\mu(d)/d; \tag{5.261}$$

and applied (in multiplicative notation) to (5.254) gives

$$\kappa_n = \prod_{d|n} (X^d - 1)^{\mu(n/d)} = \prod_{d|n} (X^{n/d} - 1)^{\mu(d)}. \tag{5.262}$$

This exhibits the polynomial κ_n as a rational function $f(X)/g(X) \in \mathbb{Q}(X)$. Now f and g are products of various $X^d - 1$ and are therefore monic polynomials in $\mathbb{Z}[X]$. Hence in the division process, as explained in (3.32), no fractional coefficients are introduced:

$$\kappa_n(X) \in \mathbb{Z}[X]. \tag{5.263}$$

This permits $\kappa_n(X)$ to be interpreted as a polynomial over any field k.

(5.264) PROPOSITION. (i) *Let k be a field and n a positive integer that is not a multiple of* char(k). *Then every primitive n*th *root of* 1 *in k is a root of κ_n. Conversely, every root of κ_n is a primitive n*th *root of* 1. *The unique factorization of κ_n in $k[X]$ contains no repeated factors.*

(ii) *For every n, κ_n is irreducible over $\mathbb{Q}$.*

Remark. It was already observed in (5.102) that if p is a prime then κ_p is irreducible over $\mathbb{Q}_p$, and hence irreducible over $\mathbb{Q}$.

Proof. (i) If ζ is a primitive nth root of 1 in k, then ζ is a root of κ_n since

$$(X^n - 1) \prod_{d|n, d>1} (X^d - 1)^{\mu(n/d)} = \kappa_n.$$

If $f = X^n - 1$ then $f' = nX^{n-1} \neq 0$ (since char$(k) \nmid n$) and g.c.d.$(f, f') = 1$. Hence f has no repeated factor and in particular no repeated root in k. It follows from

$$f = X^n - 1 = \prod_{d|n} \kappa_d$$

that κ_n has no repeated factor. This also shows that a root ζ of κ_n is a root of $X^n - 1$ but not a root of $X^m - 1 = \prod_{d|m} \kappa_d$ for any proper divisor m of n (since then it would be a root of two factors κ_n and some κ_d, hence a repeated root of $X^n - 1$). In other words, ζ is a primitive nth root of 1.

(ii) Let $\kappa_n = f_1 f_2 \cdots f_r$ be the unique factorization of κ_n in $\mathbb{Q}[X]$ into monic irreducible f_i, and suppose $r > 1$. By (3.73), $f_i \in \mathbb{Z}[X]$. Let $e^{2\pi i/n}$ be a root of f_1, say. Taking successively $j = 2, 3, \ldots$, consider the first $e^{2\pi ij/n}$ that is a root of one of the other f's, say f_2. Necessarily j is prime to n, and if we write $j = pm$ for some prime p, then $p \nmid n$ and $\zeta = e^{2\pi im/n}$ is a root of f_1 (by the minimality of j) and ζ^p a root of f_2. However, then ζ is a root of $f_2(X^p)$. Hence

$$f_2(X^p) = f_1(X) g(X)$$

for some $g \in \mathbb{Q}[X]$. In fact, $g \in \mathbb{Z}[X]$ since the f_i are in $\mathbb{Z}[X]$ and are monic. If $\bar{f}$ denotes the canonical image of an $f \in \mathbb{Z}[X]$ in $\mathbb{F}_p[X]$, we have

$$\bar{f}_2(X)^p = \bar{f}_2(X^p) = \bar{f}_1(X)\bar{g}(X). \tag{5.265}$$

Hence the irreducible factors of $\bar{f}_1$ in $\mathbb{F}_p[X]$ occur in $\bar{f}_2$. This implies that $\bar{\kappa}_n = \bar{f}_1 \bar{f}_2 \cdots$, which is the nth cyclotomic polynomial for $\mathbb{F}_p$, has a repeated factor. Since $p \nmid n$, this is a contradiction. ■

Here is another application of Möbius inversion, the **inclusion–exclusion principle**:

(5.266) PROPOSITION. *Let S be a set with N elements of which N_i have property i (i.e., belong to a certain subset S_i), where $1 \leq i \leq r$, N_{ij} have both properties i and j (i.e., belong to $S_i \cap S_j$), N_{ijk} have all three properties i, j, k, and so on. Then the number of elements that have none of the r properties is*

$$N - \sum N_i + \sum N_{ij} - \sum N_{ijk} + \cdots. \tag{5.267}$$

Proof. Choose any distinct primes $p_1, \ldots, p_r$ and put $n = p_1 \cdots p_r$. For each divisor $d = p_1^{f_1} \cdots p_r^{f_r}$ of n (each $f_i = 0$ or 1), let $f(d)$ denote the number of $s \in S$ satisfying

$$s \in S_i \quad \text{if } f_i = 0, \qquad s \notin S_i \quad \text{if } f_i = 1.$$

Thus if $i_1, \ldots, i_m$ are the subscripts for which $f_i = 0$, then

$$g(d) = \sum_{e|d} f(e) = |S_{i_1} \cap \cdots \cap S_{i_m}| = N_{i_1 \cdots i_m}.$$

Möbius inversion gives

$$f(n) = \sum_{d|n} \mu(d) g(n/d).$$

Now $g(n) = N$, and if $d = p_{j_1} \cdots p_{j_t} > 1$, then

$$g(n/d) = |S_{j_1} \cap \cdots \cap S_{j_t}| = N_{j_1 \cdots j_t},$$

and the relation is

$$f(n) = N - \sum N_i + \sum N_{ij} - \sum N_{ijk} + \cdots. \quad ■$$

As an application, let $S = \{1, 2, \ldots, N\}$, where N has the prime power factorization $p_1^{e_1} \cdots p_r^{e_r}$, and let the ith property be divisibility by p_i. Thus $N_{i_1 \cdots i_t}$ is the number of natural numbers $m \leq N$ that are divisible by each of the primes $p_{i_1}, \ldots, p_{i_t}$. By unique factorization, such m are precisely the multiples of the product $p_{i_1} \cdots p_{i_t}$ and therefore

$$N_{i_1 \cdots i_t} = N / p_{i_1} \cdots p_{i_t}.$$

The sum (5.267) is

$$N - \sum \frac{N}{p_i} + \sum \frac{N}{p_i p_j} - \cdots = N \prod \left(1 - \frac{1}{p_i}\right).$$

Since the m that have none of the properties are precisely the m relatively prime to n, we have

(5.268) COROLLARY. *If* $N = p_1^{e_1}\cdots p_r^{e_r}$ $(e_i > 0)$, *then*

$$\varphi(N) = N\prod_{p|N}\left(1-\frac{1}{p}\right) = \prod p_i^{e_i-1}(p_i-1).$$

For instance,

$$\varphi(12) = 12(1-\tfrac{1}{2})(1-\tfrac{1}{3}) = 4.$$

Recall from Chapter 3 (just after 3.20) the

(5.269) DEFINITION. A group A is **cyclic** if $A = \langle a\rangle$ (in the notation of A6.1) for some $a \in A$. This means that every element in A can be written in the form a^n for some $n \in \mathbb{Z}$. Then a is called a **generator** of A.

(5.270) REMARKS AND EXAMPLES

1. Since $a^m a^n = a^{m+n} = a^n a^m$, a cyclic group is abelian.

2. If a is an element of a group G, then the subgroup $\langle a\rangle$ generated by a is cyclic and a is a generator. For $\langle a\rangle$ consists of all a^n, $n \in \mathbb{Z}$. (Of course, these elements are not necessarily distinct.) For example, in the group of all complex roots of unity, $U_n = \langle \zeta_n\rangle$ is cyclic. If m is another natural number, then $\langle \zeta_m, \zeta_n\rangle$ in general is not generated by either ζ_m or ζ_n, although it is cyclic, generated by ζ_N, where $N =$ l.c.m.(m,n). The reason is that $\langle \zeta_N\rangle$ contains ζ_m and ζ_n since m and n are divisors of N, and if g.c.d.$(m,n) = d$, so that $N = mn/d$, and if $mx + ny = d$, $x, y \in \mathbb{Z}$, then

$$\zeta_m^y\zeta_n^x = \exp(2\pi i(y/m + x/n)) = \exp(2\pi i/N) = \zeta_N.$$

This observation will be generalized in (5.272).

3. For $n \in \mathbb{N}$, the additive group of the ring $\mathbb{Z}/n\mathbb{Z}$ is denoted variously Cyl_n, $\mathrm{Cyl}(n)$, $C(n)$. Thus Cyl_n is obtained from $\mathbb{Z}/n\mathbb{Z}$ by "forgetting" multiplication and the special status of 1. Cyl_n is cyclic since $j = j\cdot 1 = (-j)(-1)$, $\forall j \in \mathbb{Z}$, and therefore both 1 and -1 are generators. In the infinite cyclic group no other element a is a generator since $\langle a\rangle = \mathbb{Z}a$ is a proper subgroup. When $n > 0$, Cyl_n contains precisely $\varphi(n)$ generators, as we now prove. The elements of Cyl_n are represented by the integers $0,1,2,\ldots,n-1$. If m is an integer and g.c.d.$(m,n) = d$, say $dd' = n$, then in Cyl_n, $\langle m\rangle = \langle d\rangle = \{0, d, 2d, \ldots, (d'-1)d\}$, as is clear from the relations $mx + ny = d$, $dz = m$, where $x, y, z \in \mathbb{Z}$. This is the whole group iff $d = 1$ and therefore the generators of Cyl_n are represented by the $\varphi(n)$ integers between 1 and n that are relatively prime to n.

4. The list of cyclic groups Cyl_n is actually complete: A cyclic group A is isomorphic to exactly one Cyl_n. Indeed if a is a generator of A, define $f\colon \mathrm{Cyl}_0 \to A$ by $f(m) = ma$. This is a surjective group homomorphism. If $a, b \in \mathrm{Ker}(f)$ and $c \in \mathbb{Z}$, then $a+b$ and $ac \in \mathrm{Ker}(f)$; hence $\mathrm{Ker}(f)$ is an ideal, say $n\mathbb{Z}$, $n \geqslant 0$. Thus f induces an isomorphism $\bar{f}\colon \mathrm{Cyl}_n \xrightarrow{\sim} A$. No two of the groups Cyl_n are isomorphic since they consist of different numbers of elements. Thus A uniquely determines n. On the other hand, the isomorphism $\bar{f}$ is not unique (unless $n = 1$ or 2) since we are free to choose any generator a. For example, the group $U_6 = \{1, \zeta, \ldots, \zeta^5 : \zeta^6 = 1\}$, where $\zeta = \exp(\pi i/3)$ admits two isomorphisms $\bar{f}\colon \mathrm{Cyl}_6 \to U_6$. One is fixed by $f_1(1) = \zeta$, the other by $f_2(1) = \zeta^5$. An alternative way of viewing this is that Cyl_6 has a

nontrivial automorphism $f_2^{-1}f_1$ given by $m \mapsto -m$. (Of course, this is only a group automorphism of $\mathbb{Z}/6\mathbb{Z}$, not a ring automorphism.)

5. In an isomorphism $f: A \to B$ between cyclic groups, since $f(ma) = mf(a)$, generators correspond to generators. Thus (3) and (4) combined give the statement: If A is a cyclic group of order n then A has precisely $\varphi(n)$ generators; if a is one of them, then the others are a^m, where $1 \leqslant m \leqslant n$ and g.c.d.$(m, n) = 1$. In particular, if the field k contains a primitive nth root of 1, then the number of primitive nth roots of 1 in k is $\varphi(n)$, and these are the generators ζ^m of U_n. (In the next proposition we shall see that the group U_n is always cyclic and therefore k contains a primitive nth root of 1 iff $|U_n| = n$.)

6. The last remark in (4) can be amplified as follows. If A denotes the (not necessarily cyclic) additive group of the ring R and $r \in R$, then the map $a \mapsto ra$, called **left homothety by r**, is an endomorphism of A (since $r(a+b) = ra + rb$). It is an automorphism iff $r \in R^*$, for if $r \in R^*$, then the inverse automorphism is homothety by r^{-1}; conversely, if $a \mapsto ra$ is bijective, then $ra = 1$ for some a, and since $r(ar - 1) = 0$, we must have $ar - 1 = 0$; hence $r \in R^*$ with $r^{-1} = a$. Of course, similar remarks apply to right homotheties. If $r \neq 0$, the map $a \mapsto a + r$, called **translation by r**, does not preserve sums.

7. For any abelian group A and $r \in \mathbb{Z}$, $h_r(a) = ra$ defines an endomorphism of A. Hence $\operatorname{Im}(h_r)$ (which can be written rA) and $\operatorname{Ker}(h_r)$ are subgroups. We note that if A is finite cyclic and $|A| = n$, then

$$(5.271) \qquad |rA| = n/d, \qquad \text{where} \quad d = \text{g.c.d.}(r, n),$$

since by (4) we can take $A = \mathbb{Z}/n\mathbb{Z}$, and the result follows from the fact that $rx \equiv a \bmod n$ has a solution iff $d \mid a$; indeed A6.2(β) shows that if $a \in rA$, then $rx = a$ has precisely d solutions $x \in A$. This last fact (or Lagrange's theorem applied to (5.271)) implies $|\operatorname{Ker}(h_r)| = d$.

8. Every subgroup of a cyclic group is cyclic. To prove this, again by (4) we can assume that H is a subgroup of Cyl_n. Since $0 = \langle 0 \rangle$ is cyclic, we can assume that H contains a nonzero element x. Now either x or $-x$ is represented by a positive integer m, and taking m minimal, the usual argument using the division algorithm shows that the elements of H are those represented by multiples of m. Thus $H = \langle x \rangle$.

(5.272) PROPOSITION. *Let A be a finite group of order n such that, for each divisor d of n, $\{a \in A : a^d = 1\}$ consists of at most d elements (for instance when A is a finite subgroup of the multiplicative group k^* of a field k). Then A is cyclic.*

Proof. If A contains an element a of order d, then each of the d elements $x \in \langle a \rangle$ satisfies $x^d = 1$ (by A6.1(vi)), and therefore by assumption there are no other elements in A satisfying this equation. In particular, the elements of order d are precisely the generators of $\langle a \rangle$, and there are $\varphi(d)$ of these by (5.270)(5). Thus, if $\psi(d)$ denotes the number of elements of order d in A, then since the total number of elements is n, and repeating (3.64), we have

$$\psi(d) = 0 \quad \text{or} \quad \varphi(d) \qquad \text{and} \qquad \sum_{d \mid n} \psi(d) = \sum_{d \mid n} \varphi(n) = n.$$

These imply that $\psi(d)=\varphi(d)$ for every divisor d of n. In particular, $\psi(n)>0$, and therefore A is cyclic. ■

(5.273) COROLLARY. *For every finite field* $\mathbb{F}_q$, $\mathbb{F}_q{}^*$ *is cyclic. Thus the cyclotomic polynomial* κ_{q-1} *factors into linear factors over* $\mathbb{F}_q$, *and, consequently, for each prime* p, κ_{p-1} *factors into linear factors over* $\mathbb{Q}_p$.

Proof. Since $|\mathbb{F}_q{}^*|=q-1$, every $a\in\mathbb{F}_q{}^*$ satisfies $a^{q-1}=1$, i.e, $\mathbb{F}_q{}^*=U_{q-1}$, and the generators of $\mathbb{F}_q{}^*$ are precisely the $\varphi(q-1)$ primitive $(q-1)$st roots of 1. They, or integers representing these generators in the case $\mathbb{Z}/p\mathbb{Z}$, are called **primitive roots** for short. Hensel's lemma gives a root ξ of κ_{p-1} in $\mathbb{Q}_p$ satisfying $\xi\equiv g \bmod p$ for each of the $\varphi(p-1)$ primitive roots mod p satisfying $1\leqslant g\leqslant p-1$. Hence κ_{p-1} factors completely over $\mathbb{Q}_p$. ■

(The example $\kappa_4=(X-i)(X+i)\in\mathbb{Q}_5[X]$ was worked out in Section 7.)

Example. By Lagrange's theorem, the possible orders of 2 in $\mathbb{F}_{11}{}^*$ are the divisors $d=1,2,5,10$ of 10. Since $2^d\not\equiv 1 \bmod 11$ for $d=1$, 2 or 5, we conclude that 2 is a primitive root mod 11. The others are $2^3=8$, $2^7\equiv 7$, and $2^9\equiv 6$ (since 1,3,7,9 are the $\varphi(10)=4$ numbers between 1 and 10 relatively prime to 10.) As of 1980, it is not yet known whether there are infinitely many primes p for which a given number, such as 2, is a primitive root.

Let us transcribe the statements in (5.270) (7) for the case $A=\mathbb{F}_q{}^*$:

$$|\mathrm{Ker}(h_r)|=|U_r|=d=\text{g.c.d.}(d,q-1);$$

the subgroup rA is now the set of rth powers in $\mathbb{F}_q{}^*$ or, equivalently, the elements with an rth root in $\mathbb{F}_q{}^*$; (5.271) reads as follows.

(5.274) COROLLARY. *If* $r\in\mathbb{N}$ *then the number of rth powers in* $\mathbb{F}_q{}^*$ *is* $(q-1)/d$, *where* $d=\text{g.c.d.}(r,q-1)$.

For the remainder of this section p denotes an odd prime, g a primitive root mod p, and $p'=(p-1)/2$.

Since $g^{p'}\not\equiv 1$ and $(g^{p'})^2\equiv g^{p-1}\equiv 1$, we have

(5.275) $$g^{p'}\equiv -1 \mod p.$$

(5.276) COROLLARY **Wilson's theorem.** $(p-1)!\equiv -1 \bmod p$.

Proof.

$$(p-1)!\equiv\prod_{i=1}^{p-1} g^i=g^{\Sigma i}=g^{p'p}\equiv(-1)^p\equiv -1.$$ ■

By (5.274) the number of nonzero squares in $\mathbb{F}_p$ is p'; they are given by the even powers $g^2, g^4, \ldots, g^{p-1}$. If Q denotes the group of these squares, then Q is a subgroup of index 2 in $\mathbb{F}_p{}^*$, and the coset gQ of nonsquares consists of the odd powers $g, g^3, \ldots, g^{p-2}$. Of course, Q does not depend on the choice of g. For instance, when $p = 11$, $g = 2$, we have

$$Q = \{2^2 = 4, 2^4 \equiv 5, 2^6 \equiv 9, 2^8 \equiv 3, 2^{10} \equiv 1\},$$
$$2Q = \{2, 2^3 = 8, 2^5 \equiv 10, 2^7 \equiv 7, 2^9 \equiv 6\}.$$

It is customary to call an element of Q, or an integer representing such an element, a **quadratic residue** (mod p). Similarly, an element of gQ, or a representing integer, is called a **quadratic nonresidue**. If g^{2s+1} and g^{2t+1} are two quadratic nonresidues, then their product $g^{2s+2t+2}$ is a quadratic residue. Similarly, the product of a quadratic nonresidue with a quadratic residue is a quadratic nonresidue, and the product of two quadratic residues is a quadratic residue.

A convenient notation is afforded by the **Legendre symbol**: If a is an integer not divisible by p then

$$\left(\frac{a}{p}\right) = \begin{cases} 1 & \text{if} \quad a \text{ is a quadratic residue mod } p, \\ -1 & \text{if} \quad a \text{ is a quadratic nonresidue mod } p. \end{cases}$$

The rules derived above are summarized by

$$\left(\frac{ab}{p}\right) = \left(\frac{a}{p}\right)\left(\frac{b}{p}\right), \tag{5.277}$$

where a, b are any two integers not divisible by p. Also it is plain from the definition that

$$a \equiv b \bmod p \quad \Rightarrow \quad \left(\frac{a}{p}\right) = \left(\frac{b}{p}\right) \tag{5.278}$$

and

$$\left(\frac{ab^2}{p}\right) = \left(\frac{a}{p}\right). \tag{5.279}$$

(5.280) PROPOSITION (**Euler's criterion**).

$$\left(\frac{a}{p}\right) \equiv a^{p'} \mod p.$$

Proof. If $(a/p) = 1$, then $a \equiv g^{2s}$ for some integer s and $a^{p'} \equiv g^{(p-1)s} \equiv 1^s \equiv 1$; if $(a/p) = -1$, then $a \equiv g^{2s+1}$ and $a^{p'} \equiv g^{(p-1)s+p'} \equiv g^{p'} \equiv -1$ by (5.275). ■

In particular, since $(-1/p)$ and $(-1)^{p'}$ cannot differ by a multiple of $p > 2$,

$$\left(\frac{-1}{p}\right) = (-1)^{p'} = \begin{cases} +1, & \text{if} \quad p = 4n+1, \quad p' = 2n, \\ -1, & \text{if} \quad p = 4n-1, \quad p' = 2n-1. \end{cases} \tag{5.281}$$

For instance, $(-1/29)=1$, so -1 has a square root in the field $\mathbb{F}_{29}$ though Euler's criterion gives no clue as to its value; in fact $(\pm 12)^2 \equiv -1 \bmod 29$.

Here is the celebrated **law of quadratic reciprocity**:

(5.282) THEOREM. *If p, q are distinct odd primes then*

$$\left(\frac{p}{q}\right)\left(\frac{q}{p}\right)=(-1)^{p'q'}.$$

In other words, $(p/q)=(q/p)$ unless both p and $q \equiv 3 \bmod 4$ and then $(p/q)=-(q/p)$.

Proof. Let θ, ζ be complex numbers satisfying

$$\theta \neq 1, \qquad \theta^{p-1}=1, \qquad \zeta \neq 1, \qquad \zeta^p=1;$$

hence $1+\theta+\cdots+\theta^{p-2}=(\theta^{p-1}-1)/(\theta-1)=0$, and let

$$F(\theta,\zeta)=\sum_{s=0}^{p-2}\theta^s\zeta^{g^s}$$

(a special type of Gauss sum).

(5.283) LEMMA. (i) *For $a \not\equiv 0 \bmod p$, say $a \equiv g^t$, $F(\theta,\zeta^a)=\theta^{-t}F(\theta,\zeta)$.*
(ii) $F(\theta,\zeta)F(\theta^{-1},\zeta)=p\theta^{p'}$.

Proof of the lemma. (i) Since $\theta^s=\theta^r$ and $\zeta^{g^s}=\zeta^{g^r}$, if $s \equiv r \bmod p-1$, we can allow the variable s to range over any complete set of residues mod $p-1$ in the sum. Thus, writing r for $s+t$,

$$F(\theta,\zeta^a)=\sum_s \theta^s\zeta^{g^{s+t}}=\sum_r \theta^{r-t}\zeta^{g^r}=\theta^{-t}F(\theta,\zeta).$$

(ii) For $0 \leqslant k \leqslant p-2$, the coefficient of θ^k in $F(\theta,\zeta)F(\theta^{-1},\zeta)$ is

$$\alpha_k=\sum_{s=0}^{p-2}\zeta^{g^s+g^{s+k}}.$$

However, as $s=0,1,\ldots,p-2$, $g^s \equiv 1,2,\ldots,p-1 \bmod p$ in some order, and therefore $g^s+g^{s+k}=g^s(1+g^k)\equiv 1,2,\ldots,p-1 \bmod p$ in some order, provided $g^k \not\equiv -1 \bmod p$, i.e., provided $k \neq p'$. Thus

$$\alpha_k=\zeta+\zeta^2+\cdots+\zeta^{p-1}=-1 \qquad \text{if} \quad k \neq p',$$

and

$$\alpha_{p'}=1+\cdots+1=p-1.$$

Hence

$$F(\theta,\zeta)F(\theta^{-1},\zeta)=-(1+\theta+\cdots+\theta^{p-2})+p\theta^{p'}=p\theta^{p'}. \quad \blacksquare$$

To prove the theorem we take $F=F(-1,\zeta)$. Let A denote the subring $\mathbb{Z}[\zeta]$ of $\mathbb{C}$ and let $q\equiv g^t \bmod p$. Then

$$\begin{aligned} F^q &\equiv \sum(-1)^{qs}\zeta^{qg^s} \mod qA \qquad \text{by (3.52)} \\ &= F(-1,\zeta^q) \qquad \text{since } (-1)^q=-1 \\ &= (-1)^t F \qquad \text{by (i) of the lemma} \\ &= \left(\frac{q}{p}\right)F. \end{aligned}$$

Hence

$$\begin{aligned} F^{q+1} &\equiv \left(\frac{q}{p}\right)F^2 \mod qA \\ &= \left(\frac{q}{p}\right)(-1)^{p'}p \qquad \text{by (ii) of the lemma.} \end{aligned}$$

However,

$$\begin{aligned} F^{q+1} = F^{2(q'+1)} &= \left[(-1)^{p'}p\right]^{q'+1} \\ &\equiv (-1)^{p'q'}\left(\frac{p}{q}\right)(-1)^{p'}p \mod q \end{aligned}$$

by Euler's criterion, and therefore (since $\exists x\in\mathbb{Z}\ni px\equiv 1 \bmod q$)

$$\left(\frac{q}{p}\right)\equiv(-1)^{p'q'}\left(\frac{p}{q}\right) \mod qA.$$

This means that

$$\left(\frac{q}{p}\right)=(-1)^{p'q'}\left(\frac{p}{q}\right)+q\left(c_0+c_1\zeta+\cdots+c_{p-1}\zeta^{p-1}\right)$$

for some $c_i\in\mathbb{Z}$. Since $\{1,\zeta,\ldots,\zeta^{p-1}\}$ is linearly independent over $\mathbb{Q}$, $c_i=0$ for $i>0$; finally, since the Legendre symbols are ± 1 and $q>2$, also $c_0=0$. ∎

As a numerical example we determine the p for which 5 is a quadratic residue. Here $q=5$, $q'=2$, $(-1)^{p'q'}=1$ and $(5/p)=(p/5)$. Since the quadratic residues mod 5 are ± 1, we have proved

(5.284) COROLLARY. 5 *is a quadratic residue modulo primes of the form* $5n\pm 1$ *and a quadratic nonresidue modulo primes of the form* $5n\pm 2$.

By combining this with (5.281) we can say when $(-5/p)=1$: since $(-5/p)=(-1/p)(5/p)$, this occurs when $(-1/p)=(5/p)=1$ or $(-1/p)=(5/p)=-1$. Thus we have

(5.285) COROLLARY. $(-5/p)=1$ (*resp.* -1) *when* $p\equiv 1,3,7,9$ (*resp.* $-1,-3,-7,-9$) mod 20.

Similarly, if we wished to know when $(21/p)=1$ we could first determine $(3/p)$ and $(7/p)$ and then combine the results. However, there is an extended version of the reciprocity law that greatly facilitates such calculations. It uses a generalization of the Legendre symbol called the **Jacobi symbol** that is defined for odd positive "denominators" $d=p_1p_2\cdots p_r$, where the p_i are not necessarily distinct odd primes: If a is not divisible by any of the p_i, then

$$\left(\frac{a}{d}\right)=\left(\frac{a}{p_1}\right)\cdots\left(\frac{a}{p_r}\right).$$

The symbols on the right are Legendre symbols. For example,

$$\left(\frac{2}{15}\right)=\left(\frac{2}{3}\right)\left(\frac{2}{5}\right)=(-1)(-1)=1.$$

This example points out the fact that $(a/d)=1$ is only necessary, not in general sufficient (unless d is prime), that $x^2\equiv a \bmod d$ have a solution.

(5.286) PROPOSITION. *For integers such that the Jacobi symbols are defined (denominator odd and positive, numerator relatively prime to the denominator)*:

(i) $(ab/d)=(a/d)(b/d)$;
(ii) $(a/cd)=(a/c)(a/d)$;
(iii) $a\equiv b \bmod d\Rightarrow(a/d)=(b/d)$;
(iv) $(ab^2/d)=(a/d)$;
(v) $(-1/d)=(-1)^{d'}$, *where* $d'=(d-1)/2$;
(vi) $(d/c)=(-1)^{c'd'}(c/d)$, *where* $c'=(c-1)/2$;
(vii) $(2/d)=(-1)^{d''}$, *where* $d''=(d^2-1)/8$.

Proof. (i)–(iv) follow trivially from the corresponding properties of the Legendre symbol.

(v) If x and y are odd, then

$$(x-1)(y-1)\equiv 0 \mod 4,$$

or

$$xy-1\equiv x+y-2 \mod 4,$$

whence

$$\frac{xy-1}{2}\equiv\frac{x-1}{2}+\frac{y-1}{2} \mod 2.$$

Thus, if $d=p_1\cdots p_r$, repeated application gives

$$(*)\qquad d'=\frac{p_1\cdots p_r-1}{2}\equiv\frac{p_1-1}{2}+\cdots+\frac{p_r-1}{2} \mod 2;$$

hence

$$\left(\frac{-1}{d}\right)=\prod\left(\frac{-1}{p_i}\right)=\prod(-1)^{p_i'}=(-1)^{\Sigma p_i'}=(-1)^{d'}.$$

(vi) Let $d=p_1\cdots p_r$ and $c=q_1\cdots q_s$. Then

$$\left(\frac{d}{c}\right)=\prod_{i,j}\left(\frac{p_i}{q_j}\right)=(-1)^t\prod_{i,j}\left(\frac{q_j}{p_i}\right)=(-1)^t\left(\frac{c}{d}\right),$$

where

$$\begin{aligned} t&=\sum_{i,j}p_i'q_j' \qquad \text{by the law of reciprocity}\\ &=\left[\sum_i p_i'\right]\left[\sum_j q_j'\right]\\ &\equiv d'c' \mod 2 \qquad \text{by } (*). \end{aligned}$$

(vii) The formula is correct when $d=1$, and we proceed by induction. If $d\geqslant 3$, then

$$\begin{aligned} \left(\frac{2}{d}\right)&=\left(\frac{-1}{d}\right)\left(\frac{-2}{d}\right)=(-1)^{d'}\left(\frac{d-2}{d}\right) \qquad \text{by (iii) and (v)}\\ &=(-1)^{d'}\left(\frac{d}{d-2}\right) \qquad \text{by (vi)} \end{aligned}$$

(since one of $d, d-2$ is $\equiv 1 \mod 4$ and therefore $d'(d-2)'\equiv 0 \mod 2$); hence

$$\begin{aligned} \left(\frac{2}{d}\right)&=(-1)^{d'}\left(\frac{2}{d-2}\right) \qquad \text{by (iii)}\\ &=(-1)^x, \end{aligned}$$

where by induction $x=d'+((d-2)^2-1)/8=d''$. ■

By examining the four cases $d=8n+i$, it is easily ascertained that d'' is even when $d\equiv\pm 1 \mod 8$ and odd when $d\equiv\pm 3 \mod 8$. Hence

(5.287) COROLLARY. *2 is a quadratic residue mod primes of the form* $8n\pm 1$ *and a quadratic nonresidue mod primes of the form* $8n\pm 3$.

We close this section with a numerical example illustrating the various rules for the Jacobi symbol:

$$\begin{aligned} \left(\frac{83}{97}\right)&=\left(\frac{97}{83}\right)=\left(\frac{14}{83}\right)=\left(\frac{2}{83}\right)\left(\frac{7}{83}\right)=(-1)(-1)\left(\frac{83}{7}\right)=\left(\frac{6}{7}\right)\\ &=\left(\frac{2}{7}\right)\left(\frac{3}{7}\right)=(+1)(-1)\left(\frac{7}{3}\right)=-\left(\frac{1}{3}\right)=-1. \end{aligned}$$

Hence $x^2\equiv 83 \mod 97$ has no solution.

EXERCISES

1. If $n = p^e m$, where p is prime and $p \nmid m$, then

$$\kappa_n(X) = \kappa_m(X^{p^e})/\kappa_m(X^{p^{e-1}}).$$

2. Factorize $X^5 + 1$ and $X^7 - 1$ into irreducible factors in $\mathbb{R}[X]$ (cf. Exercise 5 after Section 20).

3. If m and n are natural numbers with g.c.d. d, then

$$(*) \qquad \text{g.c.d.}(X^m - 1, X^n - 1) = X^d - 1$$

in $\mathbb{Q}[X]$. Next, $X^d - 1 = (X^m - 1)f + (X^n - 1)g$ with $f, g \in \mathbb{Z}[X]$ (cf. the hint for A3.7). Deduce that $(*)$ is true in $k[X]$ for every field k, and generalize A3.7 in the form of $(*)$.

4. Let m, n be relatively prime numbers and $f = (1 - X^m)^{-1}(1 - X^n)^{-1}$.

(a) If we regard $f = \Sigma a_k X^k \in \mathbb{Q}((X))$, then a_k is the number of solutions $(x, y) \in \mathbb{M} \times \mathbb{M}$ of $k = mx + ny$.

(b) In $\mathbb{C}(X)$, verify the partial fraction decomposition

$$f = \frac{a_1}{1 - X} + \frac{a_2}{(1 - X)^2} + \sum_{s=1}^{m-1} \frac{b_s}{1 - \sigma^s X} + \sum_{t=1}^{n-1} \frac{c_t}{1 - \tau^t X},$$

where $a_1 = (m + n - 2)/2mn$, $a_2 = 1/mn$, $\sigma = e^{2\pi i/m}$, $\tau = e^{2\pi i/n}$, $b_s = 1/(m(1 - \sigma^{-ns}))$, $c_t = 1/((n(1 - \tau^{-mt}))$.

(c) Hence the number of solutions of $k = 2x + 3y$ is

$$\frac{k}{6} + \frac{5}{12} + \frac{1}{4}(-1)^k + \frac{1}{3}\cos\frac{2\pi k}{3} - \frac{1}{3\sqrt{3}}\sin\frac{2\pi k}{3}$$

$$= \left\lfloor \frac{k}{6} \right\rfloor + \begin{cases} 1 & \text{if } k \not\equiv 1 \mod 6, \\ 0 & \text{if } k \equiv 1 \mod 6. \end{cases}$$

5. For $a, n \in \mathbb{N}$, the polynomial $(X - 1)(X^2 - 1) \cdots (X^n - 1)$ divides $(X^a - 1)(X^{a+1} - 1) \cdots (X^{a+n-1} - 1)$.

6. Find the complex roots of $(Z + 1)^n = Z^n$.

7. Use the inclusion–exclusion principle to determine the number of positive integers whose decimal expansions consist of n digits each of which is one of 1,2,3 and such that each of 1,2,3 occurs at least once.

8. For $m, n \in \mathbb{N}$ and $d = \text{g.c.d.}(m, n)$, $\varphi(mn)\varphi(d) = \varphi(m)\varphi(n)d$.

9. $\varphi(n) = n/2 \Leftrightarrow n = 2^k, k \geqslant 1$.

10. In $k((X))$, the **Lambert series**

$$\sum_{n\in\mathbb{N}} a_n X^n(1-X^n)^{-1}$$

converges X-adically to $\Sigma b_n X^n$, where $b_n = \Sigma_{d|n} a_d$. In particular,

$$\Sigma \frac{\mu(n)X^n}{1-X^n} = X, \qquad \Sigma \frac{\varphi(n)X^n}{1-X^n} = \frac{X}{(1-X)^2}, \qquad \Sigma \frac{X^n}{1-X^n} = \Sigma\, \sigma_0(n)X^n,$$

where $\sigma_0(n) = \Sigma_{d|n} 1$ (see A12.5).

11. (i) If p is prime and $q|2^p - 1$, then $q \equiv \pm 1 \bmod 8$. (*Hint*: The order of 2 in the group $(\mathbb{Z}/q\mathbb{Z})^*$ is p.)
(ii) If p is a Fermat prime (cf. Supplementary Exercise 1 of Chapter 2), then every quadratic nonresidue of p is a primitive root of p.

12. (i) Let G be a finite group with p elements, p a prime. Then G is cyclic and every element other than 1 is a generator.
(ii) For each n in the range $0 \leqslant n \leqslant 16$ list the subgroups of Cyl(n).
(iii) Cyl$(m) \times$ Cyl(n) is cyclic iff g.c.d.$(m,n) = 1$.

13. If p is a prime, then

$$\sum_{k=1}^{p-1} k^n \equiv \begin{cases} 0 & \bmod p, \quad \text{if} \quad n \not\equiv 0 \quad \bmod p-1, \\ -1 & \bmod p, \quad \text{if} \quad n \equiv 0 \quad \bmod p-1. \end{cases}$$

(*Hint*: There exists a primitive root mod p.) Generalize to $\Sigma_{x\in\mathbb{F}_q^*} x^n$.

14. Generalize Euler's criterion to dth powers ($d \in \mathbb{N}$): If $a \in \mathbb{F}_q^*$, then a is a dth power iff $a^m = 1$, where $m = (q-1)/\text{g.c.d.}(d, q-1)$. Deduce that (for instance) for primes p of the form $3n+2$, every element in $\mathbb{F}_p$ has a unique cube root, while for primes of the form $3n+1$, exactly one-third of the nonzero elements have cube roots, and consequently each of these has three distinct cube roots.

15. Let p be an odd prime and $1 \leqslant m < p$. Then

$$(m-1)!(p-m)! \equiv (-1)^m \mod p;$$

in particular, $(p'!)^2 \equiv -(-1)^{p'}$, where $p' = (p-1)/2$. Hence, when $p \equiv 1$ mod 4, $\sqrt{-1} = \pm p'!$ in $\mathbb{F}_p$.

16. Use the fact from Supplementary Exercises 38 of Chapter 4 that the ring $\mathbb{Z}[i]$ is a U.F.D. and (5.281) to prove that every prime $p \equiv 1$ mod 4 is a sum of two squares in $\mathbb{Z}$: $p = N\pi = \pi\bar{\pi}$ for some irreducible $\pi \in \mathbb{Z}[i]$. Also, a prime $q \equiv 3$ mod 4 cannot so be written, and consequently such q are "inert"—they remain prime in $\mathbb{Z}[i]$.

17. Show that the Jacobi symbol obeys

$$\left(\frac{a}{b}\right)=\left(\frac{a}{c}\right) \quad \text{if} \quad b \equiv c \mod 4a, \qquad \forall a;$$

$$\left(\frac{a}{b}\right)=\left(\frac{a}{c}\right) \quad \text{if} \quad b \equiv c \mod 2a, \qquad a \equiv 1 \mod 4.$$

With the aid of these rules verify the table

a	$(a/b)=1$ for b of the form
-1	$4n+1$
2	$8n \pm 1$
-2	$8n+1, 8n+3$
3	$12n \pm 1$
-3	$6n+1$
5	$10n \pm 1$
-5	$20n+1, 20n+3, 20n+7, 20n+9$
6	$24n \pm 1, 24n \pm 5$
-6	$24n+1, 24n+5, 24n+7, 24n+11$
7	$28n \pm 1, 28n \pm 3, 28n \pm 9$
-7	$14n+1, 14n+9, 14n+11$
10	$40n \pm 1, 40n \pm 3, 40n \pm 9, 40n \pm 13$

Explain why ± 1 occurs on the right iff $a>0$.

22. LOCAL FIELDS AND THE BOLZANO–WEIERSTRASS THEOREM

The original Bolzano–Weierstrass theorem states that if $a_1, a_2, \ldots$ are real numbers satisfying $|a_n| \leqslant 1$, then some subsequence converges to a real number a (and obviously $|a| \leqslant 1$). The main theorem of this section gives a complete classification of all valued fields with this property. Although the original theorem refers only to $\mathbb{R}$, we shall find it convenient to refer to the general result as the Bolzano–Weierstrass theorem. Similarly, as a matter of convenience we call Corollary (5.296) the Heine–Borel theorem, although historically that theorem dealt only with the case $\mathbb{R}$.

We begin by defining some terms. A subsequence $a_{j_1}, a_{j_2}, \ldots$ of $a_1, a_2, \ldots$, where $j_1 < j_2 < \cdots$, is indicated notationally by $(a_j)_{j \in J}$, where $J = \{j_1, j_2, \ldots\}$.

(5.288) DEFINITION. A metric space X is **countably compact** or **sequentially compact** if every sequence $a_1, a_2, \ldots$ in X contains a subsequence $(a_j)_{j \in J}$ that is cauchy with limit $a \in X$.

The subspace $X = \{\alpha \in \mathbb{R} : 0 < \alpha \leqslant 1\}$ of $\mathbb{R}$ is not countably compact since the sequence $a_n = 1/n$ has no convergent subsequence with limit in X; in fact, every subsequence converges in $\mathbb{R}$ to $0 \notin X$. The subspace $\mathbb{N}$ of $\mathbb{Q}_p$ is not countably compact for a similar reason: Every subsequence of $a_n = 1 + p + \cdots + p^n$ converges to -1. This same sequence (for any p) shows that the subspace $\mathbb{N}$ of $\mathbb{R}$ is not countably compact; in this case no subsequence is cauchy.

As we observed in (5.186) (5), if a is an element of a valued field k and $\rho \in \mathbb{R}^{>}$, then

(5.289) $$V_\rho(a) = \{b \in k : |b-a| \leqslant \rho\}$$

is a closed set. In particular, $D = V_1(0)$ is closed. A subset X of k is **bounded** if X is contained in some $V_\rho(a)$. When k is $\mathbb{R}$ this means that X has both a lower bound μ and an upper bound M; i.e., $\mu \leqslant x \leqslant M\ \forall x \in X$.

(5.290) PROPOSITION. *A countably compact subset X of a valued field k is closed and bounded.*

Proof. If X is not bounded, then it is not empty, say $a_0 \in X$, and we can choose a sequence $a_j \in X$ satisfying $|a_0 - a_j| > j$. Then

$$|a_i - a_j| \geqslant |a_0 - a_j| - |a_0 - a_i| > j - |a_0 - a_i|$$

shows that no subsequence converges.

If X is not closed, then by (5.187) there is a cauchy sequence a_j in X with limit $a \in k \setminus X$, and every subsequence converges to a. ■

This proof uses the axiom of choice. Part (i) of the following theorem, which is the Bolzano–Weierstrass theorem proper, along with the two corollaries to the theorem (as promised earlier for results pertaining explicitly to the fields $\mathbb{R}$ etc.), do not depend on the axiom. (However, part (ii) of the theorem does require the axiom.)

(5.291) THEOREM. (i) *Let k denote either* $\mathbb{F}_q$, $\mathbb{R}$, $\mathbb{C}$, *or a complete discretely valued field with finite residue field* (*e.g.*, $\mathbb{Q}_p$ *or* $\mathbb{F}_q((X))$), *and let X be a closed and bounded subset of k. Then X is countably compact.*

(ii) *Conversely, if k is a valued field for which* $D = \{a \in k : |a| \leqslant 1\}$ *is countably compact, then k is one of these fields.*

Remarks. As will appear at the end of the proof, the proof of (ii) will be temporarily incomplete with respect to one point until we prove the Gelfand–Mazur theorem in Section 23. Of course, this part of the theorem will not be used in the interim.

The infinite fields that occur in this theorem are called **local fields**. They are $\mathbb{R}$, $\mathbb{C}$, $\mathbb{F}_q((X))$, $\mathbb{Q}_p$, and (but we do not prove this) extensions of $\mathbb{Q}_p$ of finite degree.

Proof. Every subspace X of $\mathbb{F}_q$ is countably compact since X is finite (or empty) and therefore every sequence in X contains a constant subsequence.

Note that the only possible $|\ |$ on $\mathbb{F}_q$ is the trivial $|\ |$. Conversely, if $|\ |$ is trivial, then $D=k$ and $(a_1, a_2, \ldots)$ is cauchy with limit a iff $a_n = a$ for all sufficiently large n. Thus D is not countably compact when k is infinite.

Hence we can assume that $|\ |$ is nontrivial in both (i) and (ii).

(i) If $X \subset V_\rho(a)$, then it is enough to prove the result for $V_\rho(a)$, for if a_n is a sequence in X and $(a_j)_{j\in J}$ is a convergent subsequence with limit $b \in V_\rho(a)$, then by (5.187) $b \in X$.

First we derive the complex case from the real case. Let $a = u + iv$ and let $b_n = s_n + it_n$ be a sequence in $V_\rho(a)$. Since $(s_n - u)^2 + (t_n - v)^2 \leqslant \rho^2$, both $|s_n - u|$ and $|t_n - v|$ are $\leqslant \rho$. Assuming the result for $\mathbb{R}$, there is a subsequence $(b_j)_{j\in J} \ni (s_j)_{j\in J}$ is cauchy with limit $s \in \{x \in \mathbb{R} : |x-u| \leqslant \rho\}$. In turn there is a subsequence $(b_l)_{l\in L}$ of $(b_j)_{j\in J}$ (i.e., $L \subset J$) such that $(t_l)_{l\in L}$ is cauchy with limit $t \in \{x \in \mathbb{R} : |x - v| \leqslant \rho\}$. By A10.7(ii),

$$\lim_{l\in L} b_l = s + it = b,$$

say, and it remains to prove that $b \in V_\rho(a)$. If $h \in \mathbb{N}$, then for all sufficiently large $l \in L$, $|b - b_l| < 1/h$. Hence

$$|b-a| \leqslant |b-b_l| + |b_l - a| < 1/h + \rho.$$

Since h is arbitrary, this implies that $|b-a| \leqslant \rho$, as required.

Now suppose that k is $\mathbb{R}$ or is complete discretely valued with finite κ. By A12.2, for each $c \in k$, $b \mapsto b - c$ defines a continuous map $V_\rho(a) \to V_\rho(a-c)$. This map is in fact a homeomorphism since it is bijective with continuous inverse $b' \mapsto b' + a$. Similarly, if $d \in k^*$, then $b \mapsto bd$ defines a homeomorphism $V_\rho(a) \to V_{\rho|d|}(ad)$. By taking an appropriate combination of c and d we see that in the real case $V_\rho(a)$ is homeomorphic with $X = \{b : 0 \leqslant b \leqslant 1\}$, and in the ultrametric case with $X = D = \{b : |b| \leqslant 1\}$.

As a general remark, if $f\colon Y \to Z$ is a homeomorphism, then, by (5.181), a sequence $y_1, y_2, \ldots$ in Y is cauchy with limit $y \in Y$ iff $f(y_1), f(y_2), \ldots$ is cauchy in Z with limit $f(y) \in Z$. Consequently, Y is countably compact iff Z is. (This does not depend on the axiom of choice, but its generalization in A12.8 that a continuous image of a countably compact space is countably compact does.)

Thus it is sufficient to prove that X is countably compact in the two cases. Every $b \in X$ has a decimal (resp. t-adic) expansion

$$b = a_0 + a_1 t + a_2 t^2 + \cdots, \tag{5.292}$$

where $t = \frac{1}{10}$ (resp. t is a uniformizer). Thus $a_i \in S$, where S is finite, say $S = \{s_1, \ldots, s_n\}$. (When $k = \mathbb{R}$ we take $s_1 = 0, \ldots, s_{10} = 9$ and there are two restrictions on the a_i: They are not all eventually 9, and $a_0 = 0$ except for $1 = 1 + 0t + \cdots$. In the ultrametric case we choose (by finite induction) an ordering 1 to n of the elements of S.)

Let $b_1, \ldots$ be any sequence in X. Among the first digits a_0 of the various b_j, some value of a_0 must occur infinitely often. We choose the smallest i

such that $a_0 = s_i$ infinitely often and we set $\bar{a}_0 = s_i$. Inductively, suppose that infinitely many b_j have expansions beginning with $\bar{a}_0 + \cdots + \bar{a}_n t^n$. We then choose the smallest i such that among the expansions of these particular b_j, $a_{n+1} = s_i$ occurs infinitely often and we define $\bar{a}_{n+1}$ to be that s_i. Thus we obtain an element

(5.293) $$\bar{b} = \bar{a}_0 + \bar{a}_1 t + \cdots \in X.$$

(In the real case repeated 9s are harmless.) Finally, we define the subsequence $b_{j_1}, b_{j_2}, \ldots$ by j_1 = the smallest j for which the expansion of b_j begins with $\bar{a}_0, \ldots,$ and, in general, j_{r+1} is the smallest $j > j_r \ni b_j$ has expansion beginning $\bar{a}_0 + \cdots + \bar{a}_r t^r$. Then $\lim b_j = \bar{b}$.

(ii) Suppose D is countably compact. If $(a_1, a_2, \ldots)$ is cauchy, then by (5.11) $|a_n| \leqslant |b|$ for some $b \in k^*$ and all n. By assumption the sequence a_n/b has a subsequence converging to a limit $c \in D$. However, since the sequence a_n/b is cauchy, this implies $\lim a_n/b = c$ and hence $\lim a_n = bc \in k$. This proves that k is complete.

Suppose first that k is ultrametric. If $|\ |$ were not discrete, we could choose $a_i \in D$ with increasing values $|a_1| < |a_2| < \cdots$ (all < 1), and by A10.5(i) no subsequence would be cauchy—a contradiction. If κ were infinite, then S would be infinite and we could choose a sequence of distinct elements $a_n \in S$. Since $|a_m - a_n| = 1$ for $m \neq n$, no subsequence would be cauchy.

Finally, when k is archimedean the result follows from the fact that the only complete archimedean fields are $\mathbb{R}$ and $\mathbb{C}$. This fact will be obtained as a corollary of the Gelfand–Mazur theorem (and was included here merely to round out the statement of the theorem). ■

(5.294) COROLLARY. *Let k and X be as in the theorem, $X \neq \varnothing$, and $f\colon X \to \mathbb{R}$ a continuous map. Then the image $f(X)$ is closed and bounded and consequently* (*by* (5.186)(8)) *f attains its minimum and maximum values: If*

$$\mu = \inf\{f(X)\}, \qquad M = \sup\{f(X)\},$$

then $\exists a, b \in X \ni f(a) = \mu$, $f(b) = M$.

Proof. The result is trivial if X is finite, so we can assume that X and k are infinite. By the theorem, X is countably compact. (If we are willing to use the axiom of choice then $f(X)$ is countably compact by A12.8, and thus closed and bounded by (5.290).) By composing f with a suitable homeomorphism as in the proof of the theorem, we can assume that $X \subset Y$, where $Y = D$ if k is ultrametric and

$$Y = \begin{cases} \{b : 0 \leqslant b \leqslant 1\} & \text{if } k = \mathbb{R}, \\ \{b + ic : 0 \leqslant b \leqslant 1, 0 \leqslant c \leqslant 1\} & \text{if } k = \mathbb{C}. \end{cases}$$

When k is ultrametric or real, each $b \in Y$, in particular each $b \in X$, has a unique expansion as in (5.292). When $k = \mathbb{C}$ the representation of $b \in Y$

takes the form

$$b=(a_0+a_1t+\cdots)+i(c_0+c_1t+\cdots),$$

where $a_j, c_j \in \{s_1=0,\ldots,s_{10}=9\}$. We wish to prove that $f(X)$ is bounded and that if $d\in\overline{f(X)}$ (the closure of $f(X)$ in $\mathbb{R}$), then $\exists x\in X \ni f(x)=d$. We write $d=\infty$ as an abbreviation for the assumption that $f(X)$ is unbounded.

Choose a definite order for the elements in $S=\{s_1,\ldots,s_n\}$ with $s_1=0$ and write $s_i<s_j$ to mean $i<j$. Now extend $<$ to a total order on the set Y by decreeing that

$$\alpha=a_0+a_1t+\cdots \quad (+i(c_0+\cdots) \text{ if } k=\mathbb{C})$$
$$<\alpha'=a_0'+a_1't+\cdots \quad (+i(c_0'+\cdots))$$

if for some $j\geqslant 0$, $a_0=a_0',\ldots,a_{j-1}=a_{j-1}', a_j<a_j'$ (or, in the complex case, if all $a_j=a_j'$ and for some $r\geqslant 0$, $c_0=c_0',\ldots,c_{r-1}=c_{r-1}', c_r<c_r'$). The details concerning $<$ are unimportant; it is the fact that we can totally order Y that allows us to sidestep the axiom of choice.

Let A_n denote the finite set of $\alpha\in Y$ of the form $a_0+\cdots+a_nt^n(+i(c_0+\cdots+c_nt^n))$ and, for $\alpha\in A_n$, let $X_\alpha=\{x\in X:|x-\alpha|\leqslant|t|^{n+1}\}$. By (5.186), X_α is closed and, for a given n, d is in at least one $\overline{f(X_\alpha)}$. (When $d=\infty$, this means that $f(X_\alpha)$ is unbounded.) We let $\alpha_n=\bar{a}_0+\cdots+\bar{a}_nt^n(+i(\bar{c}_0+\cdots+\bar{c}_nt^n))$ denote the "smallest" such α in A_n. For all $j\geqslant n$, the initial part of the expansion of α_j has stabilized at $\bar{a}_0+\cdots+\bar{a}_nt^n+\cdots(+i(\bar{c}_0+\cdots+\bar{c}_nt^n+\cdots))$. Leaving a few details to the reader, we have

$$x=\lim\alpha_n\in X$$

since X is closed, and the continuity of f implies that $d\neq\infty$ and $f(x)=d$. ■

(5.295) DEFINITION. A metric space is **compact** if every open cover contains a finite subcover; i.e., if $\{U_j\}$ is a collection of open subsets of $X\ni\cup U_j=X$, then there exist finitely many of the U_j whose union is X (or no U_j; it is convenient to count $X=\varnothing$ as compact).

By DeMorgan's laws, the following is an equivalent formulation of this definition: If $\{V_j\}$ is a collection of closed subsets such that every intersection of finitely many of the V_j is nonempty, then $\cap V_j\neq\varnothing$. The assumption on $\{V_j\}$ is referred to as the **finite intersection property**.

(5.296) COROLLARY (**the Heine–Borel theorem**). *Every X as in the theorem is compact.*

Proof. We can assume that X, and therefore also k, are infinite. It is sufficient to prove the result when

$$(5.297)\qquad X=\begin{cases} D & \text{if} \quad k \text{ is ultrametric,} \\ \{a:0\leqslant a\leqslant 1\} & \text{if} \quad k=\mathbb{R}, \\ \{a+bi:0\leqslant a,b\leqslant 1\} & \text{if} \quad k=\mathbb{C}, \end{cases}$$

because of the following two general observations:

(i) If f: $Y\to Z$ is a homeomorphism between metric spaces and $U\subset Y$, then U is open iff $f(U)$ is open. Hence Y is compact iff Z is compact.
(ii) If V is a closed subset of a compact Y, then V is also compact, for if $\{V_j\}$ is a collection of closed subsets of V with the finite intersection property, then, since the V_j are closed in Y (cf. 5.186(4)), $\cap V_j\neq\varnothing$.

A metric space is **separable** if it contains a dense subset E that is countable or finite (or even empty—it is convenient to count $\varnothing$ as separable). Each X occurring in (5.297) is separable: take E to consist of those elements whose expansion $a_0+a_1t+\cdots(+i(c_0+\cdots))$ (as described earlier) is finite. In each case there is no difficulty in concocting a rule to assign a definite ordering $\{e_1,e_2,\ldots\}$ to the elements of E, and we shall assume that this has been done.

Now suppose that $\{U_j\}$ is an open cover of X. Claim: $\exists\delta>0\ni\forall n, D_\delta(e_n)\subset$ some U_j. To prove this, suppose no such δ exists. Then $\forall m\in\mathbb{N}$ let $f(m)$ denote the smallest $n\ni D_{1/m}(e_n)\subset$ no U_j. Thus $f(1)\leqslant f(2)\leqslant\cdots$ and, since the U_j form an open cover, $\lim f(m)=\infty$. Let $(e_t)_{t\in T}$ be a convergent subsequence of $e_{f(1)}, e_{f(2)},\ldots$ with limit $e\in X$. For some j and some $\eta>0$, we have $D_\eta(e)\subset U_j$. For all sufficiently large t, $|e_t-e|<\eta/2$, so that $D_{\eta/2}(e_t)\subset U_j$. We have a contradiction since if $t=f(m)$, then $1/m<\eta/2$ for large t.

Since E is dense in X, $\{D_\delta(e_1), D_\delta(e_2),\ldots\}$ is an open cover of X and it is sufficient to show that this contains a finite subcover, in other words, that

$$V_N=X\setminus\bigcup_{n=1}^{N}D_\delta(e_n)$$

is empty for some N. For this it is enough to show that no e_n is contained in V_N; for then, if $x\in X\setminus V_N$, let $|x-e_n|>\delta+1/h$ for $n=1,\ldots,N$. Now $\exists e_r\ni|x-e_r|<1/2h$ and also $e_r\in$ some $D_\delta(e_n), 1\leqslant n\leqslant N$. This gives the contradiction $|x-e_n|\leqslant|x-e_r|+|e_r-e_n|<\delta+1/2h$. Thus no such x can exist and $V_N=\varnothing$.

It remains to draw a contradiction from the assumption that each V_N contains some e_r. Let $g(N)$ denote the minimum such r (so $g(N)>N$) and let $(e_q)_{q\in Q}$ denote a convergent subsequence of $e_{g(1)}, e_{g(2)},\ldots$ with limit $d\in X$. Now for a given N, $e_q\in V_N$ for all sufficiently large q, and since V_N is closed, $d=\lim e_q\in V_N$. We have the contradiction $d\in\cap V_N=\varnothing$. ■

Actually a metric space X is compact iff it is countably compact, but the proof of this general fact uses the axiom of choice.

Here is a simple application of the Heine–Borel theorem:

(5.298) COROLLARY. *Let k be one of the fields of the theorem (or, more generally, a valued field whose completion is one of these fields) and Λ a nonzero additive subgroup of k. The following conditions are equivalent*:

(i) $\mu = \text{g.l.b.}\{|\lambda| : \lambda \in \Lambda, \lambda \neq 0\}$ *is positive*;
(ii) $\forall n \in \mathbb{N}$, $\{\lambda \in \Lambda : |\lambda| \leqslant n\}$ *is finite*.

Proof. We can assume that $k = \tilde{k}$.

(i)$\Rightarrow$(ii) Finitely many open discs in the set $\{D_{\mu/2}(a) : a \in k, |a| \leqslant n\}$ cover the closed disc $V_n(0)$. If $\lambda, \lambda' \in D_{\mu/2}(a) \cap \Lambda$, then $\lambda - \lambda' \in \Lambda$ and $|\lambda - \lambda'| < \mu$. Hence $\lambda = \lambda'$, so each $D_{\mu/2}(a)$ contains at most one element of Λ.

(ii)$\Rightarrow$(i) If λ_1 is any nonzero element of Λ, then μ is the smallest $|\lambda|$ for λ in the finite set $\{\lambda \in \Lambda : \lambda \neq 0, |\lambda| \leqslant |\lambda_1|\}$. ■

If F is an infinite field and $k = F(X)$ (or $F((X))$), then $\Lambda = F[X^{-1}]$ (the subring of polynomials in the variable X^{-1}) satisfies (i) with $\mu = 1$, but not (ii).

(5.299) DEFINITION. A **discrete subgroup** of a valued field k is a nonzero additive subgroup Λ of k satisfying (5.298(ii)).

For $k = \mathbb{R}$ (or $k \subset \mathbb{R}$) these were classified in (5.192): They are $\Lambda = \mathbb{Z}\mu$, where $\mu \in \mathbb{R}^{>}$.

Here is the corresponding result for $\mathbb{C}$.

(5.300) PROPOSITION. *The discrete subgroups Λ of $\mathbb{C}$ are precisely the following. Either $\Lambda = \mathbb{Z}\omega_1$ for some $\omega_1 \in C^*$, or $\Lambda = \mathbb{Z}\omega_1 + \mathbb{Z}\omega_2$ for a pair $\omega_1, \omega_2 \in C^*$ which is linearly independent/$\mathbb{R}$, i.e., $\mathbb{R}\omega_1 + \mathbb{R}\omega_2 = \mathbb{C}$.*

Remark. A Λ of the second type is the **lattice spanned by ω_1 and ω_2**. (Figure 5.22 shows a lattice in $\mathbb{C}$.) It will be seen in the proof that such a spanning pair (also called a **basis** of Λ) can be obtained by the following constructive procedure. Take any ω_1 with $|\omega_1|$ minimal, i.e., $|\omega_1| = \mu$, and then choose ω_2 to minimize $D = |\omega_1\bar{\omega}_2 - \bar{\omega}_1\omega_2| > 0$.

Proof. Suppose first that Λ is discrete and choose any ω_1 with $|\omega_1| = \mu$. If $\Lambda = \mathbb{Z}\omega_1$, we have the desired result. Thus let $\beta \in \Lambda \setminus \mathbb{Z}\omega_1$.

Now $\mathbb{R}\omega_1 + \mathbb{R}\beta = \mathbb{C}$, for otherwise $a\omega_1 - b\beta = 0$ for some $a, b \in \mathbb{R}^*$. Since $\beta = (a/b)\omega_1 \notin \mathbb{Z}\omega_1$, $\beta - \lfloor a/b \rfloor \omega_1$ is a nonzero element of Λ with absolute value $|a/b - \lfloor a/b \rfloor||\omega_1| < \mu$, a contradiction.

The set

$$\Omega = \{\lambda \in \Lambda : |\lambda| \leqslant |\omega_1| + |\beta|\}$$

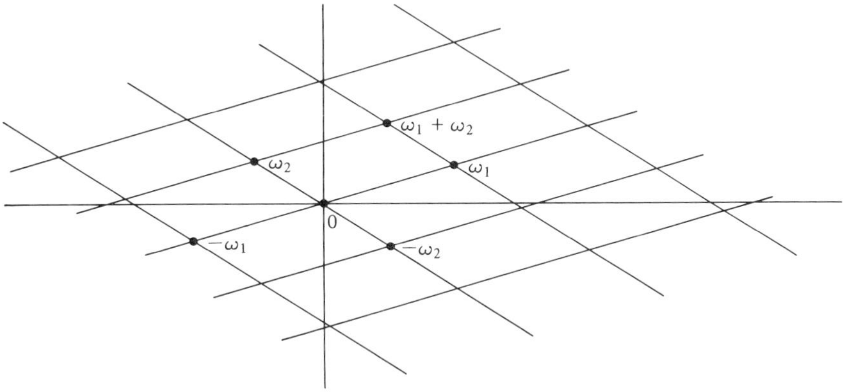

Figure 5.22 The lattice $\mathbb{Z}\omega_1 + \mathbb{Z}\omega_2$ in $\mathbb{C}$.

is finite. We now prove that $\Lambda = \mathbb{Z}\omega_1 + \mathbb{Z}\omega_2$, where ω_2 is any element of Ω such that the pair ω_1, ω_2 is linearly independent/$\mathbb{R}$ and for which $D = |\omega_1\bar{\omega}_2 - \bar{\omega}_1\omega_2|$ is minimal. (In familiar geometric terms, D is twice the area of the parallelogram spanned by ω_1 and ω_2 in the argand diagram.) If $\lambda \in \Lambda$, then $\lambda = a_1\omega_1 + a_2\omega_2$ at any rate for real a_j. Let b_j be integers such that $|a_j - b_j| \leqslant \frac{1}{2}$ and put $\omega = (a_1 - b_1)\omega_1 + (a_2 - b_2)\omega_2$. Then $|\omega| \leqslant \frac{1}{2}|\omega_1| + \frac{1}{2}|\omega_2|$, so $\omega \in \Omega$, and we wish to prove that $\omega = 0$.

If $a_2 \neq b_2$, then the pair ω_1, ω is linearly independent/$\mathbb{R}$ and $|\omega_1\bar{\omega} - \bar{\omega}_1\omega| = |a_2 - b_2| D < D$, contradicting the minimality of D. Thus $a_2 = b_2$ and $|\omega| = |a_1 - b_1|\,|\omega_1| < |\omega_1|$, and so $a_1 = b_1$ by the minimality of $|\omega_1|$.

Conversely, if $\Lambda = \mathbb{Z}\omega_1$, then $\mu = |\omega_1|$, so let $\Lambda = \mathbb{Z}\omega_1 + \mathbb{Z}\omega_2$. If $\omega_1\bar{\omega}_2 = a + bi$, then we have $b \neq 0$, since otherwise $\omega_1(\bar{\omega}_2\omega_2) = a\omega_2$, contradicting the $\mathbb{R}$-linear independence of the pair ω_1, ω_2. Since $\bar{\omega}_1\omega_2 = \overline{\omega_1\bar{\omega}_2} = a - bi$,

$$D = |\omega_1\bar{\omega}_2 - \bar{\omega}_1\omega_2| = |2bi| = 2|b| > 0,$$

and

$$|\omega_1|^2|\omega_2|^2 = a^2 + b^2 = a^2 + D^2/4.$$

Thus, for $\lambda = a_1\omega_1 + a_2\omega_2 \in \Lambda$,

$$\begin{aligned} |\lambda|^2 &= (a_1\omega_1 + a_2\omega_2)(a_1\bar{\omega}_2 + a_2\bar{\omega}_2) \\ &= a_1^2|\omega_1|^2 + 2a_1a_2a + a_2^2|\omega_2|^2 \\ &= (a_1|\omega_1| + a_2a/|\omega_1|)^2 + a_2^2D^2/4 \\ &\geqslant \begin{cases} D^2/4 & \text{if} \quad a_2 \neq 0, \\ |\omega_1|^2 & \text{if} \quad a_2 = 0, \quad a_1 \neq 0. \end{cases} \end{aligned}$$

Hence

(5.301) $$\mu \geqslant \min\{D/2, |\omega_1|\} > 0. \quad \blacksquare$$

EXERCISES

1. $\mathbb{Z}_p \backslash \{0\}$ is an open noncompact subset of $\mathbb{Z}_p$.

2. Let $\Lambda = \mathbb{Z}\omega_1 + \mathbb{Z}\omega_2$ be a lattice in $\mathbb{C}$, so $\tau = \omega_1/\omega_2 \notin \mathbb{R}$. (It is customary to take τ with positive imaginary part by interchanging ω_1 and ω_2 if necessary.) For $\alpha \in \mathbb{C}$, $\alpha\Lambda$ denotes $\{\alpha\lambda : \lambda \in \Lambda\}$.
   (a) $R(\Lambda) = \{\alpha \in \mathbb{C} : \alpha\Lambda \subset \Lambda\}$ is a subring of $\mathbb{C}$.
   (b) If $\gamma \in C^*$, then $R(\gamma\Lambda) = R(\Lambda)$. (Thus to calculate $R(\Lambda)$ we can take Λ in the form $\mathbb{Z} + \mathbb{Z}\tau$.)
   (c) $R(\mathbb{Z} + \mathbb{Z}\tau) = \mathbb{Z}$ unless τ satisfies a quadratic $\tau^2 + p\tau + q = 0$, where $p, q \in \mathbb{Q}$, and then $R \subset \mathbb{Z}[\tau]$. (An $\alpha \in R \backslash \mathbb{Z}$, which can exist only for these special Λ, is called a **complex multiplication** of Λ.)

23. NORMED VECTOR SPACES AND THE GELFAND–MAZUR THEOREM

(5.302) DEFINITION. Let k be a valued field and V a vector space over k.
(i) A **norm** on V is a map $\| \, \| : V \to \mathbb{R}^{\geqslant}$ satisfying ($\forall x, y \in V$ and $\forall a \in k$):

(AV0) $\|x\| = 0$ iff $x = 0$;
(AV2) $\|ax\| = |a| \|x\|$; and
(AV3) $\|x + y\| \leqslant \|x\| + \|y\|$.

A V equipped with such a $\| \, \|$ is called a **normed vector space** (over k).
(ii) A k-algebra V is a **normed k-algebra** if it has a norm in the sense of (i) that also satisfies ($\forall x, y \in V$)

(AV1$^\flat$) $\|1\| = 1$;
(AV2$^\flat$) $\|xy\| \leqslant \|x\| \|y\|$.

It follows from (AV1$^\flat$) and (AV2) that

(5.303) $$\|a\| = |a|, \qquad \forall a \in k,$$

and therefore there is no ambiguity in writing $|x|$ for $\|x\|$, $\forall x \in V$, which we shall usually do.

(5.304) REMARKS AND EXAMPLES
1. Every normed vector space can be regarded as a metric space since (AV0), (AV2), and (AV3) immediately translate into the metric space axioms for the metric $d(x, y) = |x - y|$. Hence, by A12.2, $x \mapsto |x|$ defines a uniformly continuous map $V \to \mathbb{R}$.
2. Simple consequences of the axioms in (ii) are

(5.305) $$|x^n| \leqslant |x|^n, \qquad \forall n \in \mathbb{N}, \quad x \in V,$$

(5.306) $$|x^{-1}| \geqslant |x|^{-1}, \qquad \forall x \in V^*,$$

of course with equality in both cases if $x \in k$. Some writers do not insist on (AV1$^\flat$) and then one has merely $\|1\| \geqslant 1$, but we shall have no need for this generality.

3. If K is a valued field containing k as a subfield and whose $|\ |$ extends that of k, then K can be regarded as a normed k-algebra (equality always holding in AV2$^\flat$). Thus $\mathbb{R}$ and $\mathbb{C}$ are normed $\mathbb{R}$-algebras.

4. If V is any vector space over the valued field k and $\{\mathbf{v}_j : j \in J\}$ is a basis, then each of the following defines a norm on V:

a. $|\Sigma a_j \mathbf{v}_j| = \max\{|a_j|\}$,

b. $|\Sigma a_j \mathbf{v}_j| = \Sigma |a_j|$, and

c. $|\Sigma a_j \mathbf{v}_j| = \sqrt{\Sigma |a_j|^2}$.

The verification of the axioms is trivial except for the triangle inequality in case c. For that see Exercise 3 at the end this section.

5. If A is a normed k-algebra (this implicitly implies that k is a valued field), then the polynomial ring $A[T]$ becomes a normed k-algebra if we set

$$|a_0 + a_1 T + \cdots| = |a_0| + |a_1| + \cdots,$$

as a simple calculation shows.

6. Let A be a commutative normed k-algebra, f a monic polynomial over A of degree $n > 1$, and I the principal ideal in $A[T]$ generated by f. Then the elements of $K = A[T]/I$ are uniquely of the form $a_0 + a_1 t + \cdots + a_{n-1} t^{n-1}$, where $t = T + I$. Again an easy calculation shows that K becomes a normed k-algebra if we define

$$(5.307) \qquad |a_0 + \cdots + a_{n-1} t^{n-1}| = |a_0| + \cdots + |a_{n-1}|$$

provided f satisfies the following condition. If

$$t^j = b_{j1} + b_{j2} t + \cdots + b_{jn} t^{n-1},$$

then

$$(5.308) \qquad |b_{j1}| + |b_{j2}| + \cdots + |b_{jn}| \leqslant 1 \qquad \text{for} \quad n \leqslant j \leqslant 2n-2.$$

This condition is satisfied for instance when $A = k$ and $f = T^2$, so that $K = k[t : t^2 = 0]$. Then $|t^2| = 0 < 1 = |t|^2$ shows that inequality can occur in (AV2$^\flat$). If $a \in k^*$ and $y = 1 + at$, then $y^{-1} = 1 - at$ and $|y| = |1| + |a| = 1 + |-a| = |y^{-1}| > 1$; hence inequality can even occur in (5.306).

7. Let $X \neq \varnothing$ denote one of the sets described in (5.291) and let $C = C(X, \mathbb{R})$ denote the set of continuous functions $f: X \to \mathbb{R}$. By A12.2(iv) C is an $\mathbb{R}$-algebra. Plainly

$$|f| = \sup\{|f(x)| : x \in X\}$$

makes C a normed $\mathbb{R}$-algebra and that inequality can occur in (AV2$^\flat$).

8. If t is an element of a normed algebra $K \ni 1 - t \in K^*$, then

$$(5.309) \qquad \frac{1}{1+|t|} \leqslant \frac{1}{|1-t|} \leqslant \left|\frac{1}{1-t}\right|$$

and if also $|t| < 1$, then

$$(5.310) \qquad \left|\frac{1}{1-t}\right| \leqslant \frac{1}{1-|t|}.$$

The first inequality in (5.309) results from $|1-t| \leqslant |1| + |-t| = 1 + |t|$ and the second from (5.306), while (5.310) is a consequence of

$$\left|\frac{1}{1-t}\right| = \left|1 + \frac{t}{1-t}\right| \leqslant 1 + |t| \left|\frac{1}{1-t}\right|.$$

(5.311) LEMMA. *If K is a normed k-algebra, then the map $K^* \to K^*$ given by $x \mapsto x^{-1}$ is continuous.*

Proof. If $x \in K^*$, we wish to show that $|y^{-1} - x^{-1}|$ is small for all y in K^* sufficiently close to x. Define $t \in K$ by $y = x(1-t)$, so

$$|t| = |1 - x^{-1}y| \leqslant |x^{-1}||x-y|,$$

which is small for all y close to x, and in particular $|t| < 1$. Then by (5.310)

$$|y^{-1} - x^{-1}| = |t(1-t)^{-1}x^{-1}| \leqslant |t|(1-|t|)^{-1}|x^{-1}|$$

which is small when $|x-y|$ is small. ∎

(5.312) THEOREM (**Gelfand–Mazur**). *If k is a complete archimedean valued field, then it is not possible to define the structure of a normed k-algebra on the field $k(X)$.*

Remark. In particular, there is no archimedean absolute value on $k(X)$ extending that of k. However, it is actually easier to prove the more general result (as will be noted during the proof). This phenomenon (that the proof of the stronger result is easier) is not uncommon. Mordell noted that it would be most awkward to prove that $1^3 + \cdots + n^3$ is a square without establishing the general formula $1^3 + \cdots + n^3 = (n(n+1)/2)^2$.

Proof. Suppose we have such a structure $|\ |: k(X) \to \mathbb{R}$. By (5.191(4i)), we have $k \supset \mathbb{R}$ and by restriction we obtain a normed $\mathbb{R}$-algebra structure on $\mathbb{R}(X)$. In the proof we shall need roots of unity so we pass to $\mathbb{C}(X)$, which can be identified with $\mathbb{R}(X)[T]/I$, in the notation of Example 7, where $f = T^2 + 1$ via the $\mathbb{R}$-algebra isomorphism $a + bi \mapsto a + bt$. Since f satisfies (5.308), $\mathbb{C}(X)$ is a normed $\mathbb{R}$-algebra; it is from this that we shall derive a contradiction.

Notice that, for $\alpha = a + bi \in \mathbb{C}$,

$$|\alpha| = |a| + |b|$$

is not the usual absolute value on $\mathbb{C}$, and inequality can occur in $|\alpha\beta| \leqslant |\alpha||\beta|$. (It is here that we profit from the flexibility of the weakened axiom ($\text{AV2}^\flat$): We do not want the problem of extending an absolute value on the field $\mathbb{R}(X)$ to one on $\mathbb{C}(X)$.) Since $|a| + |b|$ is small iff $\sqrt{a^2+b^2}$ is small, a function from $\mathbb{C}$ to a metric space is continuous with respect to the metric on $\mathbb{C}$ given by this norm (cf. Example 1) iff it is continuous with respect to the usual metric. (More precisely, the identity map on $\mathbb{C}$ is a homeomorphism between the two metric space structures.)

Since the map $\mathbb{C} \to \mathbb{C}(X)$, where $z \mapsto X - z$, is continuous, by the lemma

$$f(z) = \left|\frac{1}{X-z}\right|, \qquad z \in \mathbb{C},$$

defines a continuous function $\mathbb{C} \to \mathbb{R}^{>}$. By (AV2) and (5.310), if $z \notin V_{2|X|}(0)$, i.e., if $|z|>2|X|$, then

$$f(z)\leqslant|z|^{-1}\frac{1}{1-|X/z|}=\frac{1}{|z|-|X|}<1/|X|\leqslant f(0).$$

Hence, by (5.294), f attains a maximum value M for some $z\in V_{2|X|}(0)$. Thus

$$W=\{z: f(z)=M\}$$

is nonempty and contained in $V_{2|X|}(0)$. The required contradiction is obtained by showing that if $z\in W$ then W contains the (ordinary metric) open disc $D_{1/M}(z)$, for then $z+1/2M\in W$, and by repetition $z+j/2M\in W\ \forall j\in\mathbb{N}$. However, $z+j/2M\notin V_{2|X|}(0)$ for large j. (Alternatively, this shows that W is open. Yet $W=f^{-1}\{M\}$ is closed by A12.6(α), contradicting A12.6(γ).)

Suppose, however, that $f(z+ae^{i\theta})=M-\varepsilon$, $\varepsilon>0$, for some positive real number $a<1/M$. If $Y=X-z$, $n\in\mathbb{N}$, and $\zeta=e^{2\pi i/n}$, then

$$\frac{Y^{n-1}}{Y^n-a^n}=\frac{1}{n}\sum_{j=1}^{n}\frac{1}{Y-a\zeta^j}=s_n,$$

say. Now $|a/Y|<1$; hence $\lim(a/Y)^{n-1}=0$, and, by (5.311),

$$\text{(5.313)}\qquad \lim|s_n|=\lim\left|\frac{1}{Y-a(a/Y)^{n-1}}\right|=\left|\frac{1}{Y}\right|=M.$$

Next, since f is continuous,

$$\left|\frac{1}{Y-a\zeta^j}\right|=f(z+a\zeta^j)\leqslant M-\varepsilon/2,$$

provided $\zeta^j=e^{2\pi ij/n}$ is sufficiently close to $e^{i\theta}$, say

$$\left|\frac{2\pi i}{n}-\theta\right|<\delta.$$

If m is the number of such j, then $m\geqslant n\delta/\pi-2$. Hence

$$|s_n|\leqslant\frac{1}{n}\sum_{j=1}^{n}f(z+a\zeta^j)\leqslant\frac{1}{n}((n-m)M+m(M-\varepsilon/2))\leqslant M-\frac{\delta\varepsilon}{2\pi}+\frac{\varepsilon}{n},$$

which contradicts (5.313). ■

(5.314) COROLLARY. *The only complete archimedean valued fields are* $\mathbb{R}$ *and* $\mathbb{C}$.

Proof. If k is such a field, then by (5.191(4i)) we have $k\supset\mathbb{R}$. If $x\in k\setminus\mathbb{R}$, then the subfield $\mathbb{R}(x)$ of k has, by restriction, an archimedean absolute value. If x were transcendental, $\mathbb{R}(x)$ would be isomorphic to $\mathbb{R}(X)$, which is not possible by the theorem. Hence x is algebraic and the result follows from (5.140). ■

It follows that archimedean valued fields k can be classified as either real or complex depending on whether $\tilde{k} = \mathbb{R}$ or $\mathbb{C}$.

The following corollary is a basic result for applications in analysis. If K is an R-algebra and $x \in K$, then the set of $\lambda \in R \ni x - \lambda \notin K^*$ is the **spectrum** of x.

(5.315) COROLLARY. *If K is a normed $\mathbb{C}$-algebra, then $\forall x \in K$ the spectrum is nonempty.*

Proof. Since the subalgebra $\mathbb{C}(x)$ is normed, x must be algebraic over $\mathbb{C}$; i.e., its minimal polynomial $f \neq 0$. In $\mathbb{C}[X]$, $f = \prod(X - \lambda_j)$, say, and then in K, $0 = \prod(x - \lambda_j)$. The product of $n-1$ factors $x - \lambda_j$ is not zero since f is minimal. Therefore each $x - \lambda_j$ is a zero divisor, so each λ_j is in the spectrum of x. ■

EXERCISES

1. Let k be a valued field and let A (resp. B) be a closed (resp. countably compact) subset of k with the metric of, say, 4(a) of (5.304). Then $A + B = \{a + b : a \in A, b \in B\}$ is closed. Also show by example that the conclusion need not be true if B is only assumed to be closed.

2. Let k be a field complete with respect to a nontrivial absolute value. Then k cannot be written as a purely transcendental extension of a subfield: k is not a rational function field $F(\{X_i : i \in I\})$.

3. Prove the **Cauchy–Lagrange identity**,
$$\left(\sum_{i=1}^{n} a_i^2\right)\left(\sum_{i=1}^{n} b_i^2\right) = \left(\sum_{i=1}^{n} a_i b_i\right)^2 + \sum_{1 \leq i < j \leq n} (a_i b_j - a_j b_i)^2,$$
and hence the **Cauchy–Schwartz inequality**: For $a_1, \ldots, a_n, b_1, \ldots, b_n \in \mathbb{R}$,
$$\sqrt{\Sigma a_i^2}\,\sqrt{\Sigma b_i^2} \geqslant \Sigma a_i b_i .$$
From the latter derive the triangle inequality
$$\sqrt{\Sigma a_i^2} + \sqrt{\Sigma b_i^2} \geqslant \sqrt{\Sigma (a_i + b_i)^2} .$$
(*Hint*: Add $\Sigma a_i^2 + \Sigma b_i^2$ to both sides of Cauchy–Schwartz.)

4. For $f = a_0 + \cdots + a_n X^n \in \mathbb{C}[X]$ define $|f| = |a_0| + \cdots + |a_n|$. Then $\forall n\ \exists A \in \mathbb{R}^>$, depending only on n, $\ni A|f||g| \leqslant |f \cdot g|$ for all polynomials f, g of degree $\leqslant n$. (Clearly $|fg| \leqslant |f||g|$. (*Hint*: Reduce to the case $f, g \in T = \{h \in \mathbb{C}[X] : |h| = 1\}$. Then $(f, g) \mapsto fg$ defines a continuous function $T \times T \to \mathbb{R}^>$ whose minimum positive value is attained.)

24. FURTHER GROUP THEORY AND WEDDERBURN'S THEOREM

A **skew field** is a noncommutative ring in which every nonzero element is a unit. Wedderburn's theorem is the statement that there are no finite skew fields. The proof will use some basic ideas from group theory coupled with some facts from cyclotomy.

If G is a group and E a set, an **action** of G on E is a group homomorphism $\rho\colon G \to \mathrm{Sym}(E)$. We also say that ***G* acts on *E***. Thus each $\rho(g)$ is a permutation of the set E and we usually abbreviate $\rho(g)(e)$ to ge. The homomorphic property $\rho(gh) = \rho(g)\rho(h)$ translates into

$$(5.316)\quad (gh)(a) = g(h(a)), \qquad \text{for all} \quad g, h \in G \quad \text{and} \quad a \in E.$$

This implies that $\rho(1) = 1$, the identity permutation, and that $\rho(g^{-1}) = \rho(g)^{-1}$, or $(g^{-1})(a) = g^{-1}a$, so the notation is consistent with that used for inverse maps.

Remark. Such a ρ is also called a **left action** of G on E since we sometimes want G to act on the right. Then the requirement is

$$(5.316')\qquad a(gh) = (ag)h,$$

and $a \mapsto ag$ defines a permutation $\rho'(g)$ on the set E. Because of the way we have chosen to write maps on the left, $g \mapsto \rho'(g)$ is not a homomorphism since $\rho'(gh) = \rho'(h)\rho'(g)$. (*Exercise*: $g \mapsto \rho'(g)^{-1}$ is a homomorphism; if $a \mapsto ag$ is a right action, then $ga = ag^{-1}$ defines a left action, and conversely a left action can be converted into a right action.)

(5.317) DEFINITION. Let the group G act on the set E and let $a \in E$.

(i) The **orbit** of a is the subset $Ga = \{ga : g \in G\}$ of E.

(ii) The **stabilizer** of a is the subset $\mathrm{Sta}(a) = \{g : ga = a\}$ of G.

(5.318) PROPOSITION. *Let the group G act on the set E and let $a, b \in E$.*

(i) *The relation $b = ga$ for some $g \in G$ is an equivalence relation on E and the equivalence class containing a is Ga.*

(ii) $\mathrm{Sta}(a)$ *is a subgroup of G and, for each $g \in G$,*

$$\mathrm{Sta}(ga) = g\,\mathrm{Sta}(a)g^{-1} = \{ghg^{-1} : h \in \mathrm{Sta}(a)\}.$$

(iii) $ga \mapsto g\,\mathrm{Sta}(a)$ *is well defined and gives a bijection between Ga and the set of left cosets of* $\mathrm{Sta}(a)$ *in G. Hence the index of the stabilizer (when finite) is the number of elements in the orbit (cf. A6.1):*

$$(G : \mathrm{Sta}(a)) = |Ga|.$$

Proof. Let $H = \mathrm{Sta}(a)$ and let g, t denote elements of G.

(i) $a = 1a$, so the relation is reflexive; $b = ga \Rightarrow g^{-1}b = g^{-1}ga = a$, so the relation is symmetric; $b = ga$ and $c = tb \Rightarrow c = tga$, so the relation is transitive.

(ii) $1a=a$, so $1\in H$; if $h\in H$, i.e., $ha=a$, then $h^{-1}ha=h^{-1}a$, i.e., $a=h^{-1}a$, and so $h^{-1}\in H$; if also $j\in H$, then $hja=ha=a$, so $hj\in H$. If $t\in \mathrm{Sta}(ga)$, then $tga=ga$; hence $g^{-1}tga=g^{-1}ga=a$, so $g^{-1}tg=h$, say, is in H, and $t=ghg^{-1}\in gHg^{-1}$. Conversely, if $t=ghg^{-1}\in gHg^{-1}$, then $tga=ghg^{-1}ga=gha=ga$, so $t\in \mathrm{Sta}(ga)$.

(iii) If $ga=ta$, then $t^{-1}ga=a$, so $t^{-1}g=h$, say, is in H and $gH=thH=tH$. Thus $ga\mapsto gH$ is well defined and is obviously surjective onto the set of left cosets of H. If $gH=tH$, then $g=th$ for some $h\in H$. Hence $ga=ta$, which shows that the map is injective. ∎

(5.319) EXAMPLES

1. Let E be any ring and $G=E^*$. Then for $g\in G$ and $a\in E$, ring multiplication ga gives a G-action on E (and there is no conflict of notation) since (5.316) is true by the associativity of multiplication in E. If E is a field or skew field, then E is partitioned into just two orbits, $\{0\}$ and E^*. In the case of integral domains, the equivalence relation is the familiar one of associated elements.

2. Sometimes we want to write the elements of G as exponents. For instance, $\rho(\beta)\alpha=\alpha^{\beta}$ defines an $\mathbb{R}^*$-action on $\mathbb{R}^{>}$ since

$$\rho(\beta\gamma)\alpha=\alpha^{\beta\gamma}=(\alpha^{\gamma})^{\beta}=\rho(\beta)(\rho(\gamma)\alpha).$$

3. If V is a vector space then $\mathrm{GL}(V)$ acts on V: each automorphism of V is a special kind of permutation and $\mathrm{GL}(V)$ can be viewed as a subgroup of $\mathrm{Sym}(V)$; ρ is just the inclusion map $\mathrm{GL}(V)\subset \mathrm{Sym}(V)$. In some situations we shall want to restrict the action to some subgroup of $\mathrm{GL}(V)$. There are many similar examples where V is replaced by some algebraic structure and G is a subgroup of the full group of automorphisms. For instance, G can be a group of automorphisms of a field E.

4. If $G=E$ is a group, then the natural left action ga given by the group multiplication is not very interesting in the present context. Of more use is the action known as **conjugation**:

$$\rho(g)h=ghg^{-1}.$$

(5.136) is satisfied since

$$\rho(gt)h=ghtt^{-1}g^{-1}=\rho(g)\rho(t)h.$$

Of course, now we cannot abbreviate $\rho(g)h$ to gh. We have the following special terminology and notation for this case: Two elements $h,k\in G$ are **conjugate** if $\exists g\in G\ni k=ghg^{-1}$; **conjugacy** is the equivalence relation of (i) of the proposition. For this action, $\mathrm{Sta}(h)$ is written $Z(h)$ and is called the **centralizer** of h (in G). Thus we have

(5.320) COROLLARY. *If h is an element of the finite group G, then the number of conjugates of h in G is the index of the centralizer* $(G\colon Z(h))$.

Note that $g\in Z(h)\Leftrightarrow ghg^{-1}=h\Leftrightarrow gh=hg\Leftrightarrow h\in Z(g)$.

This notation is extended to semigroups: If x is an element of the semigroup E, then the centralizer of x in E is

$$Z(x)=\{a\in E\colon ax=xa\}.$$

The **center** of E is

$$Z = \bigcap_{x \in E} Z(x),$$

and this consists of the elements that commute with every element of E. Thus an element a is central (i.e., in Z) iff $Z(a) = E$.

An element g of a group G is central iff the conjugacy class containing g consists of g alone. When G is finite the number of elements in G is the sum of the numbers of elements in the conjugacy classes, giving the so-called **class equation**:

$$|G| = |Z| + \sum (G : Z(h)),$$

where the sum is over a set of representatives h of the noncentral conjugacy classes. In the case of S_3 (Figure 5.23), $Z = 1$ and the class equation is $|S_3| = 6 = 1 + (2 + 3)$. (*Exercise*: If E is a semigroup (resp. monoid, group, ring), then $Z(x)$ is a subsemigroup (resp. submonoid, etc.) and consequently Z is a commutative subsemigroup (resp. ...).)

Consider the case of a skew field E and $x \in E^*$. The centralizer $Z_{E*}(x)$ of x in E^* is a subgroup of E^*, while the centralizer of x in E is

$$Z_E(x) = \{0\} \cup Z_{E*}(x)$$

and is a subskewfield of E (for it is a subring by the preceding exercise, and, if $ax = xa$, $a \neq 0$, then $xa^{-1} = a^{-1}x$). Thus the center of E is a field. Under the action ρ of E^* on E given by $\rho(a)b = aba^{-1}$, E is partitioned into the subset $\{0\}$ together with the conjugacy classes of the group E^*.

We are now ready to address **Wedderburn's theorem**.

(5.321) THEOREM. *There are no finite skew fields.*

Figure 5.23 The conjugacy classes of Sym(3).

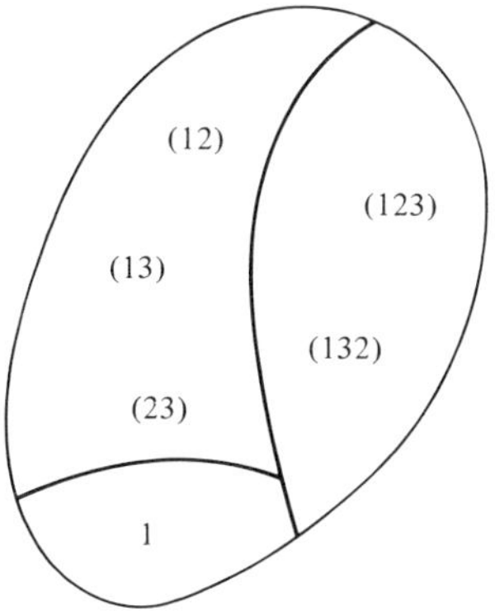

Proof. Suppose E is a finite skew field and $Z=\mathbb{F}_q$ its center. We shall obtain a contradiction. Regarding E as a vector space over Z (with scalar multiplication of $a\in E$ by $b\in Z$ being given by $ba=ab$), let $\dim_Z(E)=n$ so that $|E|=q^n$. Similarly, if $x\in E^*$ and $Z(x)$ is the centralizer of x in E, let $\dim_Z(Z(x))=n(x)$ so that $|Z(x)|=q^{n(x)}$. Removing the element 0, by (5.320) the number of conjugates of x in E^* is

$$\big(E^*: Z_{E*}(x)\big)=(q^n-1)/\big(q^{n(x)}-1\big);$$

hence $n(x)|n$ by A3.7. The class equation for E^* takes the form

$$q^n-1=q-1+\sum(q^n-1)/\big(q^{n(x)}-1\big), \tag{5.322}$$

where x runs through a set of representatives of the noncentral conjugacy classes. For such x, $n(x)<n$, and hence a primitive nth root of unity is a root of q^n-1 but not of $q^{n(x)}-1$. It follows that $(X^n-1)/(X^{n(x)}-1)$, which is a polynomial in X since $n(x)|n$, is divisible in $\mathbb{C}[X]$ by the cyclotomic polynomial $\kappa_n(X)$. Also, $\kappa_n(X)|(X^n-1)$. Therefore in (5.322) all the terms except $q-1$ are multiples of the integer $\kappa_n(q)$; hence $q-1=\kappa_n(q)m$ for some nonzero $m\in\mathbb{Z}$. However, $|\kappa_n(q)|$ is the product of the $\varphi(n)$ factors $|q-\zeta|$, ζ a primitive nth root of 1. Since $n>1,\zeta\neq 1$ and $|q-\zeta|>q-1$ by (5.142). This gives the contradiction $|m|<1$. ■

For examples of infinite skew fields, including the famous example of Hamilton quaternions—the first skew field discovered—see A12.10.

We now continue the discussion of group actions. If H is a subgroup of the group G and $g\in G$, then

$$gHg^{-1}=\{ghg^{-1}: h\in H\}$$

is a subgroup (since $1=g1g^{-1}$, $(ghg^{-1})^{-1}=gh^{-1}g^{-1}$ and $gh_1g^{-1}gh_2g^{-1}=gh_1h_2g^{-1}$), and is said to be a **conjugate** of H. This defines an action of G on the set E of subgroups of G since (cf. 5.316)

$$g_1(g_2Hg_2^{-1})g_1^{-1}=(g_1g_2)H(g_1g_2)^{-1}.$$

The stabilizer of H for this action is denoted

$$N(H)=N_G(H)=\{g\in G: gHg^{-1}=H\}$$

and called the **normalizer** of H in G. Clearly $N(H)\supset H$, and $N(H)$ contains the centralizer $Z(H)$ since, if $g\in Z(H)$, then $ghg^{-1}=h\ \forall\in H$, and therefore certainly $gHg^{-1}=H$. If $g\in N(H)$, in general $h\mapsto ghg^{-1}$ effects a permutation of the elements of H.

Proposition (5.318) applied to this case gives

(5.323) COROLLARY. *The normalizer $N(H)$ is a subgroup of G containing H. The index $(G: N(H))$, when finite, is the number of conjugates of H.*

(5.324) DEFINITION. A subgroup H of G is a **normal subgroup** if $N(H)=G$; i.e., if H has only one conjugate:

$$gHg^{-1}=H, \qquad \forall g\in G,$$

or, equivalently,

$$gH=Hg, \qquad \forall g\in G.$$

(5.325) REMARKS AND EXAMPLES

1. The notation $H\lhd G$ means that H is a normal subgroup of G. Thus, for all G, $1\lhd G$ and $G\lhd G$.

2. If G is abelian, then every subgroup H is normal since $gh=hg\ \forall h\in H$ and therefore certainly $gH=Hg$. This is true more generally for H contained in the center of G. For instance, the nonzero scalar matrices form a normal subgroup of $\mathrm{GL}_n(k)$, k a field. There is the occasional nonabelian group all of whose subgroups are normal, e.g., the **quaternion group** $G=\{\pm 1,\pm i,\pm j,\pm k\}$ (where $i^2=-1$, and so on, as in A12.10). The center is $\{\pm 1\}$ and the fact that the remaining proper subgroups $\{\pm 1,\pm i\},\{\pm 1,\pm j\},\{\pm 1,\pm k\}$ are normal follows from the next remark.

3. $(G\colon H)=2\Rightarrow H\lhd G$, for if $g\notin H$, then $G=H\amalg gH$ (cf. A6.1), and so G is split into two "equal halves" H and $gH=G\setminus H$. By the same reasoning, $Hg=G\setminus H$, so $gH=HG$ (and of course $hH=H=Hh,\ \forall h\in H$) and $H\lhd G$. For instance by (4.118), the alternating group is a normal subgroup of the symmetric group:

$$\mathrm{Alt}(n)\lhd\mathrm{Sym}(n).$$

4. In particular $\mathrm{Alt}(3)=\{1,(123),(132)\}\lhd\mathrm{Sym}(3)$. The three other proper subgroups $\{1,(12)\},\{1,(13)\},\{1,(23)\}$ form a complete conjugacy class: If $H=\{1,(12)\}$, then $N(H)=H$, which is of index 3.

5. By definition of the normalizer, $N(H)$ is the largest subgroup of G containing H as a normal subgroup: for every subgroup K of G containing $H, H\lhd K\Leftrightarrow K\subset N(H)$.

6. If H_i are subgroups, then, as we already observed in Chapter 3, $\cap H_i$ is also a subgroup. If $H_i\lhd G$, then $\cap H_i\lhd G$ since $g(\cap H_i)g^{-1}=\cap gH_ig^{-1}$. This permits us to speak of both the smallest subgroup and the smallest normal subgroup containing a given set X, which we can distinguish notationally as $\langle X\rangle$ and $\langle X\rangle_N$, respectively. We leave the following as an exercise: If $H_i\lhd G$, then $\langle\cup H_i\rangle=\langle\cup H_i\rangle_N$.

7. The set $\mathrm{Aut}(G)$ of automorphisms of the group G, that is, those $\alpha\in\mathrm{Sym}(G)$ satisfying $\alpha(hg)=\alpha(h)\alpha(g),\ \forall g,h\in G$, form a subgroup of $\mathrm{Sym}(G)$: If $\alpha,\beta\in\mathrm{Aut}(G)$, then $(\alpha\beta)(gh)=\alpha(\beta(g)\beta(h))=\alpha(\beta(g))\alpha(\beta(h))=(\alpha\beta)(g)(\alpha\beta)(h)$, so $\alpha\beta\in\mathrm{Aut}(G)$; since $\alpha(\alpha^{-1}(g)\alpha^{-1}(h))=gh$, therefore $\alpha^{-1}(g)\alpha^{-1}(h)=\alpha^{-1}(gh)$; hence $\alpha^{-1}\in\mathrm{Aut}(G)$; and of course $1\in\mathrm{Aut}(G)$. For instance, if $G=\mathrm{Cyl}(3)=\{1,g,g^2\colon g^3=1\}$, then $\mathrm{Aut}(G)$ consists of 1 and the transposition that interchanges g and g^2. Thus $\mathrm{Aut}(G)$ need not be a normal subgroup of $\mathrm{Sym}(G)$.

8. For $g\in G$, let $\bar g$ denote conjugation by g, i.e., $\bar g(h)=ghg^{-1}$. Thus $g\mapsto\bar g$ is a homomorphism (action) $G\to\mathrm{Sym}(G)$ and the set of $\bar g$, which we denote $\mathrm{Inn}(G)$, being the image of a group homomorphism, is a subgroup of $\mathrm{Sym}(G)$. In fact,

$$\mathrm{Inn}(G)\lhd\mathrm{Aut}(G). \tag{5.326}$$

First, $\bar{g} \in \operatorname{Aut}(G)$ since

$$\bar{g}(hk) = ghkg^{-1} = ghg^{-1}gkg^{-1} = \bar{g}(h)\bar{g}(k);$$

second, if $\alpha \in \operatorname{Aut}(G)$, then

$$(\alpha\bar{g}\alpha^{-1})(h) = \alpha(g\alpha^{-1}(h)g^{-1}) = \alpha(g)h\alpha(g)^{-1} = \overline{\alpha(g)}\,(h);$$

hence $\alpha\bar{g}\alpha^{-1} = \overline{\alpha(g)} \in \operatorname{Inn}(G)$. This proves that $\alpha \operatorname{Inn}(G)\alpha^{-1} \subset \operatorname{Inn}(G)$. In fact, there is equality since by replacing α by α^{-1}, $\alpha^{-1} \operatorname{Inn}(G)\alpha \subset \operatorname{Inn}(G)$, and hence $\operatorname{Inn}(G) \subset \alpha \operatorname{Inn}(G)\alpha^{-1}$. This proves (5.326).

The elements of $\operatorname{Inn}(G)$ are called **inner automorphisms**, while the elements of $\operatorname{Aut}(G) \setminus \operatorname{Inn}(G)$ (if any) are **outer automorphisms**.

In the next proposition (which includes some elementary facts already observed in Chapter 3), we see that normal subgroups are precisely those subgroups that occur as kernels of group homomorphisms. Thus they bear the same relationship to groups as ideals do to rings; just as in (3.15), there is a canonical bijection between normal subgroups and congruence relations on the containing group. (However, kernels of homomorphisms are not defined for every algebraic structure, e.g., in the case of semigroups.)

(5.327) PROPOSITION. *The homomorphism theorem for groups: Let f: $G \to K$ be a group homomorphism, let X be the set of subgroups of G containing* $\operatorname{Ker}(f)$, *and let Y be the set of subgroups of K contained in* $\operatorname{Im}(f)$.

(i) *f is injective iff* $\operatorname{Ker}(f) = 1$.

(ii) *If $H \in X$ and $L \in Y$, then $f(H) \in Y$ and $f^{-1}(L) \in X$; $H \mapsto f(H)$ and $L \mapsto f^{-1}(L)$ are mutually inverse bijections between X and Y.*

(iii) *If $L \lhd K$, then $f^{-1}(L) \lhd G$; in particular,*

$$f^{-1}(1) = \operatorname{Ker}(f) \lhd G.$$

If $H \lhd G$ and f is surjective, then $f(H) \lhd K$.

(iv) *If $H \lhd G$, then the set G/H of cosets of H in G becomes a group if we define*

$$1 = 1H, \qquad (gH)^{-1} = g^{-1}H, \qquad gH\,kH = gkH;$$

the canonical surjection $G \to G/H$ is a group homomorphism whose kernel is H. (G/H is called the **quotient group** *or* **factor group** *of G by H.)*

Proof. (i) plainly follows from the equivalences $f(g) = f(h) \Leftrightarrow f(g)f(h)^{-1} = f(gh^{-1}) = 1 \Leftrightarrow gh^{-1} \operatorname{Ker}(f)$.

(ii) If $f(h_1), f(h_2) \in f(H)$, then $f(h_1)f(h_2) = f(h_1h_2) \in f(H), f(h_1)^{-1} = f(h_1^{-1}) \in f(H)$, and $1 = f(1) \in f(H)$. Hence $f(H) \in Y$. An equally easy argument shows that $f^{-1}(L) \in X$, and the remaining statements in (ii) follow from the set theoretical facts

$$f(f^{-1}(L)) = L, \qquad f^{-1}(f(H)) = H.$$

(iii) Let $L \lhd K, h \in f^{-1}L$, and $g \in G$. Then $f(ghg^{-1}) = f(g)f(h)f(g)^{-1} \in L$, hence $ghg^{-1} \in f^{-1}L$, and therefore $f^{-1}L \lhd G$. If $H \lhd G, h \in H, f$ is surjective and $k \in K$, say $f(g) = k$, then $kf(h)k^{-1} = f(ghg^{-1}) \in fH$ since $ghg^{-1} \in H$. This proves that $f(H) \lhd K$.

(iv) We must check that the operations are well defined. Suppose $gH = g_1H$, say $g_1 = gh, h \in H$. Then $g_1{}^{-1}H = h^{-1}g^{-1}H = g^{-1}gh^{-1}g^{-1}H = g^{-1}H$ since $gh^{-1}g^{-1} \in H$ by the normality of H. Suppose also that $k_1 = kh', h' \in H$. Then $g_1k_1H = ghkh'H = gkk^{-1}hkh'H = gkH$ since $k^{-1}hk\ h' \in H$, again using $H \lhd G$. The group axioms are obviously obeyed by G/H, and $\mathrm{Ker}(G \to G/H) = \{g : gH = H\} = H$. ■

(5.328) REMARKS AND EXAMPLES

1. Let k be a field. The set H of $n \times n$ scalar matrices aI, where $a \in k^*$ (resp. where a is an nth root of unity in k) is a normal subgroup of $\mathrm{GL}_n(k)$ (resp. $\mathrm{SL}_n(k)$). The quotient group is denoted $\mathrm{PGL}_n(k)$ (resp. $\mathrm{PSL}_n(k)$) and is called the **projective general linear group** (resp. **projective special linear group**). Since $|ABA^{-1}| = |B| = 1$ for $A \in \mathrm{GL}_n(k)$ and $B \in \mathrm{SL}_n(k)$, we have $\mathrm{SL}_n(k) \lhd \mathrm{GL}_n(k)$ and part (iii) of the proposition applied to the surjective homomorphism $\mathrm{GL}_n \to \mathrm{PGL}_n$ shows that $\mathrm{PSL}_n(k) \lhd \mathrm{PGL}_n(k)$.

2. Let $G = G_1 \times G_2$ be the direct product of the groups G_1, G_2. The injection $i: G_1 \to G$ given by $x \mapsto (x,1)$ and the projection $p: G \to G_2$ given by $(x,y) \mapsto y$ are homomorphisms. G_1 is isomorphic to the subgroup $\mathrm{Im}(i)$, which is normal since it coincides with $\mathrm{Ker}(p)$. p induces an isomorphism $G/i(G_1) \approx G_2$. Of course, the roles of G_1 and G_2 can be interchanged. More generally, the kernel K_j (say) of $G = \prod_{i \in I} G_i \to G_j$ is isomorphic to $\prod_{i \in I\setminus\{j\}} G_i$, and $G/K_j \approx G_j$.

3. If $i: H \to G$ is an injective group homomorphism and $p: G \to K$ is a surjective group homomorphism for which $\mathrm{Im}(i) = \mathrm{Ker}(p)$, we call G an **extension of K by H**. It is a **split** extension if there exists a homomorphism $s: K \to G \ni ps = 1_K$. Such an s is called a (group) **section**. For example,

$$\mathbb{Z} \xrightarrow{i} \mathbb{Z} \xrightarrow{p} \mathbb{Z}/30\mathbb{Z},$$

where $i(n) = 30n$ is a nonsplit extension. (Another possibility for this sequence is $i(n) = -30n$.)

Given a group homomorphism

$$\rho: K \to \mathrm{Aut}(H),$$

an easy calculation shows that the following defines a group structure on the set $G = H \times K$; for convenience we write $\bar{k}$ for $\rho(k)$:

$$1 = (1,1),$$

$$(h,k)^{-1} = \left(\overline{k^{-1}}(h^{-1}), k^{-1}\right),$$

$$(h,k)(h',k') = \left(h\bar{k}(h'), kk'\right).$$

G is called the **semidirect product** of K by H with respect to ρ, and is denoted $H \times_\rho K$. This is the ordinary direct product when ρ is trivial ($\bar{k} = 1$, $\forall k$). Clearly $h \mapsto (h,1)$ defines an injective homomorphism $i: H \to G, (h,k) \mapsto k$ defines a surjective homomorphism $p: G \to K$, and $\mathrm{Im}(i) = \mathrm{Ker}(p)$. Thus $H \times_\rho K$ is an extension of K by H. It is split by the section $s(k) = (1, k)$. The semidirect product admits the following internal description (which in effect identifies H with $i(H)$ and K with $s(K)$): Let G be a group with subgroups H and K satisfying

$$H \lhd G, \qquad H \cap K = 1,$$

and $G = HK$, i.e., every $g \in G$ can be written $g = hk, h \in H, k \in K$. Then h and k are unique since $hk = h_1 k_1 \Rightarrow h_1{}^{-1}h = k_1 k^{-1} \in H \cap K = 1$. Also $G = KH$ since

$$hk = kk^{-1}hk = kh', \qquad \text{where} \quad h' \in H. \tag{5.329}$$

Define the group homomorphism $\rho: K \to \mathrm{Aut}(H)$ by $\rho(k) =$ the inner automorphism $g \mapsto kgk^{-1}$ restricted to H. ($\rho(k)$ is not necessarily in $\mathrm{Inn}(H)$ since there may not exist $h_1 \in H \ni khk^{-1} = h_1 h h_1{}^{-1}$ $\forall h \in H$.) Then (exercise) $(h, k) \mapsto hk$ defines an isomorphism $H \times_\rho K \to G$.

4. Let A be a commutative ring, G the group of $n \times n$ invertible upper triangular matrices over A, H the subgroup of $h \in G$ with 1s on the diagonal, and K the subgroup of diagonal $k \in G$. Then calculation shows that $H \lhd G, H \cap K = 1$, and $G = HK$. Hence G is the (internal) semidirect product of K by H.

We end this section with a basic result concerning the structure of finite groups. As already pointed out in an exercise, the group Alt(4), which has order 12, has no subgroup of order 6, so the obvious converse of Lagrange's theorem is false. However, since 12 has the prime power decomposition $4 \cdot 3$, the following guarantees that there are subgroups of orders 4 and 3:

(5.330) PROPOSITION. *Let G be a finite group of order $n = p^k m$ where p is prime and $p \nmid m$.*

(i) *G contains a subgroup of order p^k (such a subgroup is called a* **Sylow p-subgroup**).

(ii) *Any subgroup of order a power of p is contained in a Sylow p-subgroup.*

(iii) *The set Syl_p of Sylow p-subgroups form a complete conjugacy class: if $H \in \mathrm{Syl}_p$, then $gHg^{-1} \in \mathrm{Syl}_p$, $\forall g \in G$, and $K \in \mathrm{Syl}_p \Rightarrow K = gHg^{-1}$ for some g.*

(iv) $|\mathrm{Syl}_p| \equiv 1 \bmod p$.

In the proof we shall make use of the following general remark.

(5.331) LEMMA. *Let H be a finite p-group (i.e., $|H|$ is a power of p) acting on the finite set E and let E^H denote the set of fixed points $\{x \in E: hx = x \ \forall h \in H\}$.[5] Then*

$$|E^H| \equiv |E| \mod p.$$

[5]This is standard notation and the context should prevent confusion with the set of maps $H \to E$.

Proof of the lemma. $E \setminus E^H$ is the disjoint union of orbits Hy, where $\mathrm{Sta}(y)$ is a proper subgroup of H. Hence $|Hy| = (H:\mathrm{Sta}(y))$ is a power of $p > 1$, and therefore $|E \setminus E^H| \equiv 0 \bmod p$. ■

Proof. (i). Let P be the set of all subsets of G consisting of p^k elements with G acting by translation: If $X \in P$, $g \in G$, then $gX = \{gx : x \in X\} \in P$. By (4.111) and (3.54),

$$P = \binom{n}{p^k} \equiv m \mod p.$$

Thus $|P| \not\equiv 0 \bmod p$ and therefore the orbit of at least one X in P satisfies $|GX| \not\equiv 0 \bmod p$. We claim that $H = \mathrm{Sta}(X) \in \mathrm{Syl}_p$. For if $x \in X$, then $H \subset Xx^{-1}$, hence $|H| \leqslant |Xx^{-1}| = |X| = p^k$. On the other hand, $|GX| = (G:H) \not\equiv 0 \bmod p$, so $p^k \mid |H|$ by Lagrange's theorem.

(ii, iii). Let K be a subgroup of order p^r (where $r \leqslant k$ by Lagrange's theorem) and let K act on the set G/H of left cosets $\{gH : g \in G\}$ by $gH \mapsto agH$ for $a \in K$. By the lemma,

$$|(G/H)^K| \equiv |G/H| \equiv m \not\equiv 0 \mod p;$$

hence $(G/H)^K \neq \varnothing$. If $gH \in (G/H)^K$, then $K \subset gHg^{-1}$, and since $|gHg^{-1}| = |H| = p^k$, $gHg^{-1} \in \mathrm{Syl}_p$. Conversely, if $L \in \mathrm{Syl}_p$, then by what we have just proved, $L \subset gHg^{-1}$ for some g, and since these subgroups are both of order p^k, $L = gHg^{-1}$.

(iv). Let $H \in \mathrm{Syl}_p$ and let H act on Syl_p by conjugation: $L \mapsto hLh^{-1}$ for $L \in \mathrm{Syl}_p$ and $h \in H$. Since $L \lhd N_G(L)$, by (iii) $\mathrm{Syl}_p(N_G(L))$ consists of L alone, and therefore by (ii), $H \cap N_G(L) \subset L$. In other words, $h \in H \setminus L \Rightarrow hLh^{-1} \neq L$. It follows that $\mathrm{Syl}_p(G)^H$ consists of the single fixed element H, so $|\mathrm{Syl}_p{}^H| = 1$, and the congruence follows by the lemma. ■

EXERCISES

1. Let G be a group, H a subgroup, and $f: G \to \Gamma$ a surjective homomorphism with kernel K.
   - **(i)** The set $\{hk : h \in H, k \in K\}$, denoted HK, is a subgroup and $HK = KH$.
   - **(ii)** $ff^{-1}H = HK$ and $HK/K \approx fH$.
   - **(iii)** If G is finite,

     $$|G| = |\Gamma||K| \qquad \text{and} \qquad [G:HK] = [\Gamma : fH].$$

   - **(iv)** $\mathrm{Syl}_p(H) \subset \{L \cap H : L \in \mathrm{Syl}_p(G)\}$ with equality if $H \lhd G$ (more generally if H is "subnormal": There exist subgroups $H \subset H_1 \subset \cdots \subset H_n \subset G$ with $H \lhd H_1, \ldots, H_n \lhd G$.) Give an example of the situation $H \lhd H_1 \lhd G$ where H is not normal in G.

2. Find two nonconjugate elements in Alt(5) that are conjugate in Sym(5).

3. Let G be a p-group of order $p^n > 1$. Show that $Z(G)$ is nontrivial in two ways:
(a) using (5.320) and the class equation; and
(b) using (5.331).

4. Let A be the Klein 4-group Cyl(2) $\times$ Cyl(2). Then $\mathrm{Aut}(A) \approx \mathrm{Sym}(3) \approx \mathrm{GL}_2(\mathbb{F}_2)$.

5. Let H, K be normal subgroups of a group with $H \cap K = 1$. If $x \in H$ and $y \in K$, then $xy = yx$.

6. Let H be a subgroup of G such that for every pair x, y in G with $x \notin H$ $\exists h \in H \ni y^{-1}xy = h^{-1}xh$. Then $H \triangleleft G$.

7. If I is an ideal in the ring R, then

$$\{u \in R^* : u \equiv 1 \bmod I\} \triangleleft R^*.$$

8. If a finite cyclic subgroup K of G is normal in G, then every subgroup of K is normal in G.

9. Let A, B, C be subgroups of a group with C normal. Establish an isomorphism

$$\frac{A \cap BC}{A \cap C} \approx \frac{B \cap AC}{B \cap C}.$$

10. Let G be a nonabelian group with center Z. Then G/Z is not cyclic.

11. Establish the group isomorphism $\mathrm{Inn}(G) \approx G/Z$. Hence every nonabelian group has a nontrivial automorphism. (This is also true for finite abelian groups of order > 2.) Also, $Z(\mathrm{Alt}(4)) = 1$; hence $\mathrm{Inn}(\mathrm{Alt}(4)) \approx \mathrm{Alt}(4)$.

12. Let G be a group of order n, p the smallest prime dividing n, and H a subgroup of index p. Then $H \triangleleft G$. (This generalizes the fact that subgroups of index 2 are normal. *Hint*: Let G act on the set of conjugates of H.)

13. If G is a group of order pq, where $p < q$ are primes and $q \not\equiv 1 \bmod p$, then G is cyclic. (Thus Cyl(15) is the only group of order 15, while the example Sym(3) of order $2 \cdot 3$ shows that the assumption $q \not\equiv 1 \bmod p$ is essential. *Hint*: There is just one Sylow p-subgroup H, $H \triangleleft G$, and H is cyclic, say $H = \langle h \rangle$. Similarly $\mathrm{Syl}_q(G)$ consists of $L = \langle g \rangle \triangleleft G$. Consider ghg^{-1}.)

14. If k is an algebraically closed field, then there is no skew field with center k and of finite dimension over k.

15. Let k be a field and consider the following subsets of $\mathrm{GL}_n(k)$:

M consists of those matrices with a single nonzero entry in each row and in each column;

P consists of the permutation matrices; and

D consists of the diagonal matrices with nonzero diagonal entries.

Then M is a subgroup of $\mathrm{GL}_n(k)$ and is the internal semidirect product of P by D.

16. The following is a nonsplit extension of $\mathrm{Cyl}(2)=\{1,g\}$ by $\mathbb{Z}$ (the infinite cyclic group): On $\mathbb{Z}\times\{1,g\}$,

$$(a,x)(b,y)=(a+b,xy)$$

except

$$(a,g)(b,g)=(a+b+1,1).$$

Assignment 12

A12.1. Let $f\colon X\to Y, g\colon Y\to Z$ be maps between metric spaces and let $a\in X$. Prove the following statements.

(i) If f is continuous at a and g at $f(a)$, then gf is continuous at a. Hence if f and g are continuous, so is gf.

(ii) If f and g are uniformly continuous, then gf is also.

(iii) If f and g are isometries, so is gf, and if f is surjective, f^{-1} is also an isometry.

(iv) If f and g are homeomorphisms, so are gf and f^{-1}.

A12.2. **(i)** Let $X_1,\ldots,X_n$ be metric spaces with metrics $d_1,\ldots,d_n$. Show that $X=\prod X_i$ is a metric space if we define the distance between $x=(x_1,\ldots,x_n)$ and $y=(y_1,\ldots,y_n)$ to be

$$d(x,y)=\sum d_i(x_i,y_i).$$

In the following, products of metric spaces will be assumed to be equipped with this metric.

(ii) If X is a metric space, show that $(x,y)\mapsto d(x,y)$ defines a uniformly continuous function $X\times X\to\mathbb{R}$. (Hence if k is a valued field then $(x,y)\mapsto|x-y|$ is uniformly continuous and, by restriction, $x\mapsto|x|$ defines a uniformly continuous map $k\to\mathbb{R}$.)

(iii) Let k be a valued field, $\rho\in\mathbb{R}^{>}$, and $V=V_\rho(0)$. Show that the following maps are uniformly continuous:

$$+\colon k\times k\to k \qquad ((x,y)\mapsto x+y),$$

$$\cdot\colon V\times V\to k \qquad ((x,y)\mapsto xy),$$

$$^{-1}\colon k\setminus V\to k \qquad (x\mapsto x^{-1}),$$

and consequently $\cdot\colon k\times k\to k$ and $^{-1}\colon k^*\to k^*$ are continuous.

(iv) Let k be a valued field and X a metric space and let C (resp. B) denote the set of all continuous (resp. bounded and uniformly continuous) maps $X\to k$. (A map $f\colon X\to k$ is **bounded** if $\exists b\ni|f(x)|\leqslant b\ \forall x\in X$.) Show that C is a k-subalgebra of k^X and B is a k-subalgebra of C.

(v) Deduce that

$$x\mapsto a_0+a_1x+\cdots+a_nx^n,\qquad a_i\in k,$$

defines a continuous function $k\to k$ that is uniformly continuous when restricted to $V\to k$ (V as in (iii)).

(vi) Show that the following maps $\mathbb{C}\to\mathbb{C}$ (or $\mathbb{C}\to\mathbb{R}$) are uniformly continuous, where $\alpha=a+bi\in\mathbb{C}$: $\alpha\mapsto\bar{\alpha}$, $\alpha\mapsto a$, and $\alpha\mapsto b$.

(vii) Let k be a valued field, V a finite dimensional vector space over k, $\mathcal{V}=\{\mathbf{v}_1,\ldots,\mathbf{v}_n\}$ a basis, and let V equipped with the norm $|\Sigma a_i\mathbf{v}_i|=\Sigma|a_i|$ (which is obtained from the metric on k^n by means of the isomorphism $(a_1,\ldots,a_n)\mapsto\Sigma a_i\mathbf{v}_i$) be denoted $(V,\mathcal{V})$. If $(W,\mathcal{W})$ is another such space and $f\in\operatorname{Hom}(V,W)$, prove that $f:(V,\mathcal{V})\to(W,\mathcal{W})$ is continuous. Deduce that if $\mathcal{V}'$ is another basis of V then the identity map $(V,\mathcal{V})\to(V,\mathcal{V}')$ is a homeomorphism.

A12.3. If $L,M,N\in\mathbb{N}, L>1$, show that

$$\frac{ML^{1-N}}{L-1}-\log_L M\leqslant\left\lfloor\frac{M}{L^N}\right\rfloor+\left\lfloor\frac{M}{L^{N+1}}\right\rfloor+\cdots\leqslant\frac{ML^{1-N}}{L-1}.$$

(*Hint*: Write $M=a_0+a_1L+\cdots$, where $0\leqslant a_i<L$.)

A12.4. Let M be an additive submonoid of $\mathbb{R}$, let A be an integral domain, and let $B=A[M]$ be the monoid ring with M converted to multiplicative notation as in A6.7 so that the typical element of B is a finite sum $\alpha=\Sigma a_m X^m$, where $m\in M$ and $a_m\in A$. Show that B is an integral domain and that, if $0<c<1$, then

$$|\alpha|=c^{v(\alpha)},\qquad\text{where}\quad v(\alpha)=\min\{m: a_m\neq 0\}\qquad\text{if}\quad\alpha\neq 0,$$

and $|0|=0$, defines an ultrametric absolute value. (Use A10.6(i).) Show that the absolute value is discrete iff M is a discrete subgroup of $\mathbb{R}$. (Thus on the field $Q(\mathbb{Z}[\mathbb{R}])$, for instance, there is a natural nondiscrete, nontrivial absolute value.) Describe the residue field and the completion $\widetilde{Q(B)}$.

A12.5. Let A be a commutative ring.

(i) Show that $A^{\mathbb{N}}$ becomes a commutative A-algebra if we define the additive group and scalar multiplication componentwise as usual, and take for multiplication the **convolution product**

$$(f*g)(n)=\sum_{d\mid n}f(d)g(n/d),$$

and for the unit element the Kronecker function

$$\delta(n)=\begin{cases}1, & \text{if}\quad n=1,\\ 0, & \text{if}\quad n>1.\end{cases}$$

(This ring, which we denote by R in this question, is called the **ring of formal dirichlet series**. If $f,g\in R$ and we write the formal expressions

$$f=\sum_{n\in\mathbb{N}}f(n)n^{-s},\qquad g=\sum_{n\in\mathbb{N}}g(n)n^{-s},$$

then the series obtained by formally multiplying these series and collecting terms is

$$\sum_{n\in\mathbb{N}}\left[\sum_{d\mid n}f(d)g(n/d)\right]n^{-s}=\sum_{n\in\mathbb{N}}(f*g)(n)n^{-s}.)$$

(ii) Show that R is an integral domain iff A is an integral domain.

(iii) Show that $f \in R^*$ iff $f(1) \in A^*$. The **zeta function** is the element $\zeta \in R$ defined by $\zeta(n)=1$, $\forall n$. Show that ζ^{-1} is the Möbius function μ whose values $-1,0,1$ (in A) are defined as in (5.256). (Hence Möbius inversion (5.258) simply amounts to $f=g*\zeta \Leftrightarrow f*\mu=g$.)

(iv) An element $f \in R$ is **multiplicative** if $f(1)=1$ and

$$\text{g.c.d.}(m,n)=1 \quad \Rightarrow \quad f(mn)=f(m)f(n).$$

(Equivalently, $f(n)=f(p_1^{e_1})\cdots f(p_r^{e_r})$ if $n=p_1^{e_1}\cdots p_r^{e_r}$ is the prime power factorization of n and $f(1)=1$. A function satisfying $f(1)=1$ and $f(mn)=f(m)f(n)$, $\forall m,n$, is **strongly multiplicative**. For example, δ is strongly multiplicative and hence multiplicative.) Show that the multiplicative functions form a subgroup of R^*. (Hence $\mu=\zeta^{-1}$ is multiplicative and therefore, by (5.261), so is the Euler function $\varphi=\mu*\xi$, where ξ is the strongly multiplicative function $n \mapsto n$.)

(v) Now let $A=\mathbb{C}$. Deduce that for any $\nu \in \mathbb{C}$ the sum of the νth powers of the divisors of n, denoted

$$\sigma_\nu(n)=\sum_{d|n} d^\nu$$

is a multiplicative function and that, if $n=\prod p^e$, then

$$\sigma_\nu(n)=\begin{cases} \prod \dfrac{p^{(e+1)\nu}-1}{p^\nu-1}, & \text{if } \nu \notin \mathbb{R}i, \\ \prod (e+1), & \text{if } \nu=0. \end{cases}$$

A12.6. A metric space X is **connected** if the only subsets of X that are both open and closed are $\varnothing$ and X. If $\alpha,\beta \in \mathbb{R}$, then $[\alpha,\beta]$ denotes the closed interval $\{\gamma \in \mathbb{R} : \min\{\alpha,\beta\} \leqslant \gamma \leqslant \max\{\alpha,\beta\}\}$. The axiom of choice is not needed in this question.

(α) For a map $f: X \to Y$ between metric spaces show that the following are equivalent (Z denotes a subset of Y):

(i) f is continuous,

(ii) Z open in $Y \Rightarrow f^{-1}(Z)$ open in X, and

(iii) Z closed in $Y \Rightarrow f^{-1}(Z)$ closed in X.

(β) Deduce that if $f: X \to Y$ is a continuous map between metric spaces and X is connected, then so is the image $f(X)$.

(γ) Show that $\mathbb{R}$ and $\mathbb{C}$ are connected. (*Hint*: Suppose X is a nontrivial open and closed subset of $k=\mathbb{R}$ or $\mathbb{C}$. If $\alpha \in X, \beta \notin X$, then $x \mapsto (x-\alpha)/(\beta-\alpha)$ defines a homeomorphism $k \to k$, so we can assume $0 \in X, 1 \notin X$; hence $D_r(1) \cap X=\varnothing$ for some r. Consider $\gamma=$ l.u.b.$\{\delta \in \mathbb{R} \cap X : \delta < 1\}$.)

(δ) Prove the **intermediate value theorem**: If $\alpha,\beta \in \mathbb{R}$ and $f:[\alpha,\beta] \to \mathbb{R}$ is continuous, then

$$f([\alpha,\beta]) \supset [f(\alpha), f(\beta)].$$

Notice that the Weierstrass Nullstellensatz is a corollary. (*Hint*: By the argument of (γ),$[\alpha,\beta]$ is connected; if $\gamma \in [f(\alpha), f(\beta)] \setminus f(X)$, where $X=[\alpha,\beta]$, look at $f^{-1}\{\delta \in f(X) : \delta \leqslant \gamma\}$.)

(ε) Let $X \subset \mathbb{R}$ and let $f: X \to \mathbb{R}$ be an increasing continuous function: $q, r \in X$ and $q < r \Rightarrow f(q) < f(r)$. Further suppose that f has a continuous extension to $\bar{f}: \bar{X} \to \mathbb{R}$ ($\bar{f}$ is uniquely determined by f, cf. (5.188)). Show that $\bar{f}$ is "weakly increasing": If $\alpha, \beta \in \bar{X}$ and $\alpha < \beta$, then $\bar{f}(\alpha) \leqslant \bar{f}(\beta)$. Give an example where $\bar{f}$ is not increasing.

A12.7. (α) As in (5.227), show that (5.239) and (5.240) serve to define $\sin x$ and $\cos x$ $\forall x \in E \subset k$, that $\sin(-x) = -\sin x$ and $\cos(-x) = \cos x$, and that if k contains a square root i of -1, then $|i| = 1$; hence $ix \in E$ and

$$\exp(ix) = \cos x + i \sin x,$$

$$\cos x = \frac{\exp(ix) + \exp(-ix)}{2}, \qquad \sin x = \frac{\exp(ix) - \exp(-ix)}{2i},$$

$$\cos^2 x + \sin^2 x = 1.$$

From $\exp(i(x+y)) = \exp(ix)\exp(iy)$ deduce the **addition formulas**: $\forall x, y \in E$,

$$\cos(x+y) = \cos x \cos y - \sin x \sin y,$$

$$\sin(x+y) = \sin x \cos y + \cos x \sin y.$$

(β) Show that when $k = \mathbb{C}$ the zeros of $\sin x$ (the values of x for which $\sin x = 0$) are the integral multiples of π, and that the zeros of $\cos x$ are the odd integral multiples of $\pi/2$. Establish the formulas

$$\sin x = \sin(\pi - x) = \cos(\pi/2 - x),$$

$$\cos x = -\cos(\pi - x) = \sin(\pi/2 - x).$$

(γ) Show that if θ and φ both lie between 0 and π, then

$$\theta < \varphi \quad \Leftrightarrow \quad \cos\theta > \cos\varphi;$$

hence if α and β lie between $-\pi/2$ and $\pi/2$, then

$$\alpha < \beta \quad \Leftrightarrow \quad \sin\alpha < \sin\beta.$$

Hence prove that $z = a + bi (\neq 0)$ is in the first quadrant, i.e., $a \geqslant 0$ and $b \geqslant 0$, iff $0 \leqslant \operatorname{am}(z) \leqslant \pi/2$, with $\operatorname{am}(z) = 0$ (resp. $\pi/2$) corresponding to $b = 0$ (resp. $a = 0$); give analogous results for the other quadrants.

(δ) For a map $f: \mathbb{R} \to X$, X any set, define $P(f) = \{d \in \mathbb{R} : f(x+d) = f(x),\ \forall x \in \mathbb{R}\}$. f is **periodic** if $P(f) \neq 0$. Show that $P(f)$ is an additive subgroup of $\mathbb{R}$. (Referring to (5.192), if $P(f)$ is nonzero and discrete, say $P(f) = \mathbb{Z}\mu, \mu > 0$, then μ is called the **period** of f. For example, $x \mapsto e^{ix}$ defines a periodic function $\mathbb{R} \to \mathbb{C}$ with period 2π.)

(ε) The **tangent** and **secant** (resp. **cotangent** and **cosecant**) are defined for x such that $\cos x \neq 0$ (resp. $\sin x \neq 0$) by

$$\tan x = \sin x / \cos x, \qquad \sec x = 1/\cos x,$$

$$\cot x = \cos x / \sin x, \qquad \csc x = 1/\sin x.$$

When $\cos x = 0$ we write $\tan x = \infty$, and so on. These six functions, including sin and cos, are called the **trigonometric** or **circular functions**. Show that each is a periodic function $\mathbb{R} \to \mathbb{R} \amalg \{\infty\}$ and that the period of tan and cot is π, while that of the remaining four is 2π.

A12.8. Let $f\colon X \to Y$ be a continuous map between metric spaces and suppose that X is countably compact. Show that $f(X)$ is countably compact and f is uniformly continuous.

A12.9. **(a)** Let F be a field and $k = F(X)$ with the X-adic absolute value so that $\tilde{k} = F((X))$. Show that $d/dX\colon k \to k$ is uniformly continuous and that its unique uniformly continuous extension to $\tilde{k} \to \tilde{k}$ is given by

$$f = a_n X^n + a_{n+1} X^{n+1} + \cdots \mapsto n a_n X^{n-1} + (n+1) a_{n+1} X^n + \cdots.$$

Denoting the latter f', prove the rule $(fg)' = f'g + g'f$. (*Hint*: First extend d/dX from $F[X]$ to $\widetilde{F[X]} = F[\![X]\!]$ and then use (4.209).)

(b) When $\operatorname{char}(k) = 0$, show that in $F[\![X]\!]$

$$\frac{d}{dX} e^X = e^X, \qquad \frac{d}{dX} \log(1+X) = \frac{1}{1+X},$$

$$\frac{d}{dX} \sin X = \cos X, \qquad \frac{d}{dX} \cos X = -\sin X.$$

(c) Substitution of power series: Let g be a nonzero power series satisfying $|g| < 1$, i.e., $g \in XF[\![X]\!]$, and let $s\colon F[X] \to F[\![X]\!]$ be the F-algebra homomorphism determined by $X \mapsto g$. Show that s extends uniquely to a uniformly continuous F-algebra endomorphism of $\tilde{k}$. ($s(f)$ is denoted $f(g)$ and is obtained by the familiar procedure of substituting g for X and collecting terms.)

(d) If F is a valued field and a is an element of F for which a is in the circle of convergence of g (g as in (c)) and $g(a)$ is in the circle of convergence of f ($f \in F[\![X]\!]$), give an example to show that a need not be in the circle of convergence of $f(g)$. (It can be shown that $f(g)(a)$ and $f(g(a))$ coincide when they are both defined.)

(e) The **chain rule**: With g as in (c), and any $f \in \tilde{k}$, show that

$$f(g)' = f'(g) g',$$

where $'$ denotes derivative.

A12.10. Let K be a field, $s, t \in K^*$, and define the matrices

$$i = \begin{pmatrix} 0 & s & 0 & 0 \\ 1 & 0 & 0 & 0 \\ 0 & 0 & 0 & s \\ 0 & 0 & 1 & 0 \end{pmatrix}, \qquad j = \begin{pmatrix} 0 & 0 & t & 0 \\ 0 & 0 & 0 & -t \\ 1 & 0 & 0 & 0 \\ 0 & -1 & 0 & 0 \end{pmatrix},$$

$$k = \begin{pmatrix} 0 & 0 & 0 & -st \\ 0 & 0 & t & 0 \\ 0 & -s & 0 & 0 \\ 1 & 0 & 0 & 0 \end{pmatrix}.$$

(i) Identifying a scalar c with cI, show that

$$i^2 = s, \qquad j^2 = t, \qquad k = ij = -ji$$

and therefore

$$k^2 = -st, \qquad ik = -ki = sj, \qquad kj = -jk = ti.$$

(Hence the four-dimensional subspace $\langle 1, i, j, k \rangle$ is a subalgebra of $\mathrm{Mat}_4(K)$. It is denoted $(s,t)_K$ and is called the **quaternion algebra** of type (s,t). $(-1,-1)_{\mathbb{R}}$ has the special symbol $\mathbb{H}$, for Hamilton.)

(ii) Show that the center of $(s,t)_K$ consists of precisely the scalars.

(iii) If $\alpha = a + bi + cj + dk$ $(a,\ldots,d \in K)$, define $\alpha^* = a - bi - cj - dk$, called the **conjugate** of α, and the **reduced norm** and **reduced trace** by

$$N(\alpha) = \alpha\alpha^*, \qquad T(\alpha) = \alpha + \alpha^*.$$

Show that $(\alpha\beta)^* = \beta^*\alpha^*$, $N(\alpha\beta) = N(\alpha)N(\beta)$, $T(\alpha+\beta) = T(\alpha) + T(\beta)$, and

$$N(\alpha) = N(\alpha^*) = a^2 - sb^2 - tc^2 + std^2, \qquad T(\alpha) = 2a.$$

(iv) Show that α and α^* are roots of

$$X^2 - T(\alpha)X + N(\alpha).$$

(v) $(s,t)_K$ is **split** if $\exists \alpha \neq 0$ with $N(\alpha) = 0$. Show that $(s,t)_K$ is a skew field iff it is not split. Hence show that $(s,t)_K$ is a skew field in the following cases (cf. A11.3(iii)):

s	t	K any subfield of
-1	-1	$\mathbb{R}$
2	3	$\mathbb{Q}_3$
X	$1+X$	$F((X))$, where $X \in K$ and $\mathrm{char}(F) \neq 2$

(Thus $\mathbb{H}$ is a skew field. A field L containing K as a subfield is called a **splitting field** for $(s,t)_K$ if $(s,t)_L$ is split. Thus $\mathbb{C}$ is a splitting field for $\mathbb{H}$.)

(vi) Suppose that $\mathrm{char}(K) \neq 2$ and that K contains a square root of s, say $r^2 = s$. Show that

$$a + bi + cj + dk \mapsto \begin{pmatrix} a+br & ct+drt \\ c-dr & a-br \end{pmatrix}$$

gives a K-algebra isomorphism

$$(r^2,t)_K \xrightarrow{\sim} \mathrm{Mat}_2(K).$$

(Thus $\mathbb{H}$ can be identified with an $\mathbb{R}$-subalgebra of $\mathrm{Mat}_2(\mathbb{C})$ by means of

$$\alpha = a + bi + cj + dk \mapsto \begin{pmatrix} a+b\sqrt{-1} & -c-d\sqrt{-1} \\ c-d\sqrt{-1} & a-b\sqrt{-1} \end{pmatrix}.$$

The complex matrix corresponding to α^* is the *adjoint matrix*.[6]

A more elaborate calculation shows that the following are equivalent when $\mathrm{char}(K) \neq 2$:

$(s,t)_K$ is split,
$r^2/s + q^2/t = 1$ has a solution $r, q \in K$, and
$(s,t)_K \approx \mathrm{Mat}_2(K)$.)

---

[6]The **adjoint** of a complex matrix $A = (\alpha_{pq}) \in \mathrm{Mat}_{m,n}(\mathbb{C})$ is the conjugate transpose $\bar{A}^T$, that is, the $n \times m$ matrix whose pqth entry is $\bar{\alpha}_{qp}$.

25. NEWTON'S POLYGON AND PUISEUX EXPANSIONS; LIOUVILLE NUMBERS

An **algebraic closure** of a field K is a field $\bar{K}$ containing K as a subfield and such that

(i) $\bar{K}$ is algebraic over K (that is, every element of $\bar{K}$ is algebraic$/K$, i.e., has nonzero minimum polynomial), and
(ii) $\bar{K}$ is algebraically closed in the sense of (5.131).

Thus $\mathbb{C}$ is an algebraic closure of $\mathbb{R}$. Later in this section we shall prove that, for every K, $\bar{K}$ exists and is essentially unique; however, the general proof relies on the axiom of choice, and it is only for a handful of Ks that we know $\bar{K}$ at all explicitly. The first main result of this section describes the algebraic closure of $F((X))$, where F is a field of characteristic 0.

$\mathbb{C}$ is obtained from $\mathbb{R}$ by adjoining $(-1)^{1/2}$. In the case $K=F((X))$ we must first extend F to $\bar{F}$, which gives $\bar{F}((X))$, or to simplify the notation, take $F=\bar{F}$ algebraically closed to begin with. Then $\bar{K}$ is obtained by adjoining the sequence $X^{1/2}, X^{1/3}, X^{1/4},\ldots$, where $X^{1/n}$ denotes a root of Y^n-X. (When char$(K)>0$ the construction is more complicated.)

Recall that the valuation ring $D=F[[X]]$ is a local P.I.D. with irreducible element X. By Eisenstein's criterion, Y^n-X is irreducible. A K-vector space basis of $K(X^{1/n})$ is $\{1, X^{1/n},(X^{1/n})^2,\ldots,(X^{1/n})^{n-1}\}$ and

(5.332) $$\left[K(X^{1/n}):K\right]=n$$

by (4.135). In fact we shall see that the field $K(X^{1/n})$ is the *only* extension of K of degree n, i.e., every irreducible polynomial $f\in K[Y]$ of degree n has all its roots in $K(X^{1/n})$ and factors into linear factors over that field. This is easy to see directly when $n=2$ (but not when $n>2$): Since the characteristic $=0$, solving a quadratic amounts to extracting a square root, say $\sqrt{\alpha}$. If the X-adic value of α is d, we can write $\alpha=aX^d(1+a_1X+\cdots)$. Hence by the binomial theorem

$$\sqrt{\alpha}=\sqrt{a}\,X^{d/2}(1+a_1X/2+\cdots),$$

where $\sqrt{a}\in F$ since F is algebraically closed. Thus $\sqrt{\alpha}\in K(X^{1/2})$.

The typical element of $K(X^{1/n})$ has the form

$$\sum a_{0i}X^i+\left(\sum a_{1i}X^i\right)X^{1/n}+\cdots+\left(\sum a_{n-1,i}X^i\right)X^{(n-1)/n},$$

which can be rearranged as a power series in $X^{1/n}$. Hence $K(X^{1/n})=F((X^{1/n}))$, the field of power series in the variable $X^{1/n}$. Alternatively, writing X_n for $X^{1/n}$,

$$a_0+a_1X_n+a_2X_n^{\,2}+\cdots\mapsto a_0+a_1X_n^{\,n}+a_2X_n^{\,2n}+\cdots$$

is an (F-algebra) isomorphism of $F((X_n))$ with the subfield $F((X_n^{\,n}))$ of power series in the variable $X_n^{\,n}=X$.

Thus the theorem is to the effect that $\bar{K}$ consists of all formal power series of the form $\sum_i a_iX^{i/n}$ for some n, in other words, formal power series

$\Sigma a_i X^{q_i}$, where the q_i run through an increasing sequence of rational numbers with bounded denominators (and thus does not include series such as $\Sigma X^{n+1/n}$). To express this properly, we wish to form the union of the fields $F((X^{1/n}))$, but we lack a "universe" in which to perform $\cup$. This leads us to the following construction (which may seem roundabout, but actually makes checking that $\bar{K}$ is a valued field almost effortless):

$$\bar{K}=\Big(\coprod_{n\in\mathbb{N}} F((X_n))\Big)\Big/\sim,$$

where $X_1, X_2, \ldots$ now denote a sequence of indeterminates and where $\sim$ is the equivalence relation that makes the necessary identifications:

$$\sum_i a_i X_m^{\,i} \sim \sum_j b_j X_n^{\,j}$$

if there is a common multiple N of m and n, say $N=\mu m=\nu n$, such that

$$\sum_i a_i X_N^{\mu i}=\sum_j b_j X_N^{\nu j}.$$

For example, $a+bX_4^{\,2}+cX_4^{\,4}+\cdots\sim a+bX_6^{\,3}+cX_6^{\,6}+\cdots$ since $X_4^{\,2}\sim X_6^{\,3}$. Thus, if the typical element of $\bar{K}$ is denoted as an equivalence class by $[\alpha]$, where $\alpha\in F((X_n))$, for some n, then for any ν $\exists\alpha'\in F((X_{\nu n}))\ni[\alpha']=[\alpha]$. To define $[\alpha]+[\beta]$ and $[\alpha][\beta]$ we first replace α and β by representatives α' and β' in a common $F((X_N))$ and put

$$[\alpha]+[\beta]=[\alpha'+\beta'], \qquad [\alpha][\beta]=[\alpha'\beta'].$$

Because $\Sigma a_i X_n^{\,i}\mapsto\Sigma a_i X_{\nu n}^{\,\nu i}$ defines a ring homomorphism $F((X_n))\to F((X_{\nu n}))$, these operations are well defined. Similarly, $0=[0]$, $1=[1]$, $-[\alpha]=[-\alpha]$, and, when $\alpha\neq 0$, $[\alpha]^{-1}=[\alpha^{-1}]$ are well defined. The field axioms are satisfied since, for instance, $([\alpha][\beta])[\gamma]=[(\alpha'\beta')\gamma']=[\alpha'(\beta'\gamma')]=[\alpha]([\beta][\gamma])$ by taking representatives in a common $F((X_N))$. The canonical maps $F((X_n))\to\bar{K}$ (where $\alpha\mapsto[\alpha]$) are injective homomorphisms, and we can regard the $F((X_n))$ as subfields of K. In view of the identifications made, it is notationally consistent to write $X^{1/n}$ for $[X_n]$, so that finally we have a field $\bar{K}$ containing $K=F((X))$ and the roots $X^{1/2}, X^{1/3},\ldots$. Notice that if $n=md$, then $(X^{1/n})^d=X^{1/m}$, which has the corollary that X^q has a well-defined meaning in $\bar{K}$ for all $q\in\mathbb{Q}$. (In our earlier terminology, X^q is the *principal value* of $\{X^q\}$, the other values being of the form ζX^q, ζ an appropriate root of unity.)

This construction $\bar{K}$ is called the **direct limit** of the fields $F((X^{1/n}))$, and one writes

$$\bar{K}=\varinjlim F\big((X^{1/n})\big).$$

We do not elaborate on this idea here. It is better explained in the general context of category theory in order to include other types of limits.

(5.333) THEOREM. *Let F be an algebraically closed field of characteristic* 0, *let $K=F((X))$, and let $\bar{K}$ be constructed from K (as above) by adjoining $X^{1/2}, X^{1/3},\ldots$. Then $\bar{K}$ is an algebraic closure of K.*

Remark. A very short proof can be given using Hensel's lemma and some results of general valuation theory that we have not discussed. However, to actually calculate the roots of a polynomial one follows the constructive method of the proof anyway, using *Newton's polygon*. This will be made clear by an example that will be carried through the proof.

Proof. By (5.332), each element of $K(X^{1/n})$ is algebraic over K, with minimum polynomial of degree at most n. Hence $\bar{K}$ is algebraic over K.

We must show that every nonconstant

$$f=\alpha_n Y^n+\alpha_{n-1}Y^{n-1}+\cdots+\alpha_0\in\bar{K}[Y] \tag{5.334}$$

has a root

$$\eta=cX^q+c'X^{q'}+\cdots\in\bar{K}.$$

The series, where $c,c',\ldots\in F^*$ and $q<q'<\cdots$ is an increasing sequence of rational numbers with bounded denominators, is called the **Puiseux expansion** of η.

(5.335) LEMMA. *If η is a nonzero element of $\bar{K}$ with Puiseux expansion $cX^q+c'X^{q'}+\cdots$, then $v(\eta)=q$, augmented by $v(0)=\infty$, defines a (non-discrete) valuation on $\bar{K}$ extending the X-adic valuation on the subfield K.*

Proof of lemma. Let $\theta=dX^r+d'X^{r'}+\cdots$ be another element of $\bar{K}^*$ and let N be the l.c.m. of the denominators of all the qs and rs. We lift η and θ back to representatives $x=cX_N{}^h+c'X_N{}^{h'}+\cdots$ and $y=dX_N{}^k+d'X_N{}^{k'}+\cdots$ in $F((X_N))$. Since $q=h/N$, $v(\eta)=v_N(x)/N$, where v_N is the X_N-adic valuation on $F((X_N))$. Since $\eta\theta$ and $\eta+\theta$ are represented by xy and $x+y$, we have

$$v(\eta\theta)=v_N(xy)/N=v_N(x)/N+v_N(y)/N=v(\eta)+v(\theta),$$

and

$$v(\eta+\theta)=v_N(x+y)/N\geqslant\min\{v_N(x)/N,v_N(y)/N\}=\min\{v(\eta),v(\theta)\},$$

with the usual conventions concerning ∞, which concludes the proof of the lemma. ∎

We denote the valuation ring by

$$\bar{D}=\{cX^q+c'X^{q'}+\cdots:0\leqslant q<q'<\cdots\}.$$

(*Exercise*: The maximal ideal of this local ring is not finitely generated.)

Multiplying (5.334) by X^{-q}, where $q = \min\{v(\alpha_i)\}$, we can assume that $v(\alpha_i) \geqslant 0$ for all i. We shall follow the proof through with the example

$$(5.336) \quad f = Y^5 + X^3Y^3 + (X + X^2)Y^2 + (2X^2 + 2X^3)Y + X^3.$$

(Of course in general the coefficients are fractional power series, but this example will sufficiently illustrate the method of the proof.) We plot the points $P_i = (i, v(\alpha_i))$ in the plane $\mathbb{Q} \times \mathbb{Q}$, omitting any for which $v(\alpha_i) = \infty$; see Figure 5.24 for the case of (5.336).

The **Newton polygon** of f is the lower convex envelope of this graph, that is, the set of those line segments P_sP_t such that every P_iP_j lies in or above one of these segments forming the polygon. In this example, the Newton polygon consists of the two segments P_0P_2 and P_2P_5.

Recall that in a valued field if

$$x_1 + x_2 + \cdots + x_n = 0,$$

then $\min\{v(x_i)\}$ must be attained at least twice. Thus if $\eta = cX^q + \cdots$ is a root of f, then

$$v(\alpha_i\eta^i) = v(\alpha_i) + qi$$

must attain a minimum at least twice, which means that the corresponding points P_i are on a segment of the Newton polygon. In terms of the usual xy coordinates, the equation of the line containing this segment is of the form $y + qx = r$. Thus in an attempt to construct a root $\eta = cX^q + \cdots$, we choose a segment P_sP_t of the polygon, where $s < t$, say in the line $y = -qx + r$ so that the slope is $-q$. We then substitute

$$Y = X^q(c + Y_1),$$

Figure 5.24

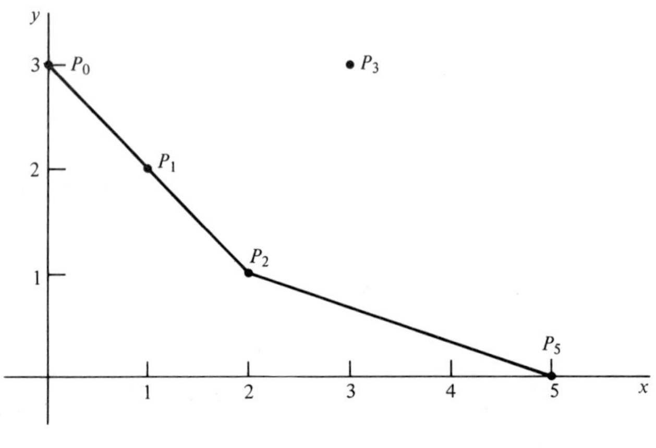

where $c \in F^*$ is to be determined, and calculate

$$f_1 = X^{-r} f$$

as a polynomial in Y_1. We shall see in a moment that the factor X^{-r} removes just the right power of X. Let I denote the set of $i \ni P_i$ is on the chosen segment, i.e., $v(\alpha_i) + qi = r$, and let J denote the set of remaining subscripts j: $v(\alpha_j) + qj > r$. Then

$$f_1 = X^{-r}\left(\sum_{i \in I} \alpha_i X^{qi}(c + Y_1)^i + \sum_{j \in J} \alpha_j X^{qj}(c + Y_1)^j \right).$$

Let the Puiseux expansion of $\alpha_i X^{qi}$ be $a_i X^r + \cdots$ and define

$$g(Z) = \sum_{i \in I} a_i Z^{i-s} \in F[Z].$$

Since P_s and P_t are the end points of the segment, a_s and a_t are nonzero and

$$d = \deg(g) = t - s > 0.$$

We choose a root $c \in F$, which is possible since F is algebraically closed, and $c \neq 0$ since $a_s \neq 0$. If

$$g(Z) = (Z - c)^m h(Z), \qquad h(c) \neq 0,$$

then

$$\begin{aligned} f_1 = X^{-r} f = {} & Y_1^m h(c + Y_1) + \sum_{i \in I} (\alpha_i X^{qi-r} - a_i)(c + Y_1)^i \\ & + \sum_{j \in J} \alpha_j X^{qj-r}(c + Y_1)^j \\ = {} & \beta_n Y_1^n + \cdots + \beta_0, \end{aligned}$$

say, where

$$\begin{aligned} & v(\beta_k) \geq 0, && \forall k \\ (5.337) \qquad & v(\beta_k) > 0, && \text{for} \quad 0 \leq k < m, \text{ and} \\ & v(\beta_m) = 0 && (\text{since } h(c) \neq 0). \end{aligned}$$

For our example we first choose the segment P_0P_2, so $s = 0, t = 2, q = 1$, $r = 3, I = \{0, 1, 2\}, d = 2$, and since $\alpha_0 = X^3$, $X^q\alpha_1 = 2X^3 + \cdots$, $X^{2q}\alpha_2 = X^3 + \cdots$,

$$g(Z) = 1 + 2Z + Z^2 = (1 + Z)^2.$$

We must take $c = -1$ with $m = 2$, and then

$$\begin{aligned} f_1 = {} & X^2Y_1^5 - 5X^2Y_1^4 + (10X^2 + X^3)Y_1^3 + (1 + X - 10X^2 - 3X^3)Y_1^2 \\ & + (5X^2 + 3X^3)Y_1 - (X + X^2 + X^3). \end{aligned}$$

Returning to general f_1, if $\beta_0 = 0$, then 0 is a root of f_1, whence cX^q is a root of f, which completes the proof. Otherwise we proceed as before, using the notation $Y_1 = X^{q_2}(c_2 + Y_2)$ and s_2 for s, and so on, except that now we must choose a segment with negative slope in order that $q_2 > 0$ and we have increasing exponents in the developing series

$$Y = X^q(c + Y_1) = cX^q + c_2 X^{q+q_2} + X^{q+q_2}Y_2.$$

This is always possible since $0 = v(\beta_m) < v(\beta_0) < \infty$ and therefore the segment containing P_0 has negative slope. In our example the Newton polygon for f_1 is that plotted in Figure 5.25. Therefore we take $s_2 = 0$, $t_2 = 2$, $q_2 = \frac{1}{2}$, $r_2 = 1$, $I_2 = \{0,2\}$, $d_2 = 2$, and

$$g_2 = -1 + Z^2 = (Z-1)(Z+1).$$

We can choose either root $c_2 = \pm 1$ with $m_2 = 1$.

Now, $m_2 = 1$ is the signal that $Y_2 = 0$ is a sufficiently close approximation to a root of f_2 to start up Hensel's lemma. For by (5.337), with the β_i now denoting the coefficients of f_2,

$$v(f_2(0)) = v(\beta_0) > 0 = 2v(\beta_1) = 2v(f_2'(0)).$$

Our example is

$$f_2 = X^{7/2}Y_2^5 + (-5X^3 + 5X^{7/2})Y_1^4 + (10X^{5/2} + \cdots)Y_1^3$$
$$+ (1 + X + \cdots)Y_1^2 + (2 + 2X + 5X^{3/2} + \cdots)Y_1$$
$$+ (5X^{3/2} - 11X^2 + \cdots).$$

The polygon algorithm could be continued, but Hensel's lemma is more efficient. In this case $c_2 = 1$ leads to

$$Y_2 = -\tfrac{5}{2}X^{3/2} + \tfrac{11}{2}X^2 + \ldots,$$

which gives the root

$$Y = -X + X^{3/2} - \tfrac{5}{2}X^3 + \tfrac{11}{2}X^{7/2} + \cdots.$$

Figure 5.25

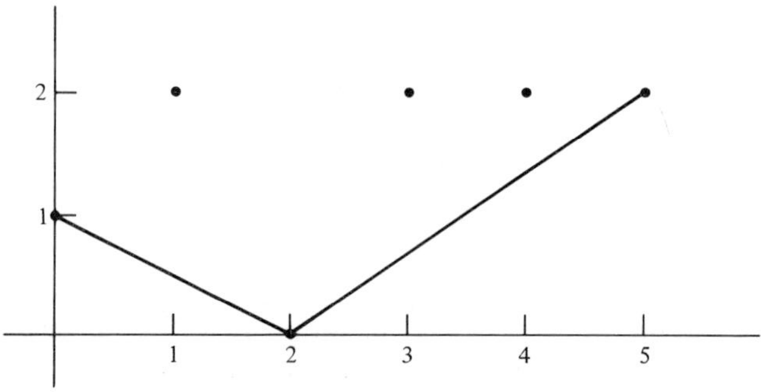

Similarly, $c_2=-1$ leads to the root

$$Y=-X-X^{3/2}-\tfrac{5}{2}X^3-\tfrac{11}{2}X^{7/2}+\cdots.$$

The remaining three roots are obtained by starting with $q=\frac{1}{3}$, with the result

$$Y=\omega X^{1/3}+\tfrac{2}{3}X+\tfrac{1}{3}\omega X^{4/3}+\cdots,$$

where ω is any one of the three roots of $\omega^3+1=0$. (The fact that the horizontal width of the segment coincides with the number of roots obtained starting with that segment will be proved in (5.340).)

In general, the polygon algorithm will give $m_i=1$ for some i, and then Hensel's lemma can be applied to f_i, provided we have taken the precaution initially of removing the factor g.c.d.(f,f') from f so that f has no multiple roots. This matter will be discussed after the proof; we can complete the proof without referring to this complication.

We must show that if the polygon algorithm is used repeatedly then

(i) the q_i have bounded denominators so that the partial sums

$$cX^q+c_2X^{q+q_2}+\cdots+c_iX^{q+q_2+\cdots+q_i}$$

converge to an element $\eta\in\overline{K}$; and

(ii) $f(\eta)=0$.

Let us fix the notation

(5.338) $$f_i(Y_i)=X^{-r_i}f_{i-1}(X^{q_i}(c_i+Y_i))=\beta_{in}Y_i^n+\cdots+\beta_{i0}$$

where $f_0=f$ and $q_1=q$, and so on. A segment with negative slope is chosen from the $(i+1)$th polygon. By (5.337) this means that

$$0\leqslant s_{i+1}<t_{i+1}\leqslant m_i.$$

Hence

$$1\leqslant m_{i+1}\leqslant t_{i+1}-s_{i+1}\leqslant m_i$$

and therefore there exists a k such that $m_k=m_{k+1}=\cdots$. Then for all $i>k$, $s_i=0$, $t_i=m_i=\deg(g_i)$; hence

$$g_i(Z)=a(Z-c_i)^{m_i}=aZ^{m_i}-\cdots\pm m_iac_i^{m_i-1}Z\mp ac_i^{m_i}$$

for some $a\in F^*$. Since char$(F)=0$ and $ac_i\neq 0$, these terms are all nonzero. This means that there is just one segment with negative slope and it contains all the points $(h,v(\beta_{i-1,h}))$ for $0\leqslant h\leqslant m_i$. Hence its slope is

$$q_i=v(\beta_{i-1,1})-v(\beta_{i-1,0}).$$

Letting N denote the l.c.m. of the denominators of $q_1,\ldots,q_k$, it follows by induction that all $\beta_{ij}\in F((X^{1/N}))$, i.e., $Nv(\beta_{ij})\in\mathbb{Z}$, and $Nq_i\in\mathbb{Z}$, $\forall i$.

Finally, since $r_i>1/N$ ($\forall i>1$) and $v(\beta_{i0})\geqslant 0$, (5.338) shows that

$$f(c_1X^{q_1}+\cdots+c_iX^{q_1+\cdots+q_i})=X^{r_1+\cdots+r_i}\beta_{i0}$$

has limit 0 as $i \to \infty$. Therefore $f(\eta)=0$ by continuity of polynomial functions (A12.2(v)). ■

Let us immediately clear up the incidental point mentioned during the proof concerning multiple roots: If f has no multiple roots, then the final constant value of m_i is 1 (and, as already explained, when that point is reached, Hensel's lemma is applicable). Suppose, using the notation of the proof, that $i>k$. Then $m_i=m_k$ and the point $(m_k,0)$ is on the segment contained in the line $y+q_ix=r_i$; hence $q_im_k=r_i$. By (5.338),

$$f(c_1X^{q_1}+\cdots+c_iX^{q_1+\cdots+q_i}+X^{q_1+\cdots+q_i}Y_i)=X^{r_1+\cdots+r_i}f(Y_i).$$

Differentiating with respect to Y_i using the chain rule A12.9(e) gives

$$f'(c_1X^{q_1}+\cdots+X^{q_1+\cdots}Y_1)=X^{a+b}f_i'(Y_i),$$

where $a=(r_1-q_1)+\cdots+(r_k-q_k)$ and $b=(r_{k+1}-q_{k+1})+\cdots+(r_i-q_i)$ $=(m_k-1)(q_{k+1}+\cdots+q_i)\geqslant(m_k-1)(i-k)/N$. Thus $m_k>1 \Rightarrow$ the root η of f is also a root of f', i.e., that η is a multiple root of f.

(5.339) COROLLARY. *Let $\eta\in\overline{K}^*$, let n be the l.c.m. of the denominators of the exponents $q,q',\ldots$ occurring in the Puiseux expansion $cX^q+c'X^{q'}+\cdots$ of η, and let $n'=[K(\eta):K]$. Then $n=n'$ and $K(\eta)=F((X^{1/n}))$. The subfields of $F((X^{1/n}))$ containing $F((X))$ are precisely $F((X^{1/m}))$, where $m|n$.*

Proof. For convenience let K_n denote $F((X^{1/n}))$. First we observe that $K_m\subset K_n$ iff $m|n$: If $md=n$, then $(X^{1/n})^d=X^{1/m}$ and hence $K_m\subset K_n$. Conversely, this implies, by (5.332) and A7.5, that $[K_m:K]=m|n=[K_n:K]$.

By the definition of n, $K(\eta)\subset K_n$, so that $n=n'd$ for some d, and by uniqueness of power series expansions in K_n, n is minimal:

$$(*)\qquad \eta\in K_m,\quad m|n \quad\Rightarrow\quad m=n.$$

If $f(Y)$ is the minimum polynomial of $X^{1/n}$ over $K(\eta)$, f is a divisor of degree $[K_n:K(\eta)]=d$ of

$$Y^n-X=\prod(Y-\zeta^jX^{1/n}),$$

where ζ^j runs through the nth roots of unity (which are in F since F is algebraically closed of characteristic 0). Thus f is a product of d terms $Y-\zeta^jX^{1/n}$ and the constant term of f has the form $aX^{1/n'}$, $a\in F^*$. This proves that $X^{1/n'}\in K(\eta)$. However, since $[K(\eta):K]=[K_{n'}:K]=n'$, this implies $K(\eta)=K_{n'}$, and $n=n'$ by $(*)$. ■

(5.340) COROLLARY. *With notation as above, let*

$$\begin{aligned}f&=Y^n+\alpha_{n-1}Y^{n-1}+\cdots+\alpha_0\in F((X))[Y]\\&=(Y-\eta_1)\cdots(Y-\eta_n),\qquad \eta_i\in\overline{K},\end{aligned}$$

where $\alpha_0 \neq 0$ so $\eta_i \neq 0$, and let $(s, v(\alpha_s)),(t, v(\alpha_t))$ with $s<t$ be the end points of a segment of the Newton polygon of f with slope $-q$. Then f has precisely $t-s$ roots $\eta_i \in \bar{K}$ satisfying $v(\eta_i)=q$. Thus $f=\prod f_q$, where $f_q = \prod\{(Y-\eta_i): v(\eta_i)=q\}$. Moreover, $f_q \in F((X))[Y]$. Hence if f is irreducible/$F((X))$ then the Newton polygon of f consists of one segment.

Remark. We allow $v(\alpha_i)<0$, so the polygon may contain points below the x axis.

Proof. Let the η_i be numbered so that

$$\begin{aligned} v(\eta_1) = \cdots &= v(\eta_{n_1}) = q_1, \\ v(\eta_{n_1+1}) = \cdots &= v(\eta_{n_2}) = q_2, \\ &\vdots \\ v(\eta_{n_h+1}) = \cdots &= v(\eta_n) = q_h, \end{aligned}$$

where $q_1 < \cdots < q_h$. (The symbol q_i had a different connotation in the proof of the theorem.) Then, recalling the formula for α_i as a symmetric function in the roots,

$$\begin{aligned} v(\alpha_{n-1}) &\geqslant \min\{v(\eta_i)\} = q_1, \\ v(\alpha_{n-2}) &\geqslant \min\{v(\eta_i\eta_j)\} = 2q_1, \\ &\vdots \\ v(\alpha_{n-n_1}) &= \min\{v(\eta_{i_1}\cdots\eta_{i_{n_1}})\} = n_1 q_1, \end{aligned}$$

with equality in the last equation because the minimum is attained by the one term $\eta_1 \cdots \eta_{n_1}$. Similarly,

$$\begin{aligned} v(\alpha_{n-n_1-1}) &\geqslant n_1 q_1 + q_2, \\ &\vdots \\ v(\alpha_{n-n_2}) &= n_1 q_1 + (n_1 - n_2) q_2, \end{aligned}$$

and so on. These imply that the vertices of the Newton polygon are $(n,0)$, $(n-n_1, n_1q_1)$, $(n-n_2, n_1q_1+(n_1-n_2)q_2), \ldots$. Hence the slopes of the segments are $-q_1, -q_2, \ldots$.

It remains to prove that f_q, where q is any one of the q_i, has coefficients in $K=F((X))$. Let η be a root with $v(\eta)=q$, let $K(\eta)=F((X^{1/m}))$, and let ζ be a primitive mth root of 1 in F. $Y^m - X$ is irreducible/K and its roots are $\zeta^i X^{1/m}$, $i=0,1,\ldots,m-1$. By (5.119), a K-algebra automorphism φ_i is defined by $X^{1/m} \mapsto \zeta^i X^{1/m}$. Thus if $\eta = cX^q + c'X^{q'} + \cdots$, where $q=p/m$, $q'=p'/m$, and so on, then

$$\varphi_i(\eta) = c\zeta^{ip}X^q + c'\zeta^{ip'}X^{q'} + \cdots \qquad (\varphi_0(\eta)=\eta).$$

We leave it as a simple exercise to prove that $K(\varphi_i(\eta))=K(\zeta^i X^{1/m})=K(X^{1/m})=K(\eta)$, and that the m elements $\varphi_i(\eta)$ of $K(\eta)$ are distinct. If g denotes the minimum polynomial of η over K, then since $\varphi_i(\alpha)=\alpha$ for $\alpha\in K$, we have $g(\varphi_i(\eta))=0$, $\forall i$. Hence

$$g(Y)=\prod_{i=0}^{m-1}(Y-\varphi_i(\eta)).$$

Since $f(Y)\in K[Y]$, $g|f$, and since all the roots of g have values $v(\varphi_i(\eta))=q$, therefore $g|f_q$. If f_q still has other roots, say η' is one of them, then the minimum polynomial h of η' is likewise a factor of f_q. Since g and h are irreducible, $gh|f$ and in this way we obtain $f=gh\cdots$ as a product of polynomials in $K[Y]$. ■

We recall from the definition at the beginning of this section that if $\bar{k}$ is an algebraic closure of the field k, then $\bar{k}$ contains k as a subfield and so may be regarded as a k-algebra.

(5.341) PROPOSITION. *Let k be a field. Then there exists an algebraic closure $\bar{k}$ of k. If k' is another algebraic closure of k, there exists a k-algebra isomorphism $\bar{k}\to k'$.*

Proof. Let S be the set of irreducible polynomials over k and let $\{X_f\colon f\in S\}$ be a set of indeterminates indexed by S. Let I be the ideal in the polynomial ring $k[\{X_f\}]$ generated by the set $\{f(X_f)\}$.[7] We claim that I is proper. For suppose

$$(*)\qquad g_1f_1+\cdots+g_nf_n=1$$

for some $f_i\in S$ and polynomials g_i. By (5.116) we can construct a field F containing roots λ_i of these finitely many f_i, and then the substitutions $X_{f_i}\mapsto\lambda_i$ for $1\leqslant i\leqslant n$, and all other $X_f\mapsto 0$ in $(*)$ give the equation $0=1$ in F, a contradiction. By A5.6, there exists a maximal ideal $M\supset I$ and $k_1=k[\{X_f\}]/M$ is a field. The canonical map $k\to k_1$ is injective, and we can regard k as a subfield of k_1.

By construction, each $f\in S$ has a root in k_1, namely, the image (class) $\bar{X}_f$ of X_f, but conceivably k_1 is not algebraically closed since there are now other polynomials with coefficients in k_1. (Actually k_1 is algebraically closed, but the proof of this is rather delicate; instead we proceed as follows.) Since each $\bar{X}_f$ is algebraic over k, k_1 is algebraic over k. Inductively we repeat the construction, obtaining a chain of fields $k\subset k_1\subset k_2\subset\cdots$, with k_{i+1} algebraic over k_i, and we set $\bar{k}=\cup k_i$. (To put this properly, $\bar{k}$ is

---

[7]Each element in $k[\{X_f\}]$ is an ordinary polynomial involving only finitely many indeterminates. The formal construction of this ring is $k[M]$, where the monoid $M=\oplus_S\mathbb{N}$ is the submonoid of $\mathbb{N}^S$ consisting of those $(\ldots,m_f,\ldots)$ with almost all $m_f=0$.

the direct limit of the k_i and has a construction $\bar{k} = \amalg k_i/\sim$ that is similar to what we used to form $\bar{K}$ in the previous theorem. We leave the details to the reader.)

$\bar{k}$ is algebraic over k: If $\alpha \in \bar{k}$, then $\alpha \in k_i$ for some i. Say it is a root of $X^n + \beta_{n-1}X^{n-1} + \cdots + \beta_0$ where all the βs are in k_{i-1}. By induction, the βs are algebraic over k; hence

$$\begin{aligned}[k(\alpha, \beta_{n-1}, \ldots, \beta_0) : k] &= [k(\alpha) : k(\beta_{n-1}, \ldots, \beta_0)] \\ &\quad \times [k(\beta_{n-1}, \ldots, \beta_0) : k] < \infty\end{aligned}$$

by A7.5(ii); i.e., α is algebraic over k.

$\bar{k}$ is algebraically closed: If $f = X^n + \gamma_{n-1}X^{n-1} + \cdots + \gamma_0 \in \bar{k}[X]$, then the γs are all contained in k_i for i sufficiently large, and f contains a root in $k_{i+1} \subset \bar{k}$.

Thus $\bar{k}$ is an algebraic closure of k. Suppose k' is another. We consider the set T of pairs (E, φ) where E is a subfield of $\bar{k}$ containing k and $\varphi: E \to k'$ is a k-algebra homomorphism. $T \neq \varnothing$ since it contains (k, ρ), where $\rho: k \to k'$ is the given embedding, and we partially order T by setting $(E, \varphi) \leqslant (F, \psi)$ when $E \subset F$ and $\psi | E = \varphi$. If (E_i, φ_i) is a chain in T, an upper bound is (E, φ), where $E = \cup E_i$ and φ is defined by $\varphi(x) = \varphi_i(x)$ if $x \in E_i$. The fact that $\varphi_j | E_i = \varphi_i$ when $E_j \supset E_i$ ensures that φ is a well-defined homomorphism.

We are in a position to apply Zorn's lemma: Let (E, φ) denote a maximal element of T. It remains to show that $E = \bar{k}$ and $\varphi(\bar{k}) = k'$.

Suppose, however, $\exists x \in \bar{k} \setminus E$. Then x is a root of an irreducible polynomial $f = X^n + \cdots + \alpha_0 \in E[X]$, and $E(x) \approx E[X]/fE[X]$. Since k' is algebraically closed, $X^n + \varphi(\alpha_{n-1})X^{n-1} + \cdots + \varphi(\alpha_0)$ has n roots $\lambda, \lambda', \ldots$ in k'. By (5.118),

$$\beta_0 + \beta_1 x + \cdots + \beta_{n-1}x^{n-1} \mapsto \varphi(\beta_0) + \varphi(\beta_1)\lambda + \cdots$$

defines a k-algebra (in fact an E-algebra) homomorphism $\varphi': E(x) \to k'$. Thus $(E, \varphi) < (E(x), \varphi')$, contradicting maximality, and we must have $E = \bar{k}$.

Finally, if $y \in k'$, then y is algebraic over k, a fortiori over $\varphi(E)$. Yet the latter is isomorphic to E, and hence is algebraically closed, and therefore the minimum polynomial of y over $\varphi(E)$ is linear. Thus $y \in \varphi(E)$ and $k' = \varphi(E)$. ■

It was only in the last paragraph that we used the assumption that k' is algebraic over k. Thus the preceding argument gives the following more general result.

(5.342) PROPOSITION. *If E is an algebraic extension of k and k' is an algebraically closed field, then a homomorphism $\rho: k \to k'$ can be extended to $E \to k'$.*

(5.343) COROLLARY. *Let k' be an algebraically closed field, k a subfield, and let l denote the* **algebraic closure of k in k'**, *i.e., the set of x in k' that are algebraic over k. Then l is an algebraic closure of k.*

Proof. If $\bar{k}$ is an algebraic closure of k, then the proposition gives an embedding $\rho: \bar{k} \to k'$. Since $\bar{k}$ is algebraic over k, so is $\rho(\bar{k})$ and therefore $\rho(\bar{k}) \subset l$. If $x \in l$, then x is algebraic over k; hence x is algebraic$/\rho(\bar{k})$. However, $\rho(\bar{k})$ is algebraically closed, so the minimum polynomial of x over $\rho(\bar{k})$ is linear. Thus $x \in \rho(\bar{k})$ and $\rho(\bar{k}) = l$. ■

For instance, the algebraic closure of $\mathbb{Q}$ in $\mathbb{C}$ is an algebraic closure of $\mathbb{Q}$; the algebraic closure of $\mathbb{C}(X)$ in the field of fractional power series over $\mathbb{C}$ is an algebraic closure of $\mathbb{C}(X)$. In both these cases the overfield is a good deal larger (in the sense of cardinal numbers) than the algebraic closure of the subfield: Most of the elements are transcendental over the subfield. (For the case $\overline{\mathbb{Q}} \subset \mathbb{C}$, see Exercise 3 at the end of this section.) However, we have yet to exhibit in either case a single explicit transcendental. This will be remedied by Liouville's construction of transcendentals after the following

(5.344) PROPOSITION. *Let k be a valued field, let H be an integral domain contained in k satisfying*

$$h \in H, \quad h \neq 0 \quad \Rightarrow \quad |h| \geqslant 1,$$

and let α be an element of k algebraic of degree n over $Q(H)$. Then there exists $C \in \mathbb{R}^{>}$ (depending on α) such that

$$|\alpha - p/q| < C/|q|^n$$

has no solution $p, q(\neq 0) \in H$ (except when $n = 1$ and $p/q = \alpha$).

Remark. Roth has given a much improved result in the archimedean case, which we state for simplicity in the best known case $H = \mathbb{Z}$, $k = \mathbb{R}$: If α is real and algebraic over $\mathbb{Q}$ and $\lambda > 2$, then $\exists C \ni |\alpha - p/q| < C/q^\lambda$ has no solution $p, q(>0) \in \mathbb{Z}$. (The exact analog of Roth's theorem in the ultrametric case is not true.)

Proof. Let $f(\alpha) = 0$, where $f = a_n X^n + \cdots + a_0$, $a_j \in H$, and f is irreducible over $Q(H)$. If $f(X) + f_1(X)Y + \cdots + f_n(X)Y^n$ is the Taylor expansion of f, choose $M \geqslant 1$ so that $|f_j(x)| < M$ for $1 \leqslant j \leqslant n$ and all x satisfying $|\alpha - x| < 1$. We show that the statement is true with $C = 1/nM$. Thus suppose that the inequality is satisfied by p/q and write $p/q = \alpha + \beta$. Since $C \leqslant 1$ and $f(\alpha) = 0$, we have $|\beta| < 1$ and

$$|f(p/q)| = |\beta f_1(p/q) + \beta^2 f_2(p/q) + \cdots| < |\beta| nM = |\beta|/C.$$

On the other hand,

$$|f(p/q)| = |a_n p^n + a_{n-1} p^{n-1} q + \cdots|/|q|^n \geqslant 1/|q|^n,$$

since the numerator $a_n p^n + \cdots \in H$ and we can assume that p/q is not one of the roots of f. Hence $|\beta| > C/|q|^n$. ■

Here is a typical application.

(5.345) COROLLARY. *Let $h_1, h_2, \ldots$ be elements of H such that $|h_j| > 1$ and, writing $u_j = h_1 h_2 \cdots h_j$, suppose that the real numbers*

$$\lambda_j = \log|u_{j+1}|/\log|u_j|$$

satisfy $\lim \lambda_j = \infty$. *Then the series*

$$(*) \qquad 1/u_1 + 1/u_2 + 1/u_3 + \cdots$$

converges to an element $\alpha \in \tilde{k}$ that is transcendental over $Q(H)$.

Proof. Choose N so that $\lambda_j > 2$ for $j \geqslant N$. By induction, $|h_j| \geqslant |u_N| = r$ (say) for $j \geqslant N$ and the absolute convergence of $1/u_N + 1/u_{N+1} + \cdots$, and thus that of $(*)$, follows by comparison with $1/r + 1/r^2 + \cdots$. We can write the jth partial sum of $(*)$ in the form p/q, where $q = u_j$ and p are elements of H. Now, for $j \geqslant N$,

$$\begin{aligned} |\alpha - p/q| &= |1/u_{j+1} + \cdots| \\ &\leqslant 1/|q|^{\lambda_j} + 1/|q|^{\lambda_{j+1}\lambda_j} + \cdots \\ &< 1/|q|^{\lambda_j} + 1/|q|^{2\lambda_j} + 1/|q|^{4\lambda_j} + \cdots \\ &< 1/\big(|q|^{\lambda_j}(1 - 1/|q|)\big), \end{aligned}$$

which is less than the $C/|q|^n$ of the proposition for sufficiently large j. Hence α cannot be algebraic of degree n over $Q(H)$. And this is true $\forall n \geqslant 1$. ■

As explicit examples, using $H = \mathbb{Z}$ and $k = \mathbb{R}$ or $\mathbb{C}$, the real number

$$0.1100010\ldots = 10^{-1!} + 10^{-2!} + 10^{-3!} + \cdots$$

and the complex number

$$10^{-1!}e^{2i} + 10^{-2!}e^{3i} + \cdots + 10^{-n!}e^{\pi_n i} + \cdots,$$

where π_n is (for instance) the nth prime number, are transcendental numbers, i.e., transcendental over $\mathbb{Q}$. For any field F, using $H = F[1/X]$, the formal power series

$$X^{1!} + X^{2!} + \cdots \in F((X))$$

is transcendental over $F(X)$.

EXERCISES

1. Let $\overline{\mathbb{Q}}$ be an algebraic closure of $\mathbb{Q}$ and $\alpha \in \overline{\mathbb{Q}} \setminus \mathbb{Q}$. Then there is a subfield K of $\overline{\mathbb{Q}}$ maximal with respect to not containing α. For any such K, $[K(\alpha):K]$ is a prime number.

2. For given $\alpha_1,\ldots,\alpha_n \in \mathbb{R}$, there are infinitely many $q \in \mathbb{N}$ such that each $q\alpha_j$ differs from an integer by at most $q^{-1/n}$, say

$$(*) \qquad |q\alpha_j - p_j| < q^{-1/n}, \qquad j=1,\ldots,n,$$

where $p_j \in \mathbb{Z}$. (Note that if we pick q "at random" and take p_j to be the integer nearest $q\alpha_j$, then we can only be sure that $|q\alpha_j - p_j| \leqslant \frac{1}{2}$. Thus the rationals p_j/q in $(*)$ are unusually good approximations to the α_j. In the case of a single α, there are infinitely many $q \ni |\alpha - p/q| \leqslant 1/q^2$ for appropriate $p \in \mathbb{Z}$; an explicit case occurs in Exercise 11 after Section 10. *Hint*: For any $N \in \mathbb{N}$ divide the "half open" unit hypercube $\{(x_1,\ldots,x_n) \in \mathbb{R}^n : 0 \leqslant x_j < 1 \text{ for } 1 \leqslant j \leqslant n\}$ into N^n boxes described by n inequalities of the form $k_j/N \leqslant x_j < (k_j+1)/N$ for various integers k_j between 0 and $N-1$. By the pigeonhole principle, two of the $N^n + 1$ vectors

$$(r\alpha_1 - \lfloor r\alpha_1 \rfloor, \ldots, r\alpha_n - \lfloor r\alpha_n \rfloor), \qquad r = 0,1,\ldots,N^n,$$

lie in the same box. Let q be the difference of the two corresponding rs.) Deduce that if $\theta_1,\ldots,\theta_n \in \mathbb{R}$, then $\forall \varepsilon \in \mathbb{R}^{>}\ \exists N \in \mathbb{N} \ni$

$$|\exp(N\theta_j i) - 1| < \varepsilon \qquad \text{for } j=1,\ldots,n.$$

3. Prove that the algebraic closure $\overline{\mathbb{Q}}$ of $\mathbb{Q}$ in $\mathbb{C}$ is a countable field. (The elements of $\overline{\mathbb{Q}}$ are called **algebraic numbers** while those of $\mathbb{C} \setminus \overline{\mathbb{Q}}$ are called **transcendental numbers**. By (4.30), $|\mathbb{C}| = |\mathbb{R} \times \mathbb{R}| = |\mathbb{R}|$; hence $\mathbb{C}$ is uncountable and "most" complex numbers are transcendental.)

Supplementary Exercises

1. [Section 3] Prove the following in succession.

(i) Every integer >6 can be written as a sum of two relatively prime integers >1.

(ii) If $p_1 = 2, p_2 = 3, \ldots$ denotes the sequence of primes, then for $n \geqslant 3$, $p_{n+1} + p_{n+2} \leqslant p_1 p_2 \cdots p_n$.

(iii) For $N \in \mathbb{N}$ let q_N denote the smallest p_n not dividing N. Then the sequence q_N/N $(N = 1,2,\ldots)$ is null with respect to the ordinary absolute value in $\mathbb{Q}$.

2. [Section 4] For real numbers, $a^2 + b^2 + c^2 = 1 \Rightarrow -\frac{1}{2} \leqslant ab + bc + ca \leqslant 1$; $pP + 2qQ + rR = 0$ and $pr - q^2 > 0 \Rightarrow PR - Q^2 \leqslant 0$.

3. [Section 4] A field is **formally real** if -1 is not a sum of squares. Prove that a field is formally real iff -1 is not a sum of 4th powers.

4. [Section 4] For $n \geqslant 2$ and $a_1,\ldots,a_n \in \mathbb{R}$,

$$\min_{i \neq j}\{(a_i - a_j)^2\} \leqslant 12(a_1^2 + \cdots + a_n^2)/n(n^2-1).$$

5. [Section 5] Let $a_1,\ldots,a_k$ be distinct real numbers with nonzero sum. Then there exist integers $n_1,\ldots,n_k \ni \Sigma n_i a_i > 0$ and $\Sigma n_i a_{\sigma(i)} < 0$, $\forall\sigma(\neq 1) \in \mathrm{Sym}(k)$.

6. [Section 10] By transport of structure (cf. Supplementary Exercise 9 of Chapter 3), for an odd natural number n, the set $\mathbb{R}$ is a field with respect to the new addition $x \oplus y = \sqrt[n]{x^n + y^n}$ and the other operations as usual.

7. [Section 10] The subset $\{\sqrt{2}, \sqrt{3}, \sqrt{5}, \sqrt{6}, \sqrt{7}, \sqrt{10}, \ldots\}$ of $\mathbb{R}$, where $2,3,5,\ldots$ are the square free integers > 1, is linearly independent over $\mathbb{Q}$. (Therefore $\{a\sqrt{2} + b\sqrt{3} + c\sqrt{6} : a, b, c \in \mathbb{Q}\}$, for instance, is a three-dimensional $\mathbb{Q}$-subspace of $\mathbb{R}$.)

8. [Section 10] For each $n \in \mathbb{N}$, $\min\{\lfloor m + n/m \rfloor : m \in \mathbb{N}\} = \lfloor \sqrt{4n+1} \rfloor$.

9. [Section 10] In the sequence $1,2,4,5,7,9,10,\ldots$ formed by taking 1 followed by the next two even numbers, then the next three odd numbers, then the next four even numbers, and so on, the nth term is $2n - \lfloor (1 + \sqrt{8n-7})/2 \rfloor$.

10. [Section 12] Let K be a commutative ring. The elements x_i of the commutative K-algebra A are **algebraically independent** if the K-algebra homomorphism $K[\{X_i\}] \to A$ determined by $X_i \mapsto x_i$ is injective. If K is a field and $A = K[Z_1,\ldots,Z_n]$, show that the elementary symmetric functions $s_1,\ldots,s_n$, as defined in (5.106), are algebraically independent.

11. [Section 14] If $1 < n_1 < \cdots < n_r$, then $1 + X^{n_1} + \cdots + X^{n_r}$ has no complex root α satisfying $|\alpha| < (\sqrt{5} - 1)/2$.

12. [Section 14] Let V denote $\mathbb{C}$ regarded as a two-dimensional vector space/$\mathbb{R}$. For $\alpha \in \mathbb{C}$, let $\tilde{\alpha} \in \mathrm{End}(V)$ be defined by $\tilde{\alpha}(\beta) = \alpha\beta$. Then $\alpha \mapsto \tilde{\alpha}$ is a ring homomorphism. In terms of the basis $\mathcal{V} = \{1, i\}$

$$(*) \qquad R_{\mathcal{V}}(\tilde{\alpha}) = \begin{pmatrix} a & -b \\ b & a \end{pmatrix}.$$

Hence $\mathrm{Tr}(\tilde{\alpha}) = 2a$, $\det(\tilde{\alpha}) = a^2 + b^2$, and α is a root of $X^2 - 2aX + a^2 + b^2$. Using $(*)$ and block multiplication (A9.1), define an $\mathbb{R}$-algebra homomorphism

$$\mathrm{Mat}_n(\mathbb{C}) \to \mathrm{Mat}_{2n}(\mathbb{R}).$$

13. [Section 14] A polynomial $f \in \mathbb{C}[X]$ is **stable** if the real part of every root is negative. (This term arises in certain applications to physical systems described by differential equations whose solutions involve $e^{\lambda t}$, where λ is a root and t denotes time.) Show that the real polynomial $X^2 + aX + b$ (resp. $X^3 + aX^2 + bX + c$, $X^4 + aX^3 + bX^2 + cX + d$) is stable iff all the coefficients are positive and, for the cubic $ab > c$, and for the quartic $abc > a^2 d + c^2$. Now apply the criterion for the quartic to $(X^2 + \alpha X + \beta)(X^2 + \bar{\alpha} X + \bar{\beta})$ to determine when a complex quadratic is stable.

14. [A11.1] Using $a+b>2\sqrt{ab}$ for appropriate a, b, prove that

$$\sqrt{2n+1}<\frac{2}{1}\cdot\frac{4}{3}\cdots\frac{2n}{2n-1}<2\sqrt{n+1}\,.$$

15. [A11.1]

(i) Adapt the proof that the arithmetic mean is greater than the geometric mean to the following result of Jensen: Let X be a subset of $\mathbb{R}$ with the property that $x_1,\ldots,x_n\in X$ (any $n\geqslant 1)\Rightarrow(x_1+\cdots+x_n)/n\in X$, and let $f\colon X\to\mathbb{R}$ satisfy

$$(*)\qquad \frac{f(x_1)+f(x_2)}{2}\leqslant f\left(\frac{x_1+x_2}{2}\right),\qquad \forall x_1,x_2\in X.$$

Then

$$(**)\qquad \frac{f(x_1)+\cdots+f(x_n)}{n}\leqslant f\left(\frac{x_1+\cdots+x_n}{n}\right)$$

for all $x_i\in X$ and all n. Also, if equality holds in $(*)$ only when $x_1=x_2$, then equality holds in $(**)$ only when $x_1=\cdots=x_n$.

(ii) Let a_1, b_1 be real numbers satisfying $0<a_1<b_1$ and define

$$a_{n+1}=\sqrt{a_nb_n}\,,\qquad b_{n+1}=\frac{a_n+b_n}{2}.$$

Then

$$a_1<a_2<a_3<\cdots<b_3<b_2<b_1$$

and $\lim a_n=\lim b_n$. (This common limit is called the **arithmetic–geometric mean of Gauss**. It is known from the theory of elliptic functions that its value is

$$\pi b_1\Big/2\int_0^{\pi/2}(1-m\sin^2\theta)^{-1/2}\,d\theta,$$

where $m=1-(a_1/b_1)^2$.)

16. [Section 15] Discuss the validity of the following. By adding and subtracting

$$\left(\frac{1+X}{2}\right)^m=\left(1+\frac{1-X}{1+X}\right)^{-m},\qquad \left(\frac{1+X}{2X}\right)^m=\left(1-\frac{1-X}{1+X}\right)^{-m}$$

we obtain

$$(1+X)^m=\frac{2^{m+1}X^m}{1+X^m}\left[1+\binom{m+1}{2}\left(\frac{1-X}{1+X}\right)^2+\binom{m+3}{4}\left(\frac{1-X}{1+X}\right)^4+\cdots\right]$$

and

$$(1+X)^m=\frac{2^{m+1}X^m}{1-X^m}\left[\binom{m}{1}\left(\frac{1-X}{1+X}\right)+\binom{m+2}{3}\left(\frac{1-X}{1+X}\right)^3+\cdots\right].$$

17. [Section 15] Verify these expansions for

$$u_n=\left(X+\sqrt{1+X^2}\right)^n+\left(X-\sqrt{1+X^2}\right)^n.$$

n even—

$$u_n=2\sum_{i=0}^{\infty}\frac{X^{2i}}{(2i)!}\prod_{j=0}^{i-1}\left(n^2-(2j)^2\right);$$

n odd—

$$u_n=2n\sum_{i=0}^{\infty}\frac{X^{2i+1}}{(2i+1)!}\prod_{j=0}^{i-1}\left(n^2-(2j+1)^2\right).$$

(As usual, an empty product has the value 1.)

18. [Section 15] The proofs of the following variants of the (finite) binomial theorem involve some work:

Abel—

$$(X+Y)^n=X\sum_{m=0}^{n}\binom{n}{m}(X+m)^{m-1}(Y-m)^{n-m};$$

Cauchy—

$$(1+XZ)(1+X^2Z)\cdots(1+X^nZ)=$$

$$1+\sum_{m=1}^{n}\frac{(1-X^n)(1-X^{n-1})\cdots(1-X^{n-m+1})}{(1-X)(1-X^2)\cdots(1-X^m)}X^{m(m+1)/2}Z^m;$$

hence

$$(1+XZ)(1+X^3Z)\cdots(1+X^{2n-1}Z)=$$

$$1+\sum_{m=1}^{n}\frac{(1-X^{2n})(1-X^{2n-2})\cdots(1-X^{2n-2m+2})}{(1-X^2)(1-X^4)\cdots(1-X^{2m})}X^{m^2}Z^m.$$

19. [Section 19] Use Exercise 5 after Section 12 to show that $s(n-1,m)/s(n,m)$ decreases as m increases.

20. [Section 19] Use the power series expansion of $\exp(1/(1-X))$ to show that if

$$A_m=\sum_{n=1}^{\infty}\frac{1}{n!}\binom{-n}{m},$$

then $A_{m+2}=(2m+3)A_{m+1}-m(m+1)A_m(m\geqslant 1)$.

21. [Section 19] For $a\in\mathbb{R}^{\geqslant}$, the sequence $a_1=a, a_{n+1}=a^{a_n}$ converges for $e^{-e}\leqslant a\leqslant e^{1/e}$ and otherwise diverges.

22. [Section 20] The **infinite product** $\prod_{n=1}^{\infty}(1+a_n)$, where a_n are in the valued field k, **converges** if the sequence of partial products $p_N=\prod_{n=1}^{N}(1+a_n)$ is cauchy with limit $p \neq 0$. (It is convenient to disallow $p=0$. Thus the real product $\Pi \frac{1}{2}$ *diverges* to 0.)

(i) For convergence it is necessary that no $a_n = -1$ and that $\lim a_n = 0$. When k is ultrametric these conditions are also sufficient. (To avoid certain trivial complications, we assume in the rest of the exercise that $|a_n| < 1\ \forall n$.) *Example*: In $F((X))$, F any field, $(1+X)(1+X^2)(1+X^3)\cdots = 1/(1-X)(1-X^3)(1-X^5)\cdots$.

(ii) If k is real or ultrametric of characteristic 0, then $\Pi(1+a_n)$ converges iff $\Sigma \log(1+a_n)$ converges. Then, if the limits are p and s (and in the l-ultrametric case, $|a_n| < |l|^{1/(l-1)}\ \forall n$), $p = \exp(s)$.

(iii) $\Pi(1+a_n)$ is **absolutely convergent** if the real product $\Pi(1+|a_n|)$ is convergent. This is so iff Σa_n is absolutely convergent.

(iv) An absolutely convergent product is convergent. (The hard part is to show $p \neq 0$.)

(v) When $k = \mathbb{R}$, $\Pi(1-(-1)^n/n)$ is convergent but not absolutely convergent. When $k = \mathbb{C}$, $\Pi(1+i/n)$ diverges while $\Pi|1+i/n|$ converges.

(vi) In the ultrametric case, $\Pi(1+a_n)$ converges iff Σa_n converges. However, when $k = \mathbb{R}$,

(a) if $a_n = (-1)^n/\sqrt{n+1}$, Σa_n converges but $\Pi(1+a_n)$ diverges; and

(b) if x stands for $1/\sqrt{n+1}$ and $a_{2n-1} = -x$, $a_{2n} = x + x^2 + x^3$, then $\Pi(1+a_n)$ converges while Σa_n and $\Sigma a_n{}^2$ diverge.

(vii) When p runs over the primes (and $k = \mathbb{R}$), $\Sigma 1/p$ and $\Pi(1-1/p)$ both diverge.[8] (*Hint*:

$$\sum_{1}^{N} 1/n \leqslant \prod_{j=1}^{N} \left(1-1/p_j\right)^{-1} \leqslant \exp\left(2\sum_{j=1}^{N} 1/p_j\right).\Bigg)$$

23. [Section 21] Let p be a prime, k a field containing the pth roots of 1, and let $a \in k$. Then $X^p - a$ is either irreducible or factors into linear factors in $k[X]$.

24. [Section 21] For $n \in \mathbb{N}$ let $\varphi_r(n) = \Sigma\{m^r : 1 \leqslant m \leqslant n, \text{g.c.d.}(m,n)=1\}$. Thus $\varphi_0(n) = \varphi(n)$. Then, if $p, q, \ldots$ are the distinct primes dividing n (so $\varphi(n) = n(1-1/p)(1-1/q)\cdots$), $\varphi_1(n) = \frac{1}{2}n(p-1)(q-1)\cdots$ and $\varphi_2(n) = \frac{1}{3}n^3(1-1/p)(1-1/q)\cdots + \frac{1}{6}n(1-p)(1-q)\cdots$.

25. [Section 21] The number of monic irreducible polynomials/$\mathbb{F}_q$ of degree n is $(1/n)\Sigma_{d|n}\mu(n/d)q^d$.

26. [Section 21] Two applications of (5.258): Let $f, g: \mathbb{R} \to A$, where A is an abelian group.

(a)

$$g(x) = \sum_{n=1}^{\lfloor x \rfloor} f(x/n) \qquad \forall x > 0$$

---

[8] For more precise results, see G. M. Hardy and E. M. Wright, *The Theory of Numbers*, $\geqslant$ 3rd ed., Oxford University Press, London, 1954, Chapter 22.

iff

$$f(x)=\sum_{n=1}^{\lfloor x\rfloor}\mu(n)g(x/n)\qquad \forall x>0.$$

(b) With suitable restrictions of f and g to ensure convergence,

$$g(x)=\sum_{n=1}^{\infty}f(nx)\qquad\Leftrightarrow\qquad f(x)=\sum_{n=1}^{\infty}\mu(n)g(nx).$$

27. [Section 21] If p is prime and $\zeta=e^{2\pi i/p}$, then

$$(1-\zeta)(1-\zeta^2)\cdots(1-\zeta^{p-1})=p.$$

Hence in $\mathbb{Z}[G]$, where $G=\mathrm{Cyl}(p)=\{1,g,\ldots,g^{p-1}:g^p=1\}$, $(1-g)(1-g^2)\cdots(1-g^{p-1})=p-(1+g+g^2+\cdots+g^{p-1})$.

28. [Section 21] Let $n_1,\ldots,n_r\in\mathbb{N}$ and let $G=\mathrm{Cyl}(n_1)\times\cdots\times\mathrm{Cyl}(n_r)$ be the additive group of $\mathbb{Z}/n_1\mathbb{Z}\times\cdots\times\mathbb{Z}/n_r\mathbb{Z}$. (It is a fact that every finite abelian group is of this form.) Thus the elements of G can be written as $g_1=1,\ldots,g_n$, where $n=n_1\cdots n_r$ and $g_i=(a_{i1},\ldots,a_{ir})$, $a_{it}\in(\mathbb{Z}/n_t\mathbb{Z})$. Let k be a field whose characteristic does not divide n and that contains the nth roots of 1, and define $M=(m_{ij})\in\mathrm{Mat}_n(k[X_1,\ldots,X_n])$ by $m_{ij}=X_h$ if $g_i^{-1}g_j=g_h$. Prove the **Dedekind determinant formula** (formerly the Frobenius determinant formula)

$$\det(M)=\prod_{\zeta}\sum_i\zeta_1^{a_{i1}}\cdots\zeta_r^{a_{ir}}X_i,$$

where the product is over all r-tuples $\zeta=(\zeta_1,\ldots,\zeta_r)$ and ζ_t is an n_tth root of 1. For example, when $G=\mathrm{Cyl}(3)$,

$$\det(M)=\begin{vmatrix}X_1&X_2&X_3\\X_3&X_1&X_2\\X_2&X_3&X_1\end{vmatrix}$$

$$=X_1^3+X_2^3+X_3^3-3X_1X_2X_3$$

$$=(X_1+X_2+X_3)(X_1+\omega X_2+\omega^2X_3)(X_1+\omega^2X_2+\omega X_3),$$

where ω is a primitive cube root of 1. (*Hint*: Ingredients are column operations $E_j(\zeta_1^{a_{j1}}\cdots\zeta_r^{a_{jr}})$, row operations $E_{i1}(\zeta_1^{-a_{i1}}\cdots\zeta_r^{-a_{ir}})$, and unique factorization in $k[X_1,\ldots]$.)

29. [Section 21] For a prime $p>5$, there exist primes r and n less than $p\ni(r/p)=1$, $(n/p)=-1$.

30. [Section 21]

(i) Suppose the field k contains a primitive nth root of unity ζ. Prove the polynomial identity

$$\sum_{j=1}^{n}(X+\zeta^j)^N=n\left(X^N+\binom{N}{n}X^{N-n}+\binom{N}{2n}X^{N-2n}+\cdots\right).$$

Deduce the result of Exercise 13 following Section 21.

(ii) Let $q=p^n$ be an odd prime power and for $a\in\mathbb{F}_q^*$ let $[a/q]=\pm 1$ denote the obvious generalization of the Legendre symbol: 1 if $x^2=a$ has a solution $x\in\mathbb{F}_q$, -1 if not. (We use square brackets to avoid confusion with the Jacobi symbol.) Prove Euler's criterion: if $q'=(q-1)/2$ then $a^{q'}\in\mathbb{F}_p$ and $[a/q]\equiv a^{q'} \bmod p$. This is true also for $a=0$ if we define $[0/q]=0$; then the number of solutions of $x^2=a$ is $1+[a/q]$, $\forall a\in\mathbb{F}_q$.

(iii) Let $a,b,c\in\mathbb{F}_q^*$ and let N denote the number of solutions $(x,y)\in\mathbb{F}_q\times\mathbb{F}_q$ of

$$(*)\qquad ax^2+by^2=c.$$

Fill in the details of the following proof that $N\geqslant p-1$. (In algebraic geometry the fact that $N>0$ becomes the statement that every conic over $\mathbb{F}_q$ has a rational point, i.e., a point with coordinates in $\mathbb{F}_q$.)

$$N=\sum_{x\in\mathbb{F}_q}\left(1+\left[\frac{bc-abx^2}{q}\right]\right).$$

Hence N is even and

$$N\equiv\left[\frac{bc}{q}\right]+\sum_{x\neq 0}(bc-abx^2)^{q'} \mod p$$

$$\equiv\left[\frac{bc}{q}\right]+\left[\frac{-ab}{q}\right](q-1)\left(\left[\frac{-ac}{q}\right]+1\right) \qquad \text{by (i)}$$

$$\equiv-\left[\frac{-ab}{q}\right],$$

so $N=pt-[-ab/q]$ where t is odd.

31. [Section 21] Let $\mathbb{F}_q$ denote a q-element field, say $q=p^n$, where p is prime, let $\mathbb{F}_q^*=\langle g\rangle$, and let m denote the minimum polynomial of g over $\mathbb{F}_p$.

(i) $\deg(m)=n$, so the elements of $\mathbb{F}_q$ are uniquely expressible as $a_0+a_1g+\cdots+a_{n-1}g^{n-1}$, $a_i\in\mathbb{F}_p$.

(ii) m divides the $(q-1)$st cyclotomic polynomial κ_{q-1}.

(iii) $\mathrm{SL}_2(\mathbb{F}_q)$ is generated by the $n+1$ elements (cf. A9.8(vi)).

$$\sigma=\begin{pmatrix}0&1\\-1&0\end{pmatrix},\qquad \tau_j=\begin{pmatrix}1&0\\g^j&1\end{pmatrix},\qquad 0\leqslant j<n.$$

(iv) There is, up to isomorphism, exactly one p^2-element field. (As mentioned earlier, this uniqueness extends to every prime power. *Hint*: For odd $q=p^2$, $\mathbb{F}_q$ is obtained from $\mathbb{F}_p$ by adjoining the square root of a quadratic nonresidue.)

32. [Section 21] Let p be a prime $\equiv 3 \bmod 4$, $p>3$, and $\zeta=e^{2\pi i/p}$. Then

$$\prod(1+\zeta^r)=\left(\frac{2}{p}\right),$$

where r runs through the quadratic residues mod p.

33. [Section 22] For k a field, $Z(\mathrm{GL}_n(k))=\{cI: c\in k^*\}$ and $Z(\mathrm{SL}_n(k))=\{cI: c^n=1\}$.

34. [Section 22] Let $\sigma\in\mathrm{Sym}(n)$ and in the unique factorization of σ into disjoint cycles (with cycles of length 1 included so that each of the n symbols appears exactly once in the factorization) let there be $f(\sigma,i)$ cycles of length i $(1\leqslant i\leqslant n)$. Then σ and τ are conjugate iff $f(\sigma,i)=f(\tau,i)$ $\forall i$. Hence the number of conjugacy classes in $\mathrm{Sym}(n)$ is the number of partitions $p(n)$ (equal to the number of ways of writing n as a sum of natural numbers, e.g., $p(5)=6$ since 5 can be written $1+1+1+1+1$, $2+1+1+1$, $2+2+1$, $3+1+1$, $3+2$, and 5).

35. [Section 22] If S is a set with more than one element and $s\in S$, then with respect to the natural action of $\mathrm{Sym}(S)$, $\mathrm{Sta}(s)$ is a maximal (proper) subgroup.

36. [Section 22] Let the group G_i act on the set E_i, let $G=\prod G_i$, $E=\coprod E_i$, and regard $G_i\subset G$, $E_i\subset E$ canonically. Define an action of G on E that restricts to the given action of G_i on E_i $\forall i$.

37. [Section 24] Let H be a subgroup of the group G.

(i) If $f: K\to G$ is a group homomorphism, then $f^{-1}(N_G(H))\subset N_K(f^{-1}(H))$ with equality if f is surjective. Now let $f\in\mathrm{Aut}(G)$, so $f(N(H))=N(fH)$; in particular, for $g\in G$, $g(N(H))g^{-1}=N(gHg^{-1})$, and $H\lhd G\Rightarrow fH\lhd G$.

(ii) $(G:H)<\infty\Rightarrow(G:fH)=(G:H)$. Hence the number of conjugates of fH is the same as that of H.

38. [Section 24]

(i) If H,K are subgroups of finite index in the group G satisfying $H\supset K$, then $(G:K)=(G:H)(H:K)$.

(ii) For any subgroup H of G, $\cap_{g\in G}gHg^{-1}\lhd G$.

(iii) **Poincaré's theorem**: The intersection of finitely many subgroups of finite index is a subgroup of finite index. In fact,

$$(G:H_1\cap\cdots\cap H_n)\leqslant(G:H_1)\cdots(G:H_n).$$

Hence a subgroup of finite index contains a normal subgroup of finite index.

(iv) Let $(G:H)=m$, $(G:K)=n$ be finite. Then $(G:H\cap K)\geqslant\mathrm{l.c.m.}(m,n)$ with equality if $\mathrm{g.c.d.}(m,n)=1$. Also, $(G:H)\geqslant(K:K\cap H)$.

(v) If H is a subgroup of G of finite index, then $\cup_{g\in G}gHg^{-1}\neq G$. (*Hint*: Reduce to the case of finite G by replacing G by $G/\cap gHg^{-1}$.)

39. [Section 24] A subgroup H of G is **characteristic** if $\alpha H=H$ $\forall\alpha\in\mathrm{Aut}(G)$.

(i) A characteristic subgroup is normal, but the Klein 4-group $\mathrm{Cyl}(2)\oplus\mathrm{Cyl}(2)$ gives an example of a normal subgroup that is not characteristic.

(ii) The following subgroups of G are characteristic: the center $Z(G)$, the Frattini subgroup $\Phi(G)$ (cf. Supplementary Exercise 17 of Chapter 3); the **commutator subgroup** (the subgroup generated by the set of elements of the form $xyx^{-1}y^{-1}$), and $\rho(G)=\{g\in G:(G:Z(g))<\infty\}$.

40. [Section 24] let $f_i: G_i \to G_{i+1}$ $(1 \leqslant i \leqslant n)$ be homomorphisms of finite groups $\ni \mathrm{Ker}(f_{i+1}) = \mathrm{Im}(f_i)$ for $1 \leqslant i \leqslant n-1$ (a so-called exact sequence) and $G_1 = G_{n+1} = 1$. Then $\Pi |G_i|^{(-1)^i} = 1$.

41. [Section 24] Three examples of the semidirect product.

(i) Describe the one-dimensional affine group over the ring A (cf. Supplementary Exercise 15 of Chapter 3) as a semidirect product.

(ii) The **holomorph** of the group H is $\mathrm{Hol}(H) = H \times_1 \mathrm{Aut}(H)$ (here $\rho: K \to \mathrm{Aut}(H)$ of the general definition is 1). Show that every automorphism of H is induced by an inner automorphism of $\mathrm{Hol}(H)$, and hence that a subgroup of H is characteristic in H (cf. Exercise 39 above) iff it is normal in $\mathrm{Hol}(H)$, and $\mathrm{Hol}(H)$ is the normalizer of H in $\mathrm{Sym}(H)$. Show that $\mathrm{Hol}(\mathrm{Cyl}(3)) \approx \mathrm{Sym}(3)$.

(iii) The **wreath product** $H \wr K$ of the groups H and K is $H^K \times_\rho K$, where $(\rho(k)(f))(k') = f(k'k)$, writing the elements of H^K (= the direct product of copies of H) as functions $f: K \to H$. If $G = \mathrm{Cyl}(2) \wr \mathbb{Z}$, and $L = \mathrm{Cyl}(2)^{\mathbb{N}}$ is regarded canonically as a subgroup of $\mathrm{Cyl}(2)^{\mathbb{Z}} \subset G$, find $g \in G \ni gLg^{-1} \subsetneq L$. (Conjugation can shrink an infinite subgroup.)

42. [Section 24] The determinant function sets up a group isomorphism $\mathrm{Gl}_n(k)/\mathrm{SL}_n(k) \xrightarrow{\sim} k^*$. More generally, if H is a subgroup of k^*, for instance h^* for some subfield h, then the determinant function induces an isomorphism $\mathrm{GL}_n(k)/N \xrightarrow{\sim} k/H$, where $N = \{A \in \mathrm{GL}_n(k): \det(A) \in H\}$.

43. [Section 24]

$$|\mathrm{GL}_n(\mathbb{F}_q)| = N, \qquad |\mathrm{SL}_n(\mathbb{F}_q)| = N/(q-1),$$
$$|\mathrm{PGL}_n(\mathbb{F}_q)| = N/(q-1), \qquad |\mathrm{PSL}_n(\mathbb{F}_q)| = N/(q-1)d,$$

where $N = (q^n - 1)(q^n - q) \cdots (q^n - q^{n-1})$ and $d = \mathrm{g.c.d.}(q-1, n)$.

44. [Section 22] Let k be a field, R a k-algebra, $G = \{g_1 = 1, g_2, \ldots, g_n\}$ a finite subgroup of R^*, and $S = kg_1 + \cdots + kg_n$ the k-subspace spanned by G. Plainly S is a subalgebra: $S = k[g_1, \ldots, g_n]$. Show that $S^* = R^* \cap S$. An application, using (5.321) and (5.273) is the following: If D is a skew field of characteristic $p > 0$ and G is a finite subgroup of D^*, then G is cyclic.

45. [A12.2] Let k be a valued field, $f, g \in k[X]$, and Z the set of zeros of g in k. Then $x \mapsto f(x)/g(x)$ defines a continuous map $k \setminus Z \to k$.

46. [A12.5] Let $f(n)$ (resp. $g(n)$) denote the number of rings (resp. commutative rings) with n elements (up to isomorphism, of course). Then f and g are multiplicative functions.

47. [A12.5]

(i) $\Sigma_{d|n} \mu(d)\varphi(d) = \Pi_{p|n}(2-p)$ (p prime). (*Hint*: Both sides are multiplicative.)

(ii) $\sigma_0(n) = \varphi(n) \Leftrightarrow n = 1, 3, 8, 10, 18, 24$ or 30. (*Hint*: φ/σ_0 is multiplicative and "increasing.")

(iii) For each $a\in\mathbb{N}$ the function ζ_a defined by $\zeta_a(n)=\text{g.c.d.}(a,n)$ is multiplicative. If f is any multiplicative function, then the composed function $f\zeta_a$, where $(f\zeta_a)(n)=f(\text{g.c.d.}(a,n))$, is also multiplicative.

48. [A12.5] Let f be a strongly multiplicative function. Then

(i)

$$\sum_{d\mid n} f(d)\prod_{p(\text{prime})\mid d}(1-1/f(p))=f(n);$$

(ii)

$$\sum_{k=1}^{n}\lfloor n/k\rfloor f(k)\prod_{p(\text{prime})\mid k}(1-1/f(p))=\sum_{k=1}^{n}f(k).$$

49. [A12.5] A natural number n is **perfect** if $\sigma(n)=2n$, where $\sigma=\sigma_1$ in the notation of A12.5. For example, $\sigma(6)=1+2+3+6=12$, so 6 is perfect. Show that n is an *even* perfect number iff it is of the form $2^{m-1}(2^m-1)$, where 2^m-1 is a (Mersenne) prime. (This result dates back to Euclid. As of 1980, it is still unknown whether any odd perfect numbers exist.)

50. [A12.5] Let A be a commutative ring, B a U.F.D., and $M\subset B[X]$ the monoid of monic polynomials. Develop a theory of formal series $f\in A^M$ as in A12.5. Show that Tr: $M\to B$ defined by $\text{Tr}(1)=0$ and, for $n\geqslant 1$, $\text{Tr}(X^n+bX^{n-1}+\cdots)=-b$, is "strongly additive": $\text{Tr}(mm')=\text{Tr}(m)+\text{Tr}(m')$, in particular,

$$\text{Tr}\big((X-\lambda_1)^{e_1}\cdots(X-\lambda_r)^{e_r}\big)=e_1\lambda_1+\cdots+e_r\lambda_r,$$

while det: $M\to B$, defined by $\det(1)=1$ and $\det(X^n+\cdots+b)=(-1)^n b$, is strongly multiplicative.

51. [A12.7]

(i) Verify the following identities:

$$2\sin x\sin y=\cos(x-y)-\cos(x+y),$$

$$2\cos x\cos y=\cos(x-y)+\cos(x+y),$$

$$2\sin x\cos y=\sin(x+y)+\sin(x-y);$$

hence

$$2\sin^2 x=1-\cos 2x,\qquad 2\cos^2 x=1+\cos 2x,$$
$$2\sin x\cos x=\sin 2x.$$

Deduce that, for any x, y, z,

$$\sin x\sin y\sin(x-y)+\sin y\sin z\sin(y-z)$$
$$+\sin z\sin x\sin(z-x)+\sin(x-y)\sin(y-z)\sin(z-x)=0.$$

(ii) Verify the identities

$$\sin x=\frac{2\tan(x/2)}{1+\tan^2(x/2)},\qquad \cos x=\frac{1-\tan^2(x/2)}{1+\tan^2(x/2)},$$

$$\tan(x/2)=\sin x/(1+\cos x).$$

Deduce that

(a) $\tan(x/2) \in \mathbb{Q} \amalg \{\infty\} \Leftrightarrow \sin x$ and $\cos x \in \mathbb{Q}$, and

(b) $2\tan(x/2)$ is the harmonic mean of $\sin x$ and $\tan x$.

(iii) For $x \in \mathbb{R}, 0 < x < \pi/2$, prove that $\sin x < x < \tan x$. From this and the fact that the harmonic mean is less than the arithmetic mean deduce that for $0 < x < \pi/4$, $2x < \sin x + \tan x$.

52. [A12.7] Use DeMoivre's theorem to derive the formula

$$\tan n\theta = \frac{\binom{n}{1}\tan\theta - \binom{n}{3}\tan^3\theta + \binom{n}{5}\tan^5\theta - \cdots}{1 - \binom{n}{2}\tan^2\theta + \binom{n}{4}\tan^4\theta - \cdots}.$$

53. [A12.7]

(i) $\tan(x+y) = (\tan x + \tan y)/(1 - \tan x \tan y)$.

(ii) $\csc\theta = \cot(\theta/2) - \cot\theta$.

(iii) $\frac{1}{2} + \cos\theta + \cos 2\theta + \cdots + \cos(n-1)\theta + \frac{1}{2}\cos n\theta = \frac{1}{2}\cos(\theta/2)\sin(n\theta)$.

(iv) $2^n\cos(n\theta/2)\cos^n(\theta/2) = \sum_{m=0}^{n}\binom{n}{m}\cos m\theta$.

(v) $2^n\sin(n\theta/2)\cos^n(\theta/2) = \sum_{m=0}^{n}\binom{n}{m}\sin m\theta$.

(vi) $\sec X = 1 + \sum_{n=1}^{\infty} E_n X^{2n}/(2n)!$, where

$$E_n = \binom{2n}{2}E_{n-1} - \binom{2n}{4}E_{n-2} + \cdots + (-1)^{n-1}E_1$$

and $E_n \in \mathbb{N}$. (The first few are $E_1 = 1, E_2 = 5, E_3 = 61, E_4 = 1385$. These are the **Euler numbers**.)

54. [A12.7] The **Bernouilli polynomials** $B_n(X)$ are defined by

$$\frac{Te^{Tx}}{e^T - 1} = \sum_{n\in\mathbb{M}} B_n(X)\frac{T^n}{n!} \in \mathbb{Q}(X)((T)).$$

The **Bernouilli numbers** are $B_n = B_n(0)$.

(i) Verify that $B_0 = 1, B_1 = -\frac{1}{2}, B_2 = \frac{1}{6}, B_{2n+1} = 0$ for $n \geqslant 1, B_4 = -\frac{1}{30}$.

(ii) $B_n(X+1) - B_n(X) = nX^{n-1}$. Hence

$$\sum_{k=1}^{n} k^n = (B_{n+1}(n+1) - B_{n+1})/(n+1).$$

(iii) $dB_n(X)/dX = nB_{n-1}(X)$.

(iv) $B_n(1-X) = (-1)^n B_n(X)$.

(v) $B_n(X) = \sum_{k=0}^{n}\binom{n}{k}B_k X^k$.

(vi) $B_n = \sum_{k=0}^{n}\binom{n}{k}B_k$ (symbolically, $B_n = (B+1)^n$, where B^k is interpreted as B_k) for $n \geqslant 2$.

(vii)

$$\tan T = T + T^3/3 + 2T^5/15 + 17T^7/315 + \cdots$$
$$= \sum(-1)^{n-1}2^{2n}(2^{2n}-1)B_{2n}T^{2n-1}/(2n)!.$$

(For further properties of $B_n(X)$ and the closely related Euler polynomials $E_n(X)$, see, e.g., Knopp.[9] The Euler numbers $E_n = 2^n E_n(\frac{1}{2})$ occur in the preceding exercise.)

[9] K. Knopp, *Problem Book in the Theory of Functions*, Vol. 1, Dover, New York, 1948, p. 99.

Table of Axiom Schemes

List
of Symbols

Arrangement of list: latin alphabet, greek alphabet, numerals, positional notation, other symbols.

$\text{Alt}(n)$	alternating group	201
am	amplitude	361
$B_n, B_n(X)$	Bernouilli numbers, polynomials	434
$\text{Bil}(U \times V \to W)$	vector space of bilinear maps	156
$\mathbb{C}$	complex field	304
$c(f)$	content of polynomial	103
$C(n), \text{Cyl}_n, \text{Cyl}(n)$	cyclic group of order n	65, 372
$_nC_k$	combinations of n things k at a time	196
$\text{card}\, X$	cardinality of set X	14, 137
char	characteristic	78
cos	cosine	360
D	unit disc	232
D_n	dihedral group of order $2n$	366
$D_r(a)$	open disc with center a, radius r	251, 339
d/dX	differentiation	286, 409
$\dim_k V, \dim V$	dimension of vector space V	131
$\text{Dis}(f)$	discriminant	300
$d(x, y)$	metric	333
e	neutral element of monoid	36
e	the real number	355
E	domain of exp	354

(as in $\tilde{k}$)	completion of valued field	237
(as in $\tilde{X}$)	completion of metric space	336
$\approx$	isomorphism	70
: (as in $(G: H)$)	group index	101
(as in $[L: K]$)	degree of field extension	134
! (as in $n!$)	factorial	30
$\vert\ \vert$ (as in $\vert X\vert$)	cardinality	14, 137
(as in $\vert \mathbf{A}\vert$)	determinant	186
(as in $\vert a\vert$)	absolute value	239, 309
$\Vert v\Vert, \vert v\vert$	length or norm	390
(n)	$\{1,\ldots, n\}$ (temporary notation)	13
$X^{(n)}$	"symbolic power" $X(X-1)\cdots(X-n+1)$	134
$\binom{n}{m}$	binomial coefficient	30, 318
$\binom{n}{a,\ldots,b}$	multinomial coefficient	224
$\left(\frac{a}{d}\right)$	Legendre, Jacobi symbol	375, 378
$(s,t)_K$	quaternion algebra over K	410
$\times$ (as in $X\times Y$)	product of sets	11, 32
$\times_\rho$	semidirect product	401
$\equiv$ (as $a\equiv b \bmod I$)	congruence modulo I	59
$f(b), f(b_1,\ldots, b_n)$	substitution in polynomial f	79, 107
$\to$	map, mapping, function	11
$\mapsto$	effect of map on element	12
$\lhd$ (as in $H\lhd G$)	H is a normal subgroup of G	399
$\cup, \amalg$	union of subsets, disjoint union	15, 16
$\cap$	intersection of subsets	15
$\subset, \supset$	contained in, contains	10
$\subsetneq, \supsetneq$	proper containment	73
$\langle S\rangle$	ideal, vector subspace, subgroup, etc. generated by subset	see index
$\lfloor a\rfloor$	integral part of a	55, 239
$\lceil a\rceil$	$-\lfloor -a\rfloor$	108
$\sqrt{\ }, \sqrt[n]{\ }$	square root, nth root	276
[ ] (as in $[a]$)	equivalence class	21
(as in $[a, b]$)	the integer $a-b$ (temporary notation)	23

Index

T

U